THE NATURE AND PROPERTIES OF SOILS

THE NATURE AND PROPERTIES OF SOILS

SEVENTH EDITION

HARRY O. BUCKMAN
Late Professor of Soil Technology Emeritus, Cornell University

NYLE C. BRADY
Professor of Soil Science and Director of Research and Director of the Cornell University Agricultural Experiment Station

REVISED BY NYLE C. BRADY

The Macmillan Company / Collier-Macmillan Limited, London

PRINTING   91011   YEAR   456789

Earlier editions by T. Lyttleton Lyon and Harry O. Buckman, copyright 1922, 1929, 1937, and 1943 by The Macmillan Company. Earlier editions by Harry O. Buckman and Nyle C. Brady © copyright 1952, 1960 by The Macmillan Company. Copyright renewed 1950 by Bertha C. Lyon and Harry O. Buckman and 1957 and 1965 by Harry O. Buckman.

Library of Congress catalog card number: 69–10539

THE MACMILLAN COMPANY
866 THIRD AVENUE, NEW YORK, NEW YORK 10022
COLLIER-MACMILLAN CANADA, LTD., TORONTO, ONTARIO

Printed in the United States of America

Preface

Numerous advances have been made in the field of soil science since 1960 when the sixth edition of this book was published. Perhaps the most dramatic change has been the adoption in the United States of the new comprehensive system of soil classification. Not only does this system carry a concept quite different from that formerly in use, but it involves, except at the series and family levels, an entirely new nomenclature. Even though a logical system is followed in relating soil class names to soil properties, the student must become acquainted with a large number of names not formerly in use.

Because of the transition from one classification scheme to another it has been necessary to include a discussion of both systems. An acquaintance with the new comprehensive system is needed to understand current literature in soil science. In scientific articles published prior to about 1960 the old system was used, thereby justifying its continued inclusion in this text.

The concept of soil acidity as it relates to hydrogen and aluminum ions has been brought up to date as has the identification of the source of the charges dominant in soils at various pH levels. Because this subject is not easy for the elementary student to grasp, a number of new diagrams have been developed and included.

The increasing importance of sulfur in crop production has been recognized by adding a section dealing with this element and its reactions in soils. This section is included in the chapter dealing with nitrogen, much of which was revised on the basis of new knowledge published in recent years.

The renewed recognition of the significance of soils in relation to the world food supply led to the writing of a new chapter on this subject— the final chapter in the book. Advantage is taken of recently published estimates of the area of tillable soils of different classes to dramatize the role that soils may play in helping man feed himself.

Two other improvements over the sixth edition should make this edition more useful. First, a rather extensive glossary has been added to define many terms peculiar to soil science. Second, there has been a decided reduction in the number of specific references cited. Both changes were made in response to suggestions from professors and indirectly from their students.

References should be made to the generosity of a large number of soil scientists who provided information used in this text. Dozens of letters were written to ask for suggestions to improve the text or to request permission to use photographs and similar materials. In nearly every case the response was most enthusiastic and helpful. For this the author is indeed grateful. The number of individual scientists who contributed to changes in this text is so large as to make reference to individuals impractical. However, the junior author is indebted especially to Donald Williams, Charles E. Kellogg, and the soil survey staff of the U.S. Soil Conservation service for the new soil maps and for many new photographs used in this textbook. He also appreciates the help of two of his Cornell colleagues, M. G. Cline and D. J. Lathwell, and of his dear wife who labored into the wee hours proofreading, checking, and rechecking the manuscript and proofs for this text.

N. C. B.

Contents

Chapter 2.
The Supply and Availability of Plant Nutrients
in Mineral Soils   18

Chapter 3.
Some Important Physical Properties of Mineral Soils   41

Chapter 21.
Soils and the World's Food Supply   580

Glossary of Soil Science Terms   597

Index   631

Chapter 1

The Soil in Perspective

Man is dependent on soils—and to a certain extent good soils are dependent upon man and the use he makes of them. Soils are the natural bodies on which plants grow. Man enjoys and uses these plants because of either their beauty or their ability to supply fiber and food for himself and his animals. His very living standard is often determined by the quality of his soils and the kinds and quality of plants and animals grown on them.

Great civilizations have almost invariably had good soils as one of their chief natural resources. Furthermore, these civilizations have remained great only so long as they properly cared for their soils. The downfall of the great nations utilizing the Tigris, Euphrates, and Nile River Valleys coincided with a deterioration of soil and water management and conservation practices. Even in our own country unwise exploitation and misuse has badly damaged some soils and has called our attention to the need for stringent measures to conserve and improve this valuable resource.

1:1. WHAT IS SOIL?

The commonplace features of nature are often not well understood or appreciated. For many of us, the soil is such a feature. It can be found most everywhere and has seemingly always been with us. Because of this, the majority of us have never taken the trouble to find out what the soil is, where it comes from, and what its basic properties are. We may not have observed how the soil in one place differs from that in another. Certainly few of us know the reasons for these differences.

CONCEPTS OF SOIL. Part of our lack of concern may be due to our different concepts and viewpoints concerning this important product of nature. For example, to a mining engineer the soil is the debris covering the rocks or minerals which he must quarry. It is a nuisance and must be disposed of. To the highway engineer the soil may be the material on which a road bed is to be placed. If its properties are suitable it is useful. If its properties are unsuitable it must be removed and rock and gravel put in its place.

The average homeowner has a concept of soil. It is a pleasant one if "the ground is nice and mellow or loamy." The opposite viewpoint is associated with "hard clay" which resists being spaded up into a good seedbed for a flower garden. The housewife can differentiate between variations in the soil, especially those relating to its stickiness or tendency to cling to shoe soles and eventually to carpets.

The farmer, along with the homeowner, looks upon the soil as a habitat for plants. He makes a living from the soil and is thereby forced to pay more attention to its characteristics. To him the soil is more than useful—it is indispensable.

To learn more about the soil we must have a common concept of what it is. Furthermore, our concept must encompass the viewpoints of the engineer, the homeowner and his wife, and by all means, the farmer. In developing this concept let us first consider soil as it is found in nature.

SOIL VS. REGOLITH. Everyone has seen views such as that shown in Fig. 1:1 in which unconsolidated materials are found on underlying rocks. Above bedrock some unconsolidated debris such as that shown in the photograph is present almost universally. This material, known as *regolith*, may be negligibly shallow or hundreds of feet in thickness. It may be material which has weathered from the underlying rock, or it may have been transported by the action of wind, water,

or ice and deposited upon the bedrock. In any case, the regolith is apt
to be variable in composition from place to place.

An examination of the upper 3 to 6 feet of the regolith would often
show that it differed from the material below. Being nearer to the
atmosphere, this upper zone has been more subject to the weathering
actions of wind, water, and heat. Furthermore, it is the zone in which
most of the plant roots are found. Plant residues, deposited originally
on the surface, have become incorporated by earthworms into the
surface layers and have been disintegrated and partially decomposed
by microorganisms.

The presence of some undecomposed organic matter along with the
weathering of minerals in the soil have often resulted in the formation of
characteristic horizontal layering. This upper and biochemically weathered portion of the regolith, which is generally considered to be the
soil, may be distinguished from the material below[1] by: (1) a relatively
high organic matter content; (2) an abundance of the roots of higher

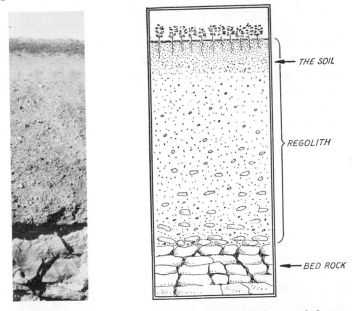

Figure 1:1. Diagram showing the relative positions of the regolith, its soil and
the underlying country rock. Sometimes the regolith is so thin that it has been
changed entirely to soil, which, in such a case, rests directly on bedrock.
(Photo courtesy Tennessee Valley Authority.)

---

[1] In cases where the regolith was relatively uniform originally, the material below
the soil is considered to have a composition similar to the *parent material* from
which the soil formed.

plants and of soil organisms; (3) more intense weathering; and (4) the presence of characteristic horizontal layers.

The scientist considers the soil to be a *natural body* having both depth and surface area. He also looks upon the soil as a product of nature resulting from both destructive and synthetic forces. Weathering and microbial decay of organic residues are examples of destructive processes, whereas the formation of new minerals, such as certain clays, and the development of characteristic layer patterns are synthetic in nature. Last, but not least, the scientist considers the soil a habitat for plants. He recognizes the contributions plants have made to soil development and realizes that the most important practical use of soils is in crop production.

THE SOIL VS. A SOIL. Man has found that characteristics of the soil vary widely from place to place. For example, on steep slopes the soil is generally not as deep and productive as when it is formed on gentle slopes. Where it has developed from sandstone it tends to be more sandy and less fertile than where it has formed from rocks such as shale. Its properties are quite different when it has developed under tropical climates as compared to temperate or arctic conditions.

Scientists have recognized these soil variations from place to place and have set up classification systems in which the soil is considered as composed of a large number of individual soils, each having its distinguishing characteristics. Therefore, *a soil*, as distinguished from *the soil*, is merely a well-defined subdivision having recognized limits in its characteristics and properties. Thus, a sandy soil, a clay soil, and a loam soil are examples of specific soils which collectively make up the over-all *soil* which covers land areas.

1:2. THE SOIL PROFILE

Let us examine the characteristics of a representative soil as found in the field. If we were to cut a section downward through this soil, the horizontal layers previously referred to would be found. Such a section is called a *profile* and the individual layers are regarded as *horizons*. These horizons above the parent material are collectively referred to as the *solum*.[2] Every well-developed, undisturbed soil has its own distinctive profile characteristics. They are made use of in soil classification and survey and are of great practical importance. In judging a soil its whole profile should be taken into consideration.

The upper layers of a soil profile generally contain considerable

---

[2] *Solum*—a Latin legal term meaning soil, land, or parcel of land.

amounts of organic matter and are usually darkened appreciably because of such an accumulation. Layers thus characterized are conveniently referred to as the major zone of organic-matter accumulation.
When a soil is plowed and cultivated, they include the familiar *surface
soil* or *furrow-slice*. The underlying *subsoil* contains comparatively less
organic matter. The various subsoil layers, especially in mature, humid-
region soils, often present two very general belts: (1) an upper zone of
transition; and (2) a lower zone of accumulation. In the latter, iron
and aluminum oxides, clay, and even calcium carbonate may gradually
concentrate. (See Fig. 1:2.)

The solum thus described extends an indefinite but moderate depth
below the surface. A depth of 3 or 4 feet is representative for temperate-
region soils. Here, the noticeable modified lower subsoil gradually merges
with the less weathered portion of the regolith. This part of the regolith
is called the *parent material* to distinguish it from the soil just above.
It is usually weathered, and its upper portion is geologically on the
point of becoming a part of the lower subsoil and hence of the solum.

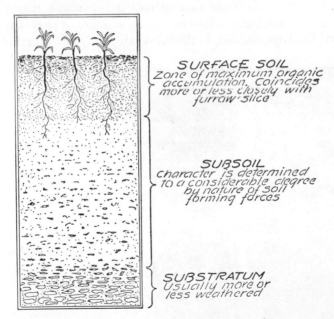

*Figure 1:2. A representative soil profile. The surface horizons are relatively
high in organic matter and become the furrow-slice when the land is plowed.
The subsoil, while markedly weathered, usually contains but little organic
matter. At variable depths it merges more or less gradually into the substratum (parent material). All of the layers above the substratum are spoken
of collectively as the* solum.

It is not to be inferred that the various layers comprising a soil profile are always distinct and well defined. In fact, the transition from one to the other is often so gradual that the establishment of boundaries is rather difficult. Nevertheless, for any particular soil the various horizons are characteristic and greatly influence the growth of higher plants.

1:3. SUBSOIL VS. SURFACE SOIL

The productivity of a soil is determined in no small degree by the nature of its subsoil. The practical importance of this fact is seen when we note that the subsoil normally is subject to little field altera- tion except by drainage. Even when roots do not penetrate deeply into the subsoil, its permeability and its chemical nature still may favorably or unfavorably influence the surface soil as a medium for plant growth. (See Fig. 1:3)

The situation in respect to the surface soil is somewhat different. In the first place, it is the major zone of root development, it carries much of the nutrients available to plants, and it supplies a large share of the water used by crops. Second, as the layer which is plowed and cultivated,

Figure 1:3. The root system of an 8-year-old juniper tree. The roots extend more than 16 feet into the soil. Moisture and nu- trients are likely absorbed to great depths in this soil. (Photo courtesy U.S. Soil Conservation Service.)

it is subject to manipulation and management. By proper cultivation and by the incorporation of organic residues, its physical condition may be modified. It can be fertilized, limed, and drained. In short, its fertility and to a lesser degree its productivity,[3] may be raised, or lowered, or satisfactorily stabilized at levels consistent with economic crop production.

This explains why much of the soil investigation and research has been expended upon the surface layer. It also explains why most of the discussion and explanation that follows, the data quoted, and the conclusions drawn concern themselves with surface soils. Plowing, cultivation, liming, and fertilization are essentially furrow-slice considerations. In fact, the term "soil," unmodified, will from here on be taken as reference to the surface layer, the so-called topsoil, or in practical terms, the furrow-slice.

1:4. MINERAL (INORGANIC) VS. ORGANIC SOILS

The profile generalizations presented above show the organic matter to be largely in the surface horizon. However, even in this zone the amounts are always comparatively low, ranging in general from 1 to 5 or 6 per cent. Because of the predominance of inorganic constituents that necessarily results, such soils are conveniently referred to as *mineral* or *inorganic soils*. Most soils are of this nature and are so common that a person involuntarily thinks of this type when the term soil is mentioned.

But in swamps, bogs, and marshes, conditions often encourage the accumulation of much organic matter. This gives rise to peat deposits and muck soils in which the organic content may range as high as 95 per cent. Perhaps 80 per cent of organic matter and 20 per cent of minerals are reliable representative figures for the organic deposits now being cultivated. A high organic content characterizes the whole profile, quite in contrast with the mineral soil sections already described. (See Fig. 13:1.) As such they are referred to as *organic* or *muck* soils.

As might be expected, muck soils are markedly different from mineral soils in many important respects and their practical handling presents problems that are both distinctive and unique. In spite of their smaller

---

[3] The term *fertility* refers to the inherent capacity of a soil to supply nutrients to plants in adequate amounts and in suitable proportions. *Productivity* is related to the ability of a soil to yield crops. Productivity is the broader term since fertility is only one of a number of factors that determine the magnitude of crop yields.

area, these soils are very important for certain crops, especially those, such as vegetables, which respond to intensive culture.

Not only are mineral soils of wider area and better known than are organic soils, but they are also in general more important agriculturally. Consequently, mineral soils deservedly receive the major attention in this text, the origin, character, and agricultural use of organic soils being considered as a unit in Chapter 13. Until then the discussion will concern itself almost exclusively with mineral soils.

1:5. THE APPROACH—EDAPHOLOGICAL VS. PEDOLOGICAL

Now that a general concept of soils has been presented, we recognize that a soil can be considered (1) as a biochemically weathered product of nature, and (2) as a habitat for the growth of plants. These conceptions illustrate the two approaches that can be used in studying soils—that of the *pedologist* in the one case and that of the *edaphologist* in the other.

Certain phases such as the origin of the soil, its classification and description, are embraced in what is designated pedology.[4] *Pedology* considers the soil purely as a natural body and lays minor emphasis on its immediate practical utilization. The pedologist studies, examines, and classifies soils as they occur in their natural environment. His findings may be as useful to highway and construction engineers as to the farmer.

Edaphology[5] is the study of the soil from the standpoint of higher plants. It considers the various properties of soils as they relate to plant production. The edaphologist is a practical man since he has the production of food and fiber as an ultimate goal. At the same time, he must be a scientist in order to determine reasons for variation in the productivity of soils and to find means of conserving and improving this productivity.

In this textbook our dominant viewpoint shall be that of the edaphologist. Pedology will be used only to the extent that it gives us a general understanding of soils as they occur in nature and as they are classified. Special attention will be given to pedology and the principles involved in this approach in only two chapters, 12 and 13. The remainder of the presentation is from an edaphological point of view.

[4] Pedology from *pedon* meaning soil or earth.

[5] Edaphology from *edaphos* also meaning soil or ground. The term *edaphology* was suggested by Dr. Horace L. Jones, Professor of the Classics, Emeritus, Cornell University. Its meaning was formulated by the authors of this text.

1:6. AN EDAPHOLOGICAL CHARACTERIZATION OF MINERAL SOILS

Mineral soils have already been designated the "upper and biologically weathered portion of the regolith." When expanded by profile and horizon study, this statement presents a pedological concept of soil origin and characterization. If, however, the production of higher plants is to be a part of the picture, a broader and more inclusive statement must be offered. In the light of the ideas already presented respecting the general function of the soil, the following edaphological definition is suggested:

The soil may be defined as a natural body, synthesized in profile form from a variable mixture of broken and weathered minerals and decaying organic matter, which covers the earth in a thin layer and which supplies, when containing the proper amounts of air and water, mechanical support and, in part, sustenance for plants.

1:7. FOUR MAJOR COMPONENTS OF SOILS

The definition just cited leads logically to an inquiry as to soil composition. This will be dealt with here in a very general way. Mineral soils consist of four major components: *mineral materials, organic matter, water,* and *air.* These, in the main, are in a rather fine state of subdivision and are intimately mixed. In fact, the contact is often so close as to render satisfactory separation rather difficult.

VOLUME COMPOSITION OF MINERAL SOILS. In Fig. 1:4 is shown the approximate volume composition of a representative silt loam surface soil in optimum condition for plant growth. Note that it contains about 50 per cent pore space (air and water). The solid space is made up by volume of about 45 per cent mineral matter and 5 per cent organic matter. At optimum moisture for plant growth, the 50 per cent of pore space possessed by this representative silt loam is divided roughly in half—25 per cent water space and 25 per cent air. The proportion of air and water is, of course, subject to great fluctuations under natural conditions, depending on the weather and other factors. (See Fig. 1:4.)

In presenting such an arbitrary volume representation of a surface mineral soil, it must be emphasized that the four main components of

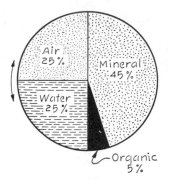

Figure 1:4. Volume composition of a silt loam surface soil when in good condition for plant growth. The air and water in a soil are extremely variable, and their proportion determines in large degree its suitability for plant growth.

the normal soil exist for the most part in an intimately mixed condition. This encourages both simple and complex reactions within and between the groups and permits an ideal environment for the growth of plants.

As might be expected, the volume composition of subsoils is somewhat different from that just described. Compared to topsoils they are lower in organic matter content and have a tendency to be somewhat more compact and to contain a higher percentage of small pores. This means they have higher percentage of minerals and water and a considerable lower content of organic matter and air.

1:8. THE MINERAL (INORGANIC) CONSTITUENTS IN SOILS

A casual examination of a sample of soil illustrates that the inorganic portion is variable in size and in composition. It is normally composed of small *rock* fragments and *minerals*[6] of various kinds. The rock fragments are remnants of massive rocks from which the regolith and in turn the soil has been formed by weathering. They are usually quite coarse. (See Table 1:1.) The minerals, on the other hand, are extremely variable in size. Some are as large as the smaller rock fragments; others, such as colloidal clay particles, are so small that they cannot be seen with the aid of an ordinary microscope. An electron microscope must be used.

Minerals such as quartz and other so-called *primary* minerals have persisted more or less unchanged in composition from the original country rock. Other minerals such as the silicate clays and iron oxides have

---

[6] The word *mineral* is used in this book in two ways: first, as a general term to describe soils dominated by inorganic constituents, and second, as a more specific term to describe distinct minerals found in nature such as *quartz* and *feldspars*. A more detailed discussion of the common soil-forming minerals and the rocks in which they are found is given in Chapter 11.

Table 1:1. Four Major Size Classes of Inorganic Particles and Their General Properties

Size Fraction	Common - Name	Visible Using	Dominant Composition
1. Very coarse	Stone, gravel	Naked eye	Rock fragments
2. Coarse	Sands	Naked eye	Primary minerals
3. Fine	Silt	Microscope	Primary and secondary minerals
4. Very fine	Clay	Electron microscope	Mostly secondary minerals

been formed by the weathering of less-resistant minerals as the regolith developed and soil formation progressed. These minerals are called *secondary* minerals. In general, the primary minerals tend to dominate the coarser fractions of soil, whereas secondary minerals are most prominent in the fine materials and especially in clays. It is obvious, therefore, that mineral particle size will have much to do with the properties of soils in the field. This will be further emphasized in a later section in which the chemical properties of clay, the finest of the mineral fractions, are considered.

1:9. THE SOIL ORGANIC MATTER

Soil organic matter represents an accumulation of partially decayed and partially resynthesized plant and animal residues. Such material is in an active state of decay, being subject to attack by soil microorganisms. Consequently, it is a rather transitory soil constituent and must be renewed constantly by the addition of plant residues.

The organic matter content of a soil is small—only about 3 to 5 per cent by weight in the case of a representative mineral topsoil. Its influence on soil properties and consequently on plant growth, however, is far greater than this low content would lead one to believe. In the first place, organic matter functions as a "granulator" of the mineral particles, being largely responsible for the loose, friable condition of productive soils. Also, organic matter is a major soil source of two important mineral elements, phosphorus and sulfur, and essentially the sole source of nitrogen. Through its effect on the physical condition of soils, organic matter also tends to increase the amounts of water a soil can hold and the proportion of this water that is available for plant growth. (See Fig. 1:5) Last, organic matter is the main source of energy for soil microorganisms. Without it, biochemical activity would come practically to a standstill.

For convenience, the soil organic matter may be considered to consist of two general groups: (1) original tissue and its partially decomposed equivalents; and (2) the humus. The original tissue includes the more or less undecomposed additions that are constantly being made—the roots and the tops of higher plants. These materials are subject to vigorous attack by soil organisms, both plant and animal, which use them as sources of energy and as tissue-building material.

The gelatinous, more-resistant products of this decomposition, both those synthesized by the microorganisms and those modified from the original plant tissue, are collectively known as *humus*. This material, usually black or brown in color, is colloidal in nature. Its capacity to hold water and nutrient ions greatly exceeds that of clay, its inorganic counterpart. Small amounts of humus thus augment tremendously the soil's capacity to promote plant production.

Figure 1:5. Soils high in organic matter are darker in color and have higher water holding capacities than do soils low in organic matter. The same amount of water was applied to each container (bottom photo).

The nonsolid or pore spaces in the soil are occupied by either water or air. Consequently the proportions of these two important components in a given soil are interrelated; as one increases, the other decreases and vice versa. An optimum balance between water and air must be maintained for best plant growth. This concept should be kept in mind as these two components are discussed in the next two sections.

1:10. SOIL WATER—
A DYNAMIC SOLUTION

Two major concepts concerning soil water are necessary in order to obtain a general idea of the significance of this major component of the soil. These are: (1) water is held within the soil pores with varying degrees of tenacity depending on the amount of water present; and (2) together with its dissolved salts, soil water makes up the so-called *soil solution* which is important as a medium for supplying nutrients to growing plants. The significance of these two facts in relation to plant growth is great.

The tenacity with which water is held by soil solids determines to a marked degree the movement of water in soils and its use by plants. An example of the latter relationship will be cited. When the moisture content of a soil is optimum for plant growth (see Fig. 1:4), plants can readily assimilate the soil water, much of which is present in pores of intermediate size. As some of the moisture is removed by the growing plants, that which remains is present in only the tiny pores and as thin films around the soil particles. The attraction of the soil solids for this water is great, and they can compete successfully with higher plants for it. Consequently, not all the water that soils can hold is available to plants. Much of it remains in the soil after plants have used some water and have wilted or even died as a consequence of water shortage. The practical significance of this available water limitation will of course be determined by the kind of soils and by the supply of rain or irrigation water.

The soil solution contains small but significant quantities of dissolved salts, many of which are essential for plant growth. There is an exchange of nutrients between these solids and the soil solution and, in turn, between the soil solution and plants. These exchanges are influenced to a degree by the concentration of salts in the solution, which in turn is determined by the total salts in the soil and by the content of soil water. Thus, we can see the dynamic nature of this solute-bearing water and its importance to plant life.

1:11. THE SOIL AIR—
ALSO A CHANGEABLE CONSTITUENT

Soil air differs from that of the atmosphere in several respects. First, the soil air is not continuous, being located in the maze of soil pores separated by soil solids. This fact accounts for its variation in composition from place to place in the soil. In local pockets, reactions involving the gases can greatly modify the composition of the soil air. Second, soil air generally has a higher moisture content than the atmosphere, the relative humidity approaching 100 per cent when soil moisture is optimum. Third, the content of carbon dioxide is generally higher and that of oxygen lower than that found in the atmosphere. Carbon dioxide is often several hundred times more concentrated than the 0.03 per cent commonly found in the atmosphere. Oxygen decreases accordingly, and in extreme cases may be no more than 10 to 12 per cent as compared to about 20 per cent for normal atmosphere.

The content and composition of soil air is determined to a large degree by the soil-water relationships. Being a mixture of gases, the air simply moves into those soil pores not occupied by water. Following a rain, the pores first vacated by the soil water are the large pores, followed by medium sized pores as water is removed by evaporation and plant utilization. Thus, the soil air generally occupies the large pores and, as the soil dries out, those intermediate in size.

This explains the tendency for soils with a high proportion of tiny pores to be poorly aerated. In such soils, water tends to dominate and the soil-air content and composition is unsatisfactory for best plant growth.

The dynamic nature of soil air is seen from the above discussion. The tendency for rapid changes in air content and composition has marked effects not only on the growth of economic plants but also upon the soil organisms, plant and animal, which occupy the soil. We shall now turn briefly to the part these organisms play in soil reactions.

1:12. THE SOIL—A TREMENDOUS
BIOLOGICAL LABORATORY

The representative mineral soil, bearing as it does so much available energy in organic form, harbors a varied population of living organisms. Indeed, the *life* of the soil plays such a prominent and indispensable role in the changes constantly occurring, that no discussion of the soil is complete without its consideration.

Representatives of both animals and plants are abundant in soils. The whole range in size from the larger rodents, worms, and insects to the tiniest bacteria commonly occurs in normal soils. Moreover, most organisms vary so much both in numbers and in amounts as to make precise statements impossible. For example, the number of bacteria alone in 1 gram of soil may range from 100,000 to several billion, depending on conditions.

The total weight of living matter, including plant roots, in an acre-furrow-slice of a representative mineral soil may be placed at 5,000 pounds at least, and 10,000 or 20,000 pounds may be more nearly correct for many soils. In any case, the quantity of living organic matter is sufficient to influence profoundly the physical and chemical trend of soil changes. Indeed it can even be said that "practically all natural soil reactions are directly or indirectly biochemical in nature." (see Fig. 1:6)

Activities of soil organisms vary from the largely physical disintegration of plant residues by insects and earthworms to the eventual complete decomposition of these residues by smaller organisms such as bacteria, fungi, and actinomycetes. Accompanying these decaying processes is the release of several nutrient elements from organic combination. Nitrogen,

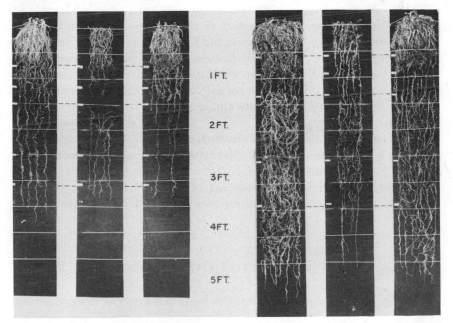

Figure 1:6. Plant roots tells us something about soil characteristics. The crop was grown on an Illinois (Cisne) soil which received no fertilizers or crop residues (left) and which received both fertilizers and crop residues (right). (Photo courtesy J. B. Fehrenbacher, University of Illinois.)

phosphorus, and sulfur are examples. By contrast, conditions in nature are such that organisms need these elements for their growth and a reversal occurs; i.e., the elements are converted again into organic combinations not available to higher plants.

Humus synthesis, exclusively a biochemical phenomenon, results from soil-organism activity. This material is certainly one of the most useful products of microbial action. We shall now turn our attention to some of the chemical properties of humus and its inorganic counterpart, clay.

1:13. CLAY AND HUMUS —
THE SEAT OF SOIL ACTIVITY

In the previous sections, attention was called to the dynamic nature of the finer portions of the soil—clay and humus. Both these constituents exist in the so-called colloidal state wherein the individual particles are characterized by extremely small size, large surface area per unit weight, and the presence of surface charges to which ions and water are attracted.

The chemical and physical properties of soils are controlled largely by clay and humus. They act as centers of activity around which chemical reactions and nutrient exchanges occur. Furthermore, by attracting ions to their surfaces, they temporarily protect essential nutrients from leaching and then release them slowly for plant use. Because of their surface charges they are also thought to act as "contact bridges" between larger particles, thus helping to maintain stable granular structure so desirable in a porous, easily worked soil.

On a weight basis, the humus colloids have greater nutrient- and water-holding capacities than does clay. The latter is generally present in larger amounts, however, and so its total contribution to the chemical and physical properties will generally equal that of humus. The best agricultural soils contain a good balance of these two important soil constituents.

1:14. THE VIEWPOINT —
A COLLOIDO-BIOLOGICAL CONCEPT

In this chapter an attempt has been made to give a very general picture of the soil in relation to its environment. A general viewpoint has been presented concerning the four major components of soil. An edaphological approach has been used because plant production is still the major function of soils.

Two major concepts presented herein should be emphasized before we move into more detailed study of soil components in succeeding chapters. First, most of the chemical activity in soils is associated with a relatively small proportion of the total soil components—the clay and humus. The soil may be visualized as possessing a basic mineral framework mostly made up of inert materials, but the physical and chemical properties are controlled to a large degree by the colloidal and extremely active fractions. Second, there is a vigorous soil organism population associated with humus and plant residues. They are responsible for a continuous turnover of organic materials including humus. Furthermore, they control, to a considerable extent, the supply of nutrient elements—both by releasing them through decomposition, and under different circumstances by competing with higher plants for them.

These two ideas lead logically to the statement that a study of soils from the standpoint of plants can best be approached from a *colloido-biological* viewpoint. This approach will be used in the chapters which follow.

Chapter 2

The Supply and Availability of Plant Nutrients in Mineral Soils

The capacity of soils to supply higher plants with certain essential elements is a fundamental problem in crop production. In this chapter we will deal with these elements as they exist and function in soils. More detailed consideration will be reserved for later chapters as will the means of supplementing the soil's supply of these necessary nutrients.[1]

2:1. FACTORS CONTROLLING THE GROWTH OF HIGHER PLANTS

The essential elements are only one of the environmental factors influencing the growth of plants. Six such external factors are generally recognized: (1) light; (2) mechanical support; (3) heat; (4) air; (5) water; and (6) nutrients. With the exception of light, the soil is an agent

---

[1] Chapters 14 through 20 deal in more detail with these subjects.

in supplying, either wholly or in part, all of these external factors.[2]

It is well to remember that plant growth is dependent upon a favorable combination of these factors and that any one of them, if out of balance with the others, can reduce or even entirely prevent the growth of plants. Furthermore, the factor which is *least* optimum will determine the level of crop production (see Fig. 2:1). This principle, sometimes called the *principle of limiting factors,* may be stated as follows:

The level of crop production can be no greater than that allowed by the most limiting of the essential plant growth factors.

This concept is a most important one and must be taken into consideration when dealing with nutrient elements. We must be concerned not only with the supply of a given element but also with its supply in relation to all other factors which may affect plant growth.

2:2. THE ESSENTIAL ELEMENTS

Research has shown that certain elements are necessary for the normal growth of plants. These *essential elements* must be present in

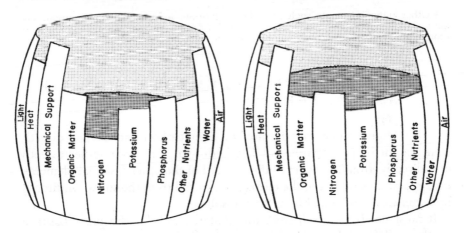

Figure 2:1. Simplified diagrams to illustrate the principle of limiting factors. The level of water in the barrels above represents the level of crop production. On the left, nitrogen is represented as being the factor that is most limiting. Even though the other elements are present in more adequate amounts, crop production can be no higher than that allowed by the nitrogen. When nitrogen is added (right) the level of crop production is raised until it is controlled by the next most limiting factor, in this case, potassium.

[2] Absence of disease and lack of serious insect pests are often mentioned as negative factors in this connection.

forms usable by plants and in concentrations optimum for plant growth. Furthermore, there must be a proper balance among the concentrations of the various soluble nutrients in the soil.[3]

Seventeen elements have been demonstrated to be essential for plant growth. They are listed in Table 2:1 and are classified according to sources—whether primarily from air and water or from soil solids—and usage—whether used by plants in relatively large or small amounts.[4]

Table 2:1. Essential Nutrient Elements and Their Sources

Essential Elements Used in Relatively Large Amounts			Essential Elements Used in Relatively Small Amounts[a]	
Mostly from Air and Water	*From Soil Solids*		*From Soil Solids*	
Carbon	Nitrogen	Calcium	Iron	Copper
Hydrogen	Phosphorus	Magnesium	Manganese	Zinc
Oxygen	Potassium	Sulfur	Boron	Chlorine
			Molybdenum	Cobalt

[a] Other minor elements such as sodium, fluorine, iodine, silicon, strontium, and barium do not seem to be universally essential, as are the seventeen already cited, although the soluble compounds of some may increase crop growth.

2:3. ESSENTIAL ELEMENTS FROM AIR AND WATER

Higher plants obtain most of their carbon and oxygen directly from the air by photosynthesis.[5] The hydrogen is derived, either directly or indirectly, from the water of the soil. All of the other essential elements, except certain supplies of the nitrogen acquired from the soil air indirectly by legumes, are obtained from the soil solids.

It must not be inferred from this that the bulk of the plant tissue is synthesized from the soil nutrients. Quite the reverse is true. Ordinarily from 94 to 99.5 per cent of fresh plant tissue is made up of carbon, hydro-

[3] Too much calcium, for example, may interfere with phosphorus and boron nutrition or may encourage chlorosis due to a reduction in the availability of the soil iron, zinc, or manganese.

[4] For instance, it is not uncommon for a crop such as corn to remove 150 pounds of nitrogen an acre. The amount of boron carried away by the same crop might be as little as 10 or 15 grams.

[5] In the process of photosynthesis, energy from the sun in the presence of chlorophyll facilitates the synthesis of sugar from CO_2 and water, the former entering the plant through the stomata, the latter being absorbed from the soil.

gen, and oxygen, and only from 0.5 to perhaps 5 or 6 per cent is from soil constituents. In spite of this, it is the nutrient elements obtained from the soil that usually limit crop development. Plant growth, except in cases of drought, cold weather, poor drainage, or disease, is not seriously retarded by a lack of carbon, hydrogen, and oxygen.[6] Hence, there is justification for the nutrient emphasis that is placed on the soil and the fourteen elements that it supplies.

2:4. ESSENTIAL ELEMENTS FROM THE SOIL[7]

MACRONUTRIENTS. Of the fourteen essential elements obtained from the soil by plants, six are used in relatively large quantities and consequently receive first attention. They are *nitrogen, phosphorus, potassium, calcium, magnesium,* and *sulfur.* Because they are used by plants in relatively large amounts, they are designated for convenience as *macronutrients.* Plant growth may be retarded because these elements are actually lacking in the soil, because they become available too slowly, or because they are not adequately balanced by other nutrients. Sometimes all three of these limitations are operative. This is often true in respect to nitrogen.

Nitrogen, phosphorus, and potassium are commonly supplied to the soil as farm manure and as commercial fertilizers. Therefore, they are often called *fertilizer* elements. In the same way, calcium and magnesium are commonly applied as lime and are styled *lime* elements. Sulfur, other than that present in rain water, usually goes into the soil as an incidental ingredient of such fertilizers as farm manure, superphosphate, and sulfate of ammonia. In special cases, sulfur is applied alone as flowers of sulfur, either to correct nutritional deficiencies or to adjust the reaction of the soil.

MICRONUTRIENTS. The other nutrient elements (*iron, manganese, copper, zinc, boron, molybdenum, chlorine,* and *cobalt*) are used by higher plants in very small amounts thereby justifying the name *micronutrients.* Such a designation does not mean that they are less essential than the so-called macronutrients. In fact, the micronutrients are fundamentally just as important (see Fig. 2:2).

---

[6] It is well to remember, however, that a serious lack of oxygen for roots may occur in heavy soils, especially if drainage is poor. This factor is important in respect to the location of orchards and is more critical than generally supposed (see p. 248).

[7] The terms *primary* and *secondary* elements are sometimes used to refer to the macronutrients. Likewise micronutrients are sometimes referred to as *trace, minor* or *rare* elements.

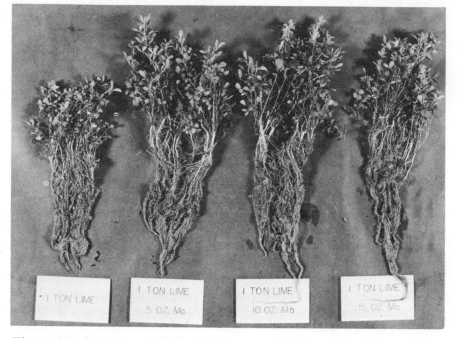

Figure 2:2. Some essential elements are required in very small quantities. Only five ounces of molybdenum per acre furrow slice were needed to nearly double the yield of the alfalfa in this experiment. (Photo courtesy W. K. Kennedy, Cornell University.)

Except for iron, and in some cases manganese, trace elements are found sparingly in most soils (see Table 2:2) and their availability to plants is often very low. Consequently, even though the removal by plants is small for any given season, the cumulative effects of crop production over a period of years may rapidly reduce the limited stores originally present. The three general soil situations where micronutrients are most apt to be a problem are: (1) sandy soils, (2) organic soils, and (3) very alkaline soils. This is due to the relatively small quantities of micronutrients in sands and organic soils and to the low availability of most of these elements under very alkaline conditions.

The deficiencies of micronutrients discovered in many of our soils in recent years have highlighted the practical significance of these elements. Because macronutrient fertility problems are more widespread, however, they will be given our first attention. Micronutrients will be considered in more detail later (Chapter 18).

FOUR NUTRIENT QUESTIONS. To arrive at a logical conclusion as to why nutrient deficiencies often occur in soils, four phases

Table 2:2. The Range in Micronutrient Content Commonly Found in Soils and a Suggested Analysis of a Representative Surface Soil

Nutrient	Normal Range		Suggested Analysis of a Representative Surface Soil
	Percentage	*p.p.m.*[a]	*p.p.m.*
Iron	.500–5.000	5000–50,000	25,000
Manganese	.020–1.000	200–10,000	2,500
Zinc	.001– .025	10– 250	100
Boron	.0005– .015	5– 150	50
Copper	.0005– .015	5– 150	50
Chlorine	.001–0.1	10– 1,000	50
Cobalt	.0001– .005	1– 50	15
Molybdenum	.00002– .0005	0.2– 5	2

[a] p.p.m = parts per million. These estimates are based on published data from a number of sources, especially R. L. Mitchell, "Trace Elements," in F. E. Bear, *Chemistry of the Soil* (New York: Reinhold, 1955), chap. 9.

of great importance must be examined. They are: (1) the amounts of the various macronutrients present in mineral soils (2) their forms of combination; (3) the processes by which these elements become available to plants; and (4) the soil solution and its pH. These phases will be considered in order.

2:5. AMOUNTS OF THE MACRONUTRIENTS PRESENT IN MINERAL SOILS

Although soils vary greatly in chemical composition, it is possible to indicate the percentage range within which the macronutrients are ordinarily found when a number of surface soils are considered. Also, analyses are suggested for representative surface soils of humid-temperate and arid-temperate regions, respectively. (See Table 2:3.)

It must be remembered, however, that such figures do not fit any particular soil, but present a very rough average of the data available. Also, it should be pointed out that the percentage values given are for topsoils only. These figures show that soils of arid regions are, in general, higher in all of the important constituents except organic matter and nitrogen. An exception, even to this, is found in the black earth soils (chernozems) of subhumid regions which sometimes may range as high as 16 per cent of organic matter and 0.70 to 0.80 per cent of nitrogen. (See p. 337.)

Table 2:3. Total Amounts of Organic Matter and Primary Nutrients Present in Temperate-region Mineral Surface Soils[a]

| | Ranges in Percentages that Ordinarily May be Expected | Representative Analyses | | | |
| | | Humid Region Soil | | Arid Region Soil | |
Constituents		Percentage	Lb to Acre Furrow-Slice	Percentage	Lb to Acre Furrow-Slice[b]
Organic matter	0.40–10.00	4.00	80,000	3.25	65,000
Nitrogen (N)	0.02– 0.50	0.15	3,000	0.12	2,400
Phosphorus (P)	0.01– 0.20	0.04	800	0.07	1,400
Potassium (K)	0.17– 3.30	1.70	34,000	2.00	40,000
Calcium (Ca)	0.07– 3.60	0.40	8,000	1.00	20,000
Magnesium (Mg)	0.12– 1.50	0.30	6,000	0.60	12,000
Sulfur (S)	0.01– 0.20	0.04	800	0.08	1,600

[a] As a supplement to the generalized figures of Table 2:2, the analyses of eight representative United States surface soils are presented as published by C. F. Marbut. For the complete set, see "Soils of the United States," *Atlas of American Agriculture,* Part 3 (U.S. Dept. of Agriculture, 1935).

Constituents	Norfolk Fine Sand, Florida %	Sassafras Sandy Loam, Virginia %	Ontario Loam, New York %	Loam from Ely, Nevada %	Hagerstown Silt Loam, Tennessee %	Cascade Silt Loam, Oregon %	Marshall Silt Loam, Iowa %	Summit Clay from Kansas %
SiO_2	91.49	85.96	76.54	61.69	73.11	70.40	72.63	71.60
TiO_2	0.50	0.59	0.64	0.47	1.05	1.08	0.63	0.81
Fe_2O_3	1.75	1.74	3.43	3.87	6.12	3.90	3.14	3.56
Al_2O_3	4.51	6.26	9.38	13.77	8.30	13.14	12.03	11.45
MnO	0.007	0.04	0.08	0.12	0.44	0.07	0.10	0.06
CaO	0.01	0.40	0.80	5.48	0.37	1.78	0.79	0.97
MgO	0.02	0.36	0.75	2.60	0.45	0.97	0.82	0.86
K_2O	0.16	1.54	1.95	2.90	0.91	2.11	2.23	2.42
Na_2O	Trace	0.58	1.04	1.47	0.20	1.98	1.36	1.04
P_2O_5	0.05	0.02	0.10	0.18	0.16	0.16	0.12	0.09
SO_3	0.05	0.07	0.08	0.12	0.07	0.21	0.12	0.11
Ignition	1.83	1.91	5.30	7.62	8.82	4.25	6.01	6.60
Nitrogen	0.02	0.02	0.16	0.10	0.27	0.08	0.17	0.09

[b] The furrow-slice of a representative mineral soil is considered to contain approximately 2,000,000 pounds of dry earth to the acre.

ORGANIC MATTER, NITROGEN, AND PHOSPHORUS. The percentage of organic matter exceeds that of any other constituent listed in Table 2:3. Yet its amount in most surface soils usually is critical. It is of prime importance in keeping the soil loose and open and is an essential source of several nutrient elements. The addition and subsequent decay of organic matter in the soil is thus highly significant both physically and chemically.

Nitrogen and phosphorus are almost always present in comparatively small amounts in mineral soils. Moreover, a large proportion of these elements at any one time is held in combinations unavailable to plants. For example, even the more simple compounds of phosphorus are relatively insoluble in many soils. As a result, this element is doubly critical —low total amounts and very low availability to plants.

POTASSIUM, CALCIUM, AND MAGNESIUM. The total quantity of potassium, in marked contrast to phosphorus, is usually plentiful except in sandy soils. The main problem is one of availability. Calcium shows great variation but it is generally present in lesser amounts than is potash. When it is lacking, soils tend to be acid. Calcium compounds, therefore, generally are added to correct this condition, although the direct nutrient influence of calcium cannot be disregarded.

Magnesium, besides its importance as a nutrient, functions in the soil much as does calcium. Its deficiency in some soils has long been suspected. Until recently, however, it has not been considered especially critical, because it is carried by most limestones, sometimes in large amounts. Where liming is practiced, its lack often is automatically rectified. In spite of this, magnesium deficiency is a major problem in many areas in eastern United States.

SULFUR. Although it is usually no more plentiful than phosphorus, sulfur is more readily available. This is because its simple inorganic compounds are not rendered insoluble by reacting with certain other soil constituents as is the case with phosphorus. As already suggested, the addition of sulfur in farm manure, rain water, and fertilizers tends in an automatic way to relieve a possible deficiency in humid-temperate regions. In certain areas of the West and South, however, specific additions of sulfur-containing compounds are required.

CRITICAL CONSTITUENTS. The above discussion seems to indicate that three constituents are likely to be critical in almost all mineral soils. Two—*organic matter* and *nitrogen*—merit particular attention because of the small amounts originally present and because of their ready loss through oxidation, leaching, or crop removal. The third, *phosphorus,* faces a double handicap as already explained—an exceptionally small amount present and a low availability to higher plants.

Under humid conditions *calcium* by all means must be included in the above list because it is sure to be much depleted by leaching. Consequently, it is needed not only as a nutrient but also as a means of controlling soil acidity. In arid regions, however, the leaching of calcium usually is negligible. Consequently, this nutrient is likely to be present in abundance, especially in the subsoil.

It is not to be inferred from the preceding generalizations, however, that *potassium, magnesium,* and *sulfur* may not be lacking in certain soils or that the problem of their supply may not at times be critical. The ever increasing use of potash fertilizers, the demand for dolomitic limestone, and the emphasis placed on sulfur additions are evidence of this.

2:6. FORMS IN WHICH THE MACRONUTRIENTS OCCUR IN SOILS

The nutrient elements generally exist in two conditions: (1) complex and rather insoluble compounds; and (2) simple more soluble forms readily available to higher plants. Due to the chemical and biochemical processes at work the general trend of the elements in the soil is from the complex to the simpler forms. (See Table 2:4.) The reverse process—that of synthesis and increased complexity—does occur, however. The building of proteins from simple nitrogen salts and the reversion of soluble phosphates to complex and insoluble compounds are examples.

SIMPLE AVAILABLE FORMS.   The simpler and more soluble constituents of soils, especially those of humid regions, tend to disappear in drainage or are used by microorganisms and higher plants. Consequently, the greater proportion of the macronutrients exists in the soil in complex conditions. From thence they gradually become available through various processes of simplification. As a result, the productive capacity of a soil depends not so much upon the total amounts of the various nutrients present as upon the ease with which transfer is made to simple and available forms. Such a situation indicates why a *total* chemical analysis is likely to be of uncertain value in deciding the fertilizer needs of a soil. It is rather discouraging that the total amount of a nutrient may be determined with great accuracy, whereas its *availability* ordinarily is susceptible to little more than a rough approximation.

ORGANIC COMBINATIONS.   The decomposition of soil organic matter allows nutrients held in this complex form to be released and simple compounds appear which are more or less available to higher plants. Practically all of the nitrogen and much of the sulfur and the phosphorus are held in organic combinations. (See Table 2:4.) Since phosphorus in complex mineral forms usually is very slowly available,

Table 2:4. Forms in Which the Macronutrients Occur in Mineral Soils

Group 1 *The More Complex and Less Active Forms*	Group 2 *Some of the Simpler and More Available Forms and Their Ionic Equivalents*	
Nitrogen		
Organic combinations: proteins, amino acids, and similar forms; colloidal and subject to decomposition.	Ammonium salts	NH_4^+
	Nitrite salts	NO_2^-
	Nitrate salts	NO_3^-
Phosphorus		
Apatite, an original source. Secondary Ca, Fe, Al phosphates.	Phosphate of Ca, K, Mg, etc.	$HPO_4^=$
Organic; phytin, nucleic acid, and other combinations.	Soluble organic forms	$H_2PO_4^=$
Potassium		
Original minerals such as feldspars and mica.	Potassium ions adsorbed by colloidal complex.	
Complex secondary aluminum silicates such as clays, especially illite.	Potassium salts, such as sulfates, carbonates, etc.	K^+
Calcium		
Minerals such as feldspars, hornblende, calcite, and dolomite.	Calcium ions adsorbed by colloidal complex.	Ca^{++}
	A variety of simple calcium salts.	
Magnesium		
Minerals such as mica, hornblende, dolomite, and serpentine.	Magnesium ions adsorbed by colloidal complex	Mg^{++}
Secondary aluminum silicates, such as clays, especially montmorillonite, chlorite and vermiculite.	Numerous simple salts of magnesium.	
Sulfur		
Mineral combinations such as pyrite and gypsum.	Various sulfites . . . . and sulfates	$SO_3^=$
Organic forms; colloidal and subject to decomposition.	of Ca, K, Mg., etc.	$SO_4^=$

there is some advantage of the organic association. Even so, organic phosphorus does not become available as easily and quickly as do organic sulfur and nitrogen.

INORGANIC COMBINATIONS. Most of the potassium, calcium, and magnesium exists in the soil in strictly inorganic forms. There is quite a difference, however, in the degree of availability of the three elements. For example, a much larger amount of calcium is held in an easily replaceable condition by the colloidal fractions of the soil. (See Fig. 2:3.) In this form it is quite readily available to plants. The quantity of this element in a replaceable or available form far exceeds that of any other macronutrient in the soil. This is reflected in humid regions in the significant losses of calcium in drainage water and the consequent need for its replacement by liming.

The situation in respect to potassium, and to a lesser extent for magnesium, is quite different. A very high percentage of the total quantities of these elements is held in the less available forms. (See Fig. 2:3.) The

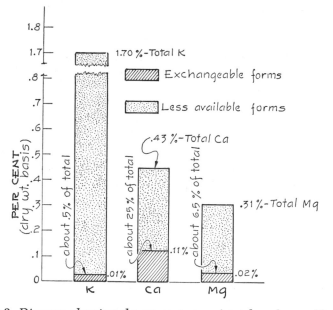

Figure 2:3. Diagram showing the percentages of total exchangeable (replaceable) K, Ca, and Mg respectively present in the representative humid-temperate regional mineral soil. Note that the amount of exchangeable Ca is approximately 10 times greater than the exchangeable K and 5 times that of the exchangeable Mg. About 25 per cent of the total Ca is represented as exchangeable, the corresponding figures for K and Mg are .50 per cent and 6.50 per cent, respectively.

exchangeable or readily available potassium, for example, usually makes up less than 1 per cent of the total quantity of this element in the soil. Although the relative content of exchangeable magnesium is usually somewhat higher, it is still lower than that of calcium.

Although sulfur is held in both mineral and organic forms (see Table 2:4), the latter combinations tend to predominate in humid-region surface soils. The availability of sulfur depends on the rate of organic decomposition. Its transfer from organic forms to inorganic salts which can be used by plants seldom gives trouble. In soils of arid regions, considerable sulfur may occur in the sulfate form as well as in organic combination. Gypsum is a common carrier of inorganic sulfur in such soils. The presence of calcium sulfate in the lower horizons of the chestnut soils of the Dakotas is an example. (See p. 337.)

The quantity of simple inorganic salts such as KCl, NaCl, and Na_2SO_4 in humid region soils is generally quite small. As one moves into more arid climates these salts are present in a somewhat higher concentration, especially in the lower horizons. Where drainage and leaching is restricted and rainfall is low, salts may be found in the plow layer or even at the soil surface in quantities sufficiently large to hinder or even prevent crop production.

2:7. THE TRANSFER OF PLANT NUTRIENTS TO AVAILABLE FORMS

The soil is such a complex body that it is impractical at this point to present in any detail the various changes that normally occur. The discussion that follows can only indicate in a very general way some of the more important transformations which affect the availability of the essential elements.

NITROGEN. Since most of the soil nitrogen is found in the organic matter, the decomposition of the latter must take place if the nitrogen is to appear in simple forms. This decomposition is a very complex, biochemical process, carried out by soil microorganisms. The nitrogen finally emerges as an ammonium compound and, if conditions are favorable, it is oxidized to the nitrite and then to the nitrate form. The two changes are spoken of as *nitrification* and are brought about by two special-purpose bacterial groups. Since most of the nitrogen utilized by higher plants is absorbed in the ammonium and nitrate forms, the importance of these processes is obvious. The transformations may be outlined in a simple way as follows:

Organic nitrogen $\longrightarrow$ Ammonium $\longrightarrow$ Nitrite $\longrightarrow$ Nitrate
(proteins amino   Salts   Salts   Salts
acids, etc.) $NH_4{}^+$ $NO_2{}^-$ $NO_3{}^-$

$\underbrace{}$ $\underbrace{}$
     Mineralization   Nitrification

Since the above transformations result largely from the activity of the soil organisms (microflora), they are influenced profoundly by soil conditions. When the soil is cold, waterlogged, or excessively acid, these biochemical changes do not progress rapidly. The nitrifying organisms are especially sensitive to these conditions.

When organic matter containing a large amount of carbon compared to nitrogen is added to a soil, the above processes may be reversed temporarily. The soil microorganisms, having large amounts of energy-producing materials at their disposal, multiply rapidly and use the nitrogen themselves, thus interfering with its simplification and appearance as ammonium and nitrates. In such cases, the soil organisms are competing directly with the higher plants. It must be concluded, therefore, that the simplification of the nitrogen is not always easy, rapid, or in proportion to the amounts present. This must, of course, be taken into consideration in the practical management of any soil.

PHOSPHORUS. When the soil phosphorus is held in organic combination, decay will encourage its simplification. The mineral phosphorus, however, presents a much more difficult problem. The various native soil phosphates are present in small quantities and are usually rather insoluble in water. Even when plant rootlets, aided by CO_2 and other root exudates, are in intimate contact with the mineral phosphates the rate of solution still is slow. A simple example illustrative of the solvent influence of carbon dioxide and water is given below, tricalcium phosphate tentatively representing the various insoluble soil phosphates:

$$Ca_3(PO_4)_2 + 4H_2O + 4CO_2 \rightarrow Ca(H_2PO_4)_2 + 2Ca(HCO_3)_2$$
Insoluble   Water-soluble   Soluble calcium
phosphate   phosphate   bicarbonate

By this means growing plants encourage an availablity that might otherwise be almost negligible. Thus, a soil may supply a crop with appreciable quantities of phosphorus, and yet the soil solution and drainage water may contain very small amounts of this element. (See Fig. 2:4.)

It should also be emphasized that simplification of phosphorus, like that of the nitrogen, may be reversed. Microorganisms readily appropriate simple and soluble phosphorus compounds and build them up into complex

Figure 2:4. A photomicrograph of dicalcium phosphate dihydrate crystals bonded to a root hair. This illustrates the intimate relationship between plant roots and some chemical fertilizers. (Photo courtesy J. R. Lehr, Tennessee Valley Authority.)

organic forms. Also such soluble fertilizer compounds as $Ca(H_2PO_4)_2$ and $NH_4H_2PO_4$ may be changed to insoluble calcium phosphates or to the equally complex and insoluble iron and aluminum combinations. Such forms liberate their phosphorus very reluctantly indeed.

POTASSIUM AND CALCIUM. It will be remembered that some of the calcium and most all the potassium occur as components of complex soil minerals. These forms slowly succumb through the years to the solvent action of water charged with carbonic and other acids. The ease with which the essential elements are rendered soluble depends upon the complexity of the soil minerals and on the intensity of weathering. The general reaction may be illustrated as follows, allowing the potash feldspar microcline to represent the complex minerals and carbonic acid the soil acids:

$$2KAlSi_3O_8 + H_2CO_3 + H_2O \rightarrow H_4Al_2Si_2O_9 + K_2CO_3 + 4SiO_2$$

Microcline		Hydrated	Soluble
feldspar		silicate	carbonate

The potassium released through such a reaction may be taken up by plants, lost in drainage, or held by the negatively charged soil colloids. The latter form of nutrient combination will now receive our attention.

A small proportion of the potassium and much of the calcium present in soils is held on the surfaces of the colloids as *adsorbed*[8] cations. These cations are easily released to the soil solution by exchanging with other cations. The general reaction may be shown as follows, assuming that hydrogen from an acid such as H_2CO_3 replaces calcium from the soil colloids:

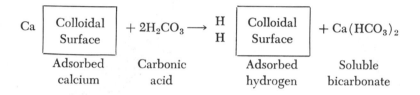

$$\text{Ca} \begin{array}{|c|} \hline \text{Colloidal} \\ \text{Surface} \\ \hline \end{array} + 2H_2CO_3 \longrightarrow \begin{array}{c} H \\ H \end{array} \begin{array}{|c|} \hline \text{Colloidal} \\ \text{Surface} \\ \hline \end{array} + \text{Ca}(HCO_3)_2$$

| Adsorbed calcium | Carbonic acid | Adsorbed hydrogen | Soluble bicarbonate |

A great deal of the calcium becomes mobile by this type of reaction. The replacement, or *ionic exchange* as it is called, takes place with surprising ease and rapidity, and undoubtedly is one of the most important types of reactions occurring in soils. Because of this situation, soils, although containing in general considerably more total potassium than total calcium (see Fig. 2:3), release the latter element to the soil solution and to leaching much more lavishly. This has a direct bearing on calcium nutrition, soil acidity, liming, and other practical considerations.[9]

MAGNESIUM. Since magnesium is held in the soil in much the same condition as is calcium, the exchange reaction cited for the latter shows how the magnesium may be released to the soil solution. However, some of the magnesium comes directly from the soil minerals by weathering, much as does the potassium. Hence, the illustrations cited for the transfer of potassium and calcium will serve for magnesium also. It is only necessary to visualize the formation and solution of magnesium bicarbonate by the breakdown of minerals in one case and by ionic exchange in the other.

Just as in the case of nitrogen and phosphorus, the release of potassium,

---

[8] *Adsorption* refers to the adhesion of substances to the surfaces of solids. In soils it has to do with the attraction of ions and of water molecules to colloidal particles. The ions are not too tightly held, being replaceable by or exchangeable with ions of a like charge.

Absorption in contrast refers to surface penetration such as takes place when nutrients and water enter plant roots. Thus Ca ions, for example, are absorbed as they are taken in by plant roots but adsorbed by soil colloids.

[9] The colloidal complex of the soil carries other cations besides calcium and hydrogen in a replaceable condition. Magnesium, potassium, ammonium, sodium, and other ions are present in minor amounts.

calcium, and magnesium to the soil solution may easily be reversed. Thus, when soluble compounds of potassium, calcium, or magnesium are added to a soil, the colloidal matter adsorbs large quantities of the metallic ions. Indeed, potassium may be even more firmly fixed as a molecular part of the mineral colloids.

SULFUR. As in the case of the nitrogen, the sulfur transformations are largely biological. They go on readily in most soils and while probably subject to marked retardation at times, such influences are apparently not as serious as in the case of nitrogen. The transformations may be indicated in a general way as follows:

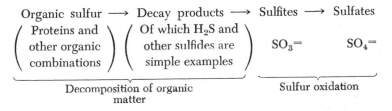

The last stage, sulfur oxidation, is, like nitrification, brought about largely by certain types of bacteria. The sulfate compounds that result (see Table 2:4) are the source of most of the sulfur acquired by higher plants.

Again, soil organisms, especially bacteria and fungi, utilize sulfur as well as the metals already mentioned. Their synthetic activities are excellent examples of a practical reversal of the simplifying processes. While such transpositions temporarily compete with higher plants, they tend to conserve nutrients by reducing the loss of valuable constituents in drainage water.

2:8. MORE ABOUT THE SOIL SOLUTION —ITS pH

It has already been emphasized that because of its segregation in the large and small pore spaces of the soil, the soil solution is not always continuous. (See Section 1:10.) As a result, not all the water can move freely. Also, the soil solution is exceedingly changeable, varying as to the gross amount present, as well as to the amount and proportion of its soluble constituents.

CONCENTRATION OF SOIL SOLUTION. As the soil moisture content is reduced by evaporation, the concentration of soluble salts in the soil solution rises. Moisture fluctuation in a humid-region mineral soil is of sufficient range to permit a variation in the concentration of the soil solution from a few parts per million, say 100, to 30,000 parts per million. Under ordinary conditions the acre-furrow-slice of an arable humid-region mineral soil contains from 500 to 1,000 pounds of soluble salts.

In arid and semiarid regions, the soil solution is usually somewhat more concentrated than where the rainfall is heavier. Under conditions of low rainfall and restricted drainage, salt concentrations are so high as to interfere at times with the growth of plants. The presence of even 0.5 per cent of total soluble salts is considered serious. This would mean about 10,000 pounds to an acre-furrow-slice.

REACTION OF THE SOIL SOLUTION. Another important property of the soil solution is its reaction—that is, whether it is *acid*, *neutral*, or *alkaline*. Without considering at this time the conditions controlling soil reaction (see p. 379), it suffices to say that some soil solutions possess a preponderance of H over OH ions and, therefore, are acid. Some, on the other hand, show the reverse and are alkaline; while others having an equal concentration of H and OH ions are neutral. (See Fig. 2:5.)

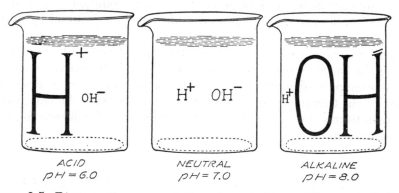

ACID
$pH = 6.0$

NEUTRAL
$pH = 7.0$

ALKALINE
$pH = 8.0$

Figure 2:5. Diagramatic representation of neutrality, acidity, and alkalinity. At neutrality the H ions and OH ions of a solution are balanced, their respective numbers being the same (pH 7).

At pH 6, the H ions are dominant, being 10 times greater while the OH ions have decreased proportionately being only 1/10 as numerous. The solution, therefore, is acid, there being 100 times more H ions than OH ions present.

At pH 8, the exact reverse is true, the OH ions being 100 times more numerous than the H ions. Hence the solution is alkaline. This mutually inverse relationship must always be kept in mind in using pH data. See note at bottom of page.

The exact relationship in any particular case is usually evaluated in terms of H ion concentration which is usually expressed in terms of pH. A soil is said to be *acid* if the pH is less than 7, *neutral* if at 7, and *alkaline* if the pH is above 7. Thus, as the H ions of the soil solution increase, the pH decreases and vice versa. On the other hand, as the OH ion concentration increases, the pH of the solution goes up accordingly.[10]

It is not to be inferred that we are, dealing with a homogeneous distribution of the H and OH ions in the soil solution. Hydrogen ions usually are adsorbed by soils to a much greater degree than are the OH ions. Consequently, one is prepared to visualize the H ions (1) as being especially concentrated at and near the colloidal interfaces, and (2) as becoming less numerous as the outer portions of the water films are approached. (See Fig 14:3.) Since the OH ions vary in numbers inversely with H ions, this makes for a higher pH in the outer moisture zones. Such a situation has many nutritional consequences in respect to both microorganisms and higher plants and will receive more attention later (pp. 398 and 399).

RANGES IN pH. In Fig. 2 : 6 are shown the ranges of soil pH encountered as well as the relationship between pH values and terms commonly used to describe soil reaction. For mineral soils the extreme range in pH extends from near 3.5 to perhaps 10 or above. It is to be noted in this connection that certain peat soils may show a pH of less than 3. At the other extreme are alkali soils, some of which may reach a pH near 11.

The common ranges in pH shown by soils of humid regions and arid regions, respectively, are sharply in contrast with the extreme spread noted above. That for soils of humid regions extends roughly from somewhat below 5 to above 7. It is to be noted that the latter figure overlaps the range common to soils of arid regions whose usual pH spread is from a little below 7 to approximately 9.

---

[10] If the reader is not definitely familiar with pH values, it would be well to consult a good textbook on chemistry. It may be pointed out here, however, that the pH value of a solution is the logarithm of the reciprocal of the H ion concentration. It may be stated conveniently as follows:

$$pH = \log \frac{1}{[H+]}$$

Also, it should be noted that the concentration of the H ion (and consequently the pH) is related mathematically to the concentration of the OH ion. In any solution in which water is the solvent the product of the concentration of these two ions is approximately 10^{-14}. Thus:

$$Con. H+ \times Conc. OH- = 10^{-14}$$

If, for example, the pH = 6 the H ion concentration is 10^{-6} equivalents per liter and the OH ion concentration is

$$\frac{10^{-14}}{10^{-6}} = 10^{-8} \text{ equivalents per liter.}$$

2:9. THE NUTRITIONAL IMPORTANCE OF SOIL pH

The soil pH may influence nutrient absorption and plant growth in two ways: (1) through the *direct* effect of the hydrogen ion; or (2) *indirectly*, through its influence on nutrient availability and the presence of toxic ions. In most soils the latter effect is of great significance. Although at extreme pH values the direct toxic effect of the hydrogen ion can be demonstrated, most plants are able to tolerate a wide range in the concentration of this ion as long as a proper balance of the other elements is maintained. Unfortunately, the availability of several of the essential nutrients is drastically affected by soil pH as is the solubility of certain elements that are toxic to plant growth. Examples of these effects will be cited.

Several essential elements tend to become less available as the pH is raised from say 5.0 to 7.5 or 8.0. Iron, manganese, and zinc are good examples. Molybdenum availability, on the other hand, is affected in the opposite way, being higher at the higher pH levels. The case of phosphorus in respect to pH is especially interesting. While this nutrient is never readily soluble in the soil, it seems to be held with less tenacity in a pH range centering around 6.5. (See p. 480 and Fig. 17:2.) Here, most plants seem to be able to extract it from the soil with least difficulty.

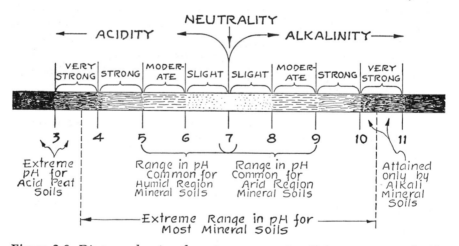

Figure 2:6. Diagram showing the extreme range in pH for most mineral soils and the range commonly found in humid-region and arid-region soils respectively. The maximum alkalinity for alkali soils is also indicated, as well as the minimum pH likely to be encountered in very acid peat soils.

At pH values below 5.0 to 5.5, aluminum, iron, and manganese are often soluble in sufficient quantities to be toxic to the growth of some plants. At very high pH values, the bicarbonate ion is sometimes present in sufficient quantities to interfere with the normal uptake of other ions and thus is detrimental to optimum growth. These few examples of the indirect effects of soil pH show why much importance must be placed on this characteristic in the diagnosis of fertility problems.

2:10. FORMS OF ELEMENTS USED BY PLANTS

There are two general sources of readily available nutrients in the soil. These are (1) nutrients adsorbed on the colloids; and (2) salts in the soil solution. In both cases the essential elements are present as ions such as K^+, Ca^{++}, Cl^-, SO_4^{--}. The positively charged ions (cations) such as K^+ are mostly adsorbed by the colloids, whereas the negatively charged ions (anions) and a small fraction of the cations are found in the soil solution. The more important ions present in the soil solution or on the soil colloids may be tabulated as follows:

Nitrogen	NH_4^+, NO_2^-, NO_3^-	Calcium	Ca^{++}
Phosphorus	HPO_4^{--}, $H_2PO_4^-$	Magnesium	Mg^{++}
Potassium	K^+	Sulfur	SO_3^{--}, SO_4^{--}
Iron	Fe^{++}, Fe^{+++}	Zinc	Zn^{++}
Molybdenum	MoO_4^{--}	Boron	BO_3^{---}
Manganese	Mn^{++}, Mn^{++++}	Chlorine	Cl^-
Copper	Cu^+, Cu^{++}	Water	H^+, OH^-
Carbon	CO_3^{--}, HCO_3^-		

NITROGEN, PHOSPHORUS, AND SULFUR. An explanation should be made regarding the use of certain ions by plants. Most of the nitrogen, for example, is absorbed in either the ammoniacal or nitrate forms, depending on the conditions of the soil, the kind of plant, and its stage of growth. In general, the presence of both ions seems most favorable. The nitrite ion is generally present in small quantities only, because it is so readily oxidized to the nitrate form. This is fortunate as any concentration of nitrite nitrogen is likely to be toxic to plants.

The particular phosphate ion presented to higher plants seems to be determined to a considerable extent by the pH of the soil. When the latter is distinctly alkaline, the HPO_4^{--} ion is the form in which soluble phosphorus occurs. As the pH is lowered and the soil becomes slightly to moderately acid, both HPO_4^{--} and $H_2PO_4^-$ ions prevail; at high acidities, the phosphorus is present largely as $H_2PO_4^-$ ion. Both these forms are considered to be absorbed by higher plants. It is well to note that soluble organic forms of phosphorus cannot be used to any extent directly by higher plants but must undergo mineralization and appear in the mineral forms before appreciable utilization takes place.

The intake of sulfur by higher plants apparently is largely as the SO_4^{--} ion. This is the final product of oxidation and if the sulfur organisms are vigorous, few SO_3^{--} ions can accumulate. The situation in some respects resembles that already cited regarding nitrite oxidation.

OTHER ELEMENTS. Little need be said at this point regarding potassium, calcium, magnesium, zinc, boron, and chlorine as they occur in the soil solution in only one ionic form respectively. But iron, manganese, and copper are in a little different category. The oxidation-reduction condition of the soil is a factor here. If the soil is well aerated, the ion of higher valence in each case tends to predominate. But if drainage is poor, reduction may occur and the lower-valent forms will be present. Thus, aeration is of tremendous nutritive importance.

The carbon dioxide of the atmosphere in its photosynthetic role is the direct source of most of the carbon acquired by higher plants, but not necessarily of all. In the soil solution carbonate and bicarbonate ions occur, and there is some evidence that these may be adsorbed by higher plants. In fact, at times a considerable amount of carbon probably enters the plant directly from the soil.

2:11.   SOIL AND PLANT INTERRELATIONS

It must not be assumed that nutrient solubility and availability are strictly soil phenomena with the plant simply absorbing in a passive way that which is presented to it. Nutrient solubility is markedly affected by root exudates and by microbial activity in the vicinity of the roots (the rhizosphere). Furthermore, once nutrients are solubilized their entrance into root cells is determined to a large extent by reactions associated with the plant. Aerobic respiration of root cells is thought to supply energy for nutrient absorption, and reactions within the root cell membrane determine the rate at which any given element can be absorbed.

Ions are thought to move across a root cell membrane with the help of so-called nutrient carriers (Fig. 2:7). The carrier for a given element (C) is "energized" by the process of respiration and in this state selec-

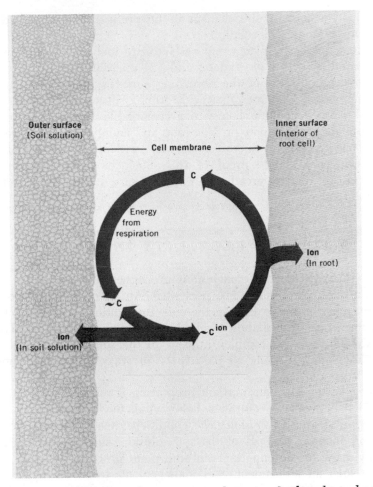

Figure 2:7. An illustration of how nutrient elements are thought to be transported from the soil solution into the root cell. An organic carrier C is specific for a given ion or group of ions. It can be energized through the process of respiration. In this state (∼C) it will bind ions of a specific element and transport them across the membrane. At the inner surface of the membrane the carrier releases the ion into the interior of the root cell. (From Hanson, J. B. "Roots—selectors of plant nutrients" Plant Food Review, Spring 1967 p. 8.)

tively binds ions from the soil solution. The carrier, coupled with the ion, moves across the cell membrane and releases the ion into the interior of the cell. This process makes possible the movement of ions from a dilute soil solution into a more concentrated solution in the cell. Furthermore, because a carrier is specific for one ion or a group of ions, it permits the ions of one element to be preferentially absorbed over others present in the soil solution.

Nutrient uptake by plants requires intimate root-soil association. It is accentuated by: (1) root exudates and (2) microbial activity in the immediate neighborhood of the absorbing surfaces. Plant roots give off large amounts of CO_2 and other acid-forming substances as well. These, no doubt, speed up interchange to a remarkable degree. Also, organic excretions from plant roots provide food and energy for microorganisms. The concentration of microbial activity within the plant-root zone (rhizosphere) is ample proof of this. Such biochemical phenomena cannot fail to increase greatly the rate and ease of transfer of nutrients from soil to plant.

2:12. SOIL FERTILITY INFERENCES

Certain practical conclusions are inescapable in respect to the plant-nutrient relationships just presented. An adequate supply of each nutrient must be maintained in the soil. In addition, provision must be made for a rate of availability suitable to normal crop growth. This involves a more or less complex transfer to the soil solution and to the plant, the latter seeming to participate in ways other than those of mere absorption.

Moreover, an adequate nutrient proportion is requisite, the total concentration of available nutrients being vital. Such a balance tends to insure the desirable physiological conditions necessary for successful plant production. The pH of the soil solution, since it influences profoundly many of the important soil and plant processes, plays a critical role in such an adjustment. Soil management, to be successful, must encompass all of these phases.

Chapter 3

Some Important Physical
Properties of Mineral Soils

Physically, a mineral soil is a porous mixture of inorganic particles, decaying organic matter, and air and water. The larger mineral fragments usually are imbedded in and coated over with colloidal and other fine materials. In some cases, the larger mineral particles predominate and a gravelly or sandy soil results. In other cases, the mineral colloids are more prevalent giving the soil clayey characteristics. All gradations between these extremes are found in nature. Organic matter acts as a binding agent to encourage the individual particles to cluster into clumps or aggregates.

Two very important physical properties of soils will be considered in this chapter: *soil texture* and *soil structure*. Soil texture is concerned with the size of mineral particles. Specifically it refers to the relative proportion of the various size-groups in a given soil. No less important is soil structure, which is the arrangement of soil particles into groups or aggregates. Together, these properties help determine, not only the nutrient-supplying ability of soil solids but also the supply of water and

41

air, so important to plant life. We shall start our consideration of these properties with a brief discussion of soil particle-size and its significance.

3:1. CLASSIFICATION OF SOIL PARTICLES AND MECHANICAL ANALYSIS

In the time covered by a generation of man, the soil processes, while surprisingly active, usually do not alter appreciably the size of the individual mineral particles. Thus, a sandy soil remains sandy, and a clay soil remains a clay. For this reason the proportion of various size-groups in a given soil (the texture) assumes added significance. It cannot be altered and thus is considered a basic property of a soil which to an appreciable extent determines the economic value of the area.

To study successfully the mineral particles of a soil, scientists usually separate them into convenient groups according to size. The various groups are spoken of as *separates*. The analytical procedure by which the particles are thus separated is called a *mechanical analysis*. It is a determination of the particle-size distribution.

As might be expected, a number of different classifications have been devised. Two of the most important will be cited, that established by the United States Department of Agriculture and that later advanced by the International Society of Soil Science. They will be found in Table 3:1.

The first column gives the names of the various separates, and the second contains the range in size of each group according to the United States system. Columns three and four show the percentages of each separate in two very different specimen soils, a sandy loam and a clay loam. In order to obtain such figures, a sample of soil is broken up and the very fine sand and larger fractions are separated into the arbitrary groups by sieving. The silt and clay percentages are then determined by methods which depend upon the rate of settling of these two separates from suspension. This combined operation is the mechanical analysis already mentioned.[1] In the fifth column, the range in size of the four separates used in the international system is given.

---

[1] The principle involved in the method is simple. When soil particles are suspended in water they tend to sink and rapidity of settling is roughly proportional to their size. The suspension of a sample of soil is, therefore, the first step; the second step is that of settling and the withdrawal by some means of successive grades; and the third step is the determination of the percentage of each group of particles based on the original sample. The apparatus and techniques are rather complicated. For an over-all discussion consult: V. J. Kilmer and L. T. Alexander, "Methods of Making Mechanical Analyses of Soils," *Soil Sci.*, 68:15–24, 1949.

Table 3:1. The Classification of Soil Particles According to Two Systems[a] (U.S. and International) and the Mechanical Analyses of Two Soils Using the U.S. System

| Soil Separate | United States Department of Agriculture System | | | International System |
| | Diameter Limits (mm) | Analyses of Two Typical Soils | | Diameter Limits (mm) |
		sandy loam (Percentage)	clay loam (Percentage)	
Very coarse sand	2.00–1.00	3.1	2.2	
Coarse sand	1.00–0.50	10.5	4.0	2.00–0.20
Medium sand	0.50–0.25	8.2	6.3	
Fine sand	0.25–0.10	25.3	8.4	0.20–0.02
Very fine sand	0.10–0.05	22.0	9.6	
Silt	0.50–0.002	21.1	37.2	0.02–0.002
Clay	below 0.002	9.8	32.3	below 0.002

[a] From *Soil Survey Manual* (U.S. Dept. of Agriculture Handbook No. 18, 1951), p. 207.

Although stone and gravel figure in the practical examination and evaluation of a field soil, they do not enter into the analysis of the fine earth. Their amounts are usually rated separately. The organic matter, ordinarily comparatively small in quantity, either is allowed to distribute itself through the various mineral groups or more often is removed by oxidation before the mechanical separation. The percentage of total organic matter, however, is generally quoted separately as it throws additional light on the probable physical nature of the soil in question. The percentage of calcium carbonate, if it is present, may also be given.

Sand, when dominant, yields a coarse-textured soil, which has properties known to everyone as *sandy* or *light* since such a soil is easily worked. On the other hand, a fine-textured soil is made up largely of silt and clay, and its plasticity and stickiness indicate that it is likely to be difficult to work or *heavy*. The use of the terms "light" and "heavy" refer to ease of working and not to soil weight. As we shall see later, the weight of a cubic foot of dry sand is actually greater in most cases than that of clay.

Not only is a mechanical analysis valuable in picturing in a general way the physical properties of a soil but it is also of use in deciding the textural name—that is, whether a soil is a sand, sandy loam, loam, etc. This phase is considered in Section 3:5.

3:2. THE PHYSICAL NATURE OF THE SOIL SEPARATES

THE COARSE SEPARATES. Stone, gravel, and sand, because of their sizes, function as separate particles. The first two range in size from 2 mm. upward and may be more or less rounded, irregularly angular, or even flat as the case may be.[2] Sand grains also may be rounded or quite irregular, depending on the amount of abrasion that they have received. (See Fig. 3:1.) When not coated with clay and silt, such particles exhibit practically no plasticity[3] and stickiness and, as a consequence, are little influenced by changes in moisture content. Their water-holding capacity is low, and because of the large size of the spaces between the separate particles, the passage of percolating water is rapid. They, therefore, facilitate drainage and encourage good air movement. Soils dominated by sand or gravel, therefore, are of open character, possess good drainage and aeration, and are usually in a loose friable condition.

CLAY AND SILT. The clay particles commonly are mica-like in shape and highly plastic when moist. When clay is wetted with a suitable amount of water, it expands and becomes sticky. On drying, it shrinks (see Fig. 4:8) with absorption of considerable energy. On wetting again, swelling occurs with the evolution of heat. This is called the *heat of wetting*. The adsorptive capacity of clays for water, gases, and soluble

Figure 3:1. Sand grains from soil. Note that the particles are irregular as to size and shape. While quartz usually predominates, other minerals may also occur. Silt particles have about the same shape and composition, differing only in size.

[2] The distinction between gravel and stone is now technically based on size. Gravel, chert, and slate are considered to range from 2 mm. to 3 inches along their greatest diameter. Stone, cobbles, and boulders, on the other hand, exceed 3 inches in respect to their greatest dimension.

[3] *Plasticity* is the property of a material which allows one to mold it when moist into various forms by applying pressure. When the pressure is released the material will maintain its molded form.

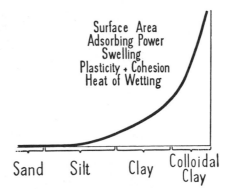

Figure 3:2. The finer the texture of a soil, the greater is the effective surface exposed by its particles. Note that adsorption, swelling, and the other physical properties cited follow the same trend and that their intensities go up rapidly as the colloidal size is approached.

Surface Area
Adsorbing Power
Swelling
Plasticity + Cohesion
Heat of Wetting

Sand   Silt   Clay   Colloidal Clay

salts is very high. The diagram in Fig. 3:2 shows how these properties increase as the particle size becomes smaller.

In contrast with the platelike clay, silt particles tend to be irregularly fragmental, diverse in shape, and seldom smooth or flat. (See Fig. 3:1.) In fact, they really are microsand particles, quartz being the dominant mineral. The silt separate possesses some plasticity, cohesion (stickiness), and adsorption due to an adhering film of clay but, of course, to a much lesser degree than the clay separate itself. In fact, the influence of silt is such as to make it a rather unsatisfactory soil constituent physically unless supplemented by adequate amounts of sand, clay, and organic matter.

The presence of silt and especially clay in a soil imparts to it a *fine texture,* and a slow water and air movement. Such a soil is highly plastic, becoming sticky when too wet, and hard and cloddy when dry unless properly handled. The expansion and contraction on wetting and drying usually are great. And the water-holding capacity of clayey and silty soils generally is high. As already mentioned, such soils are spoken of as *heavy* because of their difficult working qualities, markedly in contrast with *light,* easily tilled sandy and gravelly surface soils.

3:3. THE MINERALOGICAL AND CHEMICAL COMPOSITIONS OF SOIL SEPARATES

Although at this point our interest in soil particles is largely a physical one, a glance at their mineralogical make-up and chemical composition may not be amiss.

MINERALOGICAL CHARACTERISTICS. As already suggested, the coarsest sand particles often are fragments of rock as well as of quartz, the most prevalent mineral in this separate. Quartz also

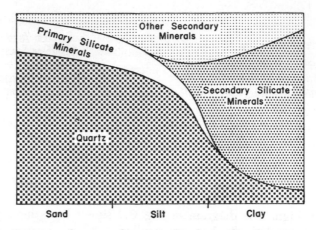

Figure 3:3. Diagram showing the general relationship between particle size and kinds of minerals present. Quartz dominates the sand and coarse silt fractions. Primary silicates such as the feldspars, hornblende, and micas are present in the sands but tend to disappear as one moves to the silt fraction. Secondary silicates dominate the fine colloidal clay. Other secondary minerals such as the oxides of iron and aluminum are prominent in the fine silt and coarse clay fractions.

commonly dominates the finer grades of sand as well as the silt separate. (See Fig. 3:1.) In addition, variable quantities of other primary minerals usually occur, such as the various feldspars and micas. (See Fig. 3:3.) Gibbsite, hematite, and limonite minerals also are found, usually as coatings on the sand grains. The latter two impart various shades of red and yellow if present in sufficient quantities. The soils of our Piedmont plateau and well-oxidized tropical earths are good examples.

Some of the clay particles, especially those in the coarser clay fractions, are composed of the minerals already cited as quartz, hematite, and gibbsite. An even more important group, however, is the complex aluminosilicates. Three main mineral types are at present recognized although others are known to occur in significant quantities—*kaolinite, illite,* and *montmorillonite.* It will suffice at this time to say that these groups vary markedly in plasticity, cohesion, and adsorption, kaolinite being lowest in each case and montmorillonite highest. It is, therefore, of considerable importance as to which clay type dominates or codominates any particular soil.

CHEMICAL MAKE-UP. Since sand and silt are dominantly quartz (SiO_2), these two fractions are generally quite inactive chemically. Even the primary minerals which may contain nutrient elements in their chemical make-up are generally so insoluble as to make their nutrient-supplying ability essentially nil. An exception to this general rule is the silt fraction of certain potassium-bearing minerals such as the micas which have been known to release this element at a sufficiently rapid rate to supply, at least in part, plant requirements.

Chemically, kaolinite and the other members of that particular group are aluminum silicates. The same is true for montmorillonite and other clays of that same crystal pattern, but they carry in addition sodium, iron, or magnesium as the case may be. Illite, often referred to as hydrous mica, is a potassium aluminum silicate. Its high potash content gives it a special nutrient significance. Obviously, the word "clay" is a term covering substances differing widely in their mineralogical and chemical compositions.

If the various soil separates, ranging as they do from very coarse sand to ultrafine clay, differ so markedly in crystal form and chemical composition, will they not also show a like contrast in respect to mineral nutrients? Logically we would expect the sands, being mostly quartz, to be lowest and the clay separate to be highest. This inference is substantiated by the data in Table 3:2. The general relationships shown by these data hold true for most soils, although some exceptions may occur.

3:4. SOIL CLASS— THE TEXTURAL NAMES OF SOILS

As soils are composed of particles varying greatly in size and shape, specific terms are needed to convey some idea of their textural make-up and to give some indication of their physical properties. For this, *class* names are used, such as sand, sandy loam, silt loam, and the like.

These class names have originated through years of soil study and classification and gradually have become more or less standardized. Three broad yet fundamental groups of soils are recognized: *sands, loams,* and *clays.* On the basis of these, additional class names have been devised.

SANDS. The *sand* group includes all soils of which the sand separates make up 70 per cent or more of the material by weight. The properties of such soils are, therefore, characteristically sandy in contrast with the stickier and more clayey nature of the heavier groups of soil. Two specific classes are recognized—*sand* and *loamy sand.*

CLAYS. A soil to be designated a clay must carry at least 35 per cent of the clay separate and in most cases not less than 40 per cent. So long as the percentage of clay is 40 or above, the characteristics of this separate are distinctly dominant and the class name is *sandy clay,*

Table 3:2. Phosphorus, Potassium and Calcium Contents of Separates from Various United States Surface Soils[a]

| Separate | Soils Developed from Indicated Materials | | | | |
	Crystalline Residual	Limestone Residual	Coastal Plain	Glacial and Loessial	Arid
			per cent P		
Sand	0.03	0.12	0.03	0.07	0.08
Silt	0.10	0.10	0.10	0.10	0.10
Clay	0.31	0.16	0.34	0.38	0.20
			per cent K		
Sand	1.33	1.21	0.31	1.43	2.53
Silt	2.0	1.52	1.10	2.00	3.44
Clay	2.37	2.17	1.34	2.55	4.20
			per cent Ca		
Sand	0.36	8.75	0.05	0.91	2.92
Silt	0.59	7.83	0.14	0.93	6.58
Clay	0.67	7.08	0.39	1.92	5.73

[a] G. H. Failyer, *et al., The Mineral Composition of Soil Particles,* Bulletin 54, Bureau of Soils, U.S. Dept. of Agric., 1908.

Data in respect to the distribution of silicon, iron, aluminum, titanium, calcium, and magnesium through the various separates as reported by Joffe and Kunin are given below. The soil fractionated was a Montalto silt loam of New Jersey, a residual product from basalt. The figures quoted are for the surface eight inch layer only.

Chemical Composition of Montalto Silt Loam Fractions[†]

Separate	SiO_2 %	Fe_2O_3 %	Al_2O_3 %	TiO_2 %	CaO %	MgO %
Sand	86.3	5.19	6.77	1.05	.37	1.02
Coarse silt	81.3	3.11	7.21	1.05	.41	.82
Fine silt	64.0	9.42	12.00	1.05	.32	2.22
Coarser clay	45.1	13.50	21.10	.96	.38	2.09
Finer clay	30.2	17.10	22.80	.88	.08	1.77

[†] J. S. Joffe and R. Kunin, "Mechanical Separates and Their Fraction in the Soil Profile: I. Variability in Chemical Composition and Its Pedogenic and Agropedogenic Implications," *Proc. Soil Sci. Soc. Amer.,* 7:187–93, 1942.

silty clay, or, the commonest of all, simply *clay.* It is well to note that sandy clays often contain more sand than clay. Likewise, the silt content of silty clays usually exceeds that of the clay fraction itself.

L O A M S .   The *loam* group, which contains many subdivisions, is more difficult to explain. An ideal loam may be defined as a mixture of sand, silt, and clay particles which exhibits light and heavy properties in about equal proportions. Roughly it is a half-and-half mixture on the basis of properties.

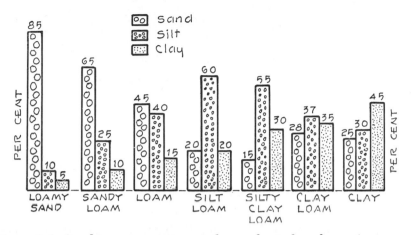

Figure 3:4. *Graphic representation of the mechanical analyses of representative mineral soils.*

Most soils of agricultural importance are some type of loam. They may possess the ideal make-up described above and be classed simply as *loam.* In most cases, however, the quantities of sand, silt, or clay present require a modified class name. Thus, a loam in which sand is dominant is classified as a *sandy loam* of some kind; in the same way there may occur *silt loams, silty clay loams,* and *clay loams.*

      VARIATIONS IN THE FIELD. It readily can be seen that the textural names already established—*sand, loamy sand, sandy loam, loam, silt loam, silty clay loam, clay loam, sandy clay, silty clay,* and *clay*—form a more or less graduated sequence from soils that are coarse in texture and easy to handle to those, the heavy clays, that are very fine and difficult to manage. It is also obvious that these class names are a reflection not only of particle-size distribution but also of tillage characteristics and other physical properties. You should be fully familiar with the concept underlying the nomenclature employed. A study of Fig. 3:4 will aid in its visualization.

      It is well to point out that for some soils qualifying factors such as stone, gravel, and the various grades of sand must be descriptively taken into consideration. Even silt and clay become qualifying terms in practice. All this will be obvious when the following lists are examined.

Sandy soils	*Loam Soils*	*Clayey Soils*
Gravelly sands	Stony-sandy loams	Stony clays
Coarse sands	Gravelly-sandy loams	Gravelly clays
Medium sands	Coarse-sandy loams	Sandy clays
Fine sands	Medium-sandy loams	Silty clays

Sandy soils	*Loam Soils*	*Clayey Soils*
Very fine sands	Fine-sandy loams	Clays
Loamy sands	Very-fine-sandy loams	
Sands	Loams, gravelly loams, and stony loams	
	Silt loams and stony-silt loams	
	Silty-clay loams	
	Clay loams and stony-clay loams	

3:5. THE DETERMINATION OF SOIL CLASS

FIELD METHOD. The common field method of determining the class name of a soil is by its *feel*. Probably as much can be judged about the texture and hence the class name of a soil merely by rubbing it between the thumb and fingers as by any other superficial means. Usually it is helpful to wet the sample in order to estimate plasticity more accurately. The way a wet soil "slicks out" gives a good idea of the amount of clay present. The sand particles are gritty; the silt has a floury or talcum-powder feel when dry and is only moderately plastic and sticky when wet. Persistent cloddiness generally is imparted by silt and clay.

The method as outlined is used in field operations such as soil survey and land classification. Accuracy in such a determination is of great practical value and depends largely on experience. Facility in class determination is one of the first things a field man should develop.

LABORATORY METHOD. A more accurate and fundamental method has been devised by the United States Department of Agriculture for the naming of soils based on a mechanical analysis. This method of identification is shown diagrammatically in Fig. 3:5. The diagram reemphasizes that a soil is a mixture of different sizes of particles and that a close correlation exists between particle size distribution and the properties of soils. Obviously, when mechanical analysis of the field soils that he has been working with are available to a surveyor, he can readily check on the accuracy of his class designations. A working knowledge of this method of naming soils is, of course, very essential. The legend explains the use of the triangular chart devised for this purpose. (See Fig. 3:5.)

3:6. THE PARTICLE DENSITY OF MINERAL SOILS

One means of expressing soil weight is in terms of the density of the solid particles making up the soil. It is usually defined as the mass

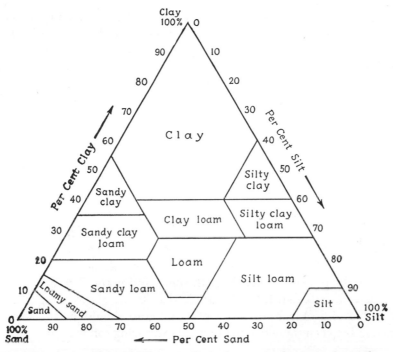

Figure 3:5. Diagram by means of which the textural name of a soil may be determined from a mechanical analysis. In using the diagram, the points corresponding to the percentages of silt and clay present in the soil under consideration are located on the silt and clay lines respectively. Lines are then projected inward, parallel in the first case to the clay side of the triangle and in the second case parallel to the sand side. The name of the compartment in which the two lines intersect is the class name of the soil in question.

(or weight) of a unit volume of soil solids and is called the *particle density*. In the metric system, particle density is usually expressed in terms of grams per cubic centimeter. Thus, if 1 cubic centimeter of soil solids weighs 2.6 grams, the particle density is 2.6 grams per cc.

Although considerable range may be observed in the density of the individual soil minerals, the figures for most mineral soils usually vary within the narrow limits of 2.60 and 2.75. This occurs because quartz, feldspar, and the colloidal silicates, with densities within this range, usually make up the major portion of mineral soils. Occasionally, however, when unusual amounts of heavy minerals such as magnetite, garnet, epidote, zircon, tourmaline, and hornblende are present, the particle density may exceed 2.75. It should be pointed out that the *fineness* of the particles of a given mineral and the arrangement of the soil solids have nothing to do with the particle density.

Since organic matter weighs much less than does an equal volume of the mineral solids, the amount of this constituent in a soil markedly affects the particle density. As a consequence, surface soils usually possess lower particle densities than do subsoils. Some highly organic mineral top soils may drop as low as 2.4, or even below, in particle density. Nevertheless, for general calculations, the average arable surface soil may be considered to have a particle density of about 2.65.

3:7. THE BULK DENSITY OF MINERAL SOILS

BULK DENSITY. This is a second and different method of expressing soil weight. In this case the *total soil space* (space occupied by solids and pore spaces combined) is taken into consideration. Bulk density is defined as the mass (weight) of a unit volume of dry soil. This volume would, of course, include both solids and pores. The comparative calculations of bulk density and particle density are shown diagrammatically in Fig. 3:6. A careful study of this figure should make clear the distinction between these two methods of expressing soil weight.

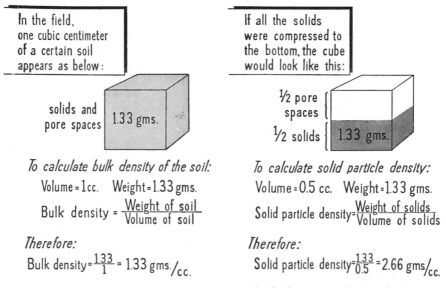

In the field, one cubic centimeter of a certain soil appears as below:

solids and pore spaces — 1.33 gms.

To calculate bulk density of the soil:

Volume = 1 cc.   Weight = 1.33 gms.

$$\text{Bulk density} = \frac{\text{Weight of soil}}{\text{Volume of soil}}$$

Therefore:

$$\text{Bulk density} = \frac{1.33}{1} = 1.33 \text{ gms.}/cc.$$

If all the solids were compressed to the bottom, the cube would look like this:

½ pore spaces
½ solids — 1.33 gms.

To calculate solid particle density:

Volume = 0.5 cc.   Weight = 1.33 gms.

$$\text{Solid particle density} = \frac{\text{Weight of solids}}{\text{Volume of solids}}$$

Therefore:

$$\text{Solid particle density} = \frac{1.33}{0.5} = 2.66 \text{ gms.}/cc.$$

Figure 3:6. A diagramatic representation of bulk density and particle density of soil. Follow the calculations through carefully and the terminology should be clear. In this particular case the bulk density is one half that of the particle density and the percentage pore space is 50.

FACTORS AFFECTING BULK DENSITY. Bulk density is a weight measurement by which the entire soil volume is taken into consideration. Unlike particle density, which is concerned with the solid particles only, bulk density is determined by the quantity of pore spaces as well as the soil solids. Thus, soils that are loose and porous will have low weights per unit volume (bulk densities) and those that are more compact will have high values. Since the particles of sandy soils generally tend to lie in close contact, such soils have high bulk densities. The low organic matter content of sandy soils further encourages this. The particles of the finer surface soils such as silt loams, clay loams, and clays, on the other hand, ordinarily do not rest so close together. This results from the fact that these surface soils are comparatively well granulated, a condition encouraged by their relatively high organic matter contents. Granulation encourages a fluffy, porous condition which results in low bulk-density values. Consequently, the bulk density of a well granulated silt loam surface soil is sure to be lower than that of a representative sandy loam.

The bulk densities of clay, clay loam, and silt loam surface soils normally may range from 1.00 to as high as 1.60 grams per cc depending on their condition. A variation from 1.20 to 1.80 may be found in sands and sandy loams. Very compact subsoils regardless of texture may have bulk densities as high as 2.0 grams per cc or even greater.

Even in soils of the same surface texture, great differences in bulk density are to be expected when similar horizon levels are compared. This is clearly shown by data in Table 3:3 respecting Wisconsin silt and clay loams. Moreover, there is a distinct tendency for the bulk density to rise with profile depth. This apparently results from a lower content of organic matter, less aggregation and root penetration, and a compaction caused by the weight of the overlying layers.

Table 3:3. Bulk Density Data for Certain Wisconsin Profiles[a]

Horizon	Marathon Silt Loam	Miami Silt Loam	Spencer Silt Loam	Superior Clay Loam
Plow layer	1.34	1.28	1.38	1.46
Upper subsoil	1.49	1.41	1.55	—
Lower subsoil	1.59	1.43	1.66	1.66
Parent material	1.72	1.49	1.63	—

[a] L. B. Nelson and R. J. Muckenhirn, "Field Percolation Rates of Four Wisconsin Soils Having Different Drainage Characteristics," *Jour. Amer. Soc. Agron.*, 33:1028–36, 1941.

The system of crop and soil management employed on a given soil is likely to influence its bulk density, especially of the surface layers. The addition of farm manure in large amounts tends to lower the weight figure of surface soils as does also a bluegrass sod. Intensive cultivation, on the other hand, operates in the opposite direction.

Data presented in Table 3:4 show this relationship very well. These data are from long-time experiments in four different states, the soils having been under cultivation for from 40 to 150 years. Cropping increased the bulk density of the topsoils in all cases.

Table 3:4. The Bulk Density and Per Cent Pore Space of Certain Cultivated Topsoils and of Nearby Uncropped Areas[a]

Soil Type	Years Cropped	Bulk Density Cropped Soil	Uncropped Soil	Per Cent Pore Space Cropped Soil	Uncropped Soil
Hagerstown loam (Penna.)	58	1.25	1.07	50.0	57.2
Marshall silt loam (Iowa)	50+	1.13	0.93	56.2	62.7
Nappanee silt loam (Ohio)	40	1.31	1.05	50.5	60.3
Ave. 19 Georgia soils	45–150	1.45	1.14	45.1	57.1

[a] The above data were obtained from several sources. See T. L. Lyon; H. O. Buckman; and N. C. Brady, *The Nature and Properties of Soils* (New York: Macmillan, 1952), p. 60.

OTHER WEIGHT FIGURES. When the bulk density of a soil is known in terms of grams per cc, its dry weight in pounds per cubic foot may be found approximately by multiplying by 62.42, the standard weight of a cubic foot of water. Clayey and silty surface soils may vary from 65 to 100 pounds to the cubic foot; sands and sandy loams may show a variation of 75 to 110 pounds. The greater the organic content, the less is this weight. Very compact subsoils, regardless of texture, may weigh as much as 125 pounds per cubic foot. The figures quoted are for the dry soil and do not include the water present.

The actual weight of a soil also may be expressed in terms of an acre-foot, referring to a volume of soil 1 acre in extent and 1 foot deep. The weight of an acre-foot of surface mineral soil commonly ranges from 3,000,000 to 4,500,000 pounds of dry substance. The figure most commonly used, however, is 2,000,000 or sometimes 2,500,000 pounds as the weight of average surface soil to a depth of 6 to 7 inches. This is considered an *acre-furrow-slice.*

3:8. THE PORE SPACE OF MINERAL SOILS

The pore space of a soil is that portion occupied by air and water. The amount of this pore space is determined largely by the arrangement of the solid particles. If they tend to lie close together, as in sands or compact subsoils, the total porosity is low. If they are arranged in porous aggregates, as is often the case in medium textured soils high in organic matter, the pore space per unit volume will be high.

The validity of the above generalizations may readily be substantiated by the use of a very simple formula[4] involving particle density and bulk density figures. A sandy soil having a bulk density of 1.50 and a particle density of 2.65 will be found to have, when these figures are properly applied to the formula below, 43.4 per cent of pore space. A silt loam in which the corresponding values are 1.30 and 2.65, respectively, possesses 50.9 per cent of air and water space. This latter value is close to the pore capacity of a normally granulated silt loam or clay loam surface soil.

FACTORS INFLUENCING TOTAL PORE SPACE. As might be expected, considerable difference in the total pore space of various soils occurs depending upon conditions. Sandy surface soils show a range of from 35 to 50 per cent, whereas medium to fine textured soils vary from 40 to 60 per cent or perhaps even more in cases of high organic matter and marked granulation. Pore space also varies with depth; some compact subsoils drop as low as 25 to 30 per cent. This accounts in part for the inadequate aeration of such horizons.

The handling of a soil exerts a marked influence upon pore space of the furrow-slice. For instance, the continuous bluegrass sod of the Hagerstown loam of Pennsylvania cited in Table 3:4 had a total porosity of 57.2 per cent, whereas the comparable rotation plot showed only 50 per cent. Additional data presented in this table from three other states

---

[4] The derivation of the formula used to calculate the percentage of total pore space in soil is as follows:

$$\% \text{ solid space} = \frac{\text{Bulk density}}{\text{Particle density}} \times 100.$$

Since,

$$\% \text{ pore space} + \% \text{ solid space} = 100$$

and

$$\% \text{ pore space} = 100 - \% \text{ solid space}$$

then

$$\% \text{ pore space} = 100 - \frac{\text{Bulk density}}{\text{Particle density}} \times 100$$

show that cropping tends to lower the total pore space below that of the virgin or uncropped soils. This reduction usually is associated with a decrease in organic matter content and a consequent lowering of granulation. Pore space in the subsoil has been found to decrease with cropping, although to a somewhat lesser degree.

SIZE OF PORES. Two types of individual pore spaces in general occur in soils—*macro-* and *micro-*. Although no sharp line of demarcation occurs, the macropores characteristically allow the ready movement of air and percolating water. In contrast, in the microtype of pore, air movement is greatly impeded, and water movement is restricted largely to slow capillary movement. Thus, in a sandy soil, in spite of the low total porosity, the movement of air and water is surprisingly rapid because of the dominance of the macrospaces.

Fine textured soils allow relatively slow gas and water movement in spite of the unusually large amount of total pore space. Here the dominating micropores often maintain themselves full of water. Aeration, especially in the subsoil, frequently is inadequate for satisfactory root development and desirable microbial activity. Thus, the *size* of the individual pore spaces rather than their combined volume is the important consideration. The loosening and granulating of fine textured soils promotes aeration, not so much by increasing the pore space in total as by raising the proportion of the macrospaces.

It has already been suggested (p. 9 and Fig. 1:4) that in a well-granulated silt loam surface-soil at optimum moisture for plant growth the total pore space will be near 50 per cent and is likely to be shared fairly equally by air and water. Soil aeration under such a condition is likely to be fairly satisfactory especially if a similar ratio of air to water extends well into the subsoil.

CROPPING AND SIZE OF PORES. Continuous cropping, particularly of soils originally very high in organic matter, often results in a reduction of large or macropore spaces. Data from a Rendzina soil in Texas presented in Table 3:5 show this effect very strikingly.

The amount of macropore space, so necessary for ready air movement, was reduced about one half by cropping the soil. This severe reduction in pore size extended into the 6- to 12-inch layer also. In fact, samples taken as deep as 42-inches showed the same trend.

A further examination of Table 3:5 shows that cultivation and cropping have appreciably reduced the total pore space. This was accompanied by a more or less proportional rise in the space given over to micropores. As would be expected, the decrease in pore size was associated with a corresponding decrease in organic matter content.

Table 3:5. The Effect of Continuous Cropping for at Least 40–50 Years on the Total Pore Space and the Macro- and Micropore Spaces in a Houston Black Clay from Texas[a]

Sampling Depth Inches	Soil Treatment	Organic Matter (%)	Pore Space		
			Total (%)	Macro (%)	Micro (%)
0–6	Virgin	5.6	58.3	32.7	25.6
	Cultivated	2.9	50.2	16.0	34.2
6–12	Virgin	4.2	56.1	27.0	29.1
	Cultivated	2.8	50.7	14.7	36.0

[a] W. D. Laws and D. D. Evans, "The Effects of Long-time Cultivation on Some Physical and Chemical Properties of Two Rendzina Soils," *Proc. Soil Sci. Soc. Amer.*, 14:15–19, 1949.

3:9. THE STRUCTURE OF MINERAL SOILS

Although *texture* undoubtedly is of great importance in determining certain characteristics of a soil, it is evident that the particular type of particle grouping that happens to predominate must exert considerable influence also. The term *structure* is used to refer to such groupings. Structure is strictly a field term descriptive of the gross, over-all aggregation or arrangement of the soil solids.

A profile may be dominated by a single structural pattern. More often, a number of types of aggregation are encountered as progress is made from horizon to horizon. It is at once apparent that soil conditions and characteristics—such as water movement, heat transfer, aeration, bulk density, and porosity—will be much influenced by structure. In fact, the important physical changes imposed by the farmer in plowing, cultivating, draining, liming, and manuring his land are structural rather than textural.

Structural forms under virgin conditions apparently have been developed from one or both of two possible nonstructural states—(1) *single grained* and (2) *massive*. In the former, the single, solid particles function as individuals. Loose sand is a good example of this. The binding influence of organic matter often modifies this original form to a certain extent by building up a weak aggregation. In the massive nonstructural case, the soil units originally are very large, irregular, and featureless as far as characteristic soil aggregates are concerned.

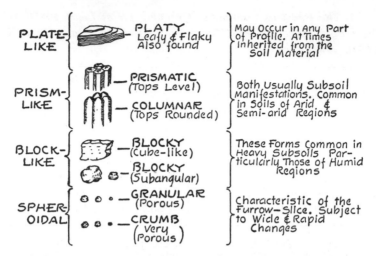

Figure 3:7. *Diagramatic representation of the various structural types found in mineral soils. Their location in the profile is suggested. In arable soils, granulation usually receives the most attention.*

TYPES OF SOIL STRUCTURE. These two extremes cited above are the theoretical boundaries of the seven structural types commonly recognized in soil profiles. They are as follows: *platy, columnar, prismatic, blocky, subangular blocky, granular,* and *crumb*. A brief description of each of these structural types with schematic drawings will be found in Fig. 3:7. A more detailed description of each follows:

1. Platelike—*Platy*—In this structural type the aggregates or groups are arranged in relatively thin horizontal plates, leaflets, or lenses. If the units are quite thin, the term *laminar* is used. Although it is most noticeable in the surface layers of virgin soils, platy structure may characterize the subsoil horizons as well.

    Although most structural features are usually a product of soil forming forces, the *platy* type is often inherited from the parent materials, especially when the latter have been laid down by water or ice.

2. Prism-like—*Columnar* and *Prismatic*—These types are characterized by vertically oriented aggregates or pillars. These elongated columns vary in length with different soils and may reach a diameter of 6 inches or more. They commonly occur in the subsoil horizons of arid and semiarid region soils and when well developed are a very striking feature of the profile.

    When the tops are rounded, the term *columnar* is used. This may occur when the profile is changing and certain horizons are degrading. When the tops of the prisms are still plane, level, and clean cut, the structural pattern is designated *prismatic*. Both the prismatic and columnar types of aggregation are divided into classes depending on the size or horizontal diameter of the prisms.

3. Blocklike—*Blocky* and *Subangular blocky*—In this case the original aggregates have been reduced to blocks, irregularly six faced, and with their three dimensions more or less equal. In size these fragments range from a fraction of an inch to 3 or 4 inches in thickness. In general, the design is so individualistic that identification is easy.

When the edges of the cubes are sharp and the rectangular faces distinct, the type is designated *blocky*. When subrounding has occurred, the aggregates are spoken of as *subangular blocky* or *nuciform*. These types usually are confined to the subsoil, and their stage of development and other characteristics have much to do with soil drainage, aeration, and root penetration.

4. Spheroidal—*Granular* and *Crumb*—All rounded aggregates may be placed in this category although the term more properly refers to those not over ½ inch in diameter. These rounded complexes usually lie loosely and are readily shaken apart. When wetted, the intervening spaces generally are not closed so readily by swelling as may be the case with a blocky structural condition. Ordinarily the aggregates are spoken of as granules and the pattern as *granular*. However, when the granules are especially porous, the term *crumb* is significantly applied.

Granular and, less frequently, crumb structures are characteristic of many surface soils, especially those high in organic matter. They are the only types of aggregation that are commonly influenced by practical methods of soil management.

As already emphasized, two or more of the structural conditions listed usually occur in the same soil solum. In humid-temperate regions, a granular aggregation in the surface horizon with a blocky, subangular blocky or platy type of some kind in the subsoil is usual, although granular subhorizons are not uncommon. In soils of arid regions the blocky type in the subsoil may be replaced by a prismatic arrangement.

GENESIS OF SOIL STRUCTURE. The mechanics of structure formation are exceedingly complicated and rather obscure. The nature and origin of the parent material are important factors as are the physical and biochemical processes of soil formation, particularly those that result in the synthesis of clay and humus. Climate is also a prime consideration. Soluble salts probably play an important role, particularly in the soils of arid regions. Nor should the downward migration of clay, iron oxides, and lime be overlooked. Undoubtedly, the accumulation of organic matter and its type of decay play a major role, especially in the development of the granular structure so common in the surface soils of grasslands. In fact, the preservation and encouragement of this particular structural type becomes one of the most important soil problems of cultivated lands. Let us turn to this phase without further delay.

3:10. AGGREGATION AND ITS PROMOTION IN ARABLE SOILS[5]

In a practical sense we are concerned with two sets of factors in dealing with soil aggregation (1) those responsible for aggregate formation; and (2) those which give the aggregates stability once they are formed. Since both sets of factors are operating simultaneously, it is sometimes difficult to separate their relative effects on stable granule development in soils.

GENESIS OF GRANULES. Although there is some uncertainty about the exact mechanism by which granules form, several specific factors are known to influence their genesis. These include: (1) wetting and drying; (2) freezing and thawing; (3) the physical activity of roots and soil animals; (4) the influence of decaying organic matter and of the slimes from the microorganisms and other forms of life; (5) the modifying effects of adsorbed cations; and (6) soil tillage.

Obviously, any action that will develop lines of weakness, shift the particles to and fro, and force contacts that otherwise might not occur, should encourage aggregation. Consequently, it is not surprising that the alternate wetting and drying, and freezing and thawing, the physical effects of root extension, and the mixing action of soil organisms and of tillage implements tend to encourage aggregate formation. The benefits of fall plowing on certain types of soil and the slaking of clods under the influence of a gentle rain have long been known and taken advantage of in seedbed preparation. And the granulating influences of earthworms and other soil organisms should not be passed unnoticed.

THE INFLUENCE OF ORGANIC MATTER. The major agency in the encouragement of granular type aggregates in surface soil horizons probably is organic matter (see Fig. 3:8) which not only binds but also lightens and expands, making possible the porosity so characteristic of individual soil aggregates. Plant roots probably promote this granulation as much or more by the decay of the distributed organic matter as by the disruptive action of their ramifications. The electrochemical properties of the humus, as well as of the clay are probably effective in the organization and the later stabilization of the aggregates. Moreover,

---

[5] A review of the theories concerning aggregation will be found in an article by R. F. Harris, et al., "Dynamics of Soil Aggregation" *Advan. in Agron.*, 18:107–169, 1966.

Figure 3:8. A puddled soil (left) and a well-granulated soil (right). Plant roots and especially humus play the major role in soil granulation. For that reason a sod tends to restore the structural condition of cultivated land. (Photo courtesy U.S. Soil Conservation Service.)

slime and other viscous microbial products probably encourage crumb development and exert a stabilizing influence as well. Granulation thus assumes a highly biological aspect.

Organic matter is of much importance in modifying effects of clay. In fact, some suspect that an actual chemical union may at times take place between the decaying organic matter and the silicate molecules. Moreover, the high adsorptive capacity of humus for water tends to intensify the disruptive effects of temperature changes and moisture fluctuations. The granulation of a clay soil apparently cannot be promoted adequately without the presence of a certain amount of humus. The maintenance of organic matter and of its synthesized products, therefore, is of great practical concern, not only chemically and biologically but also physically (see Fig. 3:8.)

THE EFFECT OF ADSORBED CATIONS. One of the outstanding characteristics of the colloidal substances of the soil, both mineral and organic, is the ability to adsorb cations (see p. 73). The domination or even partial domination of certain of these cations tends to develop more or less definite physical characteristics. For instance when sodium is a prominent adsorbed ion, the particles are dispersed and a very undesirable soil structure results.

The adsorption of calcium by contrast may encourage granulation by a phenomenon called *flocculation*. When this occurs, the colloidal matter is brought together in floccules and tends to encourage a type of structure that is quite desirable. Flocculation in itself, however, is not granulation as it usually does not provide for the *stabilization* of the aggregates. When such means are present and active as often is the case, flocculation assumes considerable practical significance.[6]

While many surface soils highly charged with native calcium exhibit granulation to a marked degree, it must not be inferred that this effect is due entirely to the direct influence of the adsorbed calcium. Exchangeable cations merely modify the influence of the other factors, especially the over-all effects of decaying organic matter. The addition of lime, therefore, is effective as a granulating agent largely through its influence on biotic forces.

INFLUENCE OF TILLAGE. Tillage has both favorable and unfavorable effects on granulation. The short-time effect is often favorable, because the implements loosen the soil and incorporate the organic matter into the soil. Tillage under the proper moisture conditions breaks up clods and makes a more favorable seedbed. A minimum amount of tillage is thus considered necessary in normal soil management.

Over longer periods, tillage operations have detrimental effects on surface soil granules. In the first place, tillage generally hastens the oxidation of organic matter from soils. Second, tillage operations, especially those involving heavy equipment, tend to break down the stable soil aggregates. The compaction[7] that soils suffer from repeatedly running over fields with heavy farm equipment is by no means slight. An indication of the effect of such traffic upon bulk density is given in Fig. 3:9. These data help explain the increased interest in recent years in techniques of drastically reducing the tillage operations where possible. (See Fig. 3:12.)

AGGREGATE STABILITY. The stability of aggregates is of great practical importance. Some granules readily succumb to the beating of rain and the rough and tumble of plowing and fitting of the land. Others resist disintegration, thus making the maintenance of a suitable soil structure comparatively easy. Differences in aggregate stability are apparently related to the presence or absence of certain binding

---

[6] The mechanics of flocculation are more fully considered on pages 105–107.

[7] For a recent review of research on soil compaction, see: N. J. Rosenberg, Response of Plants to Physical Effects of Soil Compaction," *Advan. in Agron.*, 16:181–196, 1964.

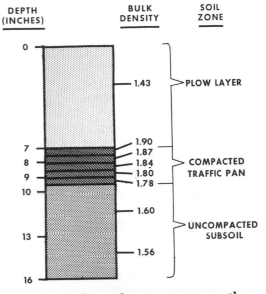

Figure 3:9. Tillage and heavy equipment traffic compacted a zone just below the plow layer of this Norfolk profile. Cotton roots would not penetrate layers with bulk densities of more than 1.8 (From C. R. Camp and J. F. Lund, "Effect of soil compaction on cotton roots." Crops and Soils 17:13–14, November 1964.)

agents. Organic compounds of various kinds are known to possess these stabilizing properties. (See Fig. 3:10.) The kind of clay influences aggregate stability, kaolinite-dominated granules being more stable than those in which montmorillonite is prominent. Other inorganic compounds, e.g., iron oxides, have a definite cementing or binding effect giving rise to stable granules.

As a general rule, the larger the aggregates present in any particular soil, the lower is their stability. This is why it is difficult to build up soil aggregation beyond a certain size of granule or crumb in cultivated land.

Figure 3:10. The aggregates of soils high in organic matter are much more stable than are those low in this constituent. The low organic matter soil aggregates fall apart when they are wetted while those high in organic matter maintain their stability.

3:11. THE STRUCTURAL MANAGEMENT OF SOILS

COARSE-TEXTURED SOILS. Looseness, friability, good aeration and drainage, and easy tillage are characteristics of sandy soils. On the other hand, such soils are often too loose and open, and lack the capacity to adsorb and hold sufficient moisture and nutrients. They are, as a consequence, likely to be droughty and lacking in fertility. They need granulation. There is only one practical method of improving the structure of such a soil—the addition of organic matter. Organic material will not only act as a binding agent for the particles but will also increase the water-holding capacity. The addition of farm manures and the growth of sod crops are practices commonly followed to improve the structural condition of sandy soils.

FINE-TEXTURED SOILS. The structural management of a silicate-clay is not such a simple problem as that of a sandy one. In the sands, the plasticity and cohesion are never great due to low content of inorganic colloids. In clays and similar soils of temperate regions, however, the potential plasticity and cohesion are always high due to the presence of large amounts of colloidal clay. The more plastic such a soil becomes, the more likely it is to *puddle*,[8] especially if worked when wet. A soil of high plasticity is prone to become hard and cloddy when dry, due to the cohesive tendencies of the small platelike particles. Such soils must be treated very carefully, especially in tillage operations. If plowed too wet, the aggregation of particles is broken down, and an unfavorable structure is sure to result. On the other hand, if plowed too dry, great clods are turned up which are difficult to work into a good seedbed. In sandy soils and the so-called hydrous-oxide clays of the tropics such difficulties usually are at a minimum.

Not only must tillage operations be carefully timed in soils high in silt and clay but granulation should be encouraged to the fullest degree. As already emphasized, organic matter is a major concern. In this respect sod crops, especially deep-rooted legumes, should be utilized to the fullest extent and the rotation planned to attain their maximum benefits. Most sod crops not only protect the land from dashing rains and erosion but also help maintain the soil organic matter.

The data shown in Table 3:6 confirm the above commonly accepted

---

[8] When a surface soil in a wet and plastic condition has been worked until its pore space is much reduced, it becomes practically impervious to air and water, and is said to be *puddled*. When a soil in this condition dries, it usually becomes hard and dense.

Table 3:6. Percentage Water-Stable Aggregation of a Marshall Silt Loam near Clarinda, Iowa, under Different Cropping Systems. (Samples Were Taken in August) [a]

Crops	Per Cent of the Water-Stable Aggregates Which Were:	
	Large (*1 mm and above*)	*Small* (*Less than 1 mm*)
Corn continuously	8.8	91.2
Corn in rotation	23.3	76.7
Meadow in rotation	42.2	57.8
Bluegrass continuously	57.0	43.0

[a] H. A. Wilson, Roger Gish, and G. M. Browning, "Cropping Systems and Season as Factors Affecting Aggregate Stability," *Proc. Soil Sci. Soc. Amer.*, 12:36–43, 1947.

observations. A Marshall silt loam near Clarinda, Iowa, was used, the cropping system employed having been in operation for a sufficient number of years for differences in their effects to develop.

A glance at the table will confirm the degranulating influence commonly ascribed to corn, less rapid, of course, when the crop is grown in a suitable rotation. The aggregating tendency of sod whether it is a meadow mixture or a bluegrass sward is likewise obvious. The data also suggest the degrees of soil granulation a person may normally expect and disclose the rapidity with which aggregation may decline. Certainly, granulation is a fluctuating, ever changing property and deserves more attention in practice than it generally receives.

3:12. SOIL CONSISTENCE

Before considering the effect of tillage on soil properties, one more important physical characteristic of soils should receive our attention. This is soil *consistence* which is a term used to describe the physical condition of a soil at various moisture contents as evidenced by the behavior of that soil toward mechanical stresses or manipulations. Soil consistence is considered a combination of soil properties which are dependent upon the forces of attraction between soil particles as influenced by soil moisture. Terms that are commonly used to describe soil consistence are as follows:

Wet soils: nonsticky, slightly sticky, sticky, very sticky, nonplastic, slightly plastic, plastic, and very plastic.

Moist soils: loose, very friable, friable, firm, very firm, and extremely firm.

Dry soils: loose, soft, slightly hard, hard, very hard, and extremely hard.

Cementation: weakly cemented, strongly cemented, and indurated.

Perhaps the best way to explain how soil consistence varies with moisture content is to use the above terms in describing how this soil property varies. A heavy clay soil soon after a rain would be quite high in soil moisture and would be *sticky* to feel. It obviously is too wet to work and if manipulated will tend to puddle or run together. Even when this soil is allowed to dry somewhat it may still be slightly sticky and will be *plastic* in nature. It can be molded into various forms by applying pressure to it. Although it can be plowed at this moisture content, the furrow-slice thus turned will likely form clods when the soil is allowed to dry. The consistence of these clods would then be considered as *hard* or *harsh*.

At a moisture content slightly below that required for plastic consistence, a soil is in optimum condition for working. If it has the appropriate properties it then may be termed as *soft* or *friable*. The exact moisture range over which this condition occurs will be different for different soils. In general, this range is much wider for medium-textured soils such as loams and some silt loams than is the case for finer-textured clays.

In using the example of the clay soil, one should not expect all soils to behave in a like manner. Sandy soils, for example, do not become plastic or sticky when wet, or hard or harsh when dry. They have a tendency to stay quite *loose* throughout their normal field moisture range. Loams and silt loams will tend to be intermediate in their behavior between the clays and sands.

Consistence can be seen to be important in determining the practical utilization of soils. The terms used to describe this soil property are meaningful to one concerned with soil tillage, compaction by farm machinery, etc. These subjects are covered in the next section.

3:13. TILTH AND TILLAGE

Although frequent mention has been made of plowing and cultivation in relation to soil structure, something must be said regarding seedbed preparation and the maintenance of its granulation throughout the season. A convenient term—*tilth*—will greatly facilitate such a discussion.

TILTH DEFINED. Simply defined, tilth refers to "the physical condition of the soil in its relation to plant growth" and hence must take cognizance of all soil physical conditions that influence crop development.

Tilth depends not only on granulation and its stability, but also on such factors as moisture content, degree of aeration, rate of water infiltration, drainage, and capillary-water capacity. As might be expected, it often changes rapidly and markedly. For instance, the working properties of fine-textured soils may be altered abruptly by a slight change in moisture.

One of the objectives of plowing and cultivation, supposedly, is the encouragement and maintenance of good tilth. Unfortunately, when improperly administered these operations may seriously impair tilth directly or set the stage for later deterioration.

TILTH AND PLOWING. The mold-board plow is a tillage implement designed to accentuate the granulation of the soil by its lifting, twisting, and shearing actions. At the same time, it turns under any organic residues that may be on or in the surface. It is a powerful tool *for good* when properly used—for *ill* if applied too frequently or under unsatisfactory conditions. Undoubtedly, it is the best implement for the preparation of sod land for cultivated crops. It cuts through the matted roots, turns the sod into the furrow, and exposes the shattered, subsurface layers for further preparation.

On fine-textured soils, the plow is indispensable if maximum crop yields are to be attained. On sandy soils, however, the advantage of the mold-board plow is not so obvious, as disking or some other type of cultivation may be as good or even better, especially if a stubble mulch is desired as is often the case in areas of low rainfall.

Table 3:7. Data Showing the Influence of Various Methods of Seedbed Preparation upon Soil Porosity in Ohio[a]

Seedbed Preparation	After Seven Years	
	Total Porosity %	Air Space Porosity %
1. Standard (plow, harrow)	56.3	25.9
2. Sod plow	56.0	24.9
3. Rotary tillage	56.9	24.2
4. Subsurface tillage	54.8	19.2
5. Subsurface tillage only	49.1	14.2
6. Standard plus straw mulch	55.8	26.9

[a] J. B. Page, C. J. Willard, and G. W. McCuen, "Progress Report on Tillage Methods in Preparing Land for Corn," *Proc. Soil Sci. Soc. Amer.*, 11:77–80, 1945.

Figure 3:11. Cotton root development under two soil conditions. Left, *a "plow pan" has developed in this soil and the cotton roots have not penetrated it.* Right, *another soil without "plow pan" with normal root penetration to a depth of 26 inches. (Photos courtesy U.S. Soil Conservation Service.)*

Undoubtedly, many farmers plow too much and at times when soil aggregation is seriously impaired. (See Fig. 3:11) This is likely to be the case when clayey soils are plowed too wet or too dry. Yet in spite of its misuse and the criticism leveled at it, the plow continues to be an important factor in the structural management of land and the maintenance of crop yields. This is clearly shown by the data of Table 3:7. When and how to plow, in this age of heavy, mechanized farm implements, are more important than ever before.

TILTH AND CULTIVATION. Cultivation is often more likely to impair tilth than is plowing. It is employed more frequently during the rotation, is performed by many types of implements, and drastically influences the upper furrow-slice that is so susceptible to degranulation. Hence, in the preparation of a seedbed only the minimum of cultivation should be applied after plowing, leaving the soil with a granular structure suitable for seeding yet coarse enough at the surface to resist erosion and the puddling effects of beating rains. (See Fig. 3:12.)

Figure 3:12. A practice which is receiving some acceptance is that of mulch tillage. The furrow is opened with a disc lister or middle buster and the crop is planted in the furrow with no other seed bed preparation. Corn and soybeans are being grown using this technique on sandy and sandy loam soils. (Photo courtesy U.S. Soil Conservation Service.)

In the spring, coarse granules at the soil surface may insure a satisfactory tilth through the critical portion of the growing season. The influence of a seedbed thus prepared usually greatly affects crop yield. Corn, for, instance, is a plant that markedly responds to the persistence of good tilth.

Cultivation during the growing season serves mainly to break up crusts induced by dashing rains, to insure adequate aeration, and to kill weeds. When herbicides are used, the control of weeds by cultivation ceases to be so important. With intertilled crops, cultivation should be kept at a minimum and ordinarily should not extend much beyond midseason. This is because serious root pruning (see Fig. 8:4) may occur as well as a loss of water by evaporation from the exposed surfaces without a compensating improvement in tilth. Directly and indirectly, cultivation may impair soil aggregation. Do not hasten the decline of tilth by too much cultivation.

Chapter 4

Soil Colloids: Their Nature and Practical Significance

It has already been emphasized that the most active portions of the soil are those in the colloidal state[1] and that the two distinct types of colloidal matter, inorganic and organic, exist in intimate intermixture. The inorganic is present almost exclusively as clay of various kinds; the organic is represented by humus. Attention will be focused to begin with on the inorganic fraction, leaving that of organic origin for later consideration (see pp. 90 and 144).

In a broad way, two groups of clays are recognized—the *silicate clays* so characteristic of temperate regions, and the *iron* and *aluminum*

[1] The colloidal state refers to a two-phase system in which one material (or materials) in a very finely divided state is dispersed through a second. Good examples of the colloidal state are milk and cheese, clouds and fog, starch, gelatin, rubber, blood, proteins, plant and animal cells, and of course soil. Obviously, the colloidal state in nature is the rule rather than the exception. The upper limit in size of the mineral colloidal particles is less than 0.001 mm, or one micron (μ), values as low as 0.5 or even 0.2 microns being commonly accepted. Because the maximum size limit of the *clay* fraction of a soil is considered to be 0.002 mm, or 2 μ, not all the clay is strictly colloidal.

hydrous-oxide clays found in the tropics and semitropics. Our immediate concern will be with the silicates, because they are dominant in the most developed agricultural regions of the world.

4:1. THE GENERAL CONSTITUTION OF SILICATE CLAYS

SHAPE. Early students of colloidal clays visualized the individual particles as more or less spherical. However, it is now definitely established that the particles are laminated, that is made up of layers of plates or flakes (see Fig. 4:1). Their individual size and shape depend upon their mineralogical organization and the conditions under which they have developed. Some of these particles are mica-like and definitely hexagonal; others are irregularly plate- or flakelike; still others seem to be lath-shaped blades or even rods. With some particles, the edges seem to be clean cut; with others the appearance is indistinctly frayed or fluffy. In all cases, however, the horizontal extension of the individual particles greatly exceeds their vertical dimension.

SURFACE AREA. Clay particles, merely because of their fineness of division, must expose a large amount of *external* surface. But this is by no means all. In some clays there are *internal* surfaces as well. This internal interface occurs between the platelike crystal units that make up each particle. (See Fig. 4:2.) Thus, the tremendous surface area that characterizes clay is accounted for not only by fineness of division but also by the platelike structure of the fine particles. As a conservative estimate, it is suggested that the active interface due to the clay fraction of an acre-furrow-slice of a representative silt or clay loam soil probably exceeds the land area of Illinois or Florida at least 40 or 50 times. The external surface area of one gram of colloidal clay is at least 1,000 times that of 1 gram of coarse sand.

ELECTRONEGATIVE CHARGE AND ADSORBED CATIONS. The minute silicate-clay colloid particles, which are referred to as *micelles* (microcell), ordinarily carry a *negative* charge. As a consequence, thousands of positively charged ions or *cations* are attracted to each colloidal crystal. This gives rise to what is known as an ionic double layer. (See Fig. 4:3.) The colloidal particle constitutes the *inner* ionic layer, being essentially a huge *anion,* the surfaces of which are highly negative in charge. The *outer* ionic layer is made up of a swarm of rather loosely held cations which surround and in some cases penetrate the particle. Thus, a clay particle is accompanied by a tremendous number of adsorbed cations.

Associated with the layer of cations that throng the adsorptive surfaces

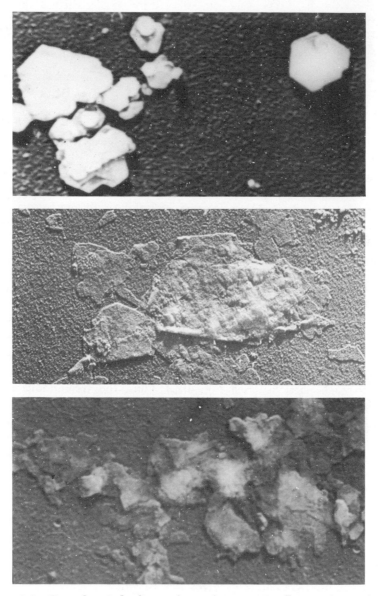

Figure 4:1. Crystals of kaolinite (upper), montmorillonite (center), and hydrous mica (illite), as pictured by the electron microscope. Note their crystalline nature and mica-like shape. The kaolinite crystals are character-istically six-sided, while the others are irregular flakes. Magnification is 38,000 for both kaolinite and montmorillonite, and 45,000 for illite. (Illite and kaolinite from work of M. L. Jackson and J. A. Kittrick, University of Wisconsin; montmorillonite by B. M. Siegel, Cornell University.)

Figure 4:2. A generalized representation of a lath-shaped clay crystal showing its platelike structure. Two types of surfaces are evident—external and internal. The latter is much more extended than the former and, except for kaolinite and similar clays, is much more important in respect to adsorptive capacity than are the external surfaces.

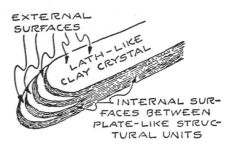

of clay particles is a large and indefinite amount of water. Part of these water molecules is carried by the adsorbed cations mentioned above since most of them are definitely hydrated. In addition, all silicate clays hold numerous water molecules packed between the plates that make up the clay micelle. These various types of water *in toto* are referred to when the hydration of clays is under consideration.

4:2. THE ADSORBED[2] CATIONS

Although all cations may be adsorbed by clay micelles, certain ones are especially prominent under natural conditions. For humid region colloids, these in the order of their numbers are H^+ and Ca^{++} first, Mg^{++} second, and K^+ and Na^+ third. (See Table 4:1.) For well-drained arid-region soils, the order of the exchangeable ions is usually Ca^{++} and Mg^{++} first, Na^+ and K^+ next, and H^+ last. The humid region clays

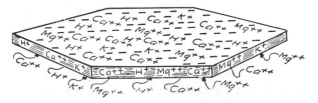

Figure 4:3. Diagramatic representation of a colloidal clay crystal (micelle) with its sheetlike structure, its innumerable negative charges, and its swarm of adsorbed cations. Note that Ca ions are dominant, but that some H, K, and Mg, and Na ions are present. No attempt has been made to show the adsorption of cations within the crystal (that is, between the platelike crystal units) or the numerous molecules of water that are held by the crystal surfaces and by the individual cations (hydrated ions).

2 For a definition of adsorption see note on page 32.

are considered to have a calcium-hydrogen complex; those in arid regions are dominated by calcium and magnesium.

When the drainage of an arid-region soil is impeded and alkaline salts accumulate, adsorbed Na ions are likely to equal or even exceed those of the adsorbed Ca. Here then would be a sodium or a sodium-calcium complex. By the same rule, in humid regions the displacement of the metallic cations by H ions gives a hydrogen or an acid clay. Since the cation, or cations, preponderant in a colloidal system has much to do with its physical and chemical properties as well as its relationship to plants, this phase of the subject is of tremendous practical importance.

Table 4:1. Relative Proportion of Adsorbed Metallic Cations Present in Certain Surface Soils of the United States (The percentage figures in each case are based on the sum of the metallic cations taken as 100. Note the geographic distribution of the soil samples.)[a]

Soils	Sum of Metallic Cations Taken as 100			
	Ca	*Mg*	*K*	*Na*
Penn Loam (N.J.)	60.8	15.8	19.0	4.4
Mardin Silt Loam (N.Y.)	90.7	5.0	3.1	1.2
Webster Series Soil (Ia.)	76.8	20.4	1.2	1.6
Sweeney Clay Loam (Calif.)	76.1	21.3	1.3	1.3
Red River Valley Soil (Minn.)	73.9	21.5	4.2	.4
Keith Silt Loam (Nebr.)	77.1	13.3	7.1	2.5
Holdrege Silt Loam (Nebr.)	66.5	20.9	11.1	1.5

[a] These data were compiled from various sources. See T. L. Lyon; H. O. Buckman; and N. C. Brady, *The Nature and Properties of Soils* (New York: Macmillan, 1952), p. 84.

4:3. THE MINERALOGICAL ORGANIZATION[3] OF THE VARIOUS TYPES OF SILICATE CLAYS

For many years, even after its colloidal nature was recognized, clays were thought to be amorphous. X-rays as well as electron-microscope examinations, however, show definitely that the clay particles, in spite of their smallness, are definitely crystalline. On the basis of their crystalline properties, three major groups of silicate clays are now rec-

[3] See Sir Laurence Bragg, G. F. Claringbull, and W. H. Taylor, *The Crystalline State*, Vol. IV *Crystal Structure of Minerals* (Ithaca, N.Y.: Cornell University Press, 1965).

ognized: (1) kaolinite; (2) montmorillonite; and (3) the hydrous micas, of which illite is representative. Recent studies have shown the importance of other groups such as vermiculite and chlorite, but their nature is not as yet too well understood.

KAOLINITE GROUP. The first group includes a number of clays: *kaolinite, halloysite, anauxite, dickite,* and several others. Of these, kaolinite is of greatest importance in soils. The crystals of this mineral are platelike in nature, being built up of flat crystal *units.* These units in turn are composed of alternate layers of octahedral or *alumina* and tetrahedral or *silica* sheets as shown by the drawing in Figure 4:4. Since every unit contains one each of the silica and alumina sheets, this group of clays are said to have a *1:1-type crystal* lattice.

The two sheets of each crystal unit of kaolinite are held together by oxygen atoms which are mutually shared by the silicon and aluminum atoms in their respective sheets. These units, in turn, are held together rather rigidly by oxygen-hydroxyl linkages. (See Fig. 4:4.) Consequently, the lattice is *fixed* and no expansion ordinarily occurs between units when the clay is wetted. Cations and water do not enter *between* the structural units of the micelle. The effective surface of kaolinite is thus restricted to its outer faces. This is one reason for its low adsorptive capacity for cations.

Kaolinite crystals usually are hexagonal with clean-cut edges. (See Fig. 4:1.) In comparison with montmorillonite particles, they are large in size, the diameter generally ranging from 0.10 to 5 microns with the majority falling within 0.2 to 2 microns. Because of the tightness with which their structural units are held together, kaolinite particles are not readily broken down into extremely thin sheets.

In contrast with the other silicate groups, the plasticity, cohesion, shrinkage, and swelling properties of kaolinite are very low. Its restricted interface and limited adsorptive capacity for cations and water molecules have already been mentioned. In general, kaolinite does not exhibit colloidal properties of a high order of intensity.

MONTMORILLONITE GROUP. The montmorillonite group also contains several clays, such as *montmorillonite, beidellite, nontronite,* and *saponite.* Of these the first is easily the most important although the others occur prominently in certain soils. The flakelike crystals of montmorillonite (see Fig. 4:1) are also composed of crystal units. These units are made up of two tetrahedral (silica) sheets with an octahedral (alumina) sheet tenaciously bound in between by mutually shared oxygen atoms. (See Fig. 4:5.) The crystal lattice is, therefore, a *2:1 type.*

The structural units themselves are so loosely held together by very

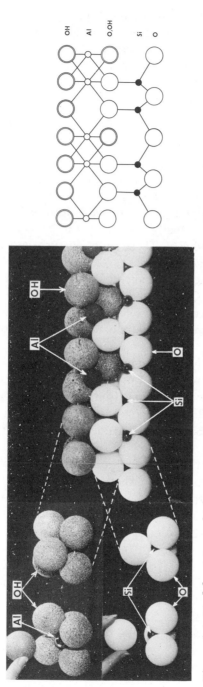

OH
Al
O,OH
Si
O

Figure 4:4. Models of ions which constitute the 1:1 type clay kaolinite. Note that the mineral is comprised of alternate octahedral (alumina) and tetrahedral (silica) layers, thus the designation "1:1." Alumina ions surrounded by six hydroxyls make up the octahedral layer (upper left). Smaller silicon ions associated with four oxygen ions constitute the tetrahedral layer. These are coupled together (center) to give a crystal unit with hydroxyls on one surface and oxygens on the other. A schematic drawing of the ions (right) shows an end view of the crystal unit.

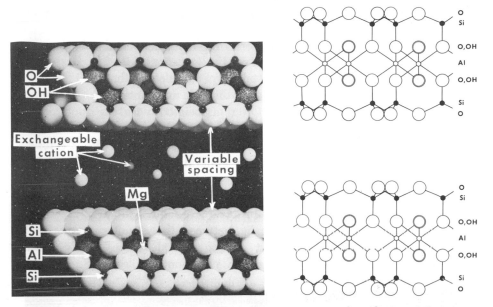

Figure 4:5. *A model of two crystal units of an expanding lattice 2:1 type clay mineral, montmorillonite. Note that each crystal is made up of an octahedral (alumina) layer sandwiched in between two tetrahedral (silica) layers. There is little attraction between oxygen ions in the bottom layer of one unit and those in the top layer of another. This permits a ready and variable expansion between units. Water and exchangeable cations occupy space between the units. This internal surface far exceeds the surface around the outside of the crystal. Note that magnesium has replaced aluminum in some sites of the octahedral layer. This gives rise to a negative charge which accounts for the high cation exchange capacity of this clay mineral.*

weak oxygen–oxygen linkages that the crystal lattice is bellows-like and *expands* very readily. As a consequence, montmorillonite crystals may be easily fractured artificially to give particles that approach the size of single structural units. Normally, however, montmorillonite crystals range in diameter from 0.01 to 1.00 microns. They are thus much smaller than the average kaolinite micelle.

Cations and water molecules are able to move in between the crystal units of montmorillonite because of its easily expanded crystal lattice. Thus, in addition to the surface of the outside of the particle, *internal surfaces* of very much greater total magnitude are presented. This internal surface is also negatively charged. Consequently, this 2:1 type of colloid has a high cation-adsorption capacity—perhaps 10 to 15 times that of kaolinite. Moreover, because of the movement of water between

miculite than for the other clay minerals. However, they do have sizeable cation exchange capacities, that of chlorite equaling illite and vermiculite equaling or exceeding montmorillonite in this respect. Vermiculite has a marked capacity to "fix" potassium similar to that of illite and montmorillonite. Like montmorillonite most of the negative charge associated with the crystal is from the internal surface.

In obtaining a general concept of clay minerals one should recognize that the specific groups do not occur independent of the other. In a given soil, one is apt to find several clay minerals in an intimate mixture. Furthermore, minerals having properties and composition intermediate between those of two well-defined minerals will be found. Such minerals are termed *mixed layer* or interstratified because within a given crystal the individual crystal units may well be of more than one type. Terms such as "chlorite-illite" and "illite-montmorillonite" are used to describe mixed-layer minerals.

4:4. GEOGRAPHIC DISTRIBUTION OF SILICATE CLAYS

The clay of any particular soil is generally made up of a mixture of different colloidal minerals. In a given soil, the mixture may vary from horizon to horizon. This occurs because the kind of clay that develops depends not only upon climatic influences and profile conditions but also upon the nature of the parent material. The situation may be further complicated by the presence in the parent material itself of clays that were formed under a preceding and perhaps an entirely different type of climatic regime. Nevertheless, some very general deductions seem possible in respect to the soils of the United States.

REGIONAL DIFFERENCES. It would seem, in general, that the clays in our Southern soils are likely to be dominated by kaolinitic minerals. (See Table 4:3.) It should be remembered, however, that montmorillonite, vermiculite, chlorite, and illite are not at all uncommon in this area. In the cool, humid regions to the north, hydrous mica often is prominent, especially if potassium-bearing minerals are present in the parent materials. Nevertheless, kaolinite still is prominent and often dominates such soils.

Shifting to the prairie soils of the Middle West, montmorillonite usually appears conspicuously and, with the hydrous mica, usually exceeds kaolinite. Vermiculite and chlorite are also found in many of these soils. Chernozems with a definitely lower rainfall show less kaolinite and much more montmorillonite and hydrous mica; in desert soils the latter two are definitely dominant.

Table 4:3. Relative Amounts of the Three Silicate Clay Groups Present in Certain Representative Soils of the United States (Expressed as Ratios)[a]

No. of Soils	Soils and Areas From Which Clays Were Obtained	Kaolinite	Sum of Groups Taken as 100	
			Hydrous Micas	Montmorillonite
	Southern Soils:			
5	Red podzolics, southern states	90	10	0
8	Red podzolics, Ala.	100	0	0
3	Black belt soils, Ala.	47	0	53
	Eastern Soils:			
8	Gray podzolics, eastern U.S.	63	37	0
4	Certain New York soils	0	100	0
	Midwestern Soils:			
5	Iowa soils	11	26	63
3	Midwestern soils	25	63	12
5	Iowa soils	16	3	81
	Western Soils:			
4	Desert soils	22	78	
12	Arizona soils	5	52	43

[a] These data were compiled from various sources throughout the United States. See T. L. Lyon; H. O. Buckman; and N. C. Brady, *The Nature and Properties of Soils* (New York: Macmillan, 1952), p. 90.

These conclusions are more or less tentative; however, they suggest that clay mixtures vary widely with different soils and that the type of clay mineral predominating is controlled to a considerable degree by climate and parent material. Nevertheless, it is often difficult to explain just why a particular clay material or mixture of clay minerals occurs in a given soil.

CLAYS OTHER THAN SILICATES. In discussing the distribution of silicate clays in the United States, it must not be forgotten that other colloidal minerals besides the ones mentioned are present. These occur either as mere accessories or as an important part of the colloidal complex. Of the latter, the oxides, of silicon, iron, and aluminum should be mentioned. While these occur frequently in temperate-region soils, the latter two are especially important in tropical and semitropical regions, giving rise to what are spoken of as *oxisols*. Although these *hydrous oxide clays* will be considered later (p. 89), it is well to note here that, as progress is made from a humid-temperate region to the humid tropics, the silicate clays often contain a larger and larger admixture of colloidal iron and aluminum hydrous oxides. The red and yellow soils of our Southern states (p. 332) provide very good evidence of this transition.

4:5. GENESIS OF SILICATE CLAYS

The silicate clays are developed most abundantly from such minerals as the feldspars, micas, amphiboles, and pyroxines. Apparently the transformation of these minerals into silicate clays has taken place in soils, and elsewhere, by at least two distinct processes: (1) a comparatively slight physical and chemical *alteration* of the primary minerals; and (2) a *decomposition* of the original minerals, with the subsequent *recrystallization* of certain of their decomposition products into the silicate clays. These processes will each be given brief consideration.

ALTERATION. Alteration of the minerals may be encouraged by chemical attacks with the consequent removal of certain soluble constituents and the substitution of others within the crystal lattice. The changes which occur as muscovite is altered to hydrous micas may be used as an example. Muscovite is a 2:1 type primary mineral with a rigid-lattice structure. As the weathering process begins, some potassium is lost from the crystal structure and water molecules enter into the lattice to give a more loose and less rigid crystal. Also, there is a relative increase in the silica content, as compared to aluminum, in the so-called silica sheet. Some of these changes, perhaps oversimplified, can be shown as follows:

$$K_2Al_4(Al_2Si_6)O_{20}(OH)_4 + Si^{+4} \xrightarrow{\ H_2O\ }$$

Muscovite
(rigid lattice)

$$(K_{0.2})(K_{0.8})Al_4(AlSi_7)O_{20}(OH)_4 + K^+ + Al^{+3}$$

Illite
(semirigid lattice)

$(K_{0.2})$ represents exchangeable potassium, and $(K_{0.8})$ represents potassium held semirigidly between crystal units.

There has been a release of potassium and aluminum, a minor change in the chemical make-up, a loosening of crystal lattice, and an initiation of exchangeable properties with little basic change in the crystal structure of the original mineral. It is still a 2:1 type, only having been *altered* in the process of weathering. Continued removal of potassium and substitution of magnesium for some of the aluminum in the alumina sheet would result in the formation of montmorillonite. (See Fig. 4:7.)

These examples illustrate the structural similarity among some of the various clay minerals. They also suggest that there may be a gradual transition from one mineral to another and that there are *intermediate* minerals with properties and characteristics in between those of the distinct groups. In verification of this, recent research has revealed the presence of so-called "mixed layer" minerals with names such as "illite-montmorillonite," "chlorite-illite," and "illite-vermiculite." These names suggest that a given colloidal crystal may contain crystal units of one mineral in between crystal units of another. Certainly they emphasize the complexity of clay mineralogy and of the soils of which these minerals are a part.

RECRYSTALLIZATION. The crystallization of silicate clays from soluble weathering products of other minerals is perhaps even more important in clay genesis than is alteration. A good example is the formation of kaolinite from solutions containing soluble aluminum and silicon. This process of recrystallization involves a complete change from the structural make-up of the original minerals and is usually the result of much more intense weathering than that required by the alteration process described above.

Moreover, such crystallization makes possible the formation of more than one kind of clay from a given mineral. The exact silicate colloid which forms apparently depends upon the condition of weathering and the ions present in the weathering solution as crystallization occurs.

RELATIVE STAGES OF WEATHERING. The more specific conditions resulting in the formation of one or more of the important types of clay are shown in Fig. 4:7. Perhaps the first generalization to be drawn from this outline is that there is a difference in the weathering stage of the minerals. The chlorite and hydrous micas apparently represent the younger-weathering stages of the silicates while kaolinite represents the oldest. Montmorillonite is considered to occupy an intermediate stage of weathering. With Fig. 4:7 as a guide, let us consider briefly the conditions which might yield each of the three groups of clays.

GENESIS OF INDIVIDUAL CLAYS. Hydrous micas represented by illite are thought to be formed, if conditions are favorable, by the alteration of the micas. This is postulated because illite is so similar to muscovite in make-up and general characteristics. Apparently, as indicated earlier, only a comparatively slight alteration is necessary to effect the changes from one to the other.

In other cases, illite has apparently been formed from original min-

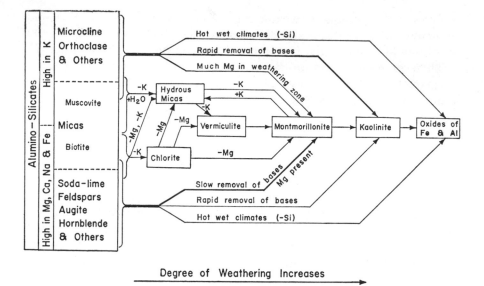

Degree of Weathering Increases ⟶

Figure 4:7. Diagram showing the general conditions for the formation of the various silicate clays and oxides of iron and aluminum. In each case, genesis is accompanied by the removal of soluble elements such as K, Na, Ca, and Mg.

erals, such as the potash feldspars, by recrystallization under conditions of an abundant potassium supply. In still other instances, illite may be formed from montmorillonite if the latter is in contact with abundant potassium. More common, however, is the reverse reaction by which illite weathers to montmorillonite by the loss of much of its potassium. (See Fig. 4:7.)

Chlorite is apparently formed by the alteration of the magnesium and iron-rich mica, biotite. This change is accompanied by a loss of some magnesium, potassium, and iron. Further alteration and weathering may yield illite (hydrous micas) or vermiculite, either of which can be altered to form montmorillonite.

Montmorillonite may be formed by recrystallization from a variety of minerals provided conditions are appropriate. Apparently, mild-weathering conditions (usually slightly acid to alkaline), a relative abundance of magnesium, and an absence of excess leaching are all conducive to the formation of this mineral. Alteration of other silicate clays, such as chlorite, illite, and vermiculite, may also yield montmorillonite.

As already stated, kaolinite represents a more advanced stage of weathering than does any of the other major types of silicate clays. It is formed from the decomposition of silicates under conditions of moderately- to strongly-acid weathering, which results in the removal of the alkali and alkaline-earth metals. The soluble aluminum and silicon products that are released may recrystallize, under proper conditions, to form kaolinite. This mineral, in turn, is subject to decomposition, especially in the tropics, with the formation of aluminum oxides and soluble silica.

As weathering of primary and secondary minerals occurs, ions of several elements are released. The more soluble ions such as sodium and potassium are usually removed in leaching waters. Others such as aluminum, iron, and silicon either may recrystallize into new silicate-clay minerals or, more commonly, may form insoluble minerals such as the hydrous oxides of iron and aluminum. As shown in Fig. 4:7, these compounds represent more advanced stages of weathering. They usually dominate soils only under tropical or semitropical conditions where intense weathering has resulted in the removal of most of the silica. (See p. 334.)

4:6. SOURCE OF THE NEGATIVE CHARGE OF SILICATE CLAYS[4]

EXPOSED CRYSTAL EDGES. There are at least two ways to account for the negative charges associated with silicate clay particles. The first method involves unsatisfied valences at the broken edges of the silica and alumina sheets. Also, the flat, external surfaces of minerals such as kaolinite have some exposed oxygen and hydroxyl groups which act as exchange sites. These groups are attached to silicon and aluminum atoms within their respective sheets. Especially at high pH, the hydrogen of these OH radicals dissociates slightly and the colloidal surface is left with a negative charge carried by the oxygen. The loosely held hydrogen is readily exchangeable. The situation may be represented as follows:

> One O Valence is
> satisfied within   —O— · H+
> the crystal by Al or Si
>
>   Adsorbed hydrogen
>
> Negative charged
> crystal surface

[4] The presence of negative charges on clay particles can be demonstrated in a number of ways. One very simple method is to treat two samples of a clay with water suspensions of gentian violet and eosin red, respectively. The particles of the former dye carry a positive charge and since they are markedly adsorbed by the clay, the clay must be negative. Conversely, the eosin particles, which are negatively charged, are only slightly adsorbed, if at all, by the clay.

The presence of thousands of such groups gives the clay particles a definite electronegativity. Consequently, they are surrounded by H ions and other cations that may have replaced such hydrogen. This phenomenon apparently accounts for most of the adsorbing capacity of 1:1 type of colloidal clays. It also is of some significance with the 2:1 types, especially at broken crystal edges.

These charge sites are thought to hold hydrogen by covalent bonding. They may be at least in part responsible for what has been termed the *pH-dependent* charge of inorganic colloids.[5] (See Fig. 4:9.) In moderately- to strongly-acid soils the hydrogen is apparently tightly held and not subject to ready replacement by other cations. Thus, the surface charge is not apparent. At pH values of 6 and above, hydrogen can be replaced by other cations such as calcium which, along with magnesium, tends to dominate these exchange sites in neutral and alkaline soils.

The magnitude of this pH-dependent charge varies with the type of colloid. It accounts for most of the charge of the 1:1 type minerals and up to one fourth of that of the 2:1 types. As will be seen later, it is the dominant type of charge for organic colloids.

IONIC SUBSTITUTION. A second source of the over-all negative charge carried by clay crystals is the substitution of one atom for another within the crystal lattice. For example, in some 2:1 type minerals such as montmorillonite, magnesium atoms have substituted for some of the aluminum atoms in the ideal alumina sheet previously described. Furthermore, the substitution is on the basis of one Mg^{++} atom for each Al^{+++} atom replaced. Therefore, each substitution results in an unsatisfied negative valence, because a three-valent atom is replaced by a two-valent one. This may be shown as follows if we assume that the three valences of the aluminum atoms were satisfied by an equivalent of one O atom and one OH group:

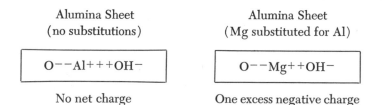

Alumina Sheet (no substitutions)	Alumina Sheet (Mg substituted for Al)
$O^{--}Al^{+++}OH^{-}$	$O^{--}Mg^{++}OH^{-}$
No net charge	One excess negative charge

Similarly, in minerals such as beidellite and illite the substitution of a three-valent atom such as Al for one of the four-valent silicon atoms in the silica sheet leaves an unsatisfied negative valence. This may be rep-

[5] Other mechanisms are also likely at work here. See pp. 379–380.

resented as follows because each Si is associated with an equivalent of 2 oxygen atoms:

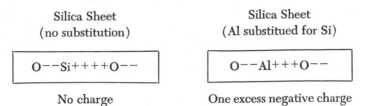

Silica Sheet	Silica Sheet
(no substitution)	(Al substitued for Si)
O--Si++++O--	O--Al+++O--
No charge	One excess negative charge

All silicate clays likely exhibit the substitution phenomenon just explained. However, the magnitude of the resulting charge is greatest in the 2:1 type clays. Substitution may have occurred in either or both the alumina and silica sheets. In montmorillonite, most of the substitution has occurred in the alumina sheet, although some may also have taken place in the silica sheet. Similarly, substitution in both sheets has occurred in illite and vermiculite, although the substitution and the source of charge lie largely in the silica sheet. In addition to the magnesium and aluminum ions, iron, manganese, and other ions may, in a similar way, enter the lattice of certain minerals.

Unlike the charge associated with the exposed crystal edges, those resulting from ionic substitution are not dependent on pH. With the exception of certain complex aluminum ions the cations attracted to these charges are subject to replacement at all common pH levels. As a consequence these charges are commonly referred to as *permanent charges*. (See Fig. 4:9) This will be dealt with in greater detail as we consider soil acidity. (See p. 379.)

4:7. THE CHEMICAL COMPOSITION OF SILICATE CLAYS

Using purified materials, chemists have long been able to determine the formulas of minerals from accurate quantitative analyses. This was done with kaolinite long before its crystal structure was known. Later such work was verified by means of X-ray diffraction patterns and other clays, hitherto unknown, were thereby discovered and classified. Once the crystal form of any particular clay mineral is known and the position of the various atoms in its lattice ascertained, its ideal formula can be written.

Because of the extensive lattice modifications and ionic substitutions common in clays, chemical formulas cannot be used to identify specifically a given mineral group. However, so-called "type" formulas can be used

Table 4:4. Chemical Formulas of Important Clay and Other Minerals Showing the Most Prominent Substitution in the Al and Si Sheets as Well as the Molecules Between Crystal Units.[a] *Readily Exchangeable Ions Are Shown in Parentheses*

Clay Mineral	Dominant Elements in Octahedral (Al Sheet)	Tetrahedral (Si Sheet)	Nos. of Oxygen and Hydroxyl	Between Crystal Units
Kaolinite	Al_4	Si_4	$O_{10}(OH)_8$	
Pyrophyllite	Al_4	Si_8	$O_{20}(OH)_4$	
Montmorillonite	$Al_{3.5}Mg_{0.5}$ $(Na_{0.5})$	Si_8	$O_{20}(OH)_4$	nH_2O
Vermiculite	Mg_6	Si_7Al $(Mg_{0.5})$	$O_{20}(OH)_4$	XH_2O, Mg^{++}
Chlorite	Mg_6	Si_6Al_2	$O_{20}(OH)_4$	$Mg_6(OH)_{12}$
Illite	Al_4	Si_7Al $(K_{0.2})$	$O_{20}(OH)_4$	$K_{0.8}$
Muscovite	Al_4	Si_6Al_2	$O_{20}(OH)_4$	K_2

[a] Note that the substitution of Mg for Al or Al for Si is compensated for by either exchangeable or intercrystal unit ions, e.g., Na. (In some vermiculites and chlorites the octahedral layer is filled with 4 aluminum atoms rather than 6 magnesium atoms as shown.)

The actual formulas of specific minerals are considerably more complicated than those shown. See R. E. Grim, *Clay Mineralogy* (New York: McGraw-Hill, 1953), pp. 43–76.

to illustrate differences in composition. Examples are shown in Table 4:4.

The (Na), (K), and (Mg) ions are considered as mostly exchangeable; the others are part of the lattice structure. Only the major substitutions have been shown. It will be noted that the differences among the formulas for montmorillonite, illite, chlorite, and vermiculite largely reflect differences in the ions dominant in the silica and alumina sheets. Intercrystal unit molecules are also illustrated.

4:8. MINERAL COLLOIDS OTHER THAN SILICATES

HYDROUS OXIDE CLAYS OF IRON AND ALUMINUM. The discussion so far has dealt only with silicate clays. However, hydrous-oxide clays also deserve attention for at least two reasons: (1) they occur in temperate regions intermixed with silicate clays; and (2) this type of colloidal matter is often dominant in the soils of the tropics and semitropics. The red and yellow soils of these regions are controlled in large degree by iron and aluminum hydrous oxides of various types.

As their name suggests, *hydrous oxides* are oxides containing associated water molecules. The exact mechanism by which these water molecules are held is somewhat uncertain. For simplicity, the hydrous oxides are often shown as actual iron and aluminum hydroxides [$Al(OH)_3$ and $Fe(OH)_3$]. Probably more correct general formulas are as follows: $Fe_2O_3 \cdot xH_2O$ and $Al_2O_3 \cdot xH_2O$. The x indicates that the quantity of associated water of hydration is different for different minerals. In soils, gibbsite ($Al_2O_3 \cdot 3H_2O$) is probably the dominant aluminum oxide; goethite ($Fe_2O_3 \cdot H_2O$) and limonite ($Fe_2O_3 \cdot xH_2O$) are the most prominent iron-hydrous oxides.

Although relatively less is known about the hydrous-oxide clays, they seem to have some properties in common with the silicates. For example, at least some of them are thought to have definite crystalline structure. The small particles may carry negative charges and thus serve as a central micelle around which a swarm of cations are attracted. The same general constitution described for the silicates may be visualized. Because of the much smaller number of negative charges per micelle, however, cation adsorption is even lower than for kaolinite. Also, most hydrous oxides are not as sticky, plastic, and cohesive as are the silicates. This accounts for the much better physical condition of soils dominated by hydrous oxides. Soils high in these minerals also have high anion adsorption capacities.

ALLOPHANE AND OTHER AMORPHOUS MINERALS.[6] In many soils significant quantities of noncrystalline colloidal matter are found. For example, part of the iron and aluminum hydrous oxides in some soils is amorphous. The same is true of part of the silica, especially in soils formed from volcanic ash. In most cases, the properties of the amorphous mineral do not differ greatly from those of the crystalline materials.

Perhaps the most significant amorphous mineral matter in soils is *allophane,* the somewhat poorly defined combinations of silica and aluminum sesquioxide. Having a composition approximating $Al_2O_3 \cdot 2SiO_2 \cdot H_2O$, this material is found as a constituent in many soils. It is most prevalent, however, in soils developed from volcanic ash.

The presence of allophane in a soil cannot be ignored, because it has

[6] See B. D. Mitchell, V. C. Farmer, and W. J. McHardy, "Amorphous Inorganic Materials in Soils," *Advan. in Agron.,* 16: 327–83, 1964.

a high cation exchange capacity. This capacity is apparently pH dependent. Allophane also has a considerable anion exchange capacity (see p. 484) which may be of some significance. Although the mechanics for the development of negative and positive charges on the colloid are not known, their presence in a soil could markedly affect its properties.

4:9. ORGANIC SOIL COLLOIDS—HUMUS

Because the clays of surface soils usually carry an appreciable admixture of humus, a brief word about organic colloids is necessary at this point. Otherwise, the soil significance of the colloidal state of matter cannot be fully visualized.

COLLOIDAL ORGANIZATION. Humus may be considered to have a colloidal organization similar to that of clay shown in Fig. 4:3. A highly charged anion (micelle) is surrounded by a swarm of adsorbed cations. As later sections will show, the reactions of these cations are essentially the same whether they are adsorbed by clay or by humus.

Some important differences should be noted, however, between humus and the inorganic micelles. First, the complex humus micelle is composed basically of carbon, hydrogen, and oxygen rather than of aluminum, silicon, and oxygen as are the silicate clays. Also, the cation-adsorptive capacity of humus far exceeds even that of montmorillonite. The humus micelle is not considered crystalline, and the size of the individual particles, although extremely variable, may be at least as small as montmorillonite. Last, humus is not as stable as clay and is thus somewhat more dynamic —being formed and destroyed much more rapidly than clay.

Because of their complexity, relatively less is known about the specific structure of humus colloids as compared to that of the silicate clays. However, it is known that humus is not a specific compound nor does it have a single structural makeup. The major sources of negative charge are thought to be carboxylic ($-COOH$) and phenolic ($> -OH$) groups, the hydrogen of which is partially replaced by other cations. These groups are associated with central units of varying size and complexity. This relationship is illustrated in a general way in Fig. 4:8; Note the similarity to that of the silicate clays.

The charge on humus colloids is pH dependent as is the case for part of the silicate clays (see p. 86). Under strongly acid conditions hydrogen is tightly bound and not replaceable by other cations. The colloid thereby exhibits a low negative charge. As the pH rises from the addition of bases, first the hydrogen from the carboxyl groups and finally that from the phenolic groups ionizes and is replaced by Ca, Mg, and other cations.

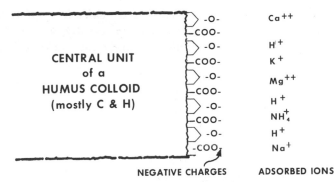

CENTRAL UNIT
of a
HUMUS COLLOID
(mostly C & H)

>-O-   Ca++
—COO-
>-O-   H+
—COO-   K+
>-O-
—COO-   Mg++
>-O-   H+
—COO-   NH₄⁺
>-O-   H+
—COO-   Na+

NEGATIVE CHARGES   ADSORBED IONS

Figure 4:8. A simplified illustration of the adsorption of cations by humus colloids. The phenolic hydroxyl groups >-O-) are attached to aromatic rings while the carboxyl groups (–COO–) are bonded to other carbon atoms in the central unit. Note the general similarity to that for the silicate clays. In this case only surface adsorption is shown, but adsorption occurs within the Micelle as well.

On the basis of solubility in acids and alkalis, humus is thought to be made up of three classes[7]: (1) fulvic acid, lowest in molecular weight and lightest in color, soluble in both acid and alkali; (2) humic acid, medium in molecular weight and color, soluble in alkali but insoluble in acid; and (3) humin, highest in molecular weight, darkest in color, and insoluble in both acid and alkali. In spite of differences in chemical and physical properties, these classes tend to have very similar properties, cation adsorption, nutrient release, etc. Consequently, they will all be considered under the general term "humus."

The information thus far presented on colloids has emphasized the complexity of the compounds and crystals of which the individual micelles are made. In spite of this complexity, however, the general organization is about the same for each of the colloidal groups. That is, a central negatively charged micelle is surrounded by a swarm of cations. Let us now consider in somewhat more detail this general organization and the reactions modifying it.

4:10. COLLOIDS—ACID SALTS

Colloidal particles regardless of their composition are made up of a complex negative radical, the micelle, and a miscellany of adsorbed

[7] See G. T. Felbeck, Jr., "Structural Chemistry of Soil Humic Substances," *Advan. in Agron.,* 17: 327–368, 1965.

cations. In a humid region, those cations of calcium, aluminum and hydrogen are by far the most numerous. Consequently, a colloidal complex may be represented in the following simple and convenient way:

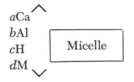

aCa
bAl
cH   Micelle
dM

The significance of the Ca, Al, and H of the formula is obvious, because in a humid region these cations jointly dominate the complex. The M stands for the small amounts of other so-called base-forming cations Mg, K, Na, etc., that are usually present in the ionic-outer layer. The a, b, c, and d indicate that the numbers of cations are variable.

The above illustration emphasizes that clays and their associated-exchangeable ions can be considered, in perhaps an oversimplified way, *complex-acid salts*. This can be verified by comparing above formula with that of $CaHPO_4$, a well-known acid salt. In both cases negatively charged radicals (anions) are associated with metallic cations and with hydrogen. The only difference is one of size and charge, the clay anion (micelle) being much larger than the phosphate and, of course, having many more negative charges per anion.

When by the proper laboratory manipulations the metallic cations are replaced entirely by H ions, a clay acid or H Micelle results. In a like manner Ca ions may be given dominance and a calcium "salt," Ca Micelle , comes into being. It should be noted that several different acids and calcium salts are possible depending upon the nature of the micelle—that is, whether we are dealing with kaolinite, montmorillonite, humus, or some other colloid. Of course, in nature, soil colloids are very seldom wholly acids or wholly salts. As illustrated by the general formula at the beginning of this section, they are actually mixtures of *complex-acid salts*.

WHY ADSORBED CA, AL, AND H IONS ARE SO PROMINENT. In the early stages of clay formation the solution surrounding the decomposing silicates contains calcium, magnesium, potassium, sodium, and aluminum which have been liberated by weathering.[8] These ions are not all held with equal tightness by the soil colloids. The order of strength of adsorption when they are present in equivalent quan-

[8] Iron may also be present, although its solubility is generally less than that of aluminum.

tities is Al > Ca > Mg > K > Na. Consequently, one would expect the
with aluminum and calcium being the most dominant and sodium the
least dominant cation. This is generally the case in most well-drained,
moderately acid, humid-region soils.

As organic matter gradually accumulates and decomposes, organic and
other acids are generated. These supply hydrogen, which influences the
cation adsorption in two ways. First, it helps solubilize or keep in solution
aluminum ions which are quickly adsorbed by the colloids. Second, the
H ions are rather tightly adsorbed themselves by both organic and inorganic micelles. The Al and H ions are very important, because between
them they characterize soil acidity and determine the amount of lime
needed for optimum plant growth. Their presence is favored by high rainfall levels, which tend to leach out the other ions, most of which are held
with relatively less tenacity.
quantity of these ions in the exchangeable form to be in the same order,

In arid and semi-arid regions, the calcium and other bases do not leach
from the soil. As a consequence these metallic cations tend to dominate
the adsorptive sites resulting in pH values of 7.0 and above. Under these
conditions the Al ions form insoluble compounds, and the adsorbed H
ions are drastically reduced in quantity.

4:11. CATION EXCHANGE[9]

With the fundamental colloidal conceptions already presented
as a background, the exchange of one cation for another on soil colloids
may be accounted for very simply. The tendency of hydrogen ions to
force such a transfer will be used to illustrate this phenomenon. Cation
exchange is one of the most common and most important of soil reactions.

A SIMPLE EXAMPLE. Consider, to begin with, a near
neutral humid-region mineral surface-soil, rather high in adsorbed calcium, and functioning under optimum conditions of moisture and temperature. A considerable amount of organic and mineral acids is formed as
the organic matter decomposes. The H ions thus generated will tend to
replace the exchangeable calcium of the colloidal complex. This occurs
not only because of mass action effect but also because under comparable
conditions ionic hydrogen is adsorbed more strongly than is the ionic
calcium. The reaction may be shown simply as follows, only one ion of
the copiously-adsorbed calcium being represented as displaced.

[9] The term *base exchange* is often used in referring to this phenomenon. *Cation
exchange,* however, is preferable because hydrogen cations as well as the base forming cations are involved in the interchange.

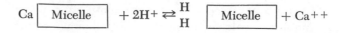

The reaction takes place fairly rapidly and the interchange of calcium and hydrogen is chemically equivalent. Moreover, if the H ion concentration were decreased for any reason or the Ca ions are increased, say by liming, the adjustment would be to the left in response to mass action. Conversely, if the H ions are increased or if the Ca ions are removed by leaching, the adjustment would be to the right. The soil is so dynamic that the equalization is constantly changing, oscillating back and forth as conditions dictate.

CATION EXCHANGE UNDER NATURAL CONDITIONS. With these principles in mind, suppose we write the reaction more completely and as it commonly occurs in humid-region surface soils. We shall assume, for the sake of simplicity, that the number of Ca, Al, H, and other metallic cations (M) are in the ratio of 40, 20, 20, and 20 per micelle, respectively. The metallic cations (M) are considered monovalent in this case.

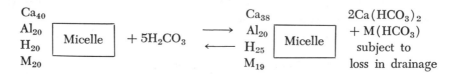

It is important to note that where sufficient precipitation is available to leach the calcium the reaction tends to go toward the right—that is, H ions are entering and calcium and other bases (M) are being forced out of the exchange complex into the soil solution.[10] This is because the establishment of equilibrium is prevented by the loss of carbonates and bicarbonates in drainage. Obviously, so long as this continues and the H ion concentration is not correspondingly diminished, the adjustment will continue as pictured.

It is to be noted also that one micelle is taken to represent the whole colloidal fraction and that the loss of metallic cations (Ca and M) is just balanced by the gain in H ions. That is, the exchange is in *chemically equivalent amounts*.

In regions of low rainfall the calcium and other salts are not easily leached from the soil as indicated. This prevents the reaction from

[10] Note that aluminum is not shown as being replaced by the hydrogen. This is because of the tenacity with which the Al ion is held. Also, an increase in acidity would likely bring more aluminum into solution, which might even increase the adsorption of this element. This situation is discussed in greater detail on p. 380.

going to completion. That is, it prevents the removal of bases from the exchange sites, thereby keeping the soil neutral or above in reaction. The interaction of climate, biological processes and cation exchange thus helps determine the properties of soils.

LOSS OF METALLIC ELEMENTS. The above reaction is an excellent illustration of cation exchange and also is one of the most important and far reaching transfers that occurs in humid-region surface soils. By this mechanism, calcium and to a lesser extent magnesium, potassium, and sodium are lost from the soil by leaching. At the same time aluminum and hydrogen ions, both of which enhance the acidic properties of the soil, are increased. Thus, cation exchange accounts for the great loss of lime suffered by humid-region surface soils. At the same time it indicates why such soils tend to become acid so quickly.[11]

INFLUENCE OF LIME AND FERTILIZER. Cation-exchange reactions are reversible. Hence, if lime is applied to an acid soil, the reverse of the replacement just cited occurs. The active calcium ions by mass action replace the hydrogen and other cations. As a result, the clay becomes higher in exchangeable calcium and lower in adsorbed hydrogen and aluminum. And as the soil solution adjusts to this altered proportion of bases and hydrogen, its pH is raised and its chemical make-up is modified.

One more illustration of cation exchange will be offered. If a soil is treated with a liberal application of a fertilizer containing potassium chloride an exchange such as follows may occur: (Again M is considered monovalent.)

$$
\begin{array}{l}
Ca_{40} \\
Al_{20} \\
H_{20} \\
M_{20}
\end{array} \boxed{\text{Micelle}} + 7KCl \xrightleftharpoons{}
\begin{array}{l}
K_{7} \\
Ca_{38} \\
Al_{20} \\
H_{19} \\
M_{19}
\end{array} \boxed{\text{Micelle}} +
\begin{array}{l}
2CaCl_2 \\
HCl \\
2MCl
\end{array}
$$

Some of the added potassium pushes its way into the colloidal complex and forces out equivalent quantities of calcium, hydrogen, and other elements which appear in the soil solution. The adsorption of the added potassium is considered to be advantageous because a nutrient so held remains largely in an available condition but is less subject to leaching than are most fertilizer salts. Hence, cation exchange is an

[11] This subject is so important in a practical way that it will receive detailed consideration in later chapters. (See p. 214.)

important consideration not only for nutrients already present in soils but also for those applied in commercial fertilizers and in other ways.[12]

4:12. CATION-EXCHANGE CAPACITY[13]

The capacity of soil colloids to adsorb nutrients can be determined rather easily. In commonly used methods, the original adsorbed nutrients are replaced by barium, potassium, or ammonium ions and then the amount of adsorbed barium, potassium or ammonium is determined.

It should be pointed out that the cation-exchange capacity in most soils increases with pH. (See Fig. 4:9.) At a very low pH value, only the so-called permanent charges of the clays (see p. 87) and a small portion of the charges of organic colloids hold ions that can be replaced by cation exchange. On the majority of the organic colloid exchange sites and on some of those of the inorganic fraction, hydrogen and perhaps aluminum hydroxy ions are held so tightly as to resist replacement. Therefore, the cation-exchange capacity is low.

As the pH is raised, the hydrogen held by the remainder of the organic and inorganic colloids becomes ionized and is replaceable. Also the adsorbed aluminum hydroxy ions are removed forming $(Al(OH)_3$, thereby releasing additional exchange sites on the mineral colloids. The net result is an increase in the cation-exchange capacity.

In most cases the cation-exchange capacity is determined at a pH of 7.0 or above. This means that it includes most of those charges dependent on pH as well as the more or less permanent ones.

The cation-exchange capacity is expressed in terms of *equivalents,* or more specifically, as *milliequivalents* per 100 grams. Before dealing with comparative exchange capacities of different colloidal materials, let us examine briefly this method of expression.

MILLIEQUIVALENTS. The term milliequivalent is defined as *one milligram of hydrogen or the amount of any other ion that will combine with or displace it.*

Thus, if a clay has a cation-exchange capacity of 1 milliequivalent (1 m.e./100g,)[14] it is capable of adsorbing and holding 1 milligram of

---

[12] It should be noted that anionic fixation may take place and in some cases assumes considerable importance. This is especially true with respect to the adsorption of phosphate ions. This phase is dealt with on p. 484.

[13] The terms "cation-exchange capacity" and "cation-adsorption capacity" are used interchangeably in this book.

[14] The abbreviation m.e. will be used to express milliequivalent throughout this book. The number of milliequivalents are usually given for each 100 grams of material. Thus, the data may be given as, for example, 20 m.e./100 g.

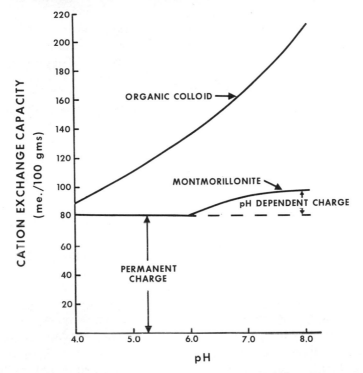

Figure 4:9. The influence of pH on the cation exchange capacity (a measure of the negative charge) of montmorillonite and humus. Note that below pH 6.0 the charge for the clay mineral is relatively constant. This charge is considered permanent and is due to ionic substitution in the crystal unit. Above pH 6.0 the charge on the mineral colloid increases due to ionization of hydrogen from exposed O–H groups of crystal edges. In contrast to the clay, essentially all the charges on the organic colloid are considered pH dependent. (Montmorillonite data from N. T. Coleman and A. Mehlich, "The Chemistry of Soil pH," a chapter in Soil the 1957 Yearbook of Agriculture, U.S.D.A., Wash., D.C. Organic colloid data from C. S. Helling et al., "Contribution of organic matter and clay to soil cation exchange capacity as affected by the pH of the saturating solution," Soil Sci. Soc. Amer. Proc. 28:517–520, 1964.)

hydrogen or its equivalent for every 100 grams of clay. This, of course is 1 milligram to 100,000 milligrams of clay or 10 parts per million. Therefore, an acre-furrow-slice of such a clay weighing 2,000,000 pounds could adsorb 20 pounds of exchangeable hydrogen or its equivalent.

It is well to note this term—*equivalent*. It indicates that other ions also may be expressed in terms of milliequivalents. For example, let us consider calcium. This element has an atomic weight of 40 compared to

1 for hydrogen. Each Ca^{++} ion has two charges and is thus equivalent to 2 H^+ ions. Therefore, the amount of calcium required to displace 1 milligram of hydrogen is 40/2 or 20 milligrams. This, then, is the weight of 1 milliequivalent of calcium. If 100 grams of a certain clay are capable of adsorbing a total of 250 milligrams of calcium, the cation-adsorption capacity is 250/20 or 12.5 m.e./100 g. The milliequivalent method of expression is so convenient and is so commonly used that a person dealing with the literature of soil science must be familiar with it.

CATION-EXCHANGE CAPACITIES OF SOIL COLLOIDS. As might be expected, the cation-exchange capacity of the colloidal fraction of soils exhibits a wide range, because humus and several minerals may be present in varying amounts. The cation-exchange capacities of humus, vermiculite, montmorillonite, hydrous mica and chlorites, kaolinite, and hydrous oxides are more or less in the order of 200, 150, 100, 30, 8, and 4 milliequivalents per 100 grams, respectively. (See Table 4:2.)

It is easy to see why the clay complex of Southern soils, when dominated by kaolinite, should have a low-exchange, capacity, ranging perhaps between 5 and 20 m.e./100 grams of soil. On the other hand, the clay mixtures functioning in the soils of the Middle West, where illite and montmorillonite are more likely to be prominent, have a much higher adsorptive capacity, ranging from 50 to possible 100 milliequivalents depending on conditions. Colloids of soils high in humus (such as mucks) will have cation exchanges in excess of 180 milliequivalents per 100 grams.

4:13. THE CATION-EXCHANGE CAPACITY (C.E.C.) OF WHOLE SOILS

VARIABILITY OF THE C.E.C. OF SOILS. Comparative cation exchange capacities of a number of soils are shown in Table 4:5. Note the great range in the figures presented, the highest approaching 60 milliequivalents per 100 grams. This is to be expected because soils vary so tremendously in humus content and in the amounts and kinds of clay present.[15] It is one thing to have kaolinite as the major clay and quite another if montmorillonite is dominant, so different are their individual capacities to adsorb cations. Moreover, humic

---

[15] From the preceding section average figures for the cation-exchange capacity of representative silicate clay (0.5 m.e. for each per cent) and for well-humified organic matter (2.0 m.e. for each per cent) might be ascertained. By using these figures, it obviously is possible to calculate in a rough way the cation-exchange capacity of a humid-temperature region surface soil from the percentages of clay and organic matter present.

Table 4:5. Cation-Exchange Capacity of a Wide Variety of Surface Soils from Various Parts of the United States (in Milliequivalents per 100 Gm of Dry Soil) [a]

Soil Type	Exch. Cap. m.e./100 gm.	Soil Type	Exch. Cap. m.e./100
Sands:		*Silt Loams:*	
Sassafras (N.J.)	2.0	Delta (Miss.)	9.4
Plainfield (Wis.)	3.5	Fayette (Minn.)	12.6
		Spencer (Wis.)	14.0
Sandy loams:		Dawes (Nebr.)	18.4
Greenville (Ala.)	2.3	Carrington (Minn.)	18.4
Sassafras (N.J.)	2.7	Penn (N.J.)	19.8
Norfolk (Ala.)	3.0	Miami (Wis.)	23.2
Cecil (S.C.)	5.5	Grundy (Ill.)	26.3
Coltneck (N.J.)	9.9		
Colma (Calif.)	17.1	*Clays and Clay loams:*	
		Cecil clay loam (Ala.)	4.0
Loams:		Cecil clay (Ala.)	4.8
Sassafras (N.J.)	7.5	Coyuco sandy clay (Calif.)	20.2
Hoosic (N.J.)	11.4	Gleason clay loam (Calif.)	31.5
Dover (N.J.)	14.0	Susquehanna clay (Ala.)	34.2
Collington (N.J.)	15.9	Sweeney clay (Calif.)	57.5

[a] These data were compiled from a number of publications. See T. L. Lyon; H. O. Buckman, and N. C. Brady, *The Nature and Properties of Soils*, 5th ed. (New York: Macmillan, 1952), p. 111.

residues developed under different climates or from diverse plant tissues do not always possess the same adsorptive power. All these factors contribute to the exceptional variability and wide range in the data presented.

RELATION OF C.E.C. TO TEXTURE AND ORGANIC MATTER. A more careful examination of the table reveals that a rough correlation exists between texture and exchange capacity. Sands and sandy loams are low in colloidal clay and are very likely to be deficient in humus also. Finer textured soils, in marked contrast, always carry more clay and generally more organic matter as well. Hence their cation-adsorption capacities are usually higher.

Although variations in exchange capacity are expected to be rather pronounced between soils of different textures, it is perhaps a little surprising to find that the differences within textural groups are at times just as striking. In some instances organic-matter differences seem to account for the deviations. This may be the case with the silt loams of

Minnesota, Wisconsin, and Nebraska and the clay soils of California cited in Table 4:5. But when the Cecil clay and clay loam of Alabama are compared with the Susquehanna clay of the same state, some other factor must be operative because all of these soils are rather low in organic matter. That the other factor might well be the type of clay present in each case is evidenced by the following tentative calculation.

INFLUENCE OF TYPE OF COLLOID. It is well known that the clay fraction of the Cecil soil is dominated by 1:1 type clays with a cation-adsorption capacity of about 8 m.e./100g. Consequently, even if its total clay content should be 30 per cent, the Cecil soil probably would not possess a cation-exchange capacity due to the clay of much more than 2 or 3 m.e. per 100 g. of soil. The low figure of Table 4:5 is thus readily accounted for.

On the other hand, the inorganic-colloidal mixture of the Susquehanna clay is dominantly montmorillonitic in nature. Assuming in this case that the exchange capacity of its clay complex is approximately 90 m.e./100 g and that the soil contained 30 per cent of this clay, its adsorptive power would be in the neighborhood of 27 m.e./100 g. This is not taking into consideration the adsorptive capacity of humus that might be present. Thus, the type of clay probably accounts for the figure quoted for the Susquehanna soil.

These findings afford an opportunity again to voice a word of caution in respect to previous generalization. It is suggested (p. 80) that the soils of our Southern states are to a considerable degree dominated by kaolinitic clays (1:1 lattice); Northern soils often are characterized by clays of the 2:1 lattice type. That such a generalization should be applied with caution is evidenced by the case of the two Southern soils discussed in the preceding paragraph—kaolinitic and montmorillonitic. Such situations are found not only in the same state but also in sites that are only a very few miles apart. Obviously then, the type of clay mixture that may characterize a soil is not necessarily determined entirely by climate. Parent material, time of weathering, drainage, and other factors participate in complicated interplay. It is not surprising, therefore, that montmorillonitic clay mixtures are found in Southern climes, and that both kaolinite and illite characterize certain Northern soils.

4:14. THE PERCENTAGE BASE SATURATION OF SOILS

Two groups of adsorbed cations tend to have opposing effects on soil acidity and alkalinity. Hydrogen and aluminum tend to dominate acid soils, both contributing to the concentration of H^+ ions in the soil solution. Adsorbed hydrogen contributes directly to the H^+ ion concentration in the soil solution. Al ions do so indirectly through hydrolysis. This may be illustrated as follows:

$$Al^{+++} + H_2O \longrightarrow Al(OH)^{++} + H^+ \text{ , and}$$
$$Al(OH)^{++} + H_2O \longrightarrow Al(OH)_2^+ + H^+$$

Most of the other cations, called exchangeable bases, move the soil toward alkalinity. The proportion of the cation exchange capacity occupied by these bases is called the *percentage base saturation*. Thus, if the percentage base saturation is 80, four fifths of the exchange capacity is satisfied by bases, the other by hydrogen and aluminum. The example in Fig. 4:10 should be helpful in showing this relationship.

PERCENTAGE BASE SATURATION AND PH. The percentage base saturation data for different soils show wide variations.

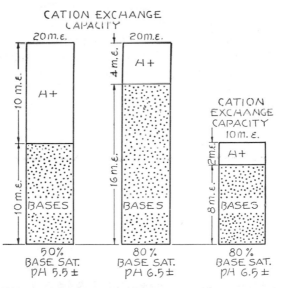

Figure 4:10. Diagrams explanatory of percentage base saturation. Three soils are pictured with percentage base saturations of 50, 80, and 80 respectively. The first is a clay loam; the second, the same soil satisfactorily limed; and the third, a sandy loam with a cation-exchange capacity of only 10 m.e.

Note especially that soil pH is correlated more or less closely with percentage base saturation. Also note that the sandy loam (right) has a higher pH than the acid clay loam (left) even though the latter contains more exchangeable bases.

For example, the colloidal complexes in arid-region soils are practically saturated with bases. On the other hand, those of humid-region soils, due to ionic exchange and leaching, are likely to be comparatively low in metallic cations and correspondingly higher in adsorbed hydrogen and aluminum. Such differences are extremely important not only from the fertility standpoint but also with respect to the H ion concentration of the soil solution.

A rather definite correlation exists between the percentage base saturation of a soil and its pH. As the base saturation is reduced, due to the loss in drainage of lime and other metallic constituents, the pH also is lowered in a more or less definite proportion.[16] This is in line with the common knowledge that leaching tends ordinarily to increase the acidity of humid-region soils. The mechanism by which colloids exert a control on soil pH will be considered later (see p. 385).

HUMID-REGION SOILS. Cation-exchange data for a representative mineral surface soil from a humid-temperate region and at an intermediate fertility level are shown in Table 4:6. The soil is about two-thirds base saturated and is distinctly acid. The notes as well as the table itself merit diligent study.

ARID-REGION SOILS. The cation-exchange situation in an arid-region surface soil is just as easily pictured. The adsorbed hydrogen and aluminum are lower and the metallic cations are higher giving a percentage base saturation of 90 or even 100. The pH, of course, is around 7 or may exceed this figure if carbonates, especially those of sodium, are present. These changes definitely indicate the differences that in general can be expected when representative humid- and arid-temperate-region soils are compared with respect to their cation-exchange characteristics, percentage base saturation, and pH of their solutions. By way of illustration, tentative exchange data for a representative chernozem surface soil, characteristic of certain semiarid, temperate regions, are offered in Table 4:6.

4:15. CATION EXCHANGE AND THE AVAILABILITY OF NUTRIENTS

It is generally assumed that adsorbed nutrients are rather readily available both to higher plants and to microorganisms. Experimental results unquestionably bear this out. We have in cation ex-

---

[16] Within the range of pH 5 to 6, the ratio for humid-temperate region mineral soils is roughly at 5 per cent base saturation change for every .10 change in pH. Thus, if the percentage base saturation is 50 per cent at pH 5.5, it should be 25 and 75 per cent at pH 5.0 and 6.0, respectively. This relationship is worth remembering.

Table 4:6. Suggested Cation-Exchange Data for Representative Mineral Surface Soils in Humid-temperature and Semi-arid-temperate Regions[a]

Characteristics	Humid Region Soil	Semiarid Region Soil
Exchangeable calcium—(Ca)	6 to 9 m.e.	13 to 16 m.e.
Other exchangeable bases (M)	2 to 3 m.e.	6 to 8 m.e.
Exchangeable hydrogen (H) and/or aluminum (Al)	4 to 6 m.e.	1 to 2 m.e.
Cation-exchange capacity	12 to 18 m.e.	20 to 26 m.e.
Percentage-base saturation	66.6	95 and 92
Probable pH	5.6 to 5.8	7±

[a] Note that the generalized formula—

$$\begin{array}{l} {}_a\text{Ca} \\ {}_b\text{Al} \\ {}_c\text{H} \\ {}_d\text{M} \end{array} \boxed{\text{Micelle}}$$

—is being evaluated.

In order that the amounts of such exchangeable cations as Ca, Mg, K, etc., may be accurately compared with the amounts of adsorbed H, they must be expressed in milliequivalents. The conversion to pounds per acre-furrow-slice is easy but follow it through until you are familiar with every step. Its mastery is essential.

One milliequivalent of any cation per 100 grams of soil is equivalent on the basis of the acre-furrow-slice. (2,000,000 lbs of dry soil) to 20 lbs of hydrogen (p. 97) or to 1,000 lbs of CaCO₃. This is a convenient conversion relation to remember. But be sure that you can prove it.

Applying this conversion to the maximum figures quoted for the humid-region soil, we find that the total exchange capacity of the soil in question is equivalent to 18,000 lbs of CaCO₃ per acre-furrow-slice and that the actual amount of exchangeable calcium present is equal to 4½ tons of CaCO₃. These figures provide a definite idea as to the magnitude of the exchange capacity of soils and as to the amount of replaceable calcium that might be present.

change a mechanism that undoubtedly facilitates the availability of nutrients. Hydrogen ions from the root hairs and soil microorganisms replace nutrient cations from the exchange complex. They are forced into the soil solution where they can be assimilated by the adsorptive surfaces of roots and soil organisms or they may be removed by drainage water.

CATION SATURATION AND NUTRIENT ABSORPTION BY PLANTS. The availability of absorbed nutrients is not always so easy as the above explanation might lead one to surmise. This is because several factors operate to expedite or retard the release of nutrients to plants. First, there is the proportion of the cation-exchange capacity of the soil occupied by the nutrient cation in question. For example, if the percentage calcium saturation of a soil is high, the displacement of this cation is comparatively easy and rapid. Thus, 6 milliequivalents of exchangeable calcium in a soil whose exchange capacity is 8 probably would mean ready availability. But 6 milliequivalents when the total exchange capacity of a soil is 30 present quite the opposite condition. This is one reason why when liming for a crop, such as alfalfa, that requires abundant calcium, the base saturation of at least part of the soil should approach or even exceed 90 per cent.

INFLUENCE OF ASSOCIATED IONS. A second important factor influencing the plant uptake of a given cation is the effects of the ions held in association with it. For example, potassium availability to plants has been shown to be limited by excessive quantities of calcium. Likewise, in some cases high potassium contents have depressed the availability of magnesium.

THE EFFECT OF TYPE OF COLLOID. Third, the several types of colloidal micelles differ in the tenacity with which they hold specific cations. This, undoubtedly, will affect the ease of cation exchange. For example, at a given percentage base saturation, the tenacity with which Ca is held by montmorillonite is much greater than that of kaolinite. As a result a montmorillonitic clay must be limed to about 70 per cent base saturation before calcium will exhibit an ease and rapidity of exchange that will satisfy growing plants. A kaolinite clay, on the other hand, seems to liberate calcium much more readily, serving as a satisfactory source of this constituent at a much more lower percentage base saturation. Obviously, the liming programs of the two soils will be somewhat different, due in part to the factor under discussion.

4:16. OTHER PROPERTIES OF COLLOIDS—PLASTICITY AND COHESION, SHRINKAGE, SWELLING, AND FLOCCULATION

Without a doubt, the cation-exchange property of colloids is outstanding. Yet, from the practical as well as the technical standpoint, certain other characteristics also assume considerable importance. Those to receive attention here are six: *plasticity, cohesion, shrinkage, swelling, flocculation,* and *dispersion.* As might be expected, they all are surface phenomena and their intensity depends upon the amount and nature of the interfaces presented by the colloids.

PLASTICITY. Many soils, especially the siliceous clays of humid regions, exhibit *plasticity,* that is, pliability and the capacity of being molded. This property is probably due to the platelike nature of the clay particles and the lubricating yet binding influence of the adsorbed water. Thus, the particles easily slide over each other much like panes of glass with films of water between them. Usually those silicate clays with a high capacity for water of hydration exhibit the greatest plasticity. Thus, montmorillonite is more markedly plastic than kaolinite. Also, the particular cation dominating the colloids is a factor, sodium encouraging a more viscous condition than calcium or hydrogen.

In a practical way, plasticity is extremely important because it encourages such a ready change in soil structure. This must be considered in tillage operations. As everyone knows, the cultivation of a fine-textured soil when it is too wet will result in a puddled condition detrimental to suitable aeration and drainage. With clayey soils, especially those of the montmorillonite type, plasticity presents a real problem. Suitable granulation therein is often difficult to establish and to maintain.

COHESION. A second characteristic somewhat related to plasticity is cohesion. As the water of a clay gel is reduced, there is an increase in the attraction of the colloidal particles for each other. This tendency of the clay particles to stick together probably is due at least in part to the mutual attraction of the clay particles for water molecules held in between them. As one might expect, montmorillonite and illite exhibit cohesion to a much more noticeable degree than does kaolinite or hydrous oxides. Humus, by contrast, tends to reduce the attraction of individual clay particles for each other.

SWELLING AND SHRINKAGE. The third and fourth characteristics of silicate clays to be considered are swelling and shrinkage. These properties are due to the relative inhibition of water, especially between the structural units of the micelles (see p. 77). If the clay in question has an expanding-crystal lattice, as is the case with montmorillonite, extreme swelling may occur upon wetting. Kaolinite and most hydrous oxides with a static lattice do not exhibit the phenomenon to any extent; illite is intermediate in this respect. After a prolonged dry spell, montmorillonitic clay-soils often are criss-crossed by wide, deep cracks which at first allow rain to penetrate rapidly. (See Fig. 4:11.) But later, because of swelling, such a soil is likely to close up and become much more impervious than one dominated by kaolinite.

Apparently, swelling, shrinkage, cohesion, and plasticity are closely related. They are dependent, not only upon the clay mixture present in a soil and the dominant adsorbed cation, but also upon the nature and amount of humus that accompanies the inorganic colloids. These properties of soils are responsible to no small degree for the development of soil structure as has been previously stressed (see pp. 60 and ff.).

FLOCCULATION AND DISPERSION. In a clay suspension the colloidal particles are dispersed; that is, they are present as separate particles and not as groups.

Figure 4:11. A field scene showing the cracks which result when a soil high in clay dries out. The type of clay in this case was likely montmorillonitic. (Photo courtesy U.S. Soil Conservation Service.)

Flocculation is a term applied to a coagulation of the dispersed particles. A very good example of flocculation is afforded by treating a colloidal clay suspension (wherein the particles are dispersed) with a small amount of calcium hydroxide. The tiny clay particles almost immediately coalesce into floccules. Because of their combined weight, these sink to the bottom of the containing vessel, leaving the supernatant liquid clear. The phenomenon is called *flocculation* because of the peculiar appearance of the aggregates. The same action apparently takes place in the soil itself, but, of course, much less rapidly.

Although the coagulating capacities of the several cations vary with the type of colloid under consideration, they may be ranked more or less in the order of Al> Ca and H> Mg> K> Na. This is fortunate as the colloidal complexes of humid-region soils are usually dominated by calcium, hydrogen, and aluminum (p. 92). Such soils gradually tend to assume a coagulated condition in the field.

In limited areas of arid regions, sodium ions have become prominent on the exchange complex. This results in a dispersed condition of the soil colloids, making the soils largely impervious to water penetration. Most plants will not grow under these conditions.

It is well to remark again (p. 62) that flocculation is not granulation, because the latter is most satisfactorily attained in the presence of organic matter. Flocculation really only sets the stage. The presence of organic matter and other cementing agents are necessary before stable granules are formed.

REASONS FOR FLOCCULATION. The reason for the greater tendency of a hydrogen- or calcium-saturated colloid to flocculate is associated with the so-called electrokinetic properties of the system. The number of negative charges responsible for the dispersion of colloidal particles is the same for a given particle regardless of the saturation cation. However, the *zeta potential* which determines the effectiveness of these charges in repelling a second particle is determined by the tightness with which the cations are held. Cations which, because of their size or hydration, are held very close to the colloidal surfaces tend to reduce the zeta potential[17] and to allow the particles to come together or to flocculate. Thus, trivalent and divalent cations, which are more tightly held than monovalent cations of the same size, result in colloid-cation systems with lower zeta potentials than do comparable monovalent cations. Also, highly hydrated ions such as sodium result in colloid-cation systems with higher zeta potential than less hydrated ions such as potassium or rubidium. The water of hydration prevents the cation from being so closely adsorbed. These facts may account for the tendency for sodium to encourage dispersion of soil colloids and for calcium to foster their flocculation.

It is clear that the six colloidal properties under discussion are of great importance in the practical management of arable soils. The field control of soil structure must definitely take them into account. With the colloidal viewpoint now provided, it might be worthwhile to review the discussion already offered (p. 64) relating to the structural management of cultivated lands.

4:17. CONCLUSION

No attempt will be made to summarize this chapter except to re-emphasize three things: (1) the unique and somewhat complicated

---

[17] The zeta potential of a colloid-cation system can be determined by measuring the movement of colloidal particles in an electrical field. The rate of movement of the silicate clay particles toward the positive pole is directly proportional to the zeta potential. Thus, sodium-saturated colloidal particles will move more rapidly in an electrical field than will those saturated with calcium.

physical and chemical organization of soil colloids; (2) their capacity to expedite certain phenomena vital to plant and animal life; and (3) the bearing of these phenomena on soil management and crop production.

Yet an understanding of these phases, even in detail, leaves the picture incomplete. The concept must be biocolloidal. Therefore, let us carry our knowledge of the colloidal state of matter with us as we consider soil organisms, soil organic matter, and the genesis of humus.

Chapter 5

The Organisms of the Soil[1]

Humus, like clay, is a product of dissolution and synthesis. And the agency responsible is the organic population of the soil. Before a proper understanding of the various organic transformations and products can be acquired, some attention must be accorded the fauna and flora, the living colloidal fraction, of the soil. In this study it is well to note at the outset that the major stress will be placed, not on classification, but upon the biochemical changes induced by the various organisms. Consequently, the grouping employed (Table 5:1) is very broad and simple.

A vast number of organisms live in the soil. By far the greater proportion of these belong to plant life. Yet animals are not to be minimized, especially in regard to the early stages of organic decomposition. Most soil oganisms, both plant and animal, are so minute as to be seen only by

[1] For a recent review of soil organisms see A. Burges and F. Raw (editors), *Soil Biology* (New York: Academic Press, 1967).

109

Table 5:1. Chart Showing the More Important Groups of Organisms That Commonly Are Present in Soils. The Grouping Is Very Broad and General as the Emphasis Is To Be Placed, Not on Classification, but upon Biochemical Activity

Animals	**Macro**	Subsisting largely on plant materials	Small mammals—squirrels, gophers, woodchucks, mice, shrew Insects—springtails, ants, beetles, grubs, etc. Millipedes Sowbugs (woodlice) Mites Slugs and snails Earthworms
		Largely predatory	Moles Insects—many ants, beetles, etc. Mites, in some cases Centipedes Spiders
	Micro	Predatory or parasitic or subsisting on plant residues	Nematodes Protozoa Rotifers

Plants	Roots of higher plants	
	Algae	Green Blue-green Diatoms
	Fungi	Mushroom fungi Yeasts Molds
	Actinomycetes of many kinds	
	Bacteria	Aerobic Anaerobic and Autotrophic Heterotrophic

the aid of the microscope. The number ranging from this size to that of the larger rodents is comparatively small. For convenience the animals will be considered first. (See Table 5:1.)

5:1. SOIL MACROANIMALS

The larger animals of the soil are chiefly: (1) rodents and insec-
tivora; (2) insects; (3) millipedes; (4) sowbugs (woodlice); (5) mites;
(6) slugs and snails; (7) centipedes; (8) spiders; and (9) earthworms.

The rodents are represented by the ground squirrel, pocket gopher,
woodchuck, kangaroo rat, and prairie dog, depending upon the particular
region under consideration. The activity of these animals results in the
pulverization, granulation, and transfer of considerable quantities of soil.
Insect-eating animals, especially moles, are equally important in many
cases. While the activities of these various animals are usually unfavorable
to agricultural operations, the effect on the soil is often beneficial and
analogous to that of tillage. Not only do these animals incorporate much
organic matter into soils but also their burrows serve to aerate and drain
the land. In some cases they so thoroughly disturb the various soil horizons as to make the original nature of soil profiles difficult to ascertain.

A great variety of insects is found in soils. Some of them have very
little influence on the organic matter, while others, such as ants, beetles,
and springtails, appreciably affect the humic constituents, either by
translocation or by digestion. In some regions, the work of ants is often
especially noticeable. In association with these insects are millipedes,
sowbugs, mites, slugs, and snails, organisms that use more or less undecomposed plant tissue as food. They thus serve to initiate the decomposition processes that are continued by bacteria and fungi. (See Fig.
5:1.)

In peat soils, the millipedes often not only have much to do with the

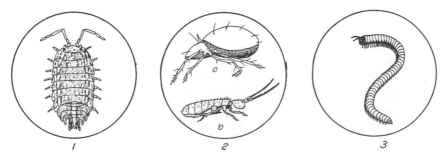

*Figure 5:1. Four animals having much to do with the digestion of the organic
matter especially of forest soils. 1, Sow-bug* (Trachelifus rathkei); *2a, mite*
(Orbata Sp.); *2b, Spring-tail* (Tomocerus Sp.); *3, millipede* (Parajulus Sp.).

digestion of the organic matter but, by forming casts, they markedly influence the structure of the horizons in which they are active. Centipedes and spiders, being in large degree predatory, are of minor importance as far as the processes of humus synthesis are concerned.

Many of the animals just mentioned are rather unimportant in organic transfers as individual groups. In mass, however, they become highly significant even if they do nothing more than contribute at death to the accumulation of decomposable tissue. A number of these organisms are of more concern as plant or animal pests. Thus they are of greater interest to the pathologist and especially the entomologist than to the student of soil science. In any case, they are a part of perhaps the most intricate biological cycle in the world.

5:2. EARTHWORMS

One of the most important of the macroanimals of the soil is the ordinary earthworm, of which there are a number of species. The *Lumbricus terrestris,* a reddish organism, and *Allolobophora caliginosa,* pale pinkish in color, are very common both in Europe and in eastern and central United States. (See Fig. 5:2.) In other parts of this country somewhat different species are dominant depending on the nature of the habitat. In the tropics and semitropics still other types are prevalent,

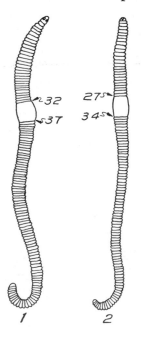

Figure 5:2. Two earthworms common in arable soils. 1, Lumbricus terrestris *and 2,* Allolobophora caliginosa. *While of about the same size, the former is darker and redder, the latter being pale and somewhat pinkish. Also there is a difference in the mouth parts. And as the diagram shows, the girdles of the organisms are located somewhat differently in respect to the segments.*

some small and others surprisingly large. In respect to species, it is rather interesting to note that *Lumbricus terrestris* probably is not native to America. As the forests and prairies were put under cultivation, this European worm rapidly replaced the native types which could not withstand the changed conditions. Virgin lands, however, still retain at least part of their native populations.

QUANTITY OF SOIL DIGESTED. Earthworms are important in many ways. The amount of soil that these creatures pass through their bodies annually may amount to as much at 15 tons of dry earth per acre, a startling figure. At such a rate, a mass of soil equivalent to the acre-furrow-slice would be so processed in a period of only sixty or seventy years. During the passage through the worms, not only the organic matter, which serves the earthworms as food, but also the mineral constituents, are subjected to digestive enzymes and to a grinding action within the animals. The rank growth of grass around earthworm casts suggests an increased availability of plant nutrients therein. Nitrogen perhaps is most markedly affected.

INFLUENCE ON SOIL FERTILITY AND PRODUCTIVITY. Earthworm casts on a cultivated field may weigh as much as 16,000 pounds an acre. Compared to the soil itself, the casts are definitely higher in organic matter, total and nitrate nitrogen, exchangeable calcium and magnesium, available phosphorus, pH and percentage base saturation, and exchange capacity. These results support the observation in the preceding paragraph regarding the increased growth of grass observed on and around earthworm casts. It has long been known that earthworms have a favorable effect on soil productivity. Studies[2] have shown that organic matter, cation-exchange capacity, and available phosphorus and potash are all increased through earthworm activity.

OTHER EFFECTS. Earthworms are important in other ways. The holes left in the soil serve to increase aeration and drainage, an important consideration in soil development. Moreover, the worms bring about a notable transportation of the lower soil to the surface. They also mix and granulate the soil by dragging into their burrows quantities of undecomposed organic matter, such as leaves and grass, which they use as food. In some cases, the accumulation is surprisingly large. In uncultivated soils, this is more important than in plowed land where organic matter is normally turned under in quantity. Without a doubt, earthworms have definitely increased both the size and stability of the soil aggregates, especially in virgin soils.

[2] Y. C. Puh, "Beneficial Influence of Earthworms on Some Chemical Properties of the Soil," *Sci. Soc. China, Biol. Lab. Contrib.*, Zool. Ser., 15, No. 9:147–55, 1941, H. Hopp and C. S. Slater, "Influence of Earthworms on Soil Productivity," *Soil Sci.*, 66:421–28, 1948.

FACTORS AFFECTING EARTHWORM NUMBERS.
Earthworms prefer a moist habitat. Therefore, they are found mostly in
medium to heavy soils where moisture capacity is high, rather than in
those of a sandy, droughty nature. They must have organic matter and
thrive best in land where this constituent is plentiful. It seems, also,
that the nutrition of some earthworms depends on certain lime-secreting
glands. Perhaps because of this, they are not usually found abundantly
in soils that are low in replaceable calcium. There are some exceptions to
this, however. Nevertheless, it is quite surprising to find how suddenly
the earthworm population at times will change as to vigor, numbers, and
even species within very short distances in response to pH and other soil
conditions.

The numbers of earthworms are markedly affected by the application
of farm manure. If we consider their dependence upon organic matter
and their response to fertility levels, this influence is to be expected.
Russell[3] quotes them as ranging from 13,000 per acre in a soil receiving
no farm manure to over 1,000,000 per acre on land to which farm manure
in quantity was applied. These data are in line with figures cited by Lutz
and Chandler[4] indicative of a range under normal conditions of from
250,000 to at least 1,000,000 individuals to the acre.

Using Russell's data as to numbers and assuming each worm to weigh
an average of ½ gram, the live weight of these animals would range from
approximately 15 pounds per acre in the one case to over 1,100 pounds in
the other. These figures are merely suggestive, but they do indicate what
may be expected in a general way as to the weight of the earthworm
population in arable soils.

EARTHWORM ECOLOGY. In a study of earthworm ecol-
ogy at College Park, Maryland, these organisms (mostly *Helodrilus
caliginosus* and *H. chloroticus*) were found to follow a distinct reproduc-
tive cycle.[5] In sod, young earthworms were fewest in the spring and
reached their peak in autumn. The numbers of mature worms were just
reversed. In the fall before they became tolerant to cold, the new generation was easily killed by freezing. Hence, in bare, cultivated soils the
population is often seriously reduced in late autumn by a sudden freeze
unless the soil surface is covered by plant debris of some kind. Frost
damage is not so likely to occur in sodded land.

Therefore, in regions where soil freezing is the rule, a surface protection

3. E. J. Russell and F. W. Russell, *Soil Conditions and Plant Growth* (New York:
Longmans, Green, 1950), p. 414.
4 H. J. Lutz and R. F. Chandler, Jr., *Forest Soils* (New York: Wiley, 1946), p. 101.
5 H. Hopp, "The Ecology of Earthworms in Cropland," *Proc. Soil Sci. Soc. Amer.*,
12:503–507, 1947. See also C. S. Slater and H. Hopp, "Relation of Fall Protection
to Earthworm Populations and Soil Physical Conditions," *Proc. Soil Sci. Soc. Amer.*,
12:508–11, 1947.

of some type is necessary as winter sets in if the earthworm population is to be carried over more or less intact. However, after the first severe weather, the earthworms not only acquire tolerance to the cold but also migrate to lower horizons where temperatures are more favorable. This penetration may range from 3 to 6 feet. For gardeners and others who wish to maintain a high earthworm population in their soils, surface protection is as essential as high organic matter, suitable moisture, good drainage and aeration, and low acidity.

5:3. SOIL MICROANIMALS

Of the abundant microscopic animal life in soils, two groups are particularly important—nematodes and protozoa. A third—the rotifers— at least deserves mention. The three groups will be considered in order. (See Table 5:1.)

NEMATODES. Nematodes, threadworms, or eelworms as they are commonly called, are found in almost all soils, often in surprisingly large numbers. A maximum of 50 to the gram of dry soil would mean about 45 billions to the acre-furrow-slice. These organisms are round and spindle-shaped, the caudal end usually being acutely pointed. In size, they are almost wholly microscopic, seldom being large enough to be seen at all readily with the naked eye. (See Fig. 5:3.)

Three groups of nematodes may be distinguished on the basis of their food demands: (1) those that live on decaying organic matter; (2) those that are predatory on other nematodes, small earthworms, and the like; and (3) those that are parasitic, attacking the roots of higher plants to pass at least a part of their life cycle imbedded in such tissue. The first and second groups are by far the most numerous in the average soil and most varied.

The last group, however, especially those of the genus Heterodera is the most important to the plant specialist. Due to their adaptable mouth

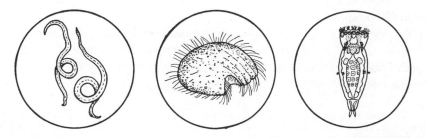

Figure 5:3. Parasitic nematodes (left), a ciliated protozoan (center), and a common rotifer (right). (First two after Waksman.)

parts and pointed form they find it easy to penetrate plant tissue. The roots of practically all plants are more or less infested even in cool temperate regions,[6] and the damage done is often very great, especially to vegetable crops grown in southern United States. Even in greenhouses, nematodes may become a serious pest unless care is taken to avoid infestation. Due to the difficulties encountered in control, an appreciable nematode infection is a serious matter.

PROTOZOA. Protozoa probably are the simplest form of animal life. Although one-celled organisms, they are considerably larger than bacteria and of a distinctly higher organization. Some are merely masses of naked protoplasm—amoeba—whereas others exhibit a much higher development and are even protected with siliceous or chitinous coverings. For convenience of discussion, soil protozoa are divided into groups: (1) amoeba, (2) ciliates or infusoria, and (3) flagellates. The presence of numerous cilia or hairs and of flagella, long whiplike appendages of protoplasm, are the bases for the two latter subdivisions. (See Fig. 5:3.) The flagellates are usually most numerous in soil followed in order by the amoeba and the ciliates.

The protozoa are the most varied and numerous in the microanimal population of soils. More than 250 species have been isolated, sometimes as many as 40 or 50 of such groups occuring in a single sample of soil. The presence of protozoa has been reported in soils from most of the countries of Europe, the United States, and many other regions. Many of these organisms are highly adaptable and occur in habitats other than that of the soil. A considerable number of serious animal and human diseases are due to protozoan infections.

The numbers of protozoa in the soil are subject to extreme fluctuation, even when conditions apparently are continuously favorable. Aeration, as well as the available food supply, is probably a very important factor. Most of the organisms are therefore confined to the surface horizons. Usually, the numbers are highest in the spring and autumn. Perhaps 1,000,000 protozoa of all kinds per gram of a representative dry soil might be considered a maximum. This might amount to a live weight of 100 or even 200 pounds to the acre.

The nutritional habits of protozoa are not well known. No doubt, most of those in the soil depend on nonliving organic matter as a source of food. There are some indications, that certain groups may ingest bacteria but no evidence that they interfere with higher plants.

---

[6] The infection of the potato soils of Long Island, New York, with the golden nematode (Heterodera Rostochiensis) is a case in point, threatening the economic production of potatoes on soils that otherwise are satisfactory in both yield and proximity to market.

ROTIFERS. That rotifers, the third group of microanimals to be considered, occur in the soil is well known and under moist conditions, especially in swampy land, their numbers may be great. As many as fifty different species have been found under such environs. These animals are mostly microscopic in size. Their anterior is modified into a retractile disk bearing circles of cilia which, in motion, give the appearance of moving wheels—hence, the name. These hairs sweep floating food materials into the animal. The posterior end of the rotifer tapers to a foot by which the rotifer can attach itself to convenient objects. (See Fig. 5:3.)

Just how important rotifers are in soils is unknown. No doubt they enter into the cycle of organic dissolution in a more or less important way, especially in peat bogs and in wet places occurring in mineral soils.

5:4. PLANT LIFE OF THE SOIL

The organisms of a plant nature are more numerous and, from some standpoints, are more important than are the animal forms. This is true especially in respect to the final stages of organic matter decomposition, the synthesis of humus and the production of compounds simple enough for the direct nutrition of higher plants. It must be remembered, however, that the initial digestion is very often due to animals such as millipedes and springtails greatly assisted by earthworms if the lime content and other conditions of the organic residues are favorable.

The plant life of the soil will be considered under five heads as follows: (1) roots of higher plants, (2) algae, (3) fungi, (4) actinomycetes, and (5) bacteria. (See Table 5:1.)

5:5. ROOTS OF HIGHER PLANTS

As a source of organic matter, the roots of higher plants are of supreme importance since they supply much more original tissue than all the other organisms combined. In fact, the life of the soil might be divided into two distinct and, in some respects, opposing groups: (1) those that supply organic residues, and (2) those that are engaged primarily in tearing such residues down. Plant roots are, of course, the all-important representative of the first group, whereas millipedes, springtails, earthworms, bacteria, molds, and actinomycetes are principals in the second type of activity.

AMOUNTS OF ORGANIC TISSUE ADDED. A good crop of oats will produce perhaps 5,000 pounds of dry matter to the acre in its aboveground parts, whereas the figure for corn on the same basis would be about 8,000 pounds. If the roots left in the soil when such crops are harvested amount to even half these weights, the added organic residues are, by no means, inconsiderable. In fact, and this is a situation seldom appreciated even by farmers, the maintenance of a satisfactory supply of organic matter in arable soils is possible only because of root residues added in this automatic way. For a photo of elongating as well as dying rootlets see Fig. 5:4.

Figure 5:4. Rootlets elongate rapidly and thereby are continually establishing new soil contacts. Were it not for this ready extension, crops growing on well drained arable soils would soon suffer from lack of moisture as well as nutrients. Since the life of these shoots is very short, they continually contribute to the supply of readily decomposable tissue and greatly stimulate microbial activity. Note the excellent granulation of this soil. (N.Y. State College of Agriculture Photo.)

The roots of higher plants also function in a more intimate manner than as a source of dead tissue for the nutrition of soil microbes. When alive, they not only influence the equilibrium of the soil solution by the withdrawal of soluble nutrients, but they also have something to do in a direct way with nutrient availability. Organic acids are formed at the root surfaces and hence become effective solvents. Again, the excretion of readily decomposable compounds such as amino acids as well as the sloughing of root tissue stimulate the microflora to an intensity of action not attained in other parts of the soil. The numbers of organisms in the immediate root zone, the *rhizosphere*, may be as many as 100 times as great as elsewhere in the soil, although a value of 10 times is probably more normal. This means that the adsorptive surfaces of the root hairs lie within the zone of unusual nutrient availability. This has already been explained (p. 38) and indicates in part why the roots of

higher plants are classified as soil organisms. They not only force a
transfer of nutrients but they also promote an availability that, under
other conditions, might be very slow.

5:6. THE MICROPLANT ORGANISMS— DIFFICULT TO STUDY

Before considering the specific groups of the microplant organisms, it may be well to mention the inadequacies of the methods used
in their study. For example, the estimation of the numbers of specific
organisms in the soil is often quite inaccurate, because all soil microorganisms do not grow equally as well on the various artificial media
commonly employed in making counts. A given species might function
very well in the soil and yet grow poorly, if at all, on any of the media
commonly used.

The above example is a reminder of the extreme complexity of the
microbiological population making it difficult to study the specific functions of the various groups. These situations should be kept in mind in
reading the following sections.

5:7. SOIL ALGAE [7]

Most algae are chlorophyll-bearing organisms and must live
at or very near the surface of the soil, if they are to survive in a habitat
of this nature. However, certain forms seem able to obtain their energy
largely from organic matter and may readily exist within and below the
surface horizon. The number of these, however, is not large. Thus, some
algae live and function much like higher plants, while others in their
nutritional habits are typical soil microorganisms. Over 60 species have
been isolated from soils, those most prominent being the same the world
over. Soil algae are divided into three general groups: (1) blue-green,
(2) green, and (3) diatoms.

Naturally, soil algae in vegetative form are most numerous in the surface layers, especially in the upper inch of arable soils. In subsoils, most
algae are present as resting spores, or cysts, or in vegetative forms that
do not depend upon chlorophyll. Grassland seems especially favorable
for the blue-green forms, whereas in old gardens diatoms are often

[7] Most of this group can carry on photosynthesis just as do higher plants. The
amounts of organic tissue thus produced, however, are small in comparison with those
supplied by higher plant residues.

numerous. All of the ordinary types of algae are greatly stimulated by the application of farm manure.

Both the green and the blue-green algae outnumber the diatoms, 100,000 to a gram of dry surface soil being an estimated minimum under favorable conditions for each in Rothamsted soils.[8] A range in algal population of 10,000 to 3,000,000 per gram soil has been reported.[9] Thus, algae undoubtedly contribute some to the organic content of the soil. Blue-green algae are especially numerous in rice soils and when such lands are waterlogged and exposed to the sun appreciable amounts of nitrogen are fixed by these organisms. Moreover, algae fixation is enhanced when the rice crop occupies the paddies. Apparently, this stimulation is due to CO_2 which is at an especially high level when the rice plants are growing most vigorously.

5:8. SOIL FUNGI

Although the influence of fungi is by no means entirely understood, it is known that they play a very important part in the transformations of the soil constitutents. Over 690 species have been identified representing 170 genera. Like the bacteria and actinomycetes, fungi contain no chlorophyll and must depend for their energy and carbon on the organic matter of the soil.

The superficial characteristic that distinguishes fungi is the filamentous nature of their vegetative forms. Their mycelial threads may be simple and restricted or profusely branched. The special spore-forming or fruiting bodies of some groups attain macroscopic sizes. Fungal organisms may thus vary from the simple microscopic yeasts to mushroom and bracket fungi of extraordinary dimensions.

For convenience of discussion, fungi may be divided into three groups as follows. (1) yeasts, (2) molds, and (3) mushroom fungi. Of these, only the last two are considered important in soils, as yeasts occur to a very limited extent in such a habitat.

MOLDS. The distinctly filamentous, microscopic, or semi-macroscopic fungi are commonly spoken of as molds. (See Fig. 5:6.) In soils, they play a role infinitely more important than the mushroom fungi, approaching or even excelling at times the influence of bacteria. They respond especially to soil aeration, their numbers and activities diminishing as air movement is retarded.

Molds will develop vigorously in acid, neutral, or alkaline soils, some

---

[8] Russell, *op. cit.,* p. 420.
[9] A. Burges and F. Raw, *op. cit.,* p. 130.

Figure 5:5. Invasion of plant roots by mycorrhizae are of considerable practical importance. (Upper left.) The pine seedling on the left was innoculated with mycorrhizal fungi at 4 months; that on the right was untreated. (Upper right.) The corn plant on the right was invaded by mycorrhizae; that on the left was not. (Lower.) A section through a red maple root is shown. Note that the hyphae appear as coils. (Tree root photos from Edward Hacskaylo, U.S. Forest Service; Corn photo from J. W. Gerdeman, Univ. of Illinois.)

being favored, rather than otherwise, by a lowered pH. (See Fig. 14:7.) Consequently, they are noticeably abundant in acid soils, where bacteria and actinomycetes offer only mild competition. This is especially important in decomposing the organic residues in acid forest soils.

The greatest numbers of molds are found in the surface layers where organic matter is ample and areation adequate. Many genera are represented, four of the more evident being Penicillium, Mucor, Fusarium, and Aspergillus. All of the common species occur in most soils, conditions determining which shall dominate. Their numbers fluctuate greatly with soil conditions, perhaps 10 to 20 million individuals to the gram of dry soil representing a more or less normal population. This might well amount to a ton of living organisms to the acre. Molds are an important part of the general-purpose, heterotrophic group of soil organisms that fluctuate so greatly in most soils.

In this connection it is interesting to note that fungal population is constantly changing not only in numbers but in respect to the species dominant. The complexity of the organic compounds being attacked seems to determine, at least in part, the particular mold or molds prevalent.

ACTIVITIES OF FUNGI. In their ability to decompose organic residues, fungi are the most versatile and perhaps the most persistent of any group. Cellulose, starch, gums, lignin, as well as the more easily affected proteins and sugars, readily succumb to their attack. In respect to the processes of humus formation and aggregate stabilization molds are perhaps more important than bacteria. This is certainly true in acid forest soils.

Moreover, fungi function more economically than bacteria in that they transform into their tissues a larger proportion of the carbon and nitrogen of the compounds attacked and give off as by-products less carbon dioxide and ammonium. As much as 50 per cent of the substances decomposed by molds may become fungal tissue. However, they apparently cannot oxidize ammonium compounds to nitrates as do certain bacteria, nor can they fix atmospheric nitrogen. Nevertheless, soil fertility depends in no small degree on molds, since they keep the decomposition processes going when bacteria and actinomycetes alone would not suffice.

MYCORRHIZAE.[10] An interesting and economically important association exists between numerous varieties of mushroom fungi and the roots of higher plants. The mycelia of the fungus infest the plant roots giving an association called *mycorrhizae,* a term meaning "fungus root." This association has been known since the latter part of the 19th century when it was first noted on certain forest tree species. It was only with the advent of specialized microbiological procedures and modern radiotracer techniques that the widespread occurrence and practical significance of mycorrhizae was firmly established.

Mycorrhizae are divided into two general classes based on the interrelation of the thread-like fungus hyphae and the root cells. In the *Ectotrophic* group the hyphae penetrate between cortex cells of the root but do not enter the cells. In contrast, the hyphae of the *Endotrophic* fungi actually penetrate the epidermal and cortex cells of the root. In each case, the fungi secrete appropriate enzymes which permit the penetration of the plant to which the fungus is adapted.

[10] An interesting review of our knowledge of mycorrhizae was given by Edward Hacskaylo, "Micorrhizae: Indispensable Invasion by Fungi," *Agric. Sci. Review* 5:13–20 First Quarter, 1967.

The Ectotrophic group are easily identified and cultured and consequently have been studied longer than Endotrophic fungi. They are common on the pine (Pinacae), birch (Betulaceae), and beech and oak (Fagaclae) families and are known to be essential for the establishment of some of the species.

The Endotrophic mycorrhizae occur on most genera of seed plants not susceptible to the Ectotrophic group. Many cultivated crops such as corn, onions, red clover, and strawberries, as well as shrubs and some trees including maple, yellow poplar, sweet gum, redwood, and apple are subject to the Endotrophic association.

The root-fungus association is of mutual benefit to the host plant and the fungi. The growth of mycorrhizae-infected plants is superior to that of uninfected plants, especially on low fertility soils (Fig. 5:5). The uptake of nutrients, particularly phosphorus, is increased markedly as a result of the association. In return, the fungi apparently absorb carbohydrates from the plant roots.

The widespread occurrence of mycorrhizae is of great practical importance. It makes possible the growth of certain forest species in areas nearly devoid of plant nutrients—growth which would not occur in the absence of the mycorrhizae. In cultivated fields, the extent of the benefit is yet to be established. However, the known increased efficiency of nutrient uptake by mycorrhizae and their widespread occurrence suggests benefits of considerable magnitude.

5:9. SOIL ACTINOMYCETES

Actinomycetes resemble molds in that they are filamentous, often profusely branched, and produce fruiting bodies in much the same way. Their mycelial threads are smaller, however, than those of fungi. Actinomycetes are similar to bacteria in that they are unicellular and of about the same diameter. When they break up into spores, they resemble bacteria often rather closely. On the basis of organization, actinomycetes occupy a position between true molds and bacteria. Although they often are classified with the fungi, they are sometimes called thread bacteria. (See Fig. 5:6.)

Actinomycetes develop best in moist, well-aerated soil. But in times of drought, they remain active to a degree not generally exhibited by either bacteria or molds. They are in general rather sensitive to acid soil conditions, their growth being practically prohibited in mineral soils at a pH of 5.0 or below. Their optimum development occurs at pH values between 6.0 and 7.5. (See Fig. 14:7.) This marked relationship to soil reaction is sometimes taken advantage of in practice, espe-

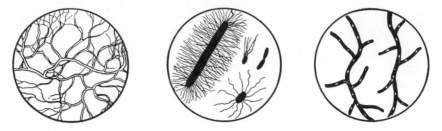

Figure 5:6. The three most important plant microorganisms of the soil, from left to right, Fungal mycelium, various types of bacteria cells, and antinomycetes threads. The bacteria and antinomycetes are much more highly magnified than the fungi.

cially in respect to potato scab, an actinomycetes disease of wide distribution. It is often possible by the use of sulfur to effect a reduction in pH sufficient to keep the disease under control. (See p. 404.)

NUMBERS AND ACTIVITIES OF ACTINOMYCETES. Except for bacteria, no other microorganisms are so numerous in the soil as the actinomycetes, their numbers sometimes reaching hundreds of millions, one tenth the number of bacteria. In actual live weight, they often excel bacteria. Under especially favorable conditions, more than a thousand pounds of actinomycetes threads and spores might be present in an acre-furrow-slice. These organisms are especially numerous in soils high in humus such as old meadows or pastures when the acidity is not too great. There they sometimes exceed in numbers all other microscopic forms of life. The addition of farm manure markedly stimulates their activities. The aroma of freshly plowed land, that is so noticeable at certain times of the year, is probably due to actinomycetes, as well as to certain molds.

Actinomycetes undoubtedly are of great importance in respect to the dissolution of soil organic matter and the liberation of nutrients therefrom. Apparently, they reduce to simpler forms even the more resistant compounds. The presence of actinomycetes in such abundance in soils long under sod is some indication of this latter capacity.

5:10. SOIL BACTERIA

CHARACTERISTICS. Bacteria are single-cell organisms, one of the simplest and smallest forms of life known. They multiply rapidly by elongating and dividing into two parts. They are, therefore, often called *fission fungi*. Their almost unlimited capacity to increase in numbers is extremely important in soils. It allows certain groups quickly to assume their normal functions under favorable conditions, even though their numbers were originally small.[11]

Bacteria may thus be considered a force of tremendous magnitude in the soil. They, with the fungi and actinomycetes, largely make up that general-purpose group of microorganisms, already mentioned, that fluctuates so markedly in response to soil conditions.

Bacteria are very small; the larger individuals seldom exceed 4 or 5 microns (0.004 to 0.005 mm) in length and the smaller ones approach the size of an average clay particle.[12] The shape of bacteria is varied in that they may be nearly round, rodlike, or spiral. In the soil, the rod-shaped organisms seem to predominate. (See Fig. 5:6.)

BACTERIAL POPULATION IN SOILS. The numbers of bacteria present in soil are variable, as many conditions markedly affect their growth. In general, the greatest population is in the surface horizons, since conditions of temperature, moisture, aeration, and food are here more favorable. It is fairly certain that the numbers of bacteria in soil are very large, normally ranging from one to three billions to a gram of soil. One thousand pounds of live weight bacterial tissue to the acre-furrow-slice of a fertile soil is probably a modest estimate. Good soils seem, in general, to carry the greatest numbers. The bacterial flora, as well as the other soil organisms, fluctuates markedly with season, the numbers in humid-temperate regions usually being the greatest in early summer and in the autumn.

In the soil, bacteria exists as mats, clumps, and filaments, called *colonies,* on and around the soil particles wherever food and other conditions are favorable. The jelly-like mixture of mineral and organic colloidal matter makes an almost ideal medium for their development. Their existence depends on soil conditions, particularly food supply. Thus, there is a constant and rapid fluctuation—multiplication and death, often by starvation.

Many of the soil bacteria are able to produce spores or similar resistant bodies, thus presenting both a vegetative and a resting stage. This latter capacity is important as it allows the organisms more readily to survive unfavorable conditions.

SOURCE OF ENERGY. Soil bacteria are commonly classified under two heads, *autotrophic* and *heterotrophic.* The former obtain

[11] If a single bacterium and every subsequent organism produced subdivided every hour, the offspring from the original cell would be about 17,000,000 in 24 hours. In six days, the organisms theoretically would greatly surpass the earth in volume.

[12] The surface exposed by soil bacteria is remarkable. Assuming that a single bacterium is, on the average, 1 μ long by 0.5 μ thick and that one billion are present to 1 g. of soil, the external surface exposed would amount to about 10 sq. ft. to the pound of dry soil, or about 460 acres to the acre-furrow-slice.

their energy from the oxidation of mineral constituents, such as ammonium, sulfur, and iron, and most of their carbon from carbon dioxide. In numbers, they are comparatively insignificant, but since they include the organisms that support nitrification and sulfur oxidation, they are tremendously important in the sustenance of higher plants.

Most soil bacteria, however, are heterotrophic, that is, their energy and carbon both come directly from the soil organic matter. The general-purpose decay and ammonifying bacteria, as well as the fungi and actinomycetes, are all heterotrophic in character.

IMPORTANCE OF BACTERIA. Bacteria, as a group, almost without exception participate vigorously in all of the organic transactions so vital if a soil is to successfully support higher plants. They not only rival but they often excel both fungi and actinomycetes in this regard. Also, they hold monopolies on three basic enzymic transformations, (1) *nitrification,* (2) *sulfur oxidation,* and (3) *nitrogen fixation.* If these were to fail, life for higher plants and for animals would be endangered. Looked at from this angle, bacteria, the simplest and most numerous of all life-forms, are perhaps basically the most consequential.

5:11. CONDITIONS AFFECTING THE GROWTH OF SOIL BACTERIA

Many conditions of the soil affect the growth of bacteria. Among the most important of these are the supplies of oxygen and moisture, the temperature, the amount and nature of the soil matter, and the H ion concentration of the soil solution as well as the amount of exchangeable calcium present. These effects are briefly outlined below:

1. Oxygen requirements
   a. Some bacteria use mostly oxygen gas (Aerobic).
   b. Some use mostly combined oxygen (Anaerobic).
   c. Some use either of the above forms (Facultative).
   d. All three of the above types usually function in a soil at one time.
2. Moisture relationships
   a. Optimum moisture level for higher plants usually best for most bacteria.
   b. The moisture content affects oxygen supply (see 1 above).
3. Suitable Temperature range
   a. From 70° to 100° F. bacterial activity generally the greatest.
   b. Ordinary soil temperature extremes seldom kill bacteria.

4. Organic Matter requirements
   a. Used as energy source for majority of bacteria (heterotrophic).
   b. Organic matter not required as energy source for others (auto-trophic).
5. Exchangeable Calcium and pH relationships
   a. High Ca, pH from 6 to 8 generally best for most bacteria.
   b. Calcium and pH values determine the specific bacteria present.
   c. Certain bacteria function at very low pH (3.0±) and others at high pH values.
   d. Exchangeable Ca seems to be more important than pH.

5:12. INJURIOUS EFFECTS OF SOIL ORGANISMS ON HIGHER PLANTS

SOIL FAUNA. It has already been suggested that certain of the soil fauna are injurious to higher plants. For instance, rodents and moles may, in certain cases, greatly damage crops. Snails and slugs in some climates are exceedingly important pests, while the activity of ants, especially as to their transfer and care of aphids on certain plants, must be diligently combated by gardeners. Protozoa, even though their effect may be indirect, also can promote a serious adverse influence. Also, most plant roots are infested with nematodes, sometimes so seriously as to make the successful growth of certain crops both difficult and expensive. Tobacco and potatoes are examples of commercial crops adversely affected by nematodes. Crop rotation and the development of resistant varieties are the most acceptable means of combatting these pests.

MICROFLORA AND PLANT DISEASES. However, it is the plant forms of soil life that, in general, exert the most devastating effects on higher plants. All three groups—bacteria, fungi, and actinomycetes—contribute their quota of plant diseases. However, fungi are responsible for most of the common soil borne diseases of crop plants. Some of the more common diseases produced by soil flora are: wilts, damping off, root rots, clubroot of cabbage and similar crops, and the actinomycetes scab of potatoes. In short, disease infestations occur in great variety, induced by many different organisms.

Injurious organisms live for variable periods in the soil. Some of them will disappear within a few years if their host plants are not grown, but others are able to maintain existence on almost any organic substance. Once a soil is infested, it is likely to remain so for a long time. Infection usually occurs easily. Organisms from infested fields may be carried on implements, plants, or rubbish of any kind. Even stable manure containing infected plants or the feces resulting from the feeding of such plants to animals act as disease carriers. Erosion, if soil is washed from one field to another, may be a means of transfer.

DISEASE CONTROL BY SOIL MANAGEMENT. Prevention is one of the best defenses against diseases produced by such soil organisms, hence the strict quarantines often attempted. Once a disease has procured a foothold, it is often very difficult to eradicate it. Rotation of crops is adequate for some diseases, but the entire absence of the host plant is often necessary.

The regulation of the pH is effective to a certain extent with potato scab and the clubroot of cabbage. If the pH is held somewhat below 5.3 or even 5.5, the former disease, which is due to an actinomycete, is much retarded. With clubroot, a fungus disease, the addition of hydroxide of lime until the pH of the soil is definitely above 7.0 seems fairly effective but is objectionable with certain types of rotation.

Wet, cold soils favor some seed rots and seedling diseases known as damping off. Good drainage and ridging help control these diseases.

Steam sterilization is a practical method of treating greenhouse soils for a number of diseases. The breeding of plants immune to particular diseases has been successful in the case of a number of other crops.

COMPETITION FOR NUTRIENTS. Another way in which soil organisms may detrimentally affect higher plants, at least temporarily, is by competition for available nutrients. Nitrogen is the element usually most vigorously contested for, although organisms may utilize appreciable quantities of phosphorus, potash, and lime to the exclusion of the crops growing on the land. Competition for trace elements may even be serious. Soil organisms usually exact their nutrient quota first and higher plants must subsist on what remains available. This subject will be considered in greater detail in the next chapter.

OTHER DETRIMENTAL EFFECTS. Under conditions of somewhat restricted drainage, active soil microflora may deplete the already limited oxygen supply of the soil. This may affect plants adversely in at least two ways. First, the plant roots require a certain minimum amount of O_2 for normal growth and nutrient uptake. Second, oxidized forms of several elements including nitrogen, sulfur, iron, and manganese will be chemically reduced by further microbial action. In the cases of nitrogen and sulfur, some of the reduced forms are gaseous and these elements may be lost to the atmosphere. Iron and manganese reduction may result in soluble forms of these elements being present in toxic quantities, especially if the soil is quite acid. Thus nutrient deficiencies and toxicities, both microbiologically induced, can result for the same basic set of conditions.

5:13. COMPETITION BETWEEN SOIL MICROORGANISMS

In addition to competition between microorganisms and higher plants, there exists in soils an intense intermicrobial rivalry for food. When fresh organic matter is added the vigorous heterotrophic soil organisms (bacteria, fungi, and actinomycetes) entirely supersede the less numerous autotrophic bacteria. Only after the rapid decay processes have spent their forces and humification is well advanced may the autotrophic bacteria function with any degree of vigor. Undoubtedly, such food competition is the rule and not the exception in soils. (See Fig. 5:7.)

Figure 5:7. Organisms compete with each other in the soil. The growth of a fungus (fusarium) was rapid when this organism was grown alone in a soil (left), but when a certain bacteria (agrobacterium) was also introduced, the fungal growth did not appear. (Photo courtesy M. A. Alexander, Cornell University.)

ANTIBIOTICS PRODUCED IN SOILS.   Besides the food competition just stressed, there is another type of microbial rivalry just as intense and even more deadly. Certain bacteria, fungi, and actinomycetes have the capacity to produce substances that will inhibit, or even actually kill, other microbes. Not only are organisms alien to the soil thus affected but also many of those that normally flourish vigorously therein.

The discovery that many soil organisms can produce *antibiotics,* as they are called, has in some respects revolutionized the treatment of certain human and animal diseases, greatly minimizing their seriousness. Many preparations carrying specific bactericidal ingredients are now on the market such as penicillin, streptomycin and aureomycin. Undoubtedly, many new and valuable substances of this type are yet to be discovered. Although the soil harbors numerous types of disease organisms, it at the same time supports others that are the source of life-saving drugs, the discovery of which marks an epochal advance in medical science.

5:14. ACTIVITIES OF SOIL ORGANISMS BENEFICIAL TO HIGHER PLANTS

In their influence on crop production, the soil fauna and flora are, of course, indispensable. Of their many beneficial effects on higher plants only the most important can be emphasized here.

ORGANIC MATTER DECOMPOSITION. Perhaps the most significant contribution of the soil fauna and flora to higher plants is that of organic matter decomposition. By this process, plant residues are broken down, thereby preventing an unwanted accumulation. Furthermore, nutrients held in organic combinations within these residues are released for use by plants; nitrogen is a prime example. At the same time, the stability of soil aggregates is enhanced not only by the slimy, intermediate products of decay, but by the more resistant portion, humus. Plants naturally profit from these beneficial chemical and physical effects.

INORGANIC TRANSFORMATIONS. The appearance in the soil of ammonium compounds and nitrates is the result of a long series of biochemical transfers beginning with proteins and related compounds. (See p. 442.) These successive changes are of vital importance to higher plants, since the latter absorb most of their nitrogen in ammoniacal and nitrate forms.

The production of sulfates is roughly analogous to the biological simplification of the nitrogen. (See p. 468.) Here again a complicated chain of enzymic activities culminates in a simple soluble product—in this case the sulfate—the only important form utilized by higher plants.

Other biologically instigated inorganic changes that may be helpful to plants are those relating to mineral elements such as iron and manganese. In well-drained soils these elements are oxidized by autotrophic organisms to their higher valent states in which forms their solubilities are very low at intermediate pH values. This keeps the greater portion of iron and manganese even under fairly acid conditions, in insoluble and nontoxic forms. If such oxidation did not occur, plant growth would be jeopardized because of toxic quantities of these elements in solution.

NITROGEN FIXATION. An outstanding relationship of tremendous practical import is the fixation of elemental nitrogen. Such nitrogen, so plentiful in the atmospheric air, cannot be used directly by higher plants. It must be in combined form before it can satisfy their nutritional needs. Two groups of bacteria participate in the capture of gaseous nitrogen: the *nodule organisms*, especially those of legumes, and the so-called *free-fixing bacteria of* several kinds.

The legume bacteria, as they are often called, use the carbohydrates of their hosts as an energy source, fix the nitrogen, and pass part of it on to the infected host. However, some is left in the root tissue and in the sloughed nodules (see Fig. 16:5). This is likely to appear later in ammoniacal and nitrate forms due to the enzymic influence of other microbial organisms.

The free-fixing soil bacteria acquire their energy from the soil organic matter, fix the free nitrogen, and make it a part of their own tissue. When they die, decay, ammonification, and nitrification render at least a part of this air nitrogen available to higher plants. Although nitrogen-fixing organisms are special purpose as to the transfer of nitrogen, they are, unlike the nitrifiers and sulfur oxidizers, heterotrophic since their energy and carbon apparently come exclusively from organic matter of various kinds.

It is obvious that the organisms of the soil must have energy and nutrients if they are to function efficiently. In obtaining them they break down organic matter, aid in the production of humus, and leave behind compounds that are useful to higher plants. These biotic features and their practical significance are considered in the next chapter which deals with soil organic matter.

Chapter 6

The Organic Matter
of Mineral Soils

Organic matter influences physical and chemical properties of soils far out of proportion to the small quantities present. It commonly accounts for at least half the cation-exchange capacity of soils and is responsible perhaps more than any other single factor for the stability of soil aggregates. Furthermore, it supplies energy- and body-building constituents for the microorganisms whose general activities have just been considered.

6:1. THE SOURCES OF SOIL ORGANIC MATTER

The original source of the soil organic matter is plant tissue. Under natural conditions, the tops and roots of trees, shrubs, grasses, and other native plants annually supply large quantities of organic residues. A good portion of the plants are commonly removed from

cropped soils, but some of the tops and all of the roots are left in the
soil. As these materials are decomposed and digested by soil organisms
of many kinds, they become part of the underlying horizons by infiltration or by actual physical incorporation. Thus, higher plant tissue is the
primary source, not only of food for the various soil organisms but of
organic matter which is so essential for soil formation. (See p. 294.)

Animals are usually considered secondary sources of organic matter.
As they attack the original plant tissues, they contribute waste products
and leave their own bodies as their life cycles are consummated. Certain
forms of animal life, especially the earthworms, centipedes, and ants,
also play an important role in the translocation of plant residues.

6:2. THE COMPOSITION OF HIGHER-PLANT TISSUE

About 75 per cent, or even more, of green tissue of higher
plants is water. The dry matter is made up of carbon, oxygen, hydrogen,
nitrogen, and mineral elements. (See Fig. 6:1.) Although over 90 per

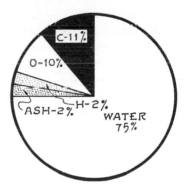

Figure 6:1. Diagram showing the general-
ized composition of green plant tissue. The
nitrogen is included in the ash. Plant tissue
is made up largely of carbon, hydrogen, and
oxygen. (After Stoddard.)

cent of the dry matter is carbon, oxygen, and hydrogen, the other elements play a vital role in plant nutrition. Nitrogen, sulfur, phosphorus,
potassium and, calcium from organic sources are particularly important.
A very large proportion of the soil nitrogen originally became a part
of the solum as a constituent of the tissue of plants and animals.

The actual compounds in plant tissue are many and varied. The general composition of representative mature and dry plant tissue has been
estimated to be about as follows:[1]

---

[1] These figures are essentially the same as those given by S. A. Waksman, *Humus*
(Baltimore: William and Wilkins, 1948), p. 95.

Carbohydrates	Sugars and starches	1– 5%
	Hemicelluloses	10–28%
	Cellulose	20–50%
Fats, waxes, tannins, etc		1– 8%
Lignins		10–30%
Proteins	Simple water soluble & crude proteins	1–15%

It should be emphasized that these figures are very general and serve only to give an idea of the range of those constituents commonly encountered in plant material.

The carbohydrates which are made up of carbon, hydrogen, and oxygen range in complexity from simple sugars to the celluloses. The fats and oils are glycerides of fatty acids such as butyric, stearic, and oleic. These are associated with resins of many kinds and are somewhat more complex than most of the carbohydrates. They too, are made up mostly of carbon, hydrogen, and oxygen.

Lignins occur in older plant tissue such as stems and other woody tissues. They are complex compounds, some of which may have so called "ring" structures. The major components of lignins are carbon, hydrogen, and oxygen. They are very resistant to decomposition.

Of the various groups, the crude proteins are probably the most complicated. They carry not only carbon, hydrogen, and oxygen, but also nitrogen and such elements as sulfur, iron, phosphorus, and others in lesser amounts. They are compounds of high molecular weight and many are of unknown constitution. As found in fresh plant tissue, they are present in the colloidal state which complicates their study.

6:3. THE DECOMPOSITION OF ORGANIC TISSUE AND THE PRODUCTS OF DECAY

RATE OF DECOMPOSITION. Regardless of the complexity of the original tissues cited above, there are research data to indicate the relative resistance of their various organic groups to decomposition—a phase of great practical significance. The compounds found in plant tissue may be listed in terms of their ease of decomposition as follows:

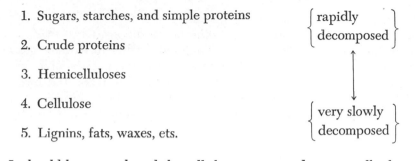

1. Sugars, starches, and simple proteins   { rapidly decomposed }

2. Crude proteins

3. Hemicelluloses

4. Cellulose   { very slowly decomposed }

5. Lignins, fats, waxes, ets.

It should be remembered that all these compounds are usually decomposing simultaneously when fresh plant tissue is added to a soil. The rate at which decomposition occurs, however, decreases as one moves from the top to the bottom of the list. Thus, sugars and water-soluble proteins are examples of readily available energy sources for soil organisms. Lignins are a very resistant source of food, although they eventually supply much total energy.

DECOMPOSITION A BURNING PROCESS. In spite of these differences in the rates of decomposition of the various organic compounds, the similarity of the ultimate end products of decay is quite striking, especially if aerobic organisms are involved. Under such conditions the major portion of all these compounds undergoes essentially a "burning" or oxidation process. The oxidizable fractions of organic materials are composed largely of carbon and hydrogen, which make up more than half of the dry weight. (See Fig. 6:1.) Consequently, we may express the complete oxidation of most of the organic compounds in the soil as follows:

$$- [C, 4H] + 2O_2 \xrightarrow[\text{Oxidation}]{\text{Enzymic}} CO_2 + 2H_2O + \text{Energy}$$

Carbon and hydro-
gen containing
compounds

It is recognized, of course, that many intermediate steps are involved in this over-all reaction. Also important side reactions are occurring simultaneously which involve elements other than carbon and hydrogen. Neither of these facts, however, detract from the importance of this basic reaction in accounting for most of the organic matter decomposition in the soil.

THE BREAKDOWN OF PROTEINS. The plant proteins and related compounds yield other very important products upon decomposition in addition to the carbon dioxide and water mentioned above.

For example, they break down into amides and amino acids[2] of various kinds, the rate of breakdown depending on conditions. Once these compounds are formed, they may be hydrolyzed readily to carbon dioxide, ammonium compounds, and other products. By the process of nitrification, ammonium compounds may be changed to nitrates, the form in which higher plants take up a large proportion of their nitrogen.

Some of the protein may combine with lignin and other resistant compounds and become a part of the soil humus. The protein is thus protected, at least for a time, from enzymic decomposition.

AN EXAMPLE OF ORGANIC DECAY. Now let us view the process of organic decay in cyclic sequence. (See Fig. 6:2.) First

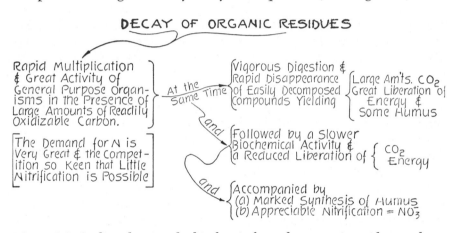

Figure 6:2. Outline showing the biochemical trend as organic residues undergo microbial digestion in the soil. Note the intense microbial competition that occurs, especially during the early stages of decomposition. This is accompanied by a copious loss of carbon as CO_2, and a great liberation of energy. Only when humification nears completion can the nitrifiers function vigorously and nitrate nitrogen appear in the soil.

assume a situation where no readily decomposable materials are present in a soil. The microbial numbers and activity are low. Now, under favorable conditions, let us introduce an abundance of fresh, decomposable tissue. A marked change immediately occurs. The multiplication of soil microorganisms suddenly increases many fold. Microbial activity is soon at its peak, as is shown by the rapid liberation of energy and the copious

---

[2] Amino acids are produced by replacing one of the alkyl hydrogens in an organic acid with NH2. Acetic acid (CH_3COOH) thereby becomes aminoacetic acid or glycocoll (CH_2NH_2COOH). Amides are formed from organic acids by replacing the hydroxyl of the carboxyl group with NH2. Acetic acid (CH_3COOH) thus becomes acetamide (CH_3CONH_2).

evolution of carbon dioxide. That great group of general-purpose decay organisms, bacteria, fungi and actinomycetes, is soon fully active, and are decomposing, as well as synthesizing at the same time.

The soil organic matter at this stage contains a great variety of substances—intermediate products of all kinds, ranging from the more stable bodies such as lignins, to microbial cells, both living and dead. Indeed, the microbial tissue may even at times account for as much as one half of the organic fraction of a soil. These dead organisms are soon subject to decay, the compounds present being attacked by the living microbes. The process is accompanied, of course, by the copious evolution of carbon dioxide.

Finally, as the readily available energy is used up and food supplies diminish, microbial activity gradually lessens, and the general-purpose soil organisms sink back again into comparative quiescence. This is associated with a release of simple products, such as nitrates and sulfates. The organic matter that now remains is a dark incoherent and heterogeneous colloidal mass and is usually referred to as *humus*. In short, we are back again to the condition first postulated after a complex cycle of decay.

It is well to emphasize that the decomposition of both plant residues and soil organic matter is nothing more than a process of enzymic digestion. It is just as truly a digestion as though the plant materials entered the stomach of a domestic animal. The products of these enzymic activities, although numerous and tremendously varied, may be listed for convenience of discussion under three headings: (1) energy appropriated by the microorganisms or liberated as heat; (2) simple end products; and (3) humus. They will be considered in order.

6:4. THE ENERGY OF THE SOIL ORGANIC MATTER AND ITS TRANSFER

The microorganisms of the soil, must not only have substance for their tissue synthesis but energy as well. For most of the microorganisms,[3] both of these are obtained from the soil organic matter. All manner of compounds are utilized as energy sources, some freely, others slowly and indifferently.

POTENTIAL ENERGY IN ORGANIC MATTER. Organic matter contains considerable potential energy, a large proportion

[3] Autotrophic bacteria such as the nitrifiers and sulfur oxidizers are good examples of exceptions to this as their carbon comes mostly from carbon dioxide and their energy largely from the oxidation of inorganic substances.

of which is readily transferable to other latent forms or is liberated as heat. Plant tissue, such as that entering the soil, has a heat value in the neighborhood of 4 or 5 kilocalories per gram of air-dry substance. The application of 10 tons of farm manure, for example, containing 5,000 pounds of dry matter, would mean an addition in round numbers of 9,000,000 to 11,000,000 kilocalories of latent energy. A soil containing 4 per cent of organic matter carries from 150,000,000 to 180,000,000 kilocalories of potential energy per acre-furrow-slice. This is equivalent in heat value perhaps to 20 to 25 tons of anthracite coal.

Of this large amount of energy carried by the soil organic matter, only a part is used by soil organisms. The remainder is left in the residues or is dissipated as heat. This heat loss represents a large and continual removal of energy from the soil.

RATE OF ENERGY LOSS FROM SOILS. Certain estimates made at the Rothamsted Experiment Station,[4] England, on two plots of the Broadbalk field, give some idea concerning the rate of energy dissipation from soils. It was calculated that 1 million kilocalories an acre were lost annually from the untreated, low-producing soil, and about 15 million kilocalories were dissipated from the more productive soil receiving liberal supplies of farm manure. The magnitude of such loss is surprising even for the poorer plot.

6:5. THE SIMPLE PRODUCTS OF ORGANIC MATTER DECOMPOSITION

As the enzymic changes of the soil organic matter proceed, simple products begin to manifest themselves. Some of these, especially carbon dioxide and water, appear immediately. Others, such as nitrate nitrogen, accumulate only after the peak of the vigorous decomposition is over and the general-purpose decay organisms have diminished in numbers.

The more common simple products that result from the activity of the soil microorganisms may be listed as follows:

Carbon	CO_2, CO_3^{--}, HCO_3^-, CH_4, elemental carbon
Nitrogen	NH_4^+, NO_2^-, NO_3^-, gaseous nitrogen
Sulfur	S, H_2S, SO_3^{--}, SO_4^{--}, CS_2
Phosphorus	$H_2PO_4^-$, HPO_4^{--}
Others	H_2O, O_2, H_2, H^+, OH^-, K^+, Ca^{++}, Mg^{++}, etc.

[4] E. J. Russell, and E. W. Russell, *Soil Conditions and Plant Growth* (London: Longmans, Green, 1950), p. 194.

Some of the significant relationships of each of the five groups are presented in the following sections. They are considered in the order listed above.

6:6. SIMPLE PRODUCTS CARRYING CARBON — THE CARBON CYCLE

Carbon is the common constituent of all organic matter. As a consequence, its movements during the microbial digestion of plant tissue are extremely significant. Much of the energy acquired by the fauna and flora within the soil comes from the oxidation of carbon. As a result, its oxide is evolved continuously and in large amounts. The various changes that this element undergoes within and without the soil are collectively designated the *carbon cycle* and are shown graphically in Fig. 6:3.

RELEASE OF CO_2. As the compounds in plant residues are digested, carbon dioxide is given off. This is the main soil source of this gas, although small amounts are excreted by plant roots and are brought down in rain water. The carbon dioxide of the soil,[5] evolved both in summer and winter, ultimately escapes in a large degree to the atmos-

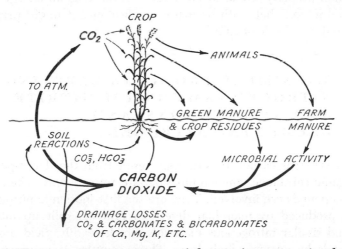

Figure 6:3. Diagrammatic representation of the transformations of carbon, commonly spoken of as the carbon cycle. *Note the stress placed on carbon dioxide both within and without the soil.*

[5] Under optimum conditions as much as 100 pounds of CO_2 per acre per day may be evolved. Twenty to 30 pounds are probably more common. See A. G. Norman, *Mineral Nutrition of Plants,* E. Truog (ed.), (Wisconsin: University of Wisconsin Press, 1951), pp. 167–86.

phere, where it may again be used by plants. Thus the cycle is completed.

A lesser amount of carbon dioxide reacts in the soil, producing carbonic acid (H_2CO_3), and the carbonates and bicarbonates of calcium, potassium, magnesium, and other bases. These salts are readily soluble and may be lost in drainage or be used by higher plants. Thus, not only are Ca, Mg, and K ions presented to the absorbing surfaces of microorganisms and higher plants, but CO_3^{--} and HCO_3^- ions are made available as well. Small amounts of carbon may enter plants in this way. Most of the carbon present in higher plants, however, is acquired from the atmosphere by photosynthesis.

OTHER CARBON PRODUCTS OF DECAY. Besides carbon dioxide, carbonates, and bicarbonates, the simplification of organic matter results in other carbon products. Elemental carbon is found in soils to a certain extent, and while not especially important, its presence is significant. Under certain conditions, methane (CH_4) and carbon bisulfide (CS_2) may be produced in small amounts. But of all the simple carbon products, carbon dioxide is by far the most abundant.

It is now obvious that the carbon cycle is all inclusive since it involves not only the soil and its teeming fauna and flora, and higher plants of every description, but also all animal life including man himself. Its failure to function properly would mean disaster to all. It is an energy cycle of such vital import that, with its many ramifications, it might properly be designated the "Cycle of Life."

6:7. SIMPLE PRODUCTS CARRYING NITROGEN—AMMONIUM, NITRITE AND NITRATE IONS, AND ELEMENTAL NITROGEN

Whereas carbon dioxide may result from the decomposition of any organic substance, ammonium salts are formed only when nitrogenous compounds are involved. They are the first inorganic nitrogen compounds produced by microbial digestion. Proteins split up into amino acids and similar nitrogenous materials which readily yield ammonium compounds by enzymic hydrolysis. These complex transformations are brought about by a large number of heterotrophic organisms—bacteria, fungi, and actinomycetes. The ammonium ion is readily available to microorganisms and most higher plants.

NITRIFICATION. If conditions are now favorable, ammonium ions are subject to ready oxidation, principally by two special-purpose organisms, the *nitrite* and the *nitrate* bacteria. The process,

nitrification, will be discussed in more detail later (see p. 444). However it may be shown simply and diagrammatically as follows:

$$2NH_4^+ + 3O_2 \xrightarrow[\text{Oxidation}]{\text{Enzymic}} 2NO_2^- + 2H_2O + 4H^+ + \text{Energy}$$

$$2NO_2^- + O_2 \xrightarrow[\text{Oxidation}]{\text{Enzymic}} 2NO_3^- + \text{Energy}$$

The autotrophic bacteria obtain energy by these transfers and leave as
a by-product nitrogen in the nitrate form. The second reaction usually
follows so closely on the first as to prevent any appreciable accumulation
of nitrites. Nitrates are a form of nitrogen that some plants seem to need
for their best growth. And it is in this combination that most of the loss
of nitrogen in drainage occurs. Such removal is often so large as to seriously deplete soils of their nitrogen supply. (See p. 214.)

The hydrogen ions formed in the first of the above reactions are of
considerable practical importance. They show that nitrification tends to
result in an increase in soil acidity. This effect is of even greater importance when dealing with commercial fertilizers containing ammonium
salts such as $(NH_4)_2SO_4$. Extra increments of lime are often added to
counteract this acidifying effect.

RELEASE OF GASEOUS NITROGEN. One more group
of end products awaits consideration—gaseous nitrogen compounds. Under certain conditions, the reduction of nitrates and nitrites takes place
in soils, and free nitrogen or oxides of nitrogen may be evolved. This
transfer is considered most likely to occur in poorly drained soils or in
acid soils containing nitrites. The processes are very complicated and as
yet are not fully understood. They apparently may be chemical as well
as biochemical. In any case, the reduction is serious since these nitrogen
gases ordinarily are relatively inert and are not recombined into compounds useful to higher plants. Some authorities believe that soils lose
considerable nitrogen in this way. (See p. 448 and ff.)

6:8. SIMPLE PRODUCTS CARRYING SULFUR — SULFITES, SULFATES, AND OTHER PRODUCTS

Many organic compounds, especially those of a nitrogenous
nature, carry sulfur, which appears in simple forms as decay progresses.
General-purpose heterotrophic types of organisms apparently simplify

the complex organic compounds. The sulfur of these simplified by-products is then subjected to oxidation by special autotrophic bacteria. The final transformation, which is carried to completion by the sulfur oxidizing organisms, may be shown diagrammatically as follows:

$$- [HS] + 2O_2 \xrightarrow[\text{Oxidation}]{\text{Enzymic}} SO_4{}^{--} + H^+ + E$$

Organic
combinations

The organisms involved obtain energy by the transfer and leave the sulfur in the sulfate form. Unlike nitrification, which occurs in two distinct steps and requires two groups of organisms, sulfur oxidation apparently occurs, as indicated above, as one continuous reaction. Thus, the sulfur originally present in complicated combinations, emerges finally as the $SO_4{}^{--}$ ion, the form in which higher plants absorb practically all of their sulfur. Considerable amounts of sulfate sulfur are lost in drainage, a phase that deserves some attention from the standpoint of fertility maintenance, especially on sandy soils.

6:9. ORGANIC PHOSPHORUS AND ITS MINERALIZATION

A large proportion of the soil phosphorus is carried in organic combinations (see p. 477) upon attack by microorganisms the organic phosphorus compounds are *mineralized*, that is they are changed to inorganic combinations. The particular forms, as we already know (p. 37), depend to a considerable degree upon soil pH. As the pH goes up, say from 5.5 to 7.5, the available phosphorus changes from $H_2PO_4{}^-$ to $HPO_4{}^{--}$. Both of these forms are available to higher plants. Since the small amount of phosphorus held in complex mineral combinations in soils usually is very slowly available, the organic sources mentioned above become especially important.

It must not be assumed, however, that the maintenance of soil organic matter at normal or even high levels will solve the phosphorus problem. Far from it. Most field soils need liberal applications of phosphatic fertilizers. Yet strangely enough, the economic use of such phosphorus depends to a considerable degree upon the organic transformation already cited. Since microorganisms utilize phosphorus freely, some of that added commercially quickly becomes part of the soil organic matter. Thus, this phosphorus is held in an organic condition and is later mineralized by microbial activity.

6 : 10. HUMUS — GENESIS AND DEFINITION

The formation of humus, although an exceedingly complicated biochemical process, may be described in general terms rather simply. As organic tissue is incorporated into a moist warm soil it is immediately attacked by a host of different soil organisms. The easily decomposed compounds quickly succumb, first yielding intermediate substances and finally the simple, soluble products already enumerated.

HUMUS FORMATION. As the above decomposition occurs two major kinds of organic compounds tend to remain in the soil: (1) resistant compounds of higher plant origin such as oils, fats, waxes, and especially lignin[6]; and (2) new compounds such as *polysaccharides* and *polyuronides* which are synthesized by microorganisms and held as part of their tissue. The lignin and similar materials are at least partially oxidized during the decomposition thereby increasing their reactivity. The compounds of microbial origin are not insignificant in quantity, studies having shown that up to ⅓ of the organic carbon may be in this form. Apparently these two groups of compounds, one modified from the original plant material and one newly synthesized by the microorganisms, provide the basic framework for humus.

As these humic substances form, there are other side reactions of great practical import. These reactions permit nitrogen to become an integral part of the humus complex. Exactly how these reactions occur is not known, nor are all the specific forms in which the nitrogen is held. Nevertheless, the nitrogen compounds are thought to react with aromatic and quinone groups, as well as polysaccharides. Among the reaction products are amino combinations, in which form about half the nitrogen occurs.

Regardless of the mechanism by which nitrogen is bound, the important fact is that the resultant product, newly formed humus, is quite resistant to further microbial attack. Its nitrogen and other essential nutrients as well are thereby protected from ready solubility and dissipation.

PROTEIN-CLAY COMBINATIONS. Another means of stabilizing nitrogen in soil is through the reaction between certain clays

---

[6] Lignin is a waxy resinous material that impregnates the cell walls of plants as they increase in age. It is exceedingly complex, and varies with different plants and different tissues of the same plant. The chemical formulae of the various lignins are in doubt.

and proteinaceous substances and other nitrogen compounds. Clays with expanding lattices, such as montmorillonite, seem to have such a faculty, the proteins and other nonionic molecules perhaps functioning as bases in satisfying the adsorption capacity of the inorganic colloids. The proteins seem to be protected against rapid decomposition. How important this is in the average soil is difficult to say. Nevertheless, it suggests that intermixed with the nitrogen-containing modified lignin and the polysaccharides, there may be clay-protein combinations, all of which tend to protect nitrogen from microbial attack.

HUMUS DEFINED. From the above discussion two facts are obvious: (1) humus is a mixture of complex compounds and is not a single material; and (2) these compounds are either (a) resistant materials which have been only modified from the original plant tissue, or (b) compounds synthesized within microbial tissue which remain as the organisms die. These two facts lead to the following definition: *humus is a complex and rather resistant mixture of brown or dark brown amorphous and colloidal substances modified from the original tissues or synthesized by the various soil organisms.* It is a natural body and although it is exceedingly variable and heterogenous, it possesses properties that distinguish it sharply from the original parent tissues and from the simple products that develop during its synthesis. Its nature is considered in the next section.

6:11. HUMUS—NATURE AND CHARACTERISTICS AS COMPARED WITH SILICATE CLAY

ADSORPTIVE CAPACITY. Humus is highly colloidal, but unlike its mineral counterpart in the soil, it is amorphous and not crystalline. Moreover, its surface area and adsorptive capacity are far in excess of those exhibited by any of the clays. The cation-exchange capacity of silicate clays commonly ranges from 8 to 150 milliequivalents per 100 grams. Comparable exchange capacities for well-developed humus from mineral soils, in sharp contrast, would range from 150 to 300. In general, the presence of 1 per cent of humus in a mineral soil under humid-temperate conditions infers an exchange capacity of perhaps 2 milliequivalents per 100 grams of soil. The comparable figure for clays would range from about 0.1 to 1.0, perhaps 0.5 being an average value.

In respect to adsorbed water, the contrast is of the same order. The fully synthesized humus of a mineral soil will adsorb from a saturated atmosphere perhaps 80 or 90 per cent of water. Clay, on the other hand, may be able to thus acquire possibly only 15 to 20 per cent. The significance of these figures in respect to soil properties is obvious.

PHYSICAL PROPERTIES. The low plasticity and cohesion of humus is a significant practical feature. The maintenance of this constituent in fine-textured soils helps alleviate unfavorable structural characteristics induced by large quantities of clay. This is due to a considerable extent to granulation which it so markedly encourages.

Another physical character that is of outstanding interest is the color imparted to soils by humus. It is well to note definitely that the development of a black pigment in humus varies with climate. In some mollisol (chernozem) soils, occurring in the northern semiarid regions with an annual rainfall around 20 inches, the pigment is very dark and abundant. In humid-temperate zones, the pigmentation is less intense, and the least coloration is found in the humus of the tropics and semitropics. Color thus in a very general way is an expression of climate. This is a point well worth remembering as it indicates that organic pigmentation cannot always be used satisfactorily as a comparative measure of the amount of organic matter present in soils.

COLLOIDAL CONSTITUTION. Soil humus, as a colloidal complex, is organized in much the same way as clay. This relationship has already been discussed. (See p. 90.) The modified lignin, polyuronides, and no doubt other constituents as well, function as complex micelles. Under ordinary conditions, these carry innumerable negative charges. But instead of being made up principally of Si, O, Al, and Fe, as are the silicate crystals, the humic micelles are composed mostly of C, H, and O with minor quantities of N, S, P, and other elements. The negative charges arise from exposed —COOH and —OH groups from which at least part of the hydrogen may be replaced by cation exchange.

The range in complexity, size, and molecular weight of the humic acids have already been discussed (see p. 91.)

The humic micelles, like the particles of clay, carry a swarm of adsorbed cations (Ca^{++}, H^+, Mg^{++}, K^+, Na^+, etc.). Thus, humus colloidally may be represented by the same structural formula used for clay

namely—
$$\begin{matrix} Ca \\ Al \\ H \\ M \end{matrix} \boxed{\text{Micelle}}$$
and the same reactions will serve to illustrate

cation exchange in both. (See p. 92.) M represents all bases other than Ca.

EFFECT OF HUMUS ON NUTRIENT AVAILABILITY. There is one particular characteristic of humus that merits attention—

the capacity of this colloid when saturated with H^+ ions to increase the availability of certain nutrient bases, such as calcium, potassium, and magnesium. It seems that an H-humus, as is the case with an H-clay, acts much like an ordinary acid and can react with soil minerals in such a way as to extract their bases. Acid humus has an unusual capacity to effect such a transfer, since the organic acid is comparatively strong. Once the exchange is made, the bases so affected are held in a loosely adsorbed condition and are easily available to higher plants. The following is a generalized reaction to illustrate this point, microcline being used as an example of the various soil minerals so affected:

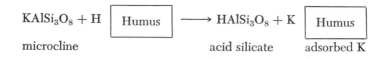

$$KAlSi_3O_8 + H \boxed{\text{Humus}} \longrightarrow HAlSi_3O_8 + K \boxed{\text{Humus}}$$

microcline   acid silicate   adsorbed K

The potassium is changed from a molecular to an adsorbed status in which condition it is rated as rather readily available to higher plants.

HUMUS-CLAY COMPLEX IN SOILS. In considering all the colloidal matter of a mineral soil, it must always be remembered that one is dealing with a mixture of many very different kinds of colloids. The crystalline clayey nucleus is markedly stable under ordinary conditions and is active mainly in respect to cation exchange. The amorphous organic micelle, on the other hand, is susceptible to slow but continuous microorganic attack and hence has a twofold activity—cation exchange and nutrient release. These contrasting details are just as important practically as the colloidal similarities already noted.

6:12. DIRECT INFLUENCE OF ORGANIC COMPOUNDS ON HIGHER PLANTS

One of the early beliefs in regard to plant nutrition was that organic matter, as such, is directly absorbed by higher plants. Although this opinion was later discarded, there is some evidence that certain organic nitrogen compounds can be absorbed by higher plants, often rather readily. Such substances ordinarily do not satisfy plant needs for nitrogen as is indicated by the ready response that most plants make to an application of nitrates.

The beneficial effects of an exceedingly small absorption of organic compounds might be accounted for by the presence of growth-promoting substances. In fact, it is quite possible that vitamin-like compounds are

developed as organic decay progresses in soils.[7] If this be the case, the
direct effect of humic substances upon higher plants might be much more
important than hitherto has been suspected. Undoubtedly, hormones and
vitamins are carried by the soil humus and may at times stimulate both
higher plants and microorganisms.

On the other hand, some soil organic compounds no doubt may be
harmful. As an example, dihydroxystearic acid may be mentioned, as
this was one of the first to be studied. This compound which is toxic to
higher plants, was isolated from 20 soils, out of a group of 60 taken in
11 states. It may be, however, that such compounds are merely
products of unfavorable soil conditions. And when such conditions are
righted, the so-called toxic matter disappears. Apparently, good drainage
and tillage, lime, and fertilizers reduce the probability of organic toxicity.

6:13. CARBON-NITROGEN RATIO

Attention has been called several times to the close relationship
that exists between the organic matter and nitrogen contents of soils.
Since carbon makes up a large and rather definite proportion of this
organic matter, it is not surprising that the *carbon to nitrogen* ratio of
soils is fairly constant. The importance of this fact in controlling the
available nitrogen, total organic matter, and the rate of organic decay,
should unfold as we consider the subject further.

RATIO IN SOILS. The ratio of carbon to nitrogen in the
organic matter of the furrow-slice of arable soils commonly ranges from
8:1 to 15:1, the median being between 10 and 12 to 1. In a given climatic
region, little variation is found in this ratio, at least in similarly managed
soils. The variations which do occur seem to be correlated in a general
way with climatic conditions, especially temperature and the amount and
distribution of rainfall. For instance, it is rather well established that the
carbon-nitrogen ratio tends to be lower in soils of arid regions than in
those of humid regions when annual temperatures are about the same.
It is also lower in warmer regions than in cooler ones, providing the
rainfalls are of about the same magnitude. Also the ratio is narrower for
subsoils, in general, than for the corresponding surface layers.

RATIO IN PLANTS, MICROBES. As one would expect,
the ratio of carbon to nitrogen of plant material is variable, ranging from
20 or 30 to 1 for legumes and farm manure to as high as 90 to 1, or even

---

[7] Evidence that some B-vitamins and other growth factors may be produced by
soil organisms is given by A. G. Lochhead, "Qualitative Studies of Soil Microorganisms; XV. Capability of the Predominant Bacterial Flora for Synthesis of Various
Growth Factors," *Soil Sci.*, 84: 395–404, 1957.

more, in certain strawy residues (see Fig. 6:5). All gradations between these extremes are found. The carbon-nitrogen ratio of the bodies of microorganisms, on the other hand, is not only more constant but much narrower, ordinarily falling between 4:1 and 9:1. Bacterial tissue, in general, is somewhat richer in protein than that of fungi and consequently has a narrower ratio.

It can be seen, therefore, that most organic residues entering the soil carry large amounts of carbon and comparatively small amounts of total nitrogen—that is, their carbon-nitrogen ratio is wide, and the C:N ratio values for soils are in between those of higher plants and the microbes.

6:14. THE SIGNIFICANCE OF THE CARBON-NITROGEN RATIO

The carbon-nitrogen ratio in soil organic matter is an important factor in a number of ways, the two most significant of which are as follows: (1) competition for available nitrogen results when residues having a high C:N ratio are added to soils; (2) due to the constancy of this ratio in soils, the maintenance of carbon, and hence soil organic matter, is dependent to no small degree on the soil nitrogen level. These two factors become obvious as we consider a practical example of the influence of highly carbonaceous material on the availability of nitrogen.

A PRACTICAL EXAMPLE. Suppose that we are dealing with a representative cultivated soil in a condition favoring vigorous nitrification. Nitrates are present in relatively large amounts and, of course, the C:N ratio is narrow. The general-purpose decay organisms are at a low level of activity as evidenced by low CO_2 production (See Fig. 6:4.)

Now suppose large quantities of organic residues with a wide C:N ratio (say 50:1) are incorporated in this soil under conditions supporting vigorous digestion. A change quickly occurs. The heterotrophic flora—bacteria, fungi, and actinomycetes—become active and multiply rapidly, yielding CO_2 in large quantities. Under these conditions, nitrate nitrogen practically disappears from the soil due to the insistent microbial demand for this element to build their tissues. And for the time being little or no nitrogen, even ammoniacal, is in a form available to higher plants. As decay occurs, the C:N ratio of the plant material decreases since carbon is being lost and nitrogen conserved.

This condition persists until humification nears completion, at which time the activities of the decay organisms gradually subside due to a lack of easily oxidizable carbon. Their numbers decrease, CO_2 formation drops off, nitrogen ceases to be at a premium and nitrification can proceed.

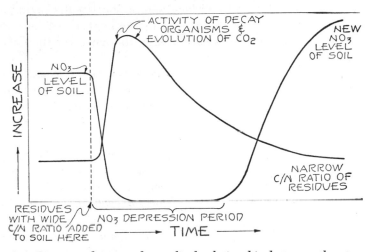

Figure 6:4. Diagram showing the cyclical relationship between the stage of decay of organic residues and the presence of nitrate nitrogen in soil. So long as the C/N ratio is wide, the general-purpose, decay organisms are dominant and the nitrifiers are more or less inactive. During the period of nitrate depression that results, higher plants can obtain but little nitrogen from the soil. The length of this period will depend upon a number of factors of which the C/N ratio is of prime importance. This figure is another version of Figure 6:2.

Nitrates again appear in quantity and the original conditions again prevail except, for the time being, the soil is somewhat richer both in nitrogen and humus. The sequence of events, an important phase of the carbon cycle, is diagramatically represented in Fig. 6:4. Study it carefully.

REASON FOR C:N CONSTANCY. As the decomposition processes above continue, both carbon and nitrogen are now subject to loss—the carbon as carbon dioxide and the nitrogen as nitrates which are leached or absorbed by plants. It is only a question of time until their percentage rate of disappearance from the soil becomes approximately the same, that is, the percentage of the total nitrogen being removed equals the percentage of the total carbon being lost. At this point the carbon-nitrogen ratio, whatever it happens to be, becomes more or less constant, always being somewhat greater than the ratios that characterize microbial tissue. As already stated, the carbon-nitrogen ratio in humid temperate region soils, especially if under cultivation, usually stabilizes in the neighborhood of 10 or 12 to 1.

PERIOD OF NITRATE DEPRESSION. The time interval of nitrate depression (Fig. 6:4), may be long or short depending on conditions. The rate of decay will lengthen or shorten the period as the case may be. And, of course, the greater the amount of residues applied the longer will nitrification be blocked. Also, the narrower the C:N ratio

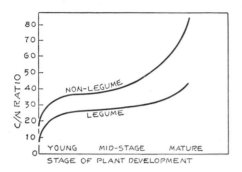

Figure 6:5. The C/N ratio of organic residues added to soil will depend upon the maturity of the plants turned under. The older the plants, the wider will be the C/N ratio and the longer will be the period of nitrate suppression. Obviously leguminous tissue will have a distinct advantage over nonlegumes since the former will promote a more rapid organic turnover in soils.

of the residues applied, the more rapidly the cycle will run its course. Hence alfalfa and clover residues should interfere least with nitrification and yield their nitrogen more quickly than if oats or wheat straw were plowed under. Also mature residues, whether legume or nonlegume, have a much higher C:N ratio than do younger succulent materials. (See Fig. 6:5). These facts are of much practical significance and should be considered when organic residues are added to a soil.

Moreover, cultivation by hastening oxidation, should encourage nitrification while a vigorous sod crop, such as bluegrass, should discourage it. This is because the root and top residues maintain a wide C:N ratio, and the small quantities of nitrate and ammonical nitrogen which appear are immediately appropriated by the sod itself. All of this is illustrative of the influence that the C:N ratio exerts upon the transfer of nitrogen in the soil and its availability to crop plants.

C : N RATIO AND ORGANIC MATTER LEVEL. Since carbon and nitrogen are reduced to a more or less definite ratio (say 11 to 1), the amount of soil nitrogen largely determines the amount of organic carbon present when stabilization occurs. Thus, the greater the amount of nitrogen present in the original residue, the greater will be the possibility of an accumulation of organically combined carbon. And since a rather definite ratio (about 1:1.7) exists between the organic carbon and the soil humus, the amount of organic matter that can be maintained in any soil is largely contingent upon the amount of organic nitrogen present.[8]

---

[8] The ratio between nitrogen and organic matter is thus rather constant. A value for the O.M./N ratio of 20/1 is commonly used for average soils. See page 152.

Practical deductions respecting the carbon-nitrogen ratio are thus clearcut. Apparently the ratio is related not only to the availability of soil nitrogen but also to the maintenance of soil organic matter. In practical handling of cultivated soils both of these phases must receive due consideration.

6:15. AMOUNTS OF ORGANIC MATTER[9] AND NITROGEN IN SOILS

The amounts of organic matter in mineral soils vary so widely that it is difficult to present representative figures. Mineral surface soil, corresponding roughly to the furrow-slice, may contain from a trace to 15 or 20 per cent of organic matter. The average organic matter and nitrogen contents of large numbers of soils from different areas of the United States are shown in Table 6:1. One is immediately impressed by

Table 6:1. *The Average Nitrogen and Organic Matter Contents of Mineral Surface Soils In Several Areas of the U.S. The Ranges Found for These Two Constituents Are Also Given*[a]

	% Organic Matter		% Nitrogen	
Soils	Range	Ave.	Range	Ave.
240 West Va. soils	0.74–15.1	2.88	.044–54	.147
15 Penn. soils	1.70– 9.9	3.60	—	—
117 Kansas soils	0.11–3.62	3.38	.017–.27	.170
30 Nebraska soils	2.43–5.29	3.83	.125–.25	.185
9 Minn. Prairie soils	3.45–7.41	5.15	.170–.35	.266
21 Southern Great Plains soils	1.16–2.16	1.55	.071–.14	.096
21 Utah soils	1.54–4.93	2.69	.088–.26	.146

[a] These data were obtained from a number of sources. See T. L. Lyon, H. O. Buckman, and N. C. Brady, *The Nature and Properties of Soils* (New York: Macmillan, 1952), p. 171.

the relatively wide ranges in organic matter encountered in these soils, even in comparatively localized areas. Thus, the West Virginia soils have

[9] It is to be noted that no figures are offered as to the amount of humus present in mineral soils. This is partly due to the fact that no very satisfactory method is available for its determination.

Unfortunately there is no very satisfactory method of determining directly the exact quantity of total organic matter present in soil. The usual procedure is to find first the amount of organic carbon which can be done quite accurately. This figure multiplied by the factor 1.7 will give the approximate amount of organic matter present.

a range from 0.74 to more than 15 per cent of organic matter. The several factors which may account for this wide variability as well as for the differences between averages in Table 6:1 will be considered in the next section.

It will be noted that the data in the table are for surface soils only. As might be expected, the organic matter contents of the subsoils are generally much lower. (See Fig 6:6) This is readily explained when we consider that most of the organic residues in both cultivated and virgin soils are incorporated in or deposited on the surface. This increases the possibility of organic matter accumulation in the upper layers.

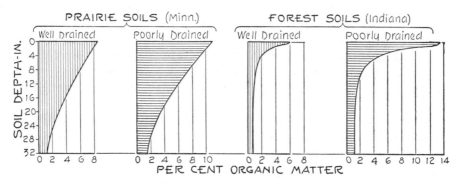

Figure 6:6. Diagrams showing the distribution of organic matter in four soil profiles. Note that the prairie soils have a higher organic matter content in the profile as a whole compared to the corresponding soils developed under forest vegetation. Poor drainage results in a higher organic matter content, particularly in the surface horizon.

THE ORGANIC MATTER TO NITROGEN RATIO. One more significant feature of the data in Table 6:1 should be considered. In comparing the average organic matter and nitrogen contents of the soils listed, one finds that there is about 20 times as much organic matter as nitrogen. This figure is fairly consistent as long as average data on a large number of soils are compared.

The explanation for the above constancy is rather simple. It will be remembered that the C:N ratio of mineral soils is rather constant, and that the organic matter content is about 1:7 times as great as the carbon content. Thus, if a C:N ratio of 11.7 to 1 is assumed, the organic matter to nitrogen ratio is 11.7 × 1.7 or about 20:1. This figure is of considerable value in making rough calculations respecting these two constituents.[10]

[10] The percentage of organic matter in a single sample of soil, when calculated from the percentage of total nitrogen by the factor (N × 20), is an extremely untrustworthy figure. But when the factor is applied in a large number of soils, it gives a comparatively accurate group figure, especially for arable soils.

6:16. VARIATIONS AND CORRELATIONS OF SOIL ORGANIC MATTER AND NITROGEN

In scanning the data presented in the preceding section, one is impressed by the variability in organic matter and nitrogen contents of representative mineral soils. Wide differences are evident, not only between soils of different physiographic provinces but also between closely contiguous areas in any particular locality. Heterogeneity seems to be the rule. This is expected by all pedologists. Let us consider the broader aspects first.

THE INFLUENCE OF CLIMATE. Climatic conditions[11] especially *temperature* and *rainfall,* exert a dominant influence on the amounts of nitrogen and organic matter found in soils. As one moves from a warmer to a cooler climate, the organic matter and nitrogen of comparable soils tend to increase. At the same time, the C:N ratio widens somewhat. In general, the decomposition of organic matter is accelerated in warm climates while a lower loss is the rule in cool regions. Within belts of uniform moisture conditions and comparable vegetation, the average total organic matter and nitrogen increase from two to three times for each 10° C fall in mean annual temperature.

The situation is well illustrated by conditions in the Mississippi Valley region. (See Fig. 6:7.) Here, the northern prairie soils and chernozems contain in general considerably greater amounts of total organic matter and nitrogen than those that lie to the south. When the amount of original tissue yearly added to the soil is taken into consideration, the tropics, where plants grow so luxuriantly, afford an even better example of the influence of temperature on the rapidity of decay and disappearance of organic materials. In spite of this, however, many tropical surface soils are surprisingly high in organic matter.

Effective soil moisture also exerts a very positive control upon the accumulation of organic matter and nitrogen in soils. In general, under comparable conditions, the nitrogen and organic matter increase as the effective moisture becomes greater. (See Fig. 6:7.) At the same time, the C:N ratio becomes wider. This is especially true for the grasslands. The explanation lies not only in the rapidity of microbial action and hence a more complete humification in areas of moderate to low rainfall but also in the scantier vegetation of these regions. In arriving at the rainfall correlation such as advanced above, it must not be forgotten that

---

[11] See H. Jenny, *Factors of Soil Formation* (New York: McGraw-Hill, 1941).

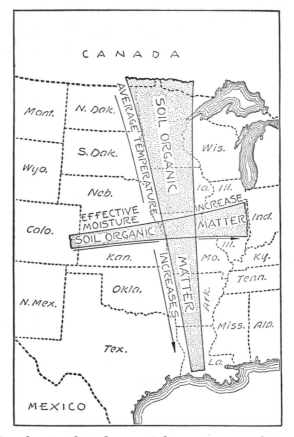

Figure 6:7. Map showing the influence of the average annual temperature and the effective moisture on the organic matter contents of grassland soils of the Midwest. Of course, the soils must be more or less comparable in all respects except for climatic differences.

Note that the higher temperatures yield soils lower in organic matter. The effect of increasing moisture is exactly opposite, favoring a higher level of this constituent. These climatic influences affect forest soils in much the same way.

the organic situation in any one soil is in large degree an expression of both temperature and precipitation plus other factors as well. Climatic influences never work singly.

THE EFFECT OF TEXTURE, DRAINAGE, AND OTHER FACTORS. Besides the two broader aspects discussed above, numerous local relationships should be mentioned. In the first place, the *texture* of the soil, other factors being constant, seems to influence the percentage of humus and nitrogen present. A sandy soil, for example, usually carries less organic matter and nitrogen than one of a finer texture. (See Table 6:2.) This is probably due to the lower moisture content and to the more ready oxidation that occurs in the lighter soils. Also the natural addition of residues normally is less with the lighter soil.

Table 6:2. The Relationship Between Soil Texture and Approximate Organic Matter Contents of a Number of North Carolina Soils[a]

Soil Type	No. of Soils	% Organic Matter	
		Topsoil	*Subsoil*
Cecil sands	15	0.80	0.50
Cecil clay loams	10	1.32	0.56
Cecil clays	27	1.46	0.64

[a] These figures were calculated by multiplying the % N by 20. The original data came from C. B. Williams, *et al., Report on the Piedmont Soils particularly with reference to their nature, plant-food requirements and adaptablity for different crops,* Bul. North Car. Dept. Agr., 36, No. 2, 1915.

Again, *poorly drained* soils because of their high moisture relations and their relatively poor aeration are generally much higher in organic matter and nitrogen than their better drained equivalents. (See Fig. 6:6.) For example, soils lying along streams are often quite high in organic matter. This is due in part to their poor drainage, as well as to the wash they receive from the uplands.

The *lime content* of a soil, its *erosion* status, and its *vegetative cover* are other factors that may exert an influence upon the accumulation and the activity of the soil organic matter and its nitrogen.

Normally, a very marked change occurs when a virgin soil, either forest or prairie, is placed under cultivation. New and usually lower levels of organic matter and nitrogen are gradually established. (See Fig. 6:8) It is not surprising, therefore, to find cultivated land much lower in organic matter and nitrogen, by perhaps 30 to 60 per cent, than its virgin equivalent. Such a drop is perfectly normal and is difficult to forestall. Hence in practice it is hardly worth while to attempt a maintenance much above certain percentages, providing good crops can be grown under these conditions. But more about that later.

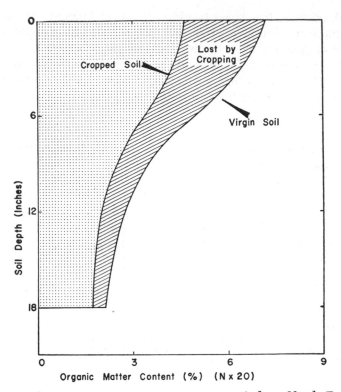

Figure **6:8.** *The average organic matter content of three North Dakota soils before and after an average of 43 years of cropping. About 25 per cent of the organic matter was lost from the 0 to 6-inch layer as a result of cropping. (From H. J. Haas, et al., "Nitrogen and Carbon Changes in Great Plains Soils as Influenced by Cropping and Soil Treatments," Tech. Bul. No. 1167, U.S. Dept. of Agric., 1957.)*

6:17. INFLUENCE OF SOIL ORGANIC MATTER ON SOIL PROPERTIES

Before discussing the practical maintenance of soil organic matter, it might be well to review very briefly what is expected from this all-important constituent.

The most obvious influences may be outlined as follows:

1. Effect on soil color—brown to black
2. Influence on physical properties
   a. Granulation encouraged
   b. Plasticity, cohesion, etc. reduced

   c. H_2O holding capacity increased
3. High cation-adsorption capacity
   a. Two to thirty times as great as mineral colloids
   b. Accounts for 30 to 90 per cent of the adsorbing power of mineral soils
4. Supply and availability of nutrients
   a. Easily replaceable cations present
   b. N, P, and S held in organic forms
   c. Extraction of elements from minerals by acid humus

6:18. THE ORGANIC MATTER PROBLEM

The fact that crop yields in areas long under cultivation have been maintained or even at times raised somewhat does not mean that organic matter and nitrogen are being held at satisfactory levels. In fact, comparisons in Ohio and Missouri[12] of soils cropped for long periods with their virgin equivalents indicate an average reduction of about 35 per cent in respect to their nitrogen. This would mean a more or less proportionate lowering on total organic matter.

That it is impossible in most cases to maintain the organic matter and nitrogen of our soils, whether forest or prairie, at their virgin levels is obvious. Nor is this necessary or even desirable. Yet a decline in organic matter content of 30 to 40 per cent is serious and should go no further. (See Fig. 6:8.) Such exploitation, if continued, may ultimately result in a definite decrease in crop yield. In practice it is not enough simply to bring to a halt this slow decline in the inherent capacity of soils to produce crops. It should be raised, not sharply or to any great degree, for this would be too expensive, but enough to insure a continuance of our present crop yields. Hence, the importance of the maintenance of soil organic matter above a certain level and with it a satisfactory nitrogen supply.

6:19. THE REGULATION OF SOIL ORGANIC MATTER

The preceding discussion has established two definite conclusions regarding the organic matter and nitrogen of soils, especially of

---

[12] R. M. Salter, R. D. Lewis, and J. A. Slipher, *Our Heritage—The Soil,* Extension Bul. 175, Ohio Agr. Exp. Sta., 1941; and A. W. Klemme and O. T. Coleman, *Evaluating Annual Changes in Soil Productivity,* Bul. 405, Missouri Agr. Exp. Sta., 1939.

those under cultivation. *First,* the inherent capacity of soils to produce crops is closely and directly related to their organic matter and nitrogen contents. *Second,* the satisfactory level of these two constituents is difficult to maintain in the majority of farm soils. Because of this situation, methods of organic matter additions and upkeep should receive early consideration in all soil management programs.

SOURCE OF SUPPLY. Organic matter may be added to cultivated soils in a number of different ways. One is the plowing under of crops when in an immature, succulent stage. This is called *green-manuring.* Such crops as rye, buckwheat, oats, peas, soybeans, and vetch, as well as others, lend themselves to this method of soil improvement. Not only do these crops help maintain the actual organic content of a soil, but in the case of legumes, at least a part of the nitrogen may be drawn from the air. This is a great advantage as such residues have a comparatively narrow C:N ratio, decay rapidly, and yield more humus than do tissues with a smaller amount of nitrogen.

A second source of organic matter supply on many farms, especially in dairy sections, is *farm manure.* When applied at the usual rates, say 10 or 15 tons per acre during a five-year rotation, perhaps from 1,000 to 1,500 pounds of dry matter go into the soil as a yearly acre average. Such additions cannot but greatly aid in organic matter maintenance.

In the same category with farm manure, but of much less concern, are *artificial farm manures* and *composts.* (p. 566). The latter are employed mostly in the management of nursery, garden and greenhouse soils.

The third, and, in general, the most important sources of organic residues, especially with arable soils, are the *current crops* themselves. Stubble, aftermath, and especially root residues of various kinds left in the soil to decay, make up the bulk of such contributions. Few farmers realize how much residual root systems aid in the conditioning of their soils. Without them, the practical maintenance of the humus in most cases would be impossible.

In this connection it should also be remembered that the maintaining of high crop yields through proper *liming* and *fertilizer practices* may be just as effective as adding manure or other organic residues. Apparently in some cases organic matter can be maintained by simply raising bumper crops. Optimum yields usually mean more residues to return to the soil and certainly increase the amount of roots remaining after harvest.

CROPS AND CROP SEQUENCE. It has already been suggested that certain sod crops, such as meadow and pasture grasses and legumes, tend to facilitate humus accumulation. This is partly due to their liberal contributions of organic residues, the slow decay of these materials and their wide C:N ratios. Under these conditions little nitrogen can appear in the soil in the nitrate form (p. 148), and hence rather slight losses of this constituent will occur. In legumes this may be offset, at least in part, by nitrogen fixation. Since the amount of humus depends to a considerable extent upon the amount of organic nitrogen (p. 147) sod crops by their nitrogen economy promote the highest possible yields of humus. Everyone knows that sod begets humus.

Cultivated crops, on the other hand, remove as much or even more nitrogen at harvest than do sod crops. Besides, tillage and other features of their management encourage an extremely rapid rate of decay and dissipation of organic matter. Thus, intertilled crops are associated with humus reduction instead of with humus accumulation. Small grains, such as oats and wheat, are in the same category—that is, they are humus wasters but to a lesser degree.

In practice crop sequences are so arranged as to offset depreciation with humus conservation. Much can be accomplished by using a suitable rotation (Table 6:3.). Also, adequate liming and fertilization to provide bumper crops encourages residues which help maintain the organic level.

ECONOMY IN HUMUS MAINTENANCE. Since the rate at which carbon is lost from the soil increases very rapidly as the

Table 6:3. *Organic Matter and Nitrogen Contents of Unfertilized Soil Plots at Wooster, Ohio, After Being Cropped in Various Ways for 32 Years*[a]

Cropping	Organic Matter Tons per Acre	Nitrogen Pounds per Acre
Original crop land	17.5	2,176
Continuous corn	6.4	840
Continuous oats	11.4	1,425
Continuous wheat	11.0	1,315
Corn, oats, wheat, clover, timothy	13.4	1,546
Corn, wheat, clover[b]	14.8	1,780

[a] R. M. Salter; R. D. Lewis; and J. A. Slipher, *Our Heritage—The Soil*, Extension Bul. 175, Ohio Agr. Exp. Sta., 1941, p. 9.
[b] Continued for 29 years instead of 32.

organic content is raised, the maintenance of the humus at a high level is not only difficult but also expensive. (See Fig. 6:9.) It is, therefore, unwise to hold the organic matter above a level consistent with crop yields that pay best. Just what this level should be will depend on climatic environments, soil conditions, and the particular crops grown and their sequence. Obviously, it should be higher in the chernozem region

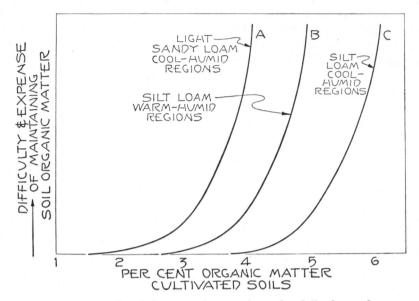

Figure **6:9.** *A generalized diagram showing how the difficulty and expense of maintaining the organic matter of cultivated soils increase as the support level is raised. While the curves are quite similar, their position in relation to the percentage of organic matter possible varies with* texture (A vs C) *and* climate (B vs C). *Other factors also are involved, especially the type of crop rotation employed.*

In practice the average amount of organic matter maintained in a cultivated soil should be held at the maximum level economically feasible.

of North Dakota than in central Kansas where the temperature is higher or in northern Montana where the effective rainfall is lower. In any event, the soil organic matter, as well as the nitrogen, should always be maintained at an economic maximum consistent with a suitable physical condition of the soil, satisfactory biochemical activity, an adequate availability of nutrients, and paying crop yields.

Good soil management, therefore, seeks to adjust the addition of organic residues, the physical and chemical conditions of the soil, the sequence of crops, and the losses through biological activity in such a way that paying crops may be harvested without reducing the humus supply of the soil below a definite level. Any system of agriculture that does not do this is impractical and unscientific.

Chapter 7

Forms of Soil Water,
Their Movement, and
Their Plant Relationships

We are interested in soil-water[1] relationships for several reasons. In the first place, large quantities of water must be supplied to satisfy the evapo-transpiration requirements of growing plants. Furthermore, this water must be available when the plants need it and most of it must come from the soil. Second, water acts as the solvent which together with the dissolved nutrients make up the soil solution. The significance of this soil component has already been adequately stressed.

As we shall see in a succeeding chapter, soil moisture also helps control two other important components so essential to normal plant growth—soil air and soil temperature. And last but not least, the control of the disposition of water as it strikes the soil determines to a large extent the

---

[1] For interesting and nontechnical articles on water in relation to soils see *The Yearbook of Agriculture* (Water), U.S. Dept. of Agriculture, 1955 and *The Yearbook of Agriculture* (Soil), U.S. Dept. of Agriculture, 1957.

incidence of soil erosion, that devastating menace which constantly threatens the impairment or even destruction of our soils.

7:1. RETENTION OF SOIL MOISTURE — A SIMPLE CASE

From a practical standpoint we are most concerned with soil properties as they affect the following factors: (1) the movement of water into and within the soil, (2) the moisture-storing capacity of soils and (3) the availability of soil moisture to higher plants. Each of these factors is related directly or indirectly to the size and distribution of soil pores and to the attraction of the soil solids for moisture. The evidence of these relationships can be seen if we follow some of the changes which take place during and following a rainstorm or the application of irrigation water.

MAXIMUM RETENTIVE CAPACITY. Assume that water is applied to the surface of a well-granulated silt loam soil which is relatively uniform in texture and structure.[2] The water might come from a heavy steady rain or from irrigation. As the water enters the soil, air is displaced and the surface soil "wets up"—that is, the soil pores, large and small, are filled with water. Continued application will result in further downward movement and air replacement. At this point, all the pores in the upper part of the soil will be filled with water. The soil is said to be saturated with respect to water and is at its *maximum retentive capacity*.[3] (Fig. 7:1.)

FIELD CAPACITY. If we now cut off the supply of water to the soil surface—that is, it stops raining or we shut off the irrigation water—there will be a continued relatively rapid downward movement of some of the water. After a day or so, this rapid downward movement will essentially cease. The soil is then said to be at its *field capacity*. At this time an examination of the soil will show that water has moved out of the larger or *macropores* and that its place has been taken by air. The *micropores* are still filled with water and it is from this source that the plants will absorb moisture for their use. Moisture movement will continue to take place but the rate of movement is quite slow since it is due primarily to capillary forces which are effective in only the micropores. (Fig. 7:1.)

___

[2] For soils containing texturally different layers the situation is much more complicated than that presented here. (See pp. 186–188.)

[3] An approximation of these conditions may be obtained if a very thin layer of soil (5 to 10 millimeters deep) is allowed to absorb water from a free water table. See E. W. Hilgard, *Soils* (New York: Macmillan, 1911) p. 209.

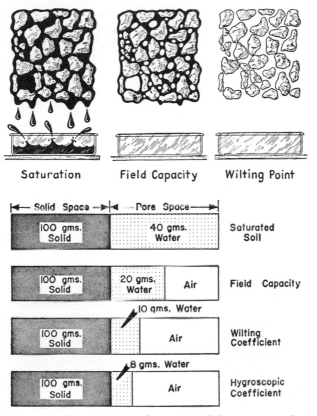

Figure 7:1. Diagrams showing the volumes of solids, water, and air in a well-granulated, silt loam soil at different moisture levels. The top bar shows the situation when a representative soil is completely saturated with moisture. This situation will usually occur for short periods of time during a rain or when the soil is being irrigated. Water will soon drain out of the larger or macro-pores. The soil is then said to be at the field capacity. *Plants will remove moisture from the soil quite rapidly until the* wilting coefficient *is approached. Permanent wilting of the plants occurs at this point even though there is still considerable moisture in the soil (wilting coefficient). A further reduction in moisture content to the* hygroscopic coefficient *is illustrated in the bottom bar. At this point, the water is held very tightly, mostly by the soil colloids. (Upper drawings modified from "Irrigation on Western Farms" published by the U.S. Depts. of Agriculture and Interior.)*

WILTING COEFFICIENT. Plants growing in our soil will absorb water and will reduce the quantity of moisture remaining in the soil. Some of the water will be translocated from the roots to the leaves where most of it will be lost by evapo-transpiration at the leaf surfaces. A second important avenue of loss is evaporation directly from the soil surface which will aid materially in the removal of soil moisture. Both of these losses are taking place simultaneously and are responsible for a markedly rapid rate of water dissipation from soils.

As the soil dries out plants will begin to show the effects of reduced soil moisture. During the daytime they will tend to wilt, especially if temperatures are high and if there is some wind movement. At first this daytime wilting will be associated with renewed nighttime turgor or plant vigor Ultimately the rate of the supply of water to the plants will be so slow that the plant will remain wilted night and day. Although not dead, the plants are now existing in a permanently wilted condition and will die if water is not added.

An examination of the soil at this point will show a considerable amount of moisture remaining. The soil moisture content at this stage is called the *wilting coefficient*[4] or the *critical moisture*. The water remaining in the soil is found in the smallest of the micropores and around individual soil particles. (See Fig. 7:1.) Obviously then, a considerable amount of water present in soils is not available to higher plants. The soil moisture must be maintained considerably above the wilting coefficient if plants are to grow and function normally.

HYGROSCOPIC COEFFICIENT. To obtain a more complete picture of the soil-moisture relations let us take a sample into the laboratory and allow the soil to dry out further. If it is kept in an atmosphere which is essentially completely saturated with water vapor, it will lose the liquid water held in even the smallest of the micropores. The remaining water will be associated with the surfaces of the soil particles, particularly the colloids, as adsorbed moisture. It is held so tightly that much of it is considered nonliquid and can move only in the vapor phase. The moisture content of the soil at this point is termed the *hygroscopic coefficient*. As might be expected, soils high in colloidal materials will hold more water under these conditions than will sandy soils and those low in clay and humus. (See Fig. 7:1.)

7:2. FORCES OF RETENTION

As we have followed the depletion of moisture from a saturated soil, two facts have become obvious: (1) moisture is held in the soil with

---

[4] The wilting coefficient is usually determined in a greenhouse using seedlings such as sunflower or some grain such as wheat or rye. This determination gives essentially the same value regardless of which of the common crops are used. Desert plants which are able to reduce their transpiration to a very low magnitude or are capable of storing water in special tissues, do not have a critical moisture in the sense used here.

a suction or tension and work must be done to remove this water; and (2) the tension with which the water is held depends upon the amount present, the smaller the amount the greater the tension.

Two forces largely account for the retention of moisture by soil solids. (See Fig. 7:2.) One is the attraction of the solid surfaces for water

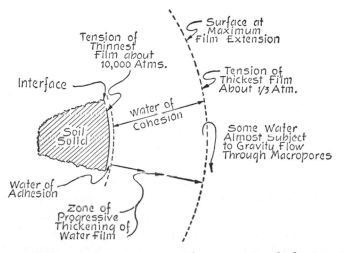

Figure 7:2. Diagramatic representation of the progressive thickening of a water film in a macropore and the corresponding decline in the tension at which the surface molecules are held. While an increment of water can be extracted easily from the surface of a thick film, a similar removal from a thin film is much more difficult. Soil water is held in two ways—adhesion and cohesion.

molecules (*adhesion*). The other is the attraction of water molecules for each other (*cohesion*). By adhesion, solids hold water molecules rigidly at their soil-water interfaces. These molecules in turn hold by cohesion other water molecules further removed from the solid surfaces. Together, these forces make it possible for the soil solids to retain water and to control its movement and utilization. Furthermore, they emphasize that energy is involved in soil-water relations and suggest that the tension with which water is held will vary with the distance of the molecules from the soil solids.

METHODS OF EXPRESSING ENERGY. Before investigating actual energy values, let us consider briefly the units in which they are expressed. One means of expressing the suction or tension is in terms of the height in centimeters of a unit water-column whose weight just equals the tension under consideration. The greater the centimeter height, the greater is the tension measured. We may thus express the tenacity with which water is held by soils in centimeters or we may convert such readings into other forms. In any case, the method of expressing the tension with which moisture films are held should be as simple as possible.

Perhaps a more generally accepted method is that of *bars* or *atmospheres*—the standard atmosphere (the average air pressure at sea level) being 14.7 pounds per square inch. The negative pressure exerted by a column of water 10 centimeters high under standard conditions is about 1/100 of an atmosphere (10 millibars); that by a column 100 centimeters high, 1/10 of an atmosphere (100 millibars); that by a 1,000 centimeter column of water, approximately 1 atmosphere of tension and so on. The table which appears below[5] presents further conversions.

7:3. THE ENERGY CONCEPT OF MOISTURE RETENTION[6]

The previous two sections have suggested that moisture is held in soils by attractive forces. Let us now examine changes in soil moisture in relation to the energy with which this important constituent is held.

TENSION VS. FILM THICKNESS. In Fig. 7:3 the inverse relationship between moisture content (film thickness) and the tension at the outer edge of the film is shown. High moisture contents (thick films) are associated with low tensions. In contrast, when the soil moisture is low, the water is held at high tensions.

This diagram should help explain some of the observations made in the last two sections. For example, during and immediately following a heavy rain or irrigation even the macropores are essentially filled with water—that is, the moisture films around and between solid particles are very thick. The tension with which the water is held at the edge of

[5] *A Table of Pressure Equivalents*

Height of a Unit Column of Water in Centimeters	Atmospheres (Bars) of Pressure Approximate
1	1 / 1000
10	1 / 100
100	1 / 10
346	1 / 3
1,000	1
10,000	10
15,849	15
31,623	31
100,000	100
1,000,000	1,000
10,000,000	10,000

[6] For further information consult L. D. Baver, *Soil Physics* (New York: Wiley, 1956), pp. 224–47.

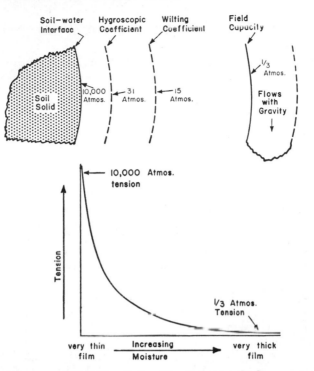

Figure 7:3. Diagrams showing relationship between thickness of water films and the tension with which the water is held at the liquid-air interface. The tension is shown in atmospheres. (Upper) Sketch of water film thickness at several moisture levels. (Lower) Logarithmic change in tension with increase in thickness of moisture film.

the film is very low. As the soil dries out or as water moves into lower layers, the average film thickness decreases and the tension at the air-water interface increases. (See Fig. 7:3). Thus, at the field capacity the tension is 0.1 to 0.5 atmosphere (averaging about ⅓ atmosphere). As plants and surface evaporation remove water the tension increases until at the wilting coefficient it is 15 atmospheres. As the film progressively decreases in thickness the tension increases to values as high as 10,000 atmospheres. These high energy of retention values emphasize the siginfi-cance of soil-water detraction in determining the water relations in soils.

ENERGY-MOISTURE CONTENT CORRELATION. By determining tension values at various moisture contents for particular soils, graphs may be constructed showing moisture-energy relationships. One such graph showing moisture-tension relationships for different soils —a sand, a sandy loam, and a silt loam—is shown in Figure 7:4. Note that atmospheres of tension are plotted against percentages of moisture based on dry soil.[7]

It is clearly apparent from the graphs that some of the water present in soils is held under tremendous negative pressures. On the other hand,

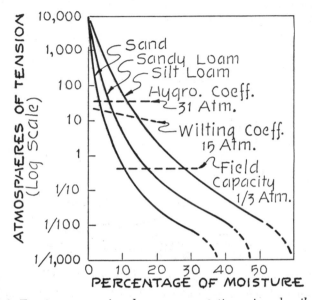

Figure 7:4. Tension curves for three representative mineral soils. The atmospheres of tension are plotted against percentage of soil moisture present. Note the rapid drop in tension as the amounts of soil moisture increase and the films thicken. The silt-loam has, of course, the greatest water capacity.

when soils are well supplied with water, a very slight suction is sufficient to withdraw a minute amount. The tension curves show all gradations between these extremes, indicating a *gradual* change in energy of retention. Thus, unless zones of demarcation are arbitrarily established, a clear-cut classification of soil water on the basis of energy units is not possible.

It must always be borne in mind that tension values express only the tension of water at the liquid-air interfaces—that is, moisture at the outer surface of the film. Thus, a thin film might be subject to a negative pressure of 100 atmospheres but, if thickened by additions, the water occupy-

[7] The usual method of expressing the amount of water present in a soil is in terms of percentage based on dry soil. Thus, if 100 g of moist soil (soil + water) when dried loses 20 g of water, the 80 g of dry matter are used as a basis for the percentage calculation. Therefore, (20 ÷ 80) × 100 = 25 per cent. The weight of the wet soil is undesirable as a basis for calculation since it changes with every moisture fluctuation.

ing the position of the original film will be subject to considerably less tension and will move much more freely than before. This must not be forgotten in the use of tension values, if a serious misconception is to be prevented.

Further examination of the illustrative curves (Fig. 7:4) will show that they vary characteristically with soil texture. The finer textured soils retain a greater percentage of moisture through the entire energy range. This is to be expected since they have a greater percentage of total colloidal matter, greater total pore space, and a much greater adsorptive surface.

7:4. THE PHYSICAL CLASSIFICATION OF SOIL MOISTURE

The moisture-tension curves in Fig. 7:3 and 7:4 remind us that as soil moisture is raised or lowered there is a *gradual* change in the tension with which the water is held. There are no sharp lines of demarcation, therefore, on which to base a classification of soil water. Just as was the case in dealing with the classification of particles according to size, however, a somewhat arbitrary classification system may be used in order to supply convenient terms for discussion. These terms should be used with caution, recognizing that there are no clear-cut lines of distinction between the different forms of soil water.

On the basis of relative degree of retention, soil water has been classified simply under three heads—*free, capillary,* and *hygroscopic.* (See Figs. 7:5 and 7:6.) Two other forms, both already mentioned—*water of crystallization* held as part of the crystal makeup of the silicate clays, and the *water vapor* of the soil air—need not be considered here.

For our purposes the following brief outline will describe the general characteristics of the three forms of water under discussion.

1. Free (drainage) water
    a. Water in the soil above that held at field capacity.
    b. Loosely held, less than 0.1 to 0.5 atmosphere tension.
    c. Undesirable, removed in drainage.
    d. Moves in response to film tension and gravitational forces.
    e. Nutrients leached with the water.
2. Capillary water
    a. Held between field capacity and hygroscopic coefficient in micropores.
    b. Tension of films varies from about 0.1 to 31 atmospheres.
    c. Not all available to plants.

    d. Moves by film adjustment from thick to thin films.

    e. Functions as the soil solution.

3. Hygroscopic water

    a. Held at the hygroscopic coefficient.

    b. Tension varies from 31 to 10,000 atmospheres.

    c. Held mostly by the soil colloids.

    d. Largely nonliquid.

    e. Moves mostly in the vapor form.

Data reported in Table 7:1 illustrate the variations in the amounts of hygroscopic and capillary water retained by soils of different texture and organic matter. The moisture equivalent figures shown are considered as approximating field capacities. Several relationships are clearly evident even from a causal examination of the data. The amounts of hy-

Table 7:1. Hygroscopic and Capillary Water Capacities of Various Soils

Soils	1 Organic Matter Per Cent	2 Hygro- scopic Coeff. Per Cent	3 Field Capacity (Moisture Equiv.) Per Cent	4 Capillary Water (Column 3–2) Per Cent	5 Maxi- mum Retentive Capacity (Tension near 0) Per Cent
Western Soils[a]					
Sandy soil (Nebr.)	1.22	3.3	7.9	4.6	34.2
Red loam (N. Mex.)	1.07	10.0	19.2	9.2	49.0
Silt loam (Nebr.)	4.93	10.2	27.8	17.8	60.9
Black adobe (Ariz.)	2.22	12.9	25.8	12.9	60.3
Iowa Soils[b]					
Dickinson fine sand	2.13	3.4	7.6	4.2	44.5
Clarion sandy loam	3.01	6.9	15.5	8.6	58.0
Marshall silt loam	3.58	10.4	24.0	13.6	76.5
Wabash silty clay	5.91	16.1	30.4	14.3	87.0

[a] F. J. Alway and G. R. McDole, "The Relation of Movement of Water in a Soil to Its Hygroscopicity and Initial Moisture," *Jour. Agr. Res.*, 10:391–428, 1917.

[b] M. B. Russell, "Soil Moisture Sorption Curves for Four Iowa Soils," *Proc. Soil Sci. Soc. Amer.*, 4:51–4, 1939.

groscopic and capillary water, as well as the maximum retentive capacity, are correlated definitely with both the texture and the organic matter contents of these soils. From what we know about colloidal characteris-

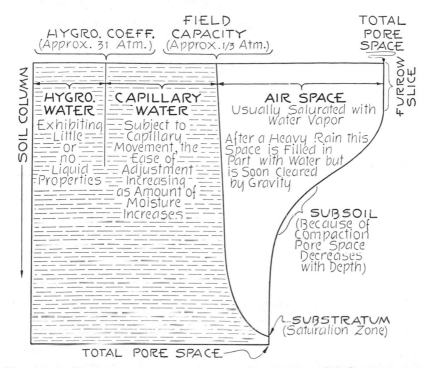

Figure 7:5. *Diagramatic representation of the moisture distribution in a soil column of uniform texture saturated at the bottom but well drained at the surface. Three forms of soil water are shown—hygroscopic, capillary, and drainage or free. The latter when present occupies the volume designated in the diagram as airspace. The tension ranges are shown in atmospheres of pressure. The exact quantity of moisture present at any particular tension will, of course, vary with the soil under consideration and its physical condition.*

tics this is no surprise but it is to be noted that the relationships are by no means uniform.

7:5. THE BIOLOGICAL CLASSIFICATION OF SOIL WATER

From the discussions already presented, it is evident that not all moisture present is available or suitable for the rapid vegetative growth of a plant. Three tentative divisions of the soil water may be made on this basis: *superfluous, desirably available,* and *unavailable.* (See Fig. 7:6.)

SUPERFLUOUS WATER. In general, moisture in excess of
that held at the field capacity is of no benefit to higher plants. When too
much of this free water is present, conditions detrimental to growth are
encouraged, the situation becoming more adverse as the saturation point
is approached. From the standpoint of plants, the free water is, therefore,
designated as *superfluous*. (See Fig 7:6.)

The unfavorable effects of such moisture on the plant arise largely from
poor aeration which deprives the roots and aerobic organisms of their
oxygen. Moreover, adverse biochemical changes may be encouraged and
nutrients may be leached especially from coarse-textured soils.

AVAILABLE WATER. The available moisture is generally
considered as that held between the field capacity and the wilting coefficient. The latter measurement is essentially the same for all common
crop plants grown on a given soil.[8] Apparently, any small differences in
the ability of plants to absorb the soil moisture is masked by the rapid
increase in tension as the moisture-film thickness decreases. The wilting
coefficient can thus be considered a characteristic of the soil and not of
the plant used to determine it. This fact must be kept in mind.

The question as to whether moisture is equally available to plants
throughout the entire range between the field capacity and the wilting
coefficient has been debated for many years. Apparently the answer
depends to a considerable extent on the crop to be grown, and the proportion of the soil profile being exploited by the crop roots. However, for
most of our common annual crop plants, the optimum moisture zone
appears to be between the field capacity and some level considerably
above the wilting coefficient. (See Fig. 7:6.)

Irrigation research indicates that for optimum crop growth, water
could be applied when from 50 to 85 per cent of the available moisture
has been used. This means that when the moisture content approaches
that of the wilting point, the rate of water uptake by plants is not rapid
enough to maintain optimum growth. The desirability of keeping the
moisture well above the wilting point has been clearly demonstrated.

UNAVAILABLE WATER. Brief mention should be made
of the so-called *unavailable* water—that held in the soil at the permanent
wilting point. Such moisture includes the hygroscopic water and that
portion of the capillary water which is removed too slowly by plants
to prevent wilting. Except for certain plants adapted to arid regions, this
inner capillary moisture is of little concern to higher-plant life. Its use

[8] It must not be inferred from this conclusion that all plants have the same drought
resistance. With humid-region plants, root spread is by far the most important factor
in this regard. Plants with the more extended root systems are, of course, able to draw
on a greater amount of water and better withstand a drought period. Moreover, some
plants can reduce their transpiration to a surprising degee, thus satisfactorily meeting
the lessened intake of water. Desert species are good examples.

by bacteria and fungi growing on the organic colloids may be advantageous but even here the rate of microbial activity is very low compared to that under more ideal moisture conditions.

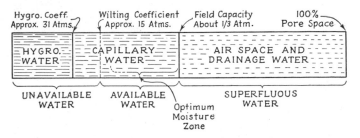

Figure 7:6. Diagram showing the relationship of the various forms of soil moisture to higher plants. By inserting the wilting coefficient, the physical classification of soil water can be converted into a biological classification and the plant significance of moisture tensions and adjustments graphically pictured.

7:6. FACTORS AFFECTING THE AMOUNT AND USE OF AVAILABLE SOIL MOISTURE

A number of plant and climatic factors have a marked effect on the amount of water which plants can absorb efficiently from a given soil. Rooting habits, resistance to drought, and stage and rate of growth, are all significant plant factors. Air temperature and humidity are climatic variables which influence the efficiency of utilization of soil water and the amount which can be lost through nonplant channels such as by evaporation from the soil surface.

Among the important soil characteristics influencing available soil moisture are: (1) moisture tension relations; (2) salt content; (3) soil depth; and (4) soil stratification or layering. Each will be discussed briefly.

MOISTURE TENSION RELATIONS. The effect of moisture tension relations on the amount of available moisture in a soil should be obvious. Those factors which affect the amount of water in a soil at the field capacity, and in turn at the wilting coefficient, will influence the available water. The texture, structure, and organic matter content, all influence the quantity of water a given soil can supply to growing plants. The general influence of texture is shown in Fig. 7:7. Note that as fineness of texture increases, there is a general increase in available moisture storage, although clays frequently have a smaller capacity than do well-granulated silt loans. The comparative available-water-holding capacities

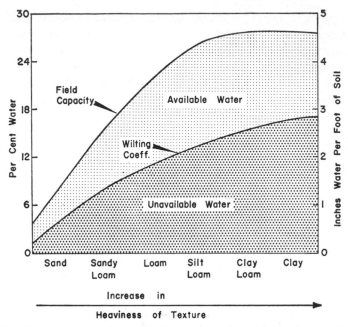

Figure 7:7. The general relationship between soil moisture characteristics and soil texture. Note that the wilting coefficient increases as the texture becomes heavier. The field capacity increases until we reach the silt loams, then levels off. Remember, these are representative curves. Individual soils would probably have values different from these shown.

in terms of inches of water per foot of soil are also shown by this graph.[9]

The influence of organic matter deserves special attention. A well-drained mineral soil containing 5 per cent organic matter will probably have a higher avaliable moisture capacity than a comparable soil with 3 per cent organic matter. One might make the mistake of assuming that this favorable effect was all due directly to the moisture-holding capacity of the organic matter. Such is not the case. Most of the benefit of organic matter in this case is due to its favorable influence on soil structure and in turn on soil porosity. Although humus does have a high field capacity, its wilting coefficient is proportionately high. Thus, the net contribution toward available moisture is less than one would suppose.

SALT CONCENTRATION. The presence of salts in soils, either from applied fertilizers or as natural-occurring compounds can

[9] These available water figures approximate those given by V. C. Jamison and O. W. Beale, *Irrigation of Corn in the Eastern United States,* U.S. Dept. of Agric. Handbook 140, 1958. The same general relationship between soil texture and available water was shown recently by P. J. Salter and J. B. Williams, "The Influence of Texture on the Moisture Characteristics of Soils. II Available Water Capacity and Moisture Release Characteristics," *Jour. Soil Sci.,* 16:310–317, 1965.

influence soil-water uptake. Osmotic pressure effects in the soil solution will tend to reduce the range of available moisture in such soils by increasing the wilting coefficient. The total moisture stress in such soils at this point is the soil moisture tension plus the osmotic pressure of the soil solution. Although in most humid-region soils this osmotic pressure effect is insignificant, it becomes of practical importance in some saline soils of arid and semiarid regions.

SOIL DEPTH AND LAYERING. All other factors being equal, deep soils will have greater available moisture-holding capacities than will shallow ones. For deep-rooted plants, this is of practical significance, especially in those subhumid and semiarid regions where supplemental irrigation is not possible. Soil moisture measurements to depths as great as 5 to 6 feet are sometimes used as bases for predicting wheat yields in the Great Plains area of the United States. Shallow soils are obviously not well suited to these climatic conditions.

Soil stratification or layering will influence markedly the available water and its movement in the soil. Hardpans or impervious layers, for example, slow down drastically the rate of movement of water and also influence unfavorably the penetration of plant roots. They sometimes restrict root growth and effectively reduce the soil depth from which moisture is drawn. Sandy layers also act as barriers to soil moisture movement from the finer-textured layers above. Movement through a sandy layer is very slow at intermediate and high tensions. The moisture tension in the overlying layers must be less than about 0.5 atmosphere before movement into the sand will take place. The explanation for this unusual situation should be apparent as we consider Sections 7:12 and 7:15 dealing with moisture movement in soils. (See Fig. 7:15.)

The available moisture-storage capacity of soils determines to a great extent their usefulness in practical agriculture. This capacity is often the buffer between an adverse climate and crop production. It becomes more significant as the ultilization of water for all purposes—industrial, domestic, as well as agricultural—begins to tax the supply of this all-important natural resource.

7:7. HOW PLANTS ARE SUPPLIED WITH WATER — CAPILLARITY AND ROOT EXTENSION

At any one time, only a small proportion of the soil water lies in the immediate neighborhood of the adsorptive surfaces of plant root systems. Consequently, a question arises as to how the immense amount of water (see p. 196) necessary to offset transpiration is so readily and steadily acquired by vigorously growing crops. Two phenomena seem to account for this acquisition: (1) the capillary movement of the soil water to plant roots; and (2) the growth of the roots into moist soil.

RATE OF CAPILLARY MOVEMENT. When plant rootlets begin to absorb water at any particular point or locality in a moist soil, the thick water films in the soil pores are thinned and their energy of retention is increased. The pull of moisture in this direction is intensified and water tends to move toward the points of plant absorption. The rate of movement depends on the magnitude of the tension gradients developed and the conductivity of the soil pores. A more complete explanation of this mechanism is offered on pages 184–185.

With some soils, the above adjustment may be comparatively rapid and the flow appreciable; in others, especially heavy and poorly granulated clays, the movement will be sluggish and the amount of water delivered meager. Thus, a root hair, by absorbing some of the moisture with which it is in contact, automatically creates a tension gradient and a flow of water is initiated toward its active surface.

How effective the above flow may be under field conditions is questionable. Many of the early investigators greatly overestimated the distance through which capillary may be effective in satisfactorily supplying plants with moisture. They did not realize that the rate of water supply is the essential factor and that capillary delivery over appreciable distances is very slow. Plants must have large amounts of water delivered rapidly and regularly. The influence of capillarity is exerted through only a few centimeters as far as the hour-by-hour needs of plants are concerned.

The above statement must not be taken to mean that capillary adjustments in the aggregate are not important. It is not always necessary for capillary water to move great distances in the soil to be of significance to plants. As roots absorb moisture, capillary movement of no more than an inch (if occurring throughout the soil volume) may be of practical importance. Capillary adjustment along with vapor movement is undoubtedly a factor in supplying water for plants growing at very low moisture contents. Since there is little root extension at moisture tensions approaching the wilting coefficient, it is likely that some water must move to the plants.

RATE OF ROOT EXTENSION. The limited water-supplying capacity of capillarity directs our attention even more forcibly to the rate of root extension and here early workers made an underestimate. They failed to recognize the rapidity with which root systems expand and the extent to which new contacts are constantly established. (See Fig. 5:4, p. 118.) During favorable growing periods, roots often elongate so rapidly that satisfactory moisture contacts are maintained even with a lessening water supply and without any great aid from capillarity. The mat of roots, rootlets, and root hairs in a meadow, between corn or potato rows, or under oats or wheat is ample evidence of the enormous root system of plants.[10]

The rate of root extension is surprising even to those engaged in plant production. On the basis of the data available, the elongation may be rapid enough to take care of practically all of the water needs of a plant growing in a soil at optimum moisture. If this be the case, the plant is more or less independent of capillary adjustment for its immediate water supply from soils which are relatively high in moisture.

As was pointed out earlier, the above generalizations may need some modification under conditions of high moisture-tension. In spite of the phenomenal number of roots and the surface area which they possess, calculations will show that these roots are probably in contact with no more than about 1 to 2 per cent of the soil solids. Under conditions wherein roots are not growing, it is obvious that moisture must move to the roots if the plants are to survive.

7:8. DETERMINATION OF SOIL MOISTURE [11]

Before considering the movement of moisture in soils, a brief comment should be made concerning the methods of determining the quantity of this important soil constituent. The major methods that are in use may be classified as follows. (1) gravimetric; (2) tensiometers; (3) resistance; (4) neutron scattering.

The *gravimetric* method is the one most commonly used. By this procedure a sample of moist soil of known weight is placed in an oven for a specified time at 100 to 110° C, and again weighed. The moisture lost by heating represents the soil moisture present in the moist sample.

Tensiometers such as the one shown in Fig. 7:8 measure the tension with which the water is held and not the absolute quantity of water present. They are most useful in determining the need for irrigation water when the moisture is being kept near the field capacity.

---

[10] H. J. Dittmer, "A Comparative Study of the Subterranean Members of Three Field Grasses," *Science*, N.S., 88: 482, 1938.

Dittmer reports as follows regarding the roots and root hairs in 1 cu. in. of soil.

Plant	Number of Roots	Number of Root Hairs	Combined Length, Feet	Combined Surface, Square Inches
Oats	110	150,000	630	15
Rye	150	300,000	1,300	30
Ky. Bluegrass	2,000	1,000,000	4,000	65

See also H. J. Dittmer, "A Quantitative Study of the Roots and Root Hairs of a Winter Rye Plant," *Amer. Jour. Bot.* 24:417–20, 1927.

[11] For a nontechnical discussion of this subject see H. R. Haise, "How to Measure the Moisture in the Soil," *The Yearbook of Agriculture(Water)*, pp. 362–71, 1955.

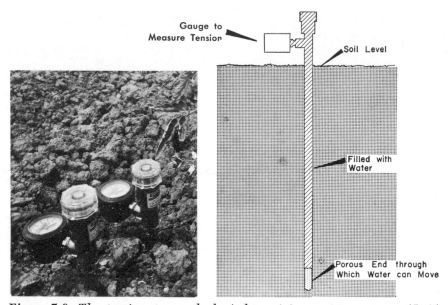

Figure 7:8. *The tensiometer method of determining moisture stress. (Left) Tensiometers in place in the field and (right) cross section showing essential components of a tensiometer. Water will move through the porous end of the instrument in response to the pull of the soil. This creates a tension which is measured by the gauge. (Photo courtesy T. W. Prosser Co., Arlington, California.)*

When *resistance* blocks which are commonly made of gypsum are placed in contact with soil, the blocks absorb moisture from the soil. The resistance of a given block to an electric current is related to the water it absorbs. By calibrating the resistance readings with soil moisture content, one can obtain an approximation of the amount of moisture in the soil. The gypsum blocks are used to measure either moisture tension or percentage and are probably most sensitive at tensions from 1 to 15 atmospheres.

The most recently developed procedure of determining soil moisture is the so-called neutron-scattering method. (See Fig. 7:9.) Advantage is taken of the fact that hydrogen atoms contained in soil water are effective in reducing the speed of fast moving neutrons, and in scattering them. Because of the scattering and change in direction of these neutrons some of them return to a point near the original source as slow moving particles. The number of these slowed neutrons is related to the quantity of hydrogen atoms (and in turn H_2O molecules) present in the soil. This method has the advantage of being one that can be used without disturbing the soil and can be used on soils containing salts.

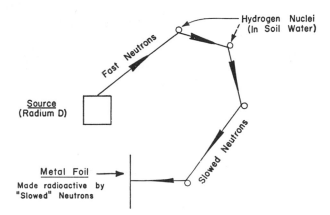

Figure 7:9. An illustration of the "neutron moderation" method of estimating soil moisture. Neutrons are emitted by the source (radium D) at a very high speed. When these neutrons collide with a small atom such as hydrogen contained in soil water their direction of movement is changed, they lose part of their energy and are slowed down. These "slowed" neutrons can be measured by using a metal foil composed of rhodium or silver which is rendered radioactive when struck by the neutrons. The more water (and thus hydrogen) present in the soil the larger will be the number of "slowed" neutrons which strike the metal foil and the greater will be the resulting radioactivity which can be measured easily.

7:9. THE MOVEMENT OF SOIL WATER—TYPES OF

In discussing the characteristics of the different forms of moisture commonly recognized in soils, movement has been stressed again and again. And rightly so, as water is a notably dynamic soil constituent. Three types of movement within the soil are recognized—*unsaturated flow, saturated flow,* and *vapor equalizations.* Since the first type of water movement—unsaturated flow—involves capillary adjustment, certain fundamentals with respect to capillarity should be kept clearly in mind. They will be briefly reviewed herewith.

7:10. CAPILLARY FUNDAMENTALS AS THEY RELATE TO SOIL WATER

First, consider an ideal case of capillarity. If the lower end of a glass tube of capillary dimensions is placed vertically in water, the liquid will rise in the tube above the level of the water surface outside. (See Fig. 7:10.) The phenomenon, called *capillarity*, is initiated by the attraction of the glass for the water (adhesion) which causes the liquid to rise around the sides of the tube. At the same time, because of the attraction of the molecules of water for each other (cohesion), that portion of the liquid unaffected directly by adhesion is progressively pulled upward, thus keeping the column intact.

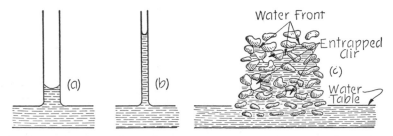

Figure 7:10. The upward capillary movement from a water table, (a) in a large glass capillary tube, (b) in a small capillary tube, and (c) in a soil column. Note the higher rise in the small capillary tube and the greater curvature of film. While the mechanism is the same in both the tubes and in the soil, the adjustment is extremely irregular in the latter due to the tortuous nature of the channels, their variability in size, and the presence of entrapped air.

In other words, surface-tension forces at the liquid-air interface are powerful enough to support that portion of the column not directly attracted by the walls of the tube. Hence, a continuous column of water rises until its weight just equals the adhesive attraction pulling the liquid upward. Thus, the mechanics of *capillary adjustment* as it operates in this particular case can be very simply stated.

It is a common observation that the smaller the capillary channel, the higher will be the rise of the water column. (See Fig. 7:10.) This is because for a unit section of the capillary tube, the amount of adhesive surface per unit weight of water is greater in a small tube than in a larger one. Thus, a longer column of water can be supported by the adhesive attraction exerted by the walls of the smaller tube.[12]

[12] This truism can be established mathematically as follows: The height (h) to which water rises in a capillary tube is expressed by the formula:

$$h = \frac{2T}{rdg}$$

where T is surface tension in dynes per centimeter, r, the radius of the tube in centimeters, d, the density of the liquid, and g, gravity in dynes per centimeter. It is obvious from the formula that the smaller the radius of the tube, the higher will be the rise of the liquid in it.

7:11. UNSATURATED FLOW FROM A SOIL WATER TABLE

When water moves upward from a water table through the micropores of a soil, the phenomenon of capillarity, sometimes called *unsaturated flow,* is identical in principle to the capillary rise already described for a glass tube. Adhesion and cohesion are active in exactly the same way. The water columns as they elongate are subject to the same mechanisms.

In contrast with the capillary adjustment in a glass tube, the unsaturated flow in soils ordinarily proceeds very irregularly. Also, the rising front of water is greatly distorted and deformed. The swelling of the soil colloids and the presence of entrapped air impede the rate of movement; many of the large soil pores cannot be bridged at all. In spite of these factors which tend to complicate unsaturated flow in soils, the same basic principles that govern capillary movement in a glass tube are at work here.

HEIGHT OF CAPILLARY RISE.   Usually the height of rise resulting from capillarity is greater with the fine-textured soils, if sufficient time is allowed, and the pores are not too small. This is readily explained on the basis of the capillary size and the continuity of the pores. With sandy soils, the adjustment is rapid, but so many of the pores are either noncapillary or only weakly exhibit this capacity, that the height of rise cannot be great. (See Fig. 7:11.)

Contrary to popular opinion, the type of capillary adjustment just described is important in only those field soils where a water table exists. This water table may be temporary or more or less permanent. In most well drained mineral soils, there is no internal accumulation of free water for any length of time. Or if a water table actually does appear within the solum, it is temporary and usually is present at a time of year when it is of no practical consequence.

However, in some cases, the type of capillary setup under discussion is of practical importance. For instance, in poorly drained, sandy soils and in peat lands, where the water table can be lowered or raised at will, the water level can be maintained near enough the surface at certain critical times to provide subirrigation by capillarity. Also, in certain poorly drained areas of the arid West where irrigation is practiced, a water table may be found within a few feet of the surface especially in the spring of year. Although this water is a source of supply for growing plants, its movement upward in the profile is sometimes accompanied by undesirable salts which tend to accumulate in the surface areas.

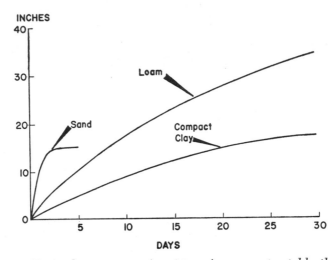

Figure 7:11. *Upward movement of moisture from a water table through soils of different textures and structures. Note the very rapid rise in the sand, but the moderate height attained. Apparently, the pores of the loam are more favorable for movement than are those in the compact clay. The rate of move- ment is thus seen to be of greater significance than the total height.*

7:12. UNSATURATED FLOW AS IT MOST COMMONLY OCCURS IN SOILS

When a large amount of water is received at the soil surface, tension adjustment, aided by gravity flow through the larger pores, will ultimately moisten the whole profile unless an impervious layer is encountered. But if the addition is limited, as is usually the case under natural conditions, the downward adjustment will soon become wholly capillary. The rate of such movement will be drastically curtailed as the moisture content is reduced below that of the field capacity. Eventually, of course, this downward movement will essentially cease.

Evaporation will now take place at the soil surface, and plants will absorb water from localized zones around their roots. These processes will result in greater moisture depletion from some soil areas than from others, and differences in the tension with which the moisture is held will be found. Unsaturated flow will occur in response to these differences in tension, the water moving from regions of low tension (high moisture) to depleted moisture zones when the water films are thin and the tensions high.

This moisture movement back and forth according to film tension represents the setup commonly operating in soils. Unlike the movement upward from a water table previously described, the unsaturated flow under discussion may be downward, upward, or lateral. The direction of movement depends on the tension of the water films surrounding and between soil particles. And what is especially important, the removal of water from any given pore initiates a movement in this direction by decreasing the film thickness and hence, increasing the pull at this point.

The type of movement just described is continually operating in soils. Yet, due to the dynamic nature of soils, capillary equilibrium is seldom attained. Of all the forms of water movement within the soil, this type of film adjustment is perhaps of greatest significance in respect to soil conditions and plant growth.

7:13. SATURATED FLOW THROUGH SOILS—PERCOLATION

As water either from rain or irrigation is added to a soil, it penetrates the surface, replacing the air in first the macro- and then the micropores. Additional water will result in downward movement by a process called saturated flow which will be encouraged by *both* gravitational and capillary forces. Such movement will continue so long as there

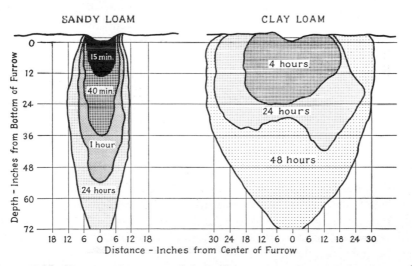

Figure 7:12. Comparative rates of irrigation water movement into a sandy loam (left) and a clay loam (right). Note the much more rapid rate of movement in the sand, especially in a downward direction. (Redrawn from J. J. Coony and J. E. Pehrson, Avocado Irrigation, *Calif. Agric. Ext. Leaflet 50, 1955.)*

is adequate moisture being supplied, and no barriers to downward movement are encountered. (See Fig. 7:12.)

AMOUNT OF PERCOLATION WATER. The quantity
of water which moves through the profile will be determined by a number
of factors, including the following: (1) the amount of water applied; (2)
infiltration capacity of the surface soil; (3) total moisture conductivity of
the lower horizons; and (4) the amount of water which the profile will
retain at its field capacity. From a practical standpoint, the texture and
structure of the various soil horizons determine to a large degree the
influence of these factors. Thus, sandy soils have high infiltration capacities and total conductivities. Their ability to hold moisture is low, and
water percolation through them takes place easily and rapidly.

COLLOIDAL SWELLING AND ENTRAPPED AIR.
In contrast to sandy soils, those finer in texture have lower percolation
rates which may be more variable because of differences in soil structure.
Certain factors undoubtedly further complicate the percolation of water
through these soils. First, clayey-colloidal matter may clog the small
connecting channels, or even the larger pores. Fine-textured soils that
crack during dry weather, at first allow rapid percolation of water. Later,
these cracks swell shut, thus reducing percolation to a minimum. Unless
granulation is encouraged by organic matter and other means, drainage
in such cases will be slow and often rather ineffective. In fact, unless a
clayey field soil possesses considerable granulation, it may not drain
rapidly enough to permit agricultural operations sufficiently early in the
spring or soon enough after a heavy rain later in the season.

Percolation water will receive more attention in connection with the
loss of nutrients and with practical means of its control. (See p. 214.)

7:14. THE RATE OF MOVEMENT
THROUGH SOILS

In discussing the mechanisms of water movement, frequent
reference has been made to the rate at which the movement takes place.
This rate is determined by two factors: (1) the water moving force; and
(2) the hydraulic conductivity. An equation showing the relationship
between these factors and the volume of water moving through the soil
may be given as follows:

$$v = kf$$

where v is the total volume moved, f is the water moving force, and k
is the hydraulic conductivity.

The water moving force, sometimes called the driving force, is determined by two factors: (1) *gravity* and (2) differences in film tension or

tension gradient. Gravity, of course, is effective only in influencing downward movement. The tension gradient, on the other hand, may act in any
direction.

If it is high, that is, if the difference in moisture tension between two
points a unit distance apart is great, water will adjust toward the higher
tension with comparative rapidity. Under comparable conditions, on the
other hand, a low gradient means a slower adjustment, and consequently
a lower delivery. This influence of tension gradient is well illustrated by
moisture curves drawn from Gardner and Widtsoe.[13] (See Fig. 7:13.)
Here the rate of water movement from a moist soil into a drier one is

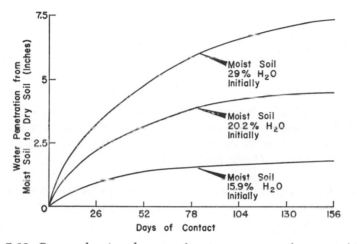

Figure 7:13. *Curves showing the rate of water movement from a moist soil at
three moisture levels to a drier one. The higher the water content of the moist
soil, the greater will be the tension gradient and the more rapid will be the
delivery. Water adjustment between two slightly moist soils at about the same
water content will be exceedingly slow. (After Gardner and Widtsoe.)*

shown. The higher the percentage of water in the moist soil, the greater
is the tension gradient, and the more rapid is the delivery. In this case
the rate of movement obviously is a function of the tension gradient.

Hydraulic conductivity is determined by a number of factors, including
pore size and the tension with which the water is held. For saturated
flow, the moisture tension is low and consequently the conductivity is
closely related to pore size, clay soils having low conductivities compared
to sands. As the moisture content is lowered to the field capacity and
below, the hydraulic conductivity, now more properly termed *capillary
conductivity*, decreases rapidly. At 0.2 atmospheres tension, for example,

[13] W. Gardner and J. A. Widtsoe, "The Movement of Soil Moisture," *Soil Sci.*, 11:
230, 1921.

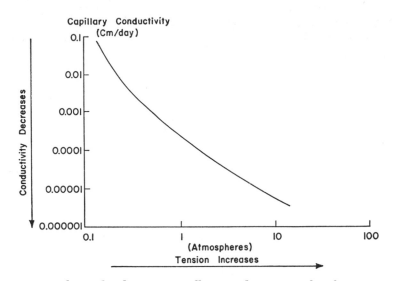

Figure 7:14. Relationship between capillary conductivity and soil moisture tension in a sandy loam soil. Note that conductivity is drastically reduced as the tension increases. (From L. A. Richards and S. J. Richards, "Soil Moisture," Yearbook of Agriculture (Soil), 1957, pp. 49–60.)

the conductivity is 10,000 times that at 10 atmospheres tension. (See Fig. 7:14.) Furthermore, this decrease in conductivity is more pronounced with sandy soils than with finer-textured soils. Apparently, at high tensions the water in sands is held only at points of contact between the relatively large sand particles. Under these conditions, there is no continuous water film and thus no opportunity for liquid movement. Water transfer, if it occurs must take place in the vapor state. This accounts for the fact previously referred to (p. 175), that layers of sand in a profile often act as moisture barriers just as do compact clay or silt pans. Apparently, the moisture tension must be 0.5 atmospheres or less before water movement will take place readily into sandy layers.

7:15. WATER MOVEMENTS IN STRATIFIED SOILS

The discussion up to now has dealt almost entirely with soils which are assumed to be quite uniform in texture and structure. In the field, of course, layers differing in physical makeup from the overlying horizons are common. Since these layers have such a profound influence on water movement, they deserve specific attention.

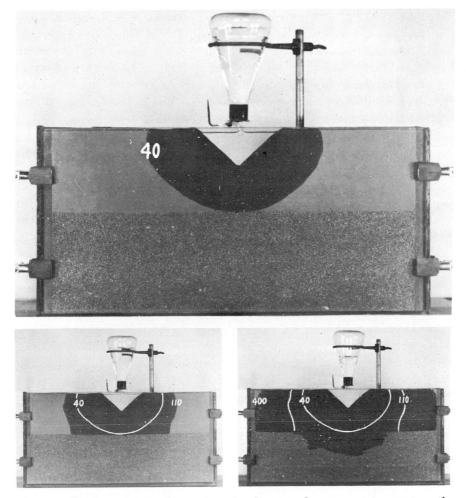

Figure 7:15. Photographs illustrating the downward water movement in soils having a stratified layer of coarse material. (Top) Water applied to the surface of a medium-textured top soil. Note that at the end of 40 minutes, downward movement is no greater than movement to the sides, indicating that in this case the gravitational force is insignificant compared to the tension gradient between dry and wet soil. (Lower left) The downward movement stops when a coarse textured layer is encountered. After 110 minutes, no movement into the sandy layer has occurred. After 400 minutes (lower right), the moisture content of the overlying layer becomes sufficiently high to give a moisture tension of 0.5 atmosphere or less, and downward movement into the coarse material takes place. Thus, sandy layers, as well as compact silt and clay, influence downward moisture movement in soils. (Photographs courtesy W. H. Gardner, Washington State College.)

Various kinds of stratification are found in many soils. Impervious silt or clay pans are common as are sand and gravel lenses or other subsurface layers. In all these cases, the effect on water movement is similar —that is—the downward movement is impeded. The influence of layering can be seen by referring to Figure 7:15. Apparently, the change in texture from that of the overlying material results in conductivity differences which prevent rapid downward movement.

The significance of this effect of stratification is obvious. For example, it definitely influences the amount of water the upper part of the soil holds at the field capacity. The layer acts as a moisture barrier until a relatively high moisture level is built up. This gives a much higher field capacity than that normally encountered in freely drained soils. It also illustrates a well known weakness of the field-capacity concept, especially if it is to be related to some definite moisture tension value.

7:16. WATER VAPOR MOVEMENT

Water vaporization as it relates to soils may be distinguished for convenience of discussion as *internal* and *external*. In the one case, the change from the liquid to the vapor state takes place within the soil, that is, in the soil pores. In the second case, the phenomenon occurs at the land surface, and the resulting vapor is lost to the atmosphere by diffusion and convection. The latter commonly is spoken of as *surface evaporation* and will be considered later (p. 192). For the present, only vaporization and vapor adjustment tendencies *within* the soil are pertinent.

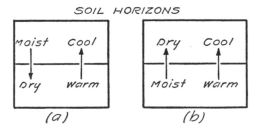

Figure 7:16. Diagram indicating the vapor movement tendencies that may be expected between soil horizons differing as to temperature and moisture. In (a) the tendencies more or less negate each other; but in (b) they are coordinated and considerable vapor transfer might be possible if the liquid water in the soil capillaries does not interfere.

RELATIVE HUMIDITY OF THE SOIL AIR. The soil air is maintained essentially saturated with water vapor so long as the moisture content is not below that of the hygroscopic coefficient. At this tension (31 atmospheres) and less, water seems to be free enough to maintain the air at approximately 100 per cent relative humidity. But when the moisture drops below the hygroscopic coefficient, and consequently is held with a greater tenacity, water vaporizes with greater and greater difficulty and its vapor pressure becomes lower and lower.

This maintenance of the soil air at or very near a relative humidity of of 100 per cent is of tremendous importance, especially in respect to biological activities. This is perhaps the most important single feature in respect to the vapor-liquid interrelations within soils. Nevertheless, the actual amount of water present in the vapor form in a soil at optimum moisture is surprisingly small, being, at any one time, perhaps not over 10 pounds to the acre-furrow-slice.

MECHANICS OF WATER VAPOR MOVEMENT. The diffusion of water vapor from one area to another in soils does occur. The motive force is due to differences in vapor pressure, the adjustment tendencies being from points of high vapor pressure to those that are lower. That is, a *vapor-pressure gradient*[14] per unit distance is operative. Thus, if a moist soil where the vapor pressure is high is in contact with an air-dry layer where the vapor pressure is lower, a diffusion into the drier area will tend to occur. Likewise, if the temperature of one part of a uniform moist soil mass is lowered, the vapor pressure of the air would be decreased and water vapor will tend to move in this direction. Heating will have the opposite effect.

The two soil conditions mentioned above—differences in relative humidity and in temperature—seem to set the stage for the movement of water vapor under ordinary field conditions. However, they may work at cross purposes and reduce vapor transfer tendencies to a minimum, or they may be so coordinated as to raise them to a maximum. The possible situation is set forth in Fig. 7:16

Undoubtedly, some vapor transfer does occur within soils. The extent of the movement by this means, however, even from one continuous macropore to another, probably is not great if the soil water is within the range optimum for higher plants. In dry soils, however, some moisture movement may take place in the vapor form. Such movement may be of some significance in supplying moisture to drought-resistant desert plants, many of which can exist at moisture levels below the commonly determined wilting coefficient.

---

[14] A *vapor-pressure* gradient is simply the difference in vapor pressure of two points a unit distance apart. The greater this difference, the more rapid diffusion tends to become and the greater is the transfer of vapor water during a unit period.

Chapter 8

Vapor Losses of Soil Moisture and Their Regulation

The ultimate objective in the field control of soil water is the maintenance of an optimum moisture condition for plants. To obtain a clear insight as to how this is done, let us first consider what happens when precipitation and irrigation water are received and utilized and the extent to which losses occur.

8:1. TYPES OF WATER LOSS FROM SOILS

The various ways by which moisture is lost from soils both before and after infiltration may be grouped for convenience of discussion under two very general heads: (1) *vapor* losses, and (2) losses in *liquid* form. The situation is presented in diagrammatic form in Fig. 8:1, in which the individual losses are shown in their proper positions. Since this sketch will be used as a basis for further discussion, its visualization, at least in a general way, will be found worth while. On the basis of both

190

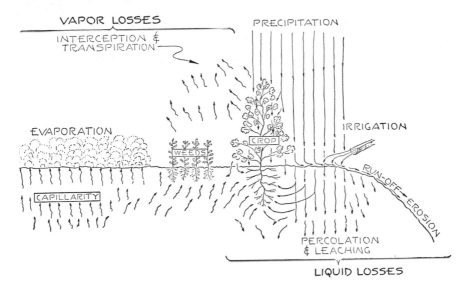

Figure 8:1. *Diagram showing the various ways by which water may be lost from soils. In practice more control can be exerted over liquid losses than over those of vaporization. Note that the latter entails only a loss of water, while in the case of drainage and runoff, losses of nutrients are also involved. Runoff often results in serious erosion in addition.*

logic and convenience, the vapor losses will be disposed of first, leaving the liquid removals for the next chapter.

8:2. INTERCEPTION OF RAIN WATER BY PLANTS

Rainfall data are often dealt with as though precipitation ordinarily reaches the soil in its entirety. Such is far from the case as a person must realize when he considers the intercepting capacity of the vegetative cover especially that presented by a dense forest. The degree to which rain is thus caught and returned to the air by evaporation is surprisingly large.

In general, the lower the rainfall the greater is the percentage diversion by the vegetative cover. And as might be expected, the proportionate loss is markedly higher when the rain is received in light showers. Such precipitation is often entirely lost as far as the soil is concerned. Forests in humid-temperate regions divert on the average perhaps 25 per cent of the yearly precipitation, allowing less than 5 per cent to run down the limbs and trunks into the soil.

Surprisingly enough, the influence of field crops, during the season that they occupy the soil, may approach that of forests in many cases. The yearly interception is, of course, much less. The figures in Table 8:1 are most significant.

Table 8:1. Seasonal Interception of Rainfall by Crops at Bethany, Missouri, and Sussex, New Jersey, Average of Three Years' Records for Alfalfa and Corn and One Year for Soybeans[a]

	Percentages in Terms of Total Seasonal Rainfall for Each Crop		
Fate of Rainfall	Alfalfa	Corn	Soybean
	%	%	%
Direct to soil	64.7	70.3	65.0
Ran down stem	13.7	22.8	20.4
Total to soil	78.4	93.1	85.4
Remainder to atmosphere	21.6	6.9	14.6

[a] J. L. Haynes, "Ground Rainfall under Vegetative Canopy of Crops," Jour. Amer. Soc. Agron., 32:176–84, 1940.

Although these data cover such short periods and are subject to very high experimental errors, they indicate something about the magnitude of rainfall interception by field crops. In general, it may be safe to conclude that from 5 to perhaps 20 per cent of the seasonal rainfall of humid-temperate regions will be caught and returned to the atmosphere by ordinary field crops. While interception losses undoubtedly reduce the economic use of rain water, little can be done to control such waste.

8:3. EVAPO-TRANSPIRATION

Vapor losses from soils occur in two ways: (1) by the *evaporation* of water at the soil surface; and (2) by *transpiration* from the leaf surfaces of water which has been absorbed by the plants and translocated to the leaves. The combined loss resulting from these two processes, termed *evapo-transpiration*, is responsible for most of the water removal from soils under normal field conditions. On irrigated soils located in arid regions, for example, it commonly accounts for the loss of 30 to 40 inches of water during the growing season of a crop such as alfalfa. Obviously, the phenomenon is of special significance to growing plants.

Before considering the magnitude of moisture losses through evapo-transpiration as it occurs in the field, let us enumerate and discuss briefly the various factors influencing this important process.

8:4. FACTORS AFFECTING EVAPO-TRANSPIRATION

The rate of water loss by evaporation either from the soil or by transpiration is determined basically by the *vapor-pressure gradient* —that is by the difference in the vapor pressure at the leaf or soil sur-

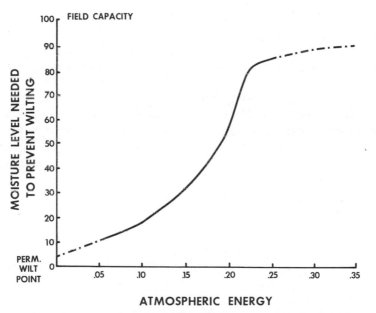

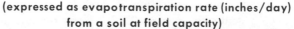

ATMOSPHERIC ENERGY

(expressed as evapotranspiration rate (inches/day)
from a soil at field capacity)

Figure 8:2. The moisture level needed to prevent turgor loss (wilting) of corn grown on a Colo silty clay loam under different conditions of atmospheric energy. The moisture level ranges from the permanent wilting point (0) to the field capacity (100). The atmospheric energy which includes factors such as temperature, wind velocity, etc. is expressed in terms of the evapo-transpiration which it causes. (Data adapted from O. T. Denmead and R. H. Shaw, "Availability of Soil Water to Plants as Affected by Soil Moisture Content and Meteorological Conditions." Agron. Jour. 45:385–390. 1962.)

face, and that of the atmosphere. The vapor-pressure gradient, in turn, is related to a number of other common climatic and soil factors. (See Fig. 8:2.)

RADIANT ENERGY. Much of thermal energy is required to evaporate water, whether from the soil directly or from leaf surfaces. The primary source of this energy is the sun. So long as ample soil moisture is available, there is a close relationship between evaporation and the absorption of this radiant energy. The potential evapo-transpiration is dependent upon the energy being absorbed from the sun as well as the other factors discussed below.

ATMOSPHERIC VAPOR PRESSURE.[1] The vapor pressure of the atmosphere helps control evaporation from soils and plants. If it is low compared to the vapor pressure at the plant and soil surfaces, evaporation takes place rapidly. If it is high, such as is the case on "humid" days, evaporation is slow. That atmospheric vapor pressure markedly influences evapo-transpiration is shown by the relatively high vapor losses from irrigated soils in arid climates. In humid regions with comparable temperatures, evapo-transpiration losses are considerably less.

TEMPERATURE. The evaporation of water is greatly influence by temperature. Consequently, during warm or hot days, the vapor pressure at the leaf surfaces or the surface of a moist soil is quite high. Temperature does not have a similar direct effect on the vapor pressure of the atmosphere. As a result, on hot days there is a large difference in vapor pressure between leaf or soil surfaces and the atmosphere— a greater vapor-pressure gradient—and evaporation proceeds rapidly. The fact that on bright, clear days plants and especially soils may be warmer than the atmosphere further emphasizes the importance of temperature in controlling evapo-transpiration.

WIND. A dry wind will continually sweep away moisture vapor from a wet surface. The moist air thus moved is replaced by air with a lower content of moisture. This tends to maintain the vapor-pressure gradient and evaporation is greatly encouraged. The drying effect of even a gentle wind is noticeable even though the air in motion may not be at a particularly low humidity level. Hence, the capacity of a high wind operating under a steep vapor-pressure gradient to enhance evaporation both from soils and plants is tremendous. Farmers of the Great Plains dread the *hot winds* characteristic of that region.

SOIL MOISTURE SUPPLY. In discussing the influence of the other factors on evapo-transpiration, the assumption has

---

[1] There is in general a correlation between relative humidity and evaporation so long as there is no drastic change in temperature.

been made that the soil and plant surfaces are plentifully supplied with moisture. Under these conditions, the climatic factors already considered will largely control vapor losses. At lower moisture contents, however, soil moisture tension will limit the rate of supply of water to the soil and plant surfaces and evapo-transpiration losses will decrease accordingly. (See Table 8:2.)

Table 8:2. The Effect of Soil Moisture Level on Evapo-transpiration Losses. Where the Surface Moisture Content Was Kept High, Total Evapo-transpiration Losses Were Greater than when Medium Level of Moisture Was Maintained[a]

Moisture Condition of Soil	Evapo-transpiration (inches)	
	Corn	Alfalfa
High	17.7	24.4
Medium	12.7	20.5

[a] Data quoted by O. J. Kelly, "Requirement and Availability of Soil Water," Ad van. in Agron., 6:67–94, 1957.
High moisture—irrigated when upper soil layers were 50 per cent depleted of available water.
Medium moisture—irrigated when upper layers were 85 per cent depleted of available water.

As moisture is depleted from the soil surface and the root zone, evaporation losses decrease. The plant responds to this moisture deficiency by the closing of leaf stomata and ultimately by wilting. In the soil, capillarity will at first partially replenish moisture lost by evaporation at the surface. With time, however, the rate of loss by evaporation and plant uptake will deplete the surface soil. Capillarity to the upper layers will then be too slow to be of much practical importance. Under these con-

Table 8:3. In a Humid Region Soil, More Than Half the Water Lost by Evapo-transpiration Came From the Surface Layer.[a] *(In Drier Areas the Lower Zones Furnish Much More Water, Especially for Deep Rooted Crops.)*

Soil Depth (Inches)	Evapo-transpiration[b] (Inches)		
	Corn	Pasture	Woods
0–7	9.66	9.38	9.31
7–72	8.30	8.47	8.89

[a] Calculated from F. R. Dreibelbis and C. R. Amerman,, "How Much Topsoil Moisture Is Available to Your Crops." Crops and Soils, 17:8–9, April-May, 1965.
[b] Period of Measurement: Corn, May 23–September 25; Pasture, April 15–August 23; Woodland, May 25–September 28.

ditions, some movement of moisture in the vapor phase from lower horizons will then take place.

Soil physicists are agreed that the depth to which soils may be depleted by evapo-capillary pumping is far short of the 4, 5, or even more feet sometimes postulated. Some investigators think that a 20- to 24-inch depth is probably a maximum range. In most cases only the water of the furrow-slice suffers appreciable diminution by surface evaporation, especially if vigorously absorbing roots are present to intercept the upward moving water. (See Table 8:3.)

8:5. MAGNITUDE OF EVAPORATION LOSSES

Let us first consider the combined losses by evaporation from the soil surface and by transpiration. Together, they account for the so-called *consumptive* use which is a measure of the total water lost by evapo-transpiration in producing crops. This is an important practical figure, especially in areas where irrigation must be employed to meet crop needs.

CONSUMPTIVE USE. As might be expected there is a marked variation in the consumptive use of water to produce different crops in different areas. All of the factors previously considered as influencing evapo-transpiration are operative. In addition, plant characteristics such as depth of rooting and length of growing season become important.

Consumptive use may vary from as little as 12 inches to as much as 85 inches or more. The low extreme might be encountered in cool mountain valleys where the growing seasons are short; the higher figure has been found in irrigated desert areas.[2] The ranges commonly encountered are 15 to perhaps 30 inches in unirrigated, humid to semiarid areas and 20 to 50 inches in hot, dry regions where irrigation is used.

From a practical standpoint, daily consumptive use figures are in some cases more significant than those for the growing season. During the hot dry periods in the summer, daily consumptive use rates for corn, for example, may be as high as 0.4 to 0.5 inches. Even with deep soils having reasonably high capacities for storing available water, this rapid rate of moisture removal soon depletes the plant root zone of easily absorbed moisture. Sandy soils, of course, may lose most of their available moisture in a matter of a few days under these conditions. The importance of these vaporization losses is obvious.

[2] See C. O. Stanberry, "Irrigation Practices for the Production of Alfalfa," *The Yearbook of Agriculture* (*Water*), 1957, 435–43.

SURFACE EVAPORATION VS. TRANSPIRATION.
It is a matter of interest to consider the comparative water losses from the soil surface and from transpiration. As one might expect, a number of factors determine these relative losses. Among them are the following: (1) plant cover in relation to soil surface; (2) efficiency of use of water by different plants; (3) proportion of time crop is on the land, especially during the summer months; and (4) climatic conditions.

In humid regions, there is some evidence that vapor losses might, in some cases, be divided about equally between evaporation from the soil and transpiration. As might be expected, this generalization would not hold in all cases since there are so many factors influencing vapor losses from both crops and soils.

Loss by evaporation from the soil is thought to be proportionately higher in semiarid regions than in humid areas. Such vapor loss has been estimated at 70 to 75 per cent of the total rainfall for the Great Plains Areas of the United States.[3] Losses by transpiration account for 20 to 25 per cent, leaving about 5 per cent for runoff.

8:6. EFFICIENCY OF WATER USE

The crop production which can be obtained from the use of a given amount of water is an important figure, especially in areas where moisture is scarce. This efficiency may be expressed in terms of (1) consumptive use (in pounds) per pound of plant tissue produced, or (2) transpiration (in pounds) per pound of plant tissue produced. The latter figure, called transpiration ratio, emphasizes the fact that large quantities of water are required to produce one pound of dry matter.

TRANSPIRATION RATIO. This figure ranges from 200 to 500 for crops in humid regions, and almost twice as much for those of arid climates. The data in Table 8:4 drawn from various investigators give some idea of the water transpired by different crops.

Much of the variation observed in the ratios arises from differences in climatic conditions. Thus in areas of more intense sunshine, the temperature is higher, the humidity is lower, and the wind velocity is frequently greater. All this tends to raise the transpiration ratio.

It is obvious from the transpiration ratios quoted that the amount of water necessary to mature the average crop is very large. For example, a representative crop of oats containing 4,000 pounds of dry matter an acre and having a transpiration ratio of 500 will withdraw from the soil during the growing season water equivalent to almost 9 inches of rain.

[3] See J. C. Hide, "Observations on Factors Influencing the Evaporation of Soil Moisture," Soil Sci. Soc. Amer. Proc., 18:234–39, 1956.

Table 8:4. Transpiration Ratios of Plants as Determined by Different In-vestigators[a]

Crop	Harpenden, England	Munich, Germany	Dahme, Germany	Madison, Wisconsin	Pusa, India	Akron, Colorado
Barley	258	774	310	464	468	534
Beans	209	...	282	...	...	736
Buckwheat	...	646	363	...	...	578
Clover	269	...	310	576	...	797
Maize	...	233	...	271	337	368
Millet	...	447	...	...	...	310
Oats	...	665	376	503	469	597
Peas	259	416	273	477	563	788
Potatoes	...	...	...	385	...	636
Rape	...	912	...	...	...	441
Rye	...	...	353	...	...	685
Wheat	247	...	338	...	544	513

[a] These data were assembled from different publications. See T. L. Lyon, H. O. Buckman, and N. C. Brady, *The Nature and Properties of Soils* (New York: Macmillan, 1952), p. 221.

The corresponding figure for corn, assuming the dry matter as 8,000 pounds and the transpiration ratio as 350, would be over 12 inches. It should be emphasized that these amounts of water, in addition to that evaporated from the surface, must be supplied during the growing season. The possibility of moisture being a critical, if not the most critical, factor in crop production is thus obvious.

FACTORS INFLUENCING EFFICIENCY. The efficiency of water use in crop production is influenced by climatic, soil, and nutrient factors. The climatic factors have already received adequate attention. (pp. 193–194). Within a given climatic zone, the other effects can be seen.

In general, highest efficiency is found where optimum crop yields are being obtained. Conversely, where yields are limited by some factor or combination of factors, efficiency is low, that is, more water is required to produce a pound of plant tissue.

In general, maintaining the moisture content of a soil too low or too high for optimum growth will increase the water required to produce one pound of dry matter. Similarly, the amount of available nutrients and their balanced condition are also concerned in the economic utilization of water. In general, the more productive the soil, the lower is the transpiration ratio, provided the water supply is held at optimum (see Fig.

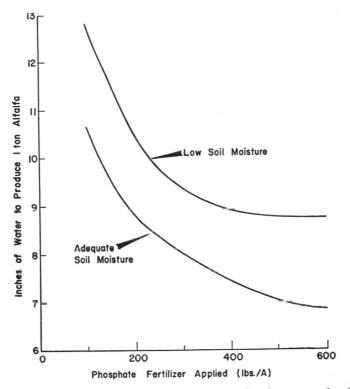

Figure 8:3. *The effect of phosphate applications and soil moisture level on the amount of water required to produce one ton of alfalfa hay. Most efficient moisture was obtained when the fertility level was high and the moisture supply adequate.* (*From O. J. Kelly, "Requirement and Availability of Soil Water," Adv. in Agron., VI:67–94, 1954.*)

8:3). Therefore, a farmer in raising the productivity of his soil by drainage, lime, good tillage, farm manure, and fertilizers provides at the same time for a greater amount of plant production for every unit of water utilized. The total quantity of water taken from the soil, however, will probably be larger. (See Table 8:2.)

8:7. EVAPORATION CONTROL— MULCHES

Any material used at the surface of a soil primarily to prevent the loss of water by evaporation, or to keep down weeds may be designated as a mulch. In some cases, foreign materials, that is substances not

Figure 8:4. For crops with high cash value, plastic mulches are being used. The plastic is installed by machine (above) and at the same time the plants are transplanted (below). The plastics help control weeds, conserve moisture, encourage rapid early growth, and eliminate need for cultivation. Their high costs make them practical only with the most high-value crops. (Photos courtesy K. Q. Stephenson, Pa. State Univ.)

already on the land, are merely spread over the soil surface. Sawdust, manure, straw, leaves, and other litter may be used successfully. Such mulches, while highly effective in checking evaporation and in preventing weed growth, are not generally applicable to most field crops, especially those that require intertillage. Their use is, therefore, limited to strawberries, blackberries, fruit trees, and such other crops as require infrequent cultivation, if any.

PAPER AND PLASTIC MULCHES. Specially prepared paper and plastics have been used as mulches. (See Fig. 8:4.) This cover is spread and fastened down either between the rows or over the rows, the plants in the latter case growing through suitable openings. This mulch can be used, however, only with crops planted in rows or in hills. As long as the ground is covered, evaporation and weeds are checked and, in some cases, remarkable crop increases have been reported. Unless the rainfall is torrential, the paper or plastic does not seriously interfere with the infiltration of the rain water.

The paper and plastic mulches have been employed with considerable success in the culture of pineapples in Hawaii, where the idea originated and with other crops elsewhere. This type of mulch is also being used to some extent in trucking and vegetable gardening in the United States. The cost of the cover and the difficulty of keeping it in place limit the use of these materials to high-valued crops.

STUBBLE MULCH. A mulch somewhat different from those already described, especially as to mode of establishment, is the *stubble* or *trash mulch* used mostly in subhumid and semiarid regions. In this case the mulching materials have been grown in place and consist of the refuse of the previous crop. Oats, stubble, and straw, corn stalks, and like residues are good examples. By the use of suitable implements, a seedbed can be prepared and the crop planted, leaving the organic trash on the surface to act as a mulch. (See Fig. 8:5.) In the case of row crops, modified tillage implements make cultivation possible without greatly disturbing the surface layer. Although the use of such a mulch has been found to conserve moisture in some cases, its main effectiveness seems to be that of controlling wind erosion.

SOIL MULCH. One of the early misconceptions with respect to the control of evaporation was that the formation of a *natural* or *soil mulch* was a desirable moisture-conserving practice. Years of experimentation and practice have shown that cultivating the surface soil to form a natural mulch does not necessarily conserve moisture. In fact, in some cases it may encourage moisture loss. This fact should be kept in mind as we consider the subject of tillage.

Figure 8:5. (*Upper.*) *The preparation of a trash mulch by incomplete incorporation of surface residues. (Lower.) In another field, the stubble mulch traps snow (right) in comparison with fallowed soil in the left. (Photos courtesy U.S. Soil Conservation Service.)*

8:8. CULTIVATION AND MOISTURE CONTROL

For many years, cultivation has been advocated in humid regions for three reasons: (1) the maintenance of a more satisfactory physical condition of the surface soil; (2) the killing of weeds; and (3) the conservation of moisture. The validity of the first two is unquestioned, if the tillage is applied with judgment, but there is much evidence to disprove the third, especially when a crop is on the land. Experimental results show that no more moisture is available to a crop which is cultivated, and thereby mulched, than is available to a comparable crop unmulched. Of course, weeds must be under control and the physical condition of the soil satisfactory in both cases. The ineffectiveness of the natural mulch seems to hold even during severe dry spells.

MOISTURE CONSERVATION VS. WEED CONTROL. Such a conclusion is borne out by research which shows that, when weeds and physical conditions are controlled, the mulching effect of cultivation is of no benefit to the crop. In fact, cultivation may at times be rather detrimental, possibly through damage to roots as well as waste of water. (See Fig. 8:6) The main service of cultivation seemed

Figure 8:6. The deep cultivation of intertilled crops such as corn (right) may result in serious root pruning. Hence cultivation for the killing of weeds should be shallow (left) even early in the season. If weeds are under control and the structure of the soil is satisfactory, further intertillage usually is unnecessary. (From L. Donald, "Don't Blame the Weather," Comm. Fert., pp. 19–24, February 1946.)

to be the killing of weeds and the encouragement of a desirable tilth.

The failure of cultivation to be of benefit is by no means limited to field crops. Thompson,[4] after six years of experimentation with vegetables on a New York sandy soil, reported that cultivation and mulch formation gave no increase in the yield of carrots, cabbage, and tomatoes over uncultivated plots also kept free of weeds.

[4] H. C. Thompson, *Experimental Studies of Cultivation of Certain Vegetable Crops*, Memoir 107, Cornell Univ. Agric. Exp. Sta., 1927.

WHY SOIL MULCHES DO NOT CONSERVE MOIS-
TURE. Three reasons are commonly advanced for the ineffectiveness
of cultivation in moisture control. In the *first* place, a large amount of
moisture always escapes by evaporation long before the soil is dry enough
for cultivation. *Second,* in many cases, this precultivation loss has already
established a thin protective surface layer of air dry soil, which may
successfully reduce evaporation. *Third,* the crop itself, if its root spread
is wide and comparatively dense, intercepts upward moving moisture
that might otherwise reach the soil surface.

8:9. VAPORIZATION CONTROL IN HUMID REGIONS

From what has been said, it seems that little in general can be
done in humid regions in respect to the control of the vaporization removal of water from farm lands. Losses due to crop transpiration and
interception are conceded as beyond control. The more vigorous the
growth of the crops, the larger will be these two removals, especially
transpiration. The ineffectiveness of a soil mulch and the waste of water
incidental to its establishment have been cited. Although stubble and
trash mulches are effective as well as feasible, they have not met with
any great favor in humid regions. Artificial mulches, although satisfactory
in gardens, nurseries, and orchards, are more or less out of the question
with field crops.

This leaves the control of weeds as about the only effective and practicable means in humid regions of influencing vaporization. Their
elimination, however, usually does not result in a reduction of soil
moisture loss *in toto* but merely insures a greater amount of water
available for crop transpiration. This, of course, is very desirable and
usually is the ultimate objective in the moisture management of field
soils. The attention now being given to improved methods of weed
control is well placed.

8:10. VAPORIZATION CONTROL IN SEMIARID AND SUBHUMID REGIONS

When the average annual rainfall of a region is very much
below 25 inches, it would seem that crop production would be impossible
without irrigation. Yet between the limits of 15 to 20 inches, certain
crop plants may be grown successfully, especially when much of the
rainfall comes in the spring and early summer. The system adopted is

often called *dry-land farming*. It consists essentially of: (1) using special varieties of such crops as wheat, corn, sorghums, and rye; (2) reducing the rate of seeding to correspond to the limited amounts of moisture that probably will be available; and (3) employing tillage practices that conserve and economize water. It is only the latter phase that need concern us here.

TILLAGE OPERATIONS. The tillage operations practiced in dry-land agriculture should keep weeds under control and at the same time reduce wind erosion to a minimum. This means rough furrows at right angles to the prevailing high winds, listing, strip-cropping, and the use of stubble mulch when practicable. At times of rain, the land should be highly permeable and retentive, and protected from water erosion if the rainfall is torrential. As to vapor losses of water from the soil, the situation in general is much the same as that already described for humid regions except for low humidity and higher wind velocities.

SUMMER FALLOW. Dry-land farming often includes a *summer fallow*, the idea being to catch and hold as much of one season's rain as possible and carry it over for use during the next. The soil profile is used as a large reservoir.

A common procedure for summer fallowing is to allow the previous year's stubble to stand on the land until the spring of the year. The soil is then tilled before appreciable weed growth has taken place and the land is kept from weeds during the summer by occasional cultivation or by the

Table 8:5. *The Influence of Summer Fallow in Alternate Years on the Moisture at Wheat Seeding Time and the Yield of Wheat Fallowing*[a]

Treatment	Available Water at Seeding Time	Wheat Yields
MANDAN, N. D. (AVE. 20 YEARS)		
Wheat after fallow	7.08 inches	4120 lbs[b]
Wheat after wheat	2.48 "	2300 lbs
HAYS, KAN. (AVE. 23 YEARS)		
Wheat after fallow	7.96 inches	27.3 Bu
Wheat after wheat	2.90 "	17.4 Bu
GARDEN CITY, KAN. (AVE. 13 YEARS)		
Wheat after fallow	4.67 inches	15.5 Bu
Wheat after wheat	1.08 "	8.2 Bu

[a] North Dakota data from J. C. Thysell, *Conservation and Use of Soil Moisture at Mandan, North Dakota*, U.S. Dept. of Agriculture, Tech. Bul. 617, 1938. Kansas data from R. I. Throckmorton and H. E. Meyers, *Summer Fallow in Kansas*, Kans. Agr. Exp. Sta., Bul. 293, 1941.
[b] Total plant yields.

use of chemical weed killers. In this way, evaporation loss is limited to that taking place at the surface of the soil.

The effectiveness of summer fallow in carrying over moisture from one year to another is somewhat variable. A conservation of perhaps one fourth of the fallow season rainfall would be expected under most conditions. Even though this efficiency of moisture-storage is lower than would be desirable, yields of succeeding crops have been augmented significantly by summer fallow. (See data in Table 8:5.)

Here, then, is a situation where an appreciable amount of moisture may be conserved by the proper handling of the land. But it is a case specific for dry-land areas and should not be confused with the situation in humid regions. In the latter, summer fallowing is detrimental and unnecessary.

8:11. EVAPORATION CONTROL ON IRRIGATED LANDS

In the areas of low rainfall, or when precipitation is so distributed as to be insufficient for crops at critical times, *irrigation*, the artificial application of water to land, is common. (See Fig. 8:7.) In the United States, most of the irrigated land lies west of the hundredth meridian and embraces perhaps twenty-one million acres. Moreover, irrigation in the more humid areas to the eastward is decidedly on the increase.

CONTROL PRINCIPLES. It is hardly necessary to emphasize that the principles already discussed relating to the movement and distribution of moisture through the soil, its losses, and its plant relationships, apply just as rigidly for irrigation water as for that reaching the soil in natural ways. Although the problems inherent to liquid water such as runoff and erosion, infiltration, percolation, and drainage are subject to better control under irrigation, they are met and solved in much the same way as for humid-region soils.

The situation regarding vapor losses is much more critical, indeed more so at times than even with contiguous soils under dry-land cropping. In irrigated areas, conditions are ideal for evaporation and transpiration loss. The climate is dry, the sunshine intense and wind velocities are often high. Furthermore, the soils are kept as moist as they are in well-drained humid-region soils. These conditions are ideal for evaporation loss.

The only practical control over evaporation under these conditions is through irrigation practices. The surface of the soil should be kept only as moist as is needed for good crop production. (See Table 8:2.) The

Figure 8:7. A typical irrigation scene. The use of easily installed siphons reduces the labor of irrigation and not only speeds up the rate of application of the water but also makes it easier to control. Note the upward capillary movement of water along the sides of the rows. (Photo courtesy U.S. Soil Conservation Service.)

irrigation schedule should be such as to keep more than just the surface soil wet. Deep penetration of roots should be encouraged.

SALT ACCUMULATION. A phenomenon closely correlated with evaporation and often met with on arid-region lands under irrigation is that of the concentration of soluble salts at or near the soil surface. So-called *saline* or even *alkali* soils may contain soluble salts in the upper horizons in sufficient quantities to inhibit the growth of many cultivated plants. Irrigation practices on these soils can improve or impair their usefulness as crop soils. By flood irrigation, some of the soluble salts can be temporarily washed down from the immediate surface. Subsequent upward movement of the water and evaporation at the soil surface may result in salt accumulation and concentration which are harmful to young seedlings. (See Fig 8:8.) Although little can be done to prevent evaporation and upward capillary movement of the salt-containing water, timing and method of irrigation may prevent the salts from being concentrated in localized areas.

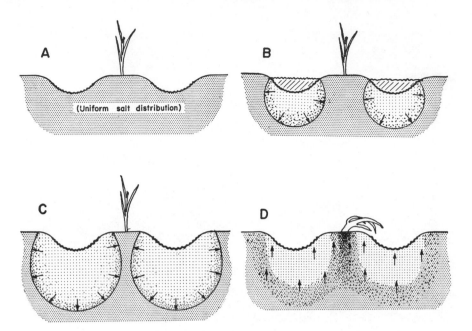

Figure 8:8. Diagrams showing the effect of irrigation on salt movement in a saline soil. (A) Soil before irrigation. Notice the relatively uniform salt distribution. (B) Water running in the furrow. Some has moved downward in the soil carrying soluble salts with it. (C) Soon after irrigation. Water continues to move downward and toward center of row. (D) A week or so after irrigation. Upward movement of water by capillarity carries salts toward the surface. Salts tend to concentrate in the center of the row, and in some cases causes injury to plants. (Concept obtained from Bernstein, et al., "The Interaction of Salinity and Planting Practice on the Germination of Irrigated Row Crops," Proc. Soil Sci. Soc. of Amer., 19:240–43, 1955.)

Chapter 9

Liquid Losses of Soil Water
and Their Control

Two types of liquid losses of water from soils are recognized: (1) the downward movement of free water (percolation) which frees the surface soil and upper subsoil of superfluous moisture; and (2) the run-off of excess water over the soil surface. (See Fig. 8:1.) Percolation results in the loss of soluble salts (leaching) and thereby depletes soils of certain nutrients. Runoff losses generally include not only water, but also appreciable amounts of soil (erosion). These two liquid losses of soil water with their concomitant effects will be considered in order.

9:1. PERCOLATION AND LEACHING — METHODS OF STUDY

Two general methods are available for the study of percolation and leaching losses—the use of an effective system of *tile drains* specially installed for the purpose, and the employment of *lysimeters*.[1] For the first method, an area should be chosen where the tile drain receives only the water from the land under study and where the drainage is efficient. The advantage of the tile method is that water and nutrient losses can be determined from relatively large areas of soil under normal field conditions.

The lysimeter method has been used most frequently to determine leaching losses. This method involves the measurement of percolation and nutrient losses under somewhat more controlled conditions. The advantages over a tile drain system are that the variations in a large field

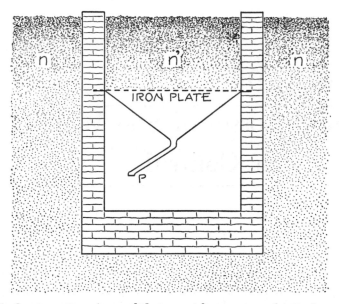

Figure 9:1. *Cross section of monolith type of lysimeter at the Rothamsted Experiment Station, England. (N') soil block under study; (N) surrounding soil not under study; (P) outlet for drainage water.*

are avoided, the work of conducting the study is not as great and the experiment is more easily controlled.

TYPES OF LYSIMETERS. Three major types of lysimeters have been used to study percolation: (1) the *block* or *monolith* type; (2) the *tank* type; and (3) the *Russian* type. In the *block* or *monolith* type of lysimeter, a small column of natural field soil is entirely isolated by appropriate means from the land surrounding it and its drainage

---

[1] From *lysi* meaning loosening and *meter*, to measure. Lysimeters are used to measure both percolation (downward movement of water through soils) and leaching (removal of soluble elements by percolation).

water measured and analyzed. (See Fig. 9:1.) Sets of these lysimeters have been used in Europe as well as in this country.

A second type of lysimeter, the *tank* type was used for much of the early work in the United States. The soil to be studied by this method is removed from the field and packed into tanks or some other suitable containers. Free drainage is allowed through the tanks and arrangements are made to collect the leachate. An example of the tank lysimeters is shown diagramatically in Fig. 9:2.

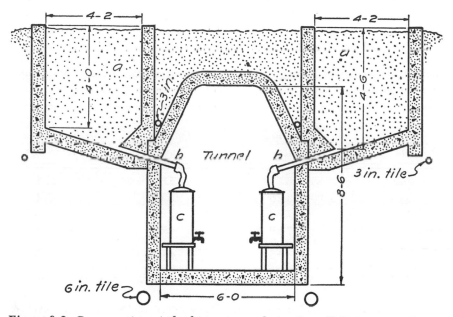

Figure 9:2. Cross section of the lysimeter tanks at Cornell University, Ithaca, New York. Each tank is one of a series, one tunnel serving two rows. Soils under investigation (a), outlet (b), and can for catching drainage water (c). Surface runoff was not allowed.

A lysimeter of an entirely different type has been perfected in Europe, called in this country the *Russian lysimeter*. A trench is dug beside the block of soil to be studied, and the small tunnels at various levels are excavated horizontally under the soil profile. In each tunnel is placed a shallow funnel-shaped pan perforated at the center. This is wedged tightly against the soil horizon above. Drainage tubes are then installed, one for each pan, and the tunnels filled with soil. Each funnel drains separately into the trench, where the water of percolation is caught in suitable receptacles and later measured and analyzed.

9:2. PERCOLATION LOSSES OF WATER

When the amount of rainfall entering a soil becomes greater than its water-holding capacity, losses by percolation will occur. Percolation losses are influenced by the amount of rainfall and its distribution, by evaporation, by the character of the soil, and by the presence of a crop.

LOSS FROM BARE SOILS. The results from the Rothamsted (England) lysimeters from 1871–1912 on a bare clay loam 5 feet deep are interesting in a comparative way (Table 9:1). The actual percolation is probably somewhat higher than under field conditions because of reduced runoff from the lysimeters.

Table 9:1. Percolation Through a 60-inch Column of Bare Clay Loam. Rothamsted Experiment Station, Annual Average of Forty-two Years[a]

Periods	Rainfall, Inches	Drainage, Inches	Percentage of Rainfall as Drainage
Dec.–Feb.	6.77	5.58	82.4
Mar.–May	5.96	2.11	35.4
June–Aug.	7.83	1.82	23.2
Sept.–Nov.	8.29	4.50	54.2
Mean Total	28.85	14.01	48.5

[a] A. D. Hall, *The Book of the Rothamsted Experiments* (New York: Dutton, 1917), p. 22.

Under the above conditions, about 50 per cent of the rainfall was lost by percolation through this bare soil. The drainage loss was much lower in summer than in winter, the ratio being about 1 to 3. This was, no doubt, due to the high evaporation during the warmer season, as the rainfall was as great for the June-August period as for the December-February interval. Such a discrepancy serves again to emphasize the great loss of water from bare soil by vaporization.

That the figures cited above are much too high for soils of low rainfall is, of course, to be expected. Percolation under arid and semiarid conditions may be nil in some cases. Nor can the figures above be applied specifically to other humid-region soils. This latter statement is clearly substantiated by data from Illinois obtained with an erosion type of monolith lysimeter by Stauffer.[2] (See Fig. 9:3.) The slope was 1.4 per

[2] R. S. Stauffer, "Runoff, Percolate, and Leaching Losses from Some Illinois Soils," *Jour. Amer. Soc. Agron.*, 34:830–35, 1942.

cent, the average annual precipitation 37.5 inches, and the duration of the study about 6.5 years. Of the six bare silt loam blocks used, one (Muscatine) allowed ready drainage; another (Cowden) permitted only slow percolation. As a result, 22.7 per cent of the annual precipitation drained through the first soil, but only 3.6 per cent was lost from the latter in this manner. Obviously, soils vary tremendously as to percolation losses.

Table 9:2. Average Annual Loss of Water by Percolation from Bare and Cropped Soils. Cornell Lysimeter Tanks (No Runoff Allowed)[a]

Conditions	Rainfall, Inches	Percolation, Inches
Dunkirk silty loam:		
Bare	32.41	24.92
Cropped	32.41	18.70
Volusia silt loam.		
Bare	33.22	20.90
Cropped	33.22	19.10

[a] T. L. Lyon; J. A. Bizzell; B. D. Wilson; and E. W. Leland, *Lysimeter Experiments, III,* Memoir 134, Cornell Univ. Agr. Exp. Sta., 1930 and T. L. Lyon and J. A. Bizzell, *Lysimeter Experiments, IV,* Memoir 194, Cornell Univ. Agr. Exp. Sta., 1936.

PERCOLATION THROUGH CROPPED SOILS. It is interesting to consider now a situation where plants were growing on the soil. In New York, a study was made of two soils, bare and cropped, held in tank-type lysimeters. The crops, grown in rotation, were corn, oats, wheat, and hay. (See Table 9:2.)

As might be expected, the presence of ordinary field crops definitely reduced the amount of drainage. If runoff had been allowed and less water had entered the soil, the influence of crops upon drainage loss would probably have been more marked. In fact, some cropped soils with annual rainfalls in excess of 30 inches show practically no percolation.[3] This occurs because of crops and evaporation draught and because runoff is high, accounting in some cases for perhaps 30 or 40 per cent of the annual precipitation. The type of rainfall, whether gentle or torrential, will be an important factor in respect to the amount of water entering the soil and hence upon the magnitude of percolation loss.

[3] V. J. Kilmer, *et al.,* "Plant Nutrients and Water Losses from Fayette Silt Loam as Measured by Monolith Lysimeters," *Jour. Amer. Soc. Agron.,* 36:249–63, 1944.

9:3. LEACHING LOSSES OF NUTRIENTS

Lysimeter data from various experiments are in fair agreement with respect to nitrogen and phosphoric acid losses by leaching. (See Tables 9:3 and 9:4.) The leaching of calcium, potassium, magnesium, and sulfur, however, was much higher from the Cornell lysimeters. Undoubtedly, this was due largely to the fact that no runoff was allowed from these tanks since the rainfall was about the same at the other locations under consideration. That the soils used in the Cornell investigation had been greatly disturbed in filling the tanks also may have been a factor.

Table 9:3. Average Annual Loss of Nutrients by Percolation through Bare and Cropped Coils. Cornell Lysimeters Average of Ten and Fifteen Years, Respectively (No Runoff Allowed)[a]

Soil Condition	Pounds per Acre per Year					
	N	P_5	K	Ca	Mg	S
Dunkirk silty clay loam:						
Bare	69.0	Trace	72	398	63	53
Rotation	7.8	Trace	57	230	44	43
Grass	2.5	Trace	62	260	50	44
Volusia silt loam:						
Bare	43.0	Trace	64	323	41	35
Rotation	6.6	Trace	57	250	27	33

[a] J. A. Bizzell and T. L. Lyon, "Composition of Drainage Waters from Lysimeters at Cornell University," *Proc. and Papers, First Internat. Cong. Soil Sci.,* II:342–57, 1927. And T. L. Lyon and J. A. Bizzell, *Lysimeter Experiment, IV,* Memoir 194, Cornell Univ. Agr. Exp. Sta., 1936.

In spite of the great variability of the data from the different sources, certain features of practical importance can be cited. In the *first* place, the amount of lime carried away by drainage usually is large for humid-region soils no matter what the soil condition or treatment may be. This, together with the loss of magnesia, accounts for the tendency of such soils to become acid. *Second,* there apparently is an extremely low loss of phosphorous by leaching. This is probably due to the small amount present in the soil and the tenacity with which it is held.[4] *Third,* the

[4] It is probable that present-day analytical methods would have shown more than a trace of phosphorus in the drainage waters of some of the earlier experiments, especially if the leachates had come from fertilized sandy soils.

Table 9:4. Average Annual Loss of Nutrients by Percolation through Soils from Three Different Areas Using the Monolith Type of Lysimeters (Runoff Allowed from Illinois and Wisconsin Lysimeters)

Condition	Pounds per Acre per Year					
	N	P	K	Ca	Mg	S
ROTATION ON A SCOTTISH SOIL[a] (AVE. 6 YEARS)						
No treatment	6.7	Trace	8.8	49.7	15.3	—
Manure and fertilizers	6.3	Trace	8.2	56.0	15.9	—
Manure, fertilizers & lime	7.9	Trace	7.6	79.5	18.7	—
UNCROPPED ILLINOIS SOILS[b] (AVE. 3½ YEARS)						
Muscatine (well drained)	76.6	—	1.2	89.8	46.3	10.5
Cowden (poorly drained)	6.1	—	0.6	10.9	3.4	1.4
FAYETTE SILT LOAM, WISCONSIN[c] (AVE. 3 YEARS)						
Fallow	—	—	1.2	37.8	18.5	2.9
Cropped to corn	—	—	0.4	14.7	5.8	0.8

[a] J. Hendrick and H. D. Welch, "The Substances Removed by the Drainage from a Scottish Soil," *Proc. and Papers, First Internat. Cong. Soil Sci.*, II:358–66, 1927.

[b] R. S. Stauffer, "Runoff, Percolate and Leaching Losses from Some Illinois Soils," *Jour. Amer. Soc. Agron.*, 34:830–35, 1942.

[c] V. J. Kilmer, *et al.*, "Plant Nutrient and Water Losses from Fayette Silt Loam as Measured by Monolith Lysimeters," *Jour. Amer. Soc. Agron.*, 36:249–63, 1944.

losses of potassium and sulfur, while appreciable, probably are not important except where the soil has been heavily fertilized. And *fourth*, crops markedly reduce the removal of all nutrients in drainage. This is especially important in respect to the nitrogen, the loss of which usually is very low from cropped soil.

The generalizations outlined above logically lead to the question of the control of leaching of essential nutrients. Can the losses be in any way reduced remembering that the removal of excess water must be facilitated? Only one suggestion of any moment can be made for field soils and this is clearly apparent from the data quoted. Keep a crop on the land as much as possible since less water passes through cropped soils than through soils that are bare. Beyond this, little more can be suggested. Obviously, it is impossible to adequately drain humid-region soils and yet hold the leaching losses, especially of lime and magnesia, at negligible levels.

LEACHING VS. CROP REMOVAL. The loss of nitrogen, potassium and especially phosphorus is much greater from crop removal than from leaching (Table 9:5), even from humid-region soils. The reverse is true for calcium, while magnesium and sulfur losses in the two directions are about equal. Of course, these generalizations can be markedly affected by factors such as fertilization levels, cropping patterns and soil characteristics such as texture and drainage.

Table 9:5. A Comparison of the Average Annual Loss of Nutrients by Drainage from a Representative Humid-region Silt Loam, Cropped to a Standard Rotation, with the Nutrients Removed by an Average Rotation Crop

Losses	Pounds per Acre, Annually					
	N	P	K	Ca	Mg	S
Leached from a representative silt loam	10	Trace	20	90	20	10
Removed by average rotation crop	100	18	80	35	25	15

9:4. LAND DRAINAGE

It is generally wise to facilitate percolation, at the same time checking the loss of available nutrients as much as possible by means of crops. The encouragement of percolation is spoken of as *land drainage*. It is the process of removing the superfluous water from the soil profile, especially from its surface layer and upper subsoil, as rapidly as possible. Although the drainage of swamps and the reclamation of overflow areas are urgent, the drainage of lands already under tillage is often much more important. Practical farm drainage is paramount in almost every community, even in arid regions, especially where irrigation is practiced.

9:5. TYPES OF DRAINAGE — TILE DRAINS

Two general types of drains are in use, *open* and *closed*. Ditch drainage represents the first group. The ditches may be deep and narrow such as those used in draining peat soils or they may be relatively shallow and broad. The latter are designed to permit *surface drainage* or the controlled removal of water from heavy soils before it infiltrates into the soil. Ditches have the advantage of large capacity and are able to carry water at a low grade. On the other hand, they waste land, are somewhat inconvenient, and demand some upkeep expenditure. Ditches have a place in land drainage; however, closed or underdrains should be used where economically feasible. (See Fig. 9:3.)

Tile drains are the most reliable means of underdrainage in the majority

Figure 9:3. The field installation of drainage tile. Left, machine for trench digging and tile laying in operation. Note that tile are being placed in the trench bottom. Right, another field after the tile was laid. Note gravel alongside and under tile to permit ease of movement of excess drainage water into the tile. (Photos courtesy U.S. Soil Conservation Service.)

of cases. While stone drains[5] are of value under certain conditions, they must always be short and are likely to clog. Besides, their drainage is slow and rather inefficient. On silty soil, they do not remain in service for any length of time. Mole drains,[6] brush drains, box drains, and the like are recommended only for special situations.

THE NATURE AND OPERATION OF TILE DRAIN. Land tile are generally 12 or more inches long with a diameter varying

[5] Stone drains are of historical interest only. They were built by arranging stone in a graded trench in such a manner as to provide a continuous channel or throat from the upper end of the drain to the lower. The spaces between the stones provided for the movement of the drainage water.

[6] A mole drain is simply an unwalled, cylindrical channel, 3 or 4 inches in diameter, located at a satisfactory distance below the soil surface. This channel is established by means of a special plow equipped with a sharp blade to which is attached the *mole*, a pointed cylindrical metal plug that looks much like the shell of a field gun. As this plug is pulled through the soil, it leaves a compressed-wall channel with the proper depth and fall.

Although this type of drain is best used on heavy mineral soils, it is employed at times in peat. Needless to say, the life of such a drain is usually short compared with that of a properly installed system of tile.

with the amount of water to be carried. They are laid end to end in strings on the bottom of a trench of sufficient slope. A carefully protected outlet should be provided. The tile are then covered with earth, straw or surface soil often being placed directly around the tile to facilitate the entrance of the water. The superfluous water enters the tile

Figure 9:4. Demonstration of the saturated flow patterns of water toward a drainage tile. The water, containing a colored dye, was added to the surface of the saturated soil and drainage was allowed through the simulated drainage tile shown by the arrow on the extreme right. (Photo courtesy G. S. Taylor, Ohio State University.)

through the joints, mostly from the sides and bottom. (See Fig. 9:4.) As a consequence, the tops of the joints may be covered with paper, cloth, or even be cemented in order to prevent the entrance of silt or quicksand. The function of a tile-drain system is twofold: (1) to facilitate the collection of the superfluous water; and (2) to discharge it quickly from the land.

Tile drains are simply a means of encouraging percolation. They are most effective when the macropores are large and numerous enough and so connected as to permit the rapid downward movement of gravity water. Good drainage is thereby established on land that might otherwise maintain a temporary water table too close to the surface at certain times of the year or that might be handicapped by a permanent water table at too high a level.

SYSTEMS OF TILE INSTALLATION. Where the land possesses considerable natural drainage, the strings of tile are laid only

along the depressions. This is spoken of as the *natural* system of drainage
in that the tile facilitate the quick removal of the water from the places
of natural accumulation. But where the land is level or gently rolling,
it often needs more uniform drainage. A *regular* system must then be
installed. This may be either of the *fishbone* or *gridiron* style, or a modification or combination of the two, natural drainage being taken advantage
of when possible. Where springs or seepage occur, a *cutoff* system must
be devised. (See Fig. 9:5.)

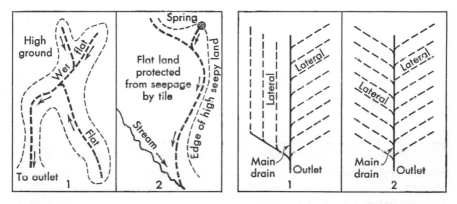
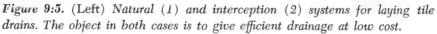

Figure 9:5. (Left) *Natural* (1) *and interception* (2) *systems for laying tile
drains. The object in both cases is to give efficient drainage at low cost.*

(Right) *Gridiron* (1) *and fishbone* (2) *system for laying tile drains. Drainage on heavy level land can be effected only by a uniform layout system.*

Every regular system consists of two parts, the laterals and the main
drain. The laterals are usually constructed of 4-, or preferably 5-inch
tile. These laterals should always enter the main at an angle of about
45 degrees. This causes a joining of the water currents with little loss
of impetus and allows the more rapidly moving lateral streams to speed
up the flow in the main drain. The size of the main depends on the
amount and intensity of the rainfall, the acreage drained, and the slope.
The main, of course, must be larger near the outlet than at any other
point. Any good text on land drainage will present tables from which the
proper size of the main drain may be determined.

The grade, or fall, necessary for the satisfactory operation of a tile-
drain system varies with the system itself and portion under consideration. The grade of the main drain may be very low, especially if the
laterals deliver their water with a high velocity. In general, the grade
will vary from 2 to 20 inches to the 100 feet, 3 to 6 inches being more
or less ideal. When the grade is reduced abruptly, the installation of a
silt-well may be advisable.

The depth of the tile beneath the surface of the land and the distance between laterals will vary with the nature of the soil. In most cases, however, a depth of about 3 feet is recommended. For sandy soils or poorly drained saline soils of arid regions, a depth of 4 feet or even more is commonly employed. On slowly permeable soils where the laterals are close together a depth of 2½ feet has been used. This is about the shallowest depth that can be used with safety on mineral soils because of the danger of tile breakage by heavy machinery.

The interval between tile lines is also reduced as the soil becomes more compact or finer in texture. On a clayey soil, the distance between the strings is sometimes as low as 30 feet, although 50 to 75 feet is commoner. (See Table 9:6.)

Table 9:6. Suggested Spacing Between Tile Laterals for Different Soil and Permeability Conditions[a]

Soil	Permeability	Spacing in Feet
Clay and clay loam	very slow	30–70
Silt and silty clay loam	slow to moderately slow	60–100
Sandy loam	moderately slow to rapid	100–300
Muck and peat	slow to rapid	50–200

[a] This table modified from K. H. Beauchamp, "Tile Drainage—Its Installation and Upkeep," *The Yearbook of Agriculture* (Water), 1955, p. 513.

The maintenance cost of a properly installed tile-drain system is low, the only special attention usually needed being the outlet. All outlets should be well protected, so that the end of the tile may not be loosened and the whole system endangered by clogging with sediment. It is well to imbed the end tile in a masonry or a concrete wall or block. The last 8 or 10 feet of tile may even be replaced by a galvanized iron pipe or with sewer tile, thus insuring against damage by frost. The end tile of the system may be covered by a gate or by wire in such a way as to allow the water to flow out freely preventing rodents from entering in dry weather.

9:6. BENEFITS OF LAND DRAINAGE

GRANULATION, HEAVING, AND ROOT ZONE. Draining the land promotes many conditions favorable to higher plants and soil organisms. By giving a freer rein to the forces of aggregation, granulation is definitely encouraged. At the same time, heaving is re-

duced, as it is only when the soil approaches saturation with water that
alternate freezing and thawing have their most disastrous effects on
plant roots. It is the heaving of small grain crops and the disruption of
such taprooted plants as alfalfa and sweet clover that are especially
feared. (See Fig. 10:8.) Also drainage, by quickly lowering the water

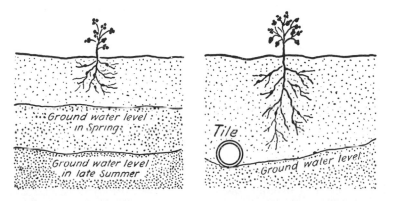

Figure 9:6. Left, *root zone restriction that occurs when natural drainage is too
slow.* Right, *lower water table and enlarged root zone that are developed by a
properly installed tile drain.*

table at critical times, maintains a sufficiently deep and effective root
zone. (See Fig. 9:6.) By this means, the quantity of nutrients available to plants is maintained at a higher level.

SOIL TEMPERATURE. The removal of excess water also
lowers the specific heat of soil, thus reducing the energy necessary to
raise the temperature of the layers thus drained. (See p. 260.) At the
same time, surface evaporation, which has a cooling effect, may be reduced. The two effects together tend to make the warming of the soil
easier. The converse of the old saying that in the spring "a wet soil is
a cold soil" applies here. Good drainage is necessary if the land is to be
satisfactorily cultivated and is imperative in the spring if the soil is to
warm up rapidly and properly. At this season of the year, an inadequately drained surface soil may be from 5° to 15° cooler than a contiguous area relieved of its excess water.

AERATION EFFECTS. It is perhaps in respect to aeration
that the greatest benefits, both directly and indirectly, are derived from
drainage. Although soil aeration problems will be dealt with in greater
detail later, their over-all significance should be recognized here.

In a well-drained soil, perhaps one half or even more of the pore space
in general may be occupied by air. Under such a condition, the furrow-
slice and the upper subsoil are usually adequately supplied with oxygen,

the air of the macropores almost equaling the atmospheric air in respect to this gas. In contrast, in poorly drained soils the oxygen supply is low and nutrient absorption as well as growth of aerobic soil organisms is adversely affected.

9:7. RUNOFF AND SOIL EROSION

In most all soils where the land is sloping or the soil is somewhat impermeable to water, a considerable amount of the moisture received is likely to be lost by runoff. Under such conditions, two considerations are important: (1) the loss of water that might otherwise enter the soil and perhaps be of use to plants; and (2) the removal of soil that usually occurs when water escapes too rapidly in this manner. This detachment and transfer of soil is spoken of as *erosion*.

EFFECTS OF RUNOFF. In some humid regions, loss by runoff may rise as high as 50 or 60 per cent of the annual precipitation. In arid sections, it is usually lower, unless the rainfall is of the torrential type as it often is in southwestern United States. While the loss of the water itself is deplorable, the erosion that accompanies it is usually even more serious. The surface soil is gradually taken away. This means not only a loss of the natural fertility but also of the nutrients that have been artificially added. Also it is the finer portion of this soil that is always removed first and this fraction, as already emphasized (p. 48), is highest in fertility. For example, the eroded material from a Collington sandy loam (New Jersey) in comparison with the original soil contained, in total, 4.7 times as much organic matter, 5.0 times as much nitrogen, 3.1 times as much phosphorous and 1.4 times as much potassium.[7] Moreover, the erodate carried almost 4 times more fine material and its available potassium was 3.7 times greater than that of the original soil.

Thus, the objectives of any scheme of soil management are seriously interfered with. The furrow-slice becomes comprised of subsoil, which usually is less fertile, and the maintenance of a satisfactory physical condition is made difficult. Many farmers, especially in southern United States, are cultivating subsoils today unaware that the surface soils have been stolen from under foot.

The destructive action of erosion in upland regions and the deplorable deposition in the lowlands have been more or less disregarded until rather recently. This is partly due to the fact that erosion has been considered as more or less uncontrollable, an ill that could not be avoided. The major factor has been a lack of observation—a failure to appreciate

[7] O. R. Neal, "Removal of Nutrients from the Soil by Crops and Erosion," *Jour. Amer. Soc. Agron.*, 36:601–07, 1944.

or measure the magnitude of the insidious removal. An effect much more easy to appreciate is the silting up of reservoirs which in many places is seriously reducing storage capacity and adding greatly to the expense of upkeep.

The early colonists of the Americas were from western Europe where erosion is not especially serious. Undoubtedly this was a contributing factor in the apathy so long existent in this part of the world in respect to erosion damage of all kinds.

EXTENT OF EROSION. Extensive soil erosion damage occurred in the United States long before its seriousness was widely recognized. Researchers had identified areas where erosion was rampant, but the public recognition of this problem came only in the 1930's. This was when the deterioration of many of our soils was emphasized by men such as H. H. Bennett, who later organized the federal support for soil erosion control. His estimates[8] indicated that nearly 50 million acres of cropland had been more or less ruined in the Continental United States, another 50 million reduced to a marginal state of productivity, while erosion is making rapid progress on 200 million acres more. Excluding the 100 million acres practically ruined, erosion is a serious

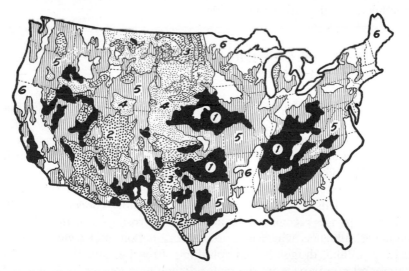

Figure 9:7. Erosion map of the United States: 1, severe sheets and gully erosion; 2, moderate to severe erosion of mesas and mountains; 3, moderate to severe wind erosion with some gullying; 4, moderate sheet and gully erosion with some wind action; 5, moderate sheet and gully erosion serious locally; 6, erosion rather unimportant. (After U.S. Soil Conservation Service.)

8 H. H. Bennett, Soil Conservation (New York: McGraw Hill, 1939) pp. 57–59.

threat to perhaps one third or even one half of the currently arable land in this country. (See Fig. 9:7.)

These estimates were made in the early years of the United States Soil Conservation Service before the erosion situation in this country had been fully investigated and undoubtedly are too high. Nor was it realized that eroded lands, if not appreciably gullied, can in many cases be readily reclaimed. Nevertheless, soil erosion ravages should not be minimized on this account. It is very serious in many sections of the United States and special precaution must be taken to insure its control. As late as 1962 a national survey by the United States Department of Agriculture showed soil erosion to be a prominent problem on about 237 million acres of cropland—more than half the total. To combat this problem, nearly 3000 soil conservation districts have been established. Furthermore, public support is being provided to partially defray the expense of erosion control methods.

The effects of erosion are no less serious in countries other than the United States—China, India, Syria, Palestine, to name but a few. Moreover, erosion in ancient times evidently was a menace—in Greece, Italy, Syria, North Africa, and Persia. Perhaps the fall of empires, such as that of Rome, was hastened by the exhausting influence on agriculture of the washing away of fertile surface soils.

9:8. ACCELERATED EROSION— MECHANICS

Water erosion is one of the commonest of geologic phenomena. It accounts in large part for the leveling of our mountains and the development of plains, plateaus, valleys, river flats, and deltas. The vast deposits that now appear as sedimentary rocks originated in this way. This is *normal* erosion. It operates slowly, yet inexorably. When erosion exceeds this normal rate and becomes unusually destructive, it is spoken of as *accelerated*. This is the water action that especially concerns agriculture.

Two steps are recognized in accelerated erosion—the *detachment* or loosening influence, which is a preparatory action, and *transportation* by floating, rolling, dragging, and splashing. Freezing and thawing, flowing water, and rain impact are the major detaching agencies. Raindrop splash and especially running water facilitate the carrying away of the loosened soil. In gullies most of the loosening and cutting is due to water flow, but on comparatively smooth soil surfaces, the beating of the raindrops effects most of the detachment.

INFLUENCE OF RAINDROPS. Raindrop impact exerts three important influences—(1) it detaches soil; (2) its beating tends to

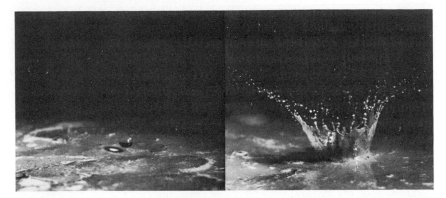

Figure 9:8. A raindrop (left) *and the splash* (right) *that it creates when the drop strikes a wet bare soil. Such rainfall impact not only tends to destroy soil granulation and encourage sheet and rill erosion but it also effects considerable transportation by splashing. A ground cover, such as sod, will largely prevent this type of erosion.(Photo courtesy U.S. Soil Conservation Service.)*

destroy granulation; and (3) its splash, under certain conditions, effects an appreciable transportation of soil. (See Fig. 9:8.) So great is the force exerted by dashing rain that soil granules not only are loosened and detached but in addition they may be beaten to pieces. Under such hammering, the aggregation of a soil so exposed practically disappears. If the dispersed material is not removed by runoff, it may develop into a hard crust upon drying. Such a layer is unfavorable in many ways. For example, certain seedlings, such as beans, have difficulty in pushing through a soil crust.

The protective importance of a vegetative shield, such as forest or bluegrass, or an artificial covering, say straw or a stubble mulch, is very great indeed. Such a protection, by absorbing the energy of rain impact, prevents the loss of both water and soil and reduces degranulation to a minimum.

TRANSPORTATION OF SOIL — SPLASH EFFECTS. In soil translocation, runoff water plays the major role. So familiar are most people with the power of water to cut and carry that little more need be said regarding these capacities. In fact, so much publicity has been given to runoff that the public, in general, ascribes to it all of the damage done by torrential rainfall.

However, splash transportation is, under certain conditions, of considerable importance. (See Fig. 9:8.) On a soil subject to easy detachment, a very heavy torrential rain may splash as much as 100 tons of soil an acre, some of the drops rising as high as 2 feet and moving horizontally perhaps 4 or 5 feet. On a slope or if the wind is blowing, splashing greatly aids and enhances runoff translocations of soil, the two together accounting for the total wash that finally occurs. Before considering methods of control let us examine the factors that influence the magnitude of accelerated erosion.

9:9. ACCELERATED EROSION — CAUSES AND RATE FACTORS

Two main factors are responsible for accelerated erosion: (1) the removal of the natural vegetative cover; and (2) the undue exposure of arable soils through the use of soil-exposing crops. Dense natural vegetation intercepts the rainfall and thus nullifies the impact of raindrops. In addition, both forest and natural grassland-cover contribute organic matter residues. These are incorporated into the surface soil thus giving greater aggregate stability and absorptive capacity. Again the plant roots hold the soil in place and thus prevent erosion even when the runoff is great.

RATE OF EROSION. The so-called "universal soil loss equation" identifies the factors on which erosion losses are dependent.[9] The equation is as follows:

$$A = RKLSCP$$

where A is the computed soil loss per unit area and the other letters represent the following factors:

R, Rainfall
K, Soil Erodibility
L, Slope Length
S, Slope Gradient
C, Crop Management
P, Erosion Control Practice

Acting together, these factors determine how much water enters the soil, how much runs off, and the manner and rate of its removal.

RAINFALL EFFECTS. Of the two phases, amount of *total rainfall* and its *intensity*, the latter is usually the more important. A heavy annual precipitation, received gently, may cause little erosion, while a lower yearly rainfall descending torrentially may result in tremendous

---

[9] For a discussion of this equation and its application to specific soil areas in the United States, see *Predicting Rainfall-Erosion Losses,* from *Cropland East of the Rocky Mountains,* Agric. Handbook No. 282, U.S. Department of Agriculture, 1965.

damage. This accounts for the marked erosion often recorded in semi-arid regions.

The *seasonal distribution* of the rainfall is also critical in determining soil erosion losses. For example, in the northern part of the United States, precipitation which runs off the land in the early spring when the soils are still frozen is ineffective in bringing about erosion. The same amount of runoff a few months later, however, often carries considerable amounts of soil with it. In any climate, heavy precipitation which occurs at a time of year when the soil is bare is likely to cause soil loss. Examples of such conditions are seedbed preparation-time and after the harvesting of crops such as beans, sugar beets, and early potatoes.

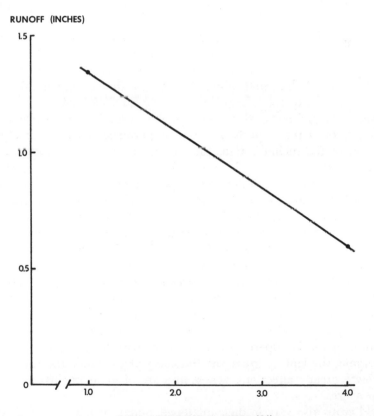

SOIL ORGANIC MATTER (%)

Figure 9:9. General relationship of runoff from 44 different Indiana soils to the organic matter content of these soils (2.5 inches of rain in 1 hour). (Source: W. H. Wischmeier and J. V. Mannering, "Effect of organic matter content of the soil on infiltration," Jour. Soil and Water Conservation 20:150–152, 1965.)

NATURE OF THE SOIL. The two most significant soil characteristics influencing erosion are: (1) the infiltration capacity, and (2) structural stability. They are closely related. The infiltration capacity is influenced greatly by structural stability, especially in the upper soil horizons. In addition, soil texture, organic content (see Fig. 9:9), the kind and amount of swelling clays, soil depth, and the presence of impervious soil layers all influence the infiltration capacity.

The stability of soil aggregates affects the extent of erosion damage in another way. Resistance of surface granules to the beating action of rain saves soil even though runoff does occur. The marked granule stability of certain tropical clay soils high in hydrous oxides of iron and aluminum accounts for the resistance of these soils to the action of torrential rains. Downpours of a similar magnitude on temperate-region clays would be disastrous.

SLOPE, TOPOGRAPHY, AND CHANNELS. The greater the *degree of slope,* other conditions remaining constant, the greater the erosion due to increased velocity of water flow. Also, more water is likely to run off. Theoretically, a doubling of the velocity enables water to move particles 64 times larger, allows it to carry 32 times more material in suspension, and makes the erosive power in total 4 times greater.

The *length* of the slope is of prime importance since the greater the extension of the inclined area, the greater is the concentration of the flooding water. For example, research in southwestern Iowa, showed doubling the length of a 9 per cent slope increased the loss of soil by 2.6 times and the runoff water by 1.8 times. This influence of slope is, of course, greatly modified by the size and general *topography* of the drainage area. Another modifying factor is the presence of *channels,* not only in the eroded area itself but in the watershed. The development of such channels controls the intensity of water concentration.

EFFECT OF VEGETATIVE COVER. Forests and grass are the best natural soil protective agencies known and are about equal in their effectiveness. But their influence varies. For instance, a forest with a heavy ground cover of organic matter and with a dense undergrowth is markedly superior to open woods with little organic accumulation. Again, the kind of grass, the thickness of its stand, and the vigor of its growth greatly affect erosiveness and are of great importance in control measures.

Field crops also vary in their influence. Some, such as wheat and oats, offer considerable obstruction to surface wash; others, especially intertilled crops, tend to encourage erosion. (See Table 9:7.) A trash or stubble mulch, where it can be utilized satisfactorily with field crops, would not only check erosion but also increase infiltration, reduce evaporation, and preserve granulation.

Table 9:7. Losses from Erosion on a Shelley Silt Loam Soil at the Missouri Agricultural Experiment Station. The Slope was 3.7 per cent, the Plots 90 Feet Long and the Average Rainfall 40 Inches. (Average of Fourteen Years)[a]

Treatment	Runoff, Per Cent of Rainfall	Tons of Soil Lost per Acre per Year	Relative Erosion, Bluegrass as 1	No. Yrs. to Erode 7 In. of Soil
No crop, plowed 4 inches deep and cultivated regularly	30.7	41.64	122	34
Corn grown continuously	29.4	19.72	58	50
Wheat grown continuously	23.3	10.10	30	100
Rotation; corn, wheat, and clover	13.8	2.78	8	368
Bluegrass sod continuously	12.0	0.34	1	3043

[a] M. F. Miller and H. H. Krusekopf, *The Influence of Systems of Cropping and Methods of Culture on Surface Runoff and Soil Erosion*, Research Bulletin 177, Mo. Agr. Exp. Sta., 1932.

EROSION-CONTROL PRACTICES. Sloping fields, especially those that are cultivated, erode easily if the rate of water runoff is not slowed down. Even sod and close-growing crops do not give sufficient protection under these conditions. Specific practices used to slow the water runoff include contour tillage, strip cropping, and terracing (see p. 233). The extent to which these practices are followed influences greatly the rate at which erosion occurs.

9:10. TYPES OF WATER EROSION

Three more or less distinct types of water erosion are generally recognized: *sheet, rill,* and *gully.* (See Figs. 9:10 and 9:11.) In the first, soil is removed more or less uniformly from every part of the slope. However, this type is often accompanied, especially on bare land newly planted or in fallow, by tiny gullies irregularly dispersed. This is *rill* erosion. But where the volume of water is concentrated, the formation of large or small ravines by undermining and downward cutting occurs. This is called *gully* erosion. While all types may be serious, the losses due to sheet and rill erosion, although less noticeable, are undoubtedly the most important from the standpoint of field soil deterioration.

Figure 9:10. The perched stones and pebbles shown in the picture are mute evidence of sheet erosion—the higher the pedestals, the greater the erosion. The soil under each rock has been protected from the beating action of the rain. The pedestal in the center is about 3 inches in height. (U.S. Soil Conservation Service photo.)

9:11. SHEET AND RILL EROSION — LOSSES UNDER REGULAR CROPPING

A number of different methods for the reduction and control of sheet and rill erosion may be currently utilized. Anything that will increase the absorptive capacity of the soil, such as surface tillage and more organic matter, will lessen the runoff over the surface. Trash and stubble mulches are of great aid. The nature of the crops grown is an especially important factor.

INFLUENCE OF CROPS. Intertilled crops such as corn or potatoes may actually encourage erosion, especially if the rows possess much slope. Small grains tend to impede such loss, whereas grasses are perhaps the most effective in checking erosion. This is so well recognized

Figure 9:11. Sheet and rill erosion on an unprotected slope with serious gully-ing imminent if protective measures are not instituted soon. Strip cropping or even terracing should be employed if cultivated crops are to be grown. Perhaps, better, the field could be seeded and used as pasture or meadow. In any case a diversion ditch well up the slope would be advisable. (U.S. Soil Conservation Service photo.)

that a sod is almost always recommended in places where serious erosion is likely to take place. A well-managed forest is of the same order of efficiency as grass.

The vegetative cover maintained by a given crop will vary depending upon its stage of growth. Runoff at different times of the year from plots at 9 corn belt research stations illustrate this point (Table 9:8).

NUTRIENT LOSSES. It is interesting to note the amount of some of the important nutrients that are swept away by erosion (Table 9:9). These losses are likely to be greater than one might expect since the finer particles of soil, much higher in fertility than the whole soil, are sorted out and carried away. This means an accelerated loss of all of the fertility elements. For comparison, tentative figures as to the nutrients withdrawn from the soil by the average crop of a standard rotation are quoted. The data, in round numbers, are shown in Table 9:9.

Table 9:8. The Effect of Crop Stage (Increase in Ground Coverage) and Return of Crop Residues on Runoff on 678 Plot-Years of Corn at 9 Research Locations in the Corn Belt States[a]

| Crop Stage | Runoff When Residues Were | |
	Removed (Inches[b])	Returned (Inches[b])
Rough Fallow (plowing to seeding)	0.62	0.37
Seedbed (0–30 days after seeding)	0.47	0.26
Establishment (30–60 days after seeding)	0.51	0.24
Growing Crop (establishment to harvest)	0.51	0.22
Residue (crop harvest to next plowing)	0.98	0.52
Total	3.09	1.61

[a] Data from W. H. Wischmeier and J. V. Mannering, "Effect of Organic Matter Content of the Soil on Infiltration," *Jour. Soil and Water Conservation,* 20:150–152, 1965.
[b] Expressed in inches per 1,000 foot-tons of computed rainfall energy per acre.

Table 9:9. Nutrients Removed Annually in Pounds to the Acre in the Missouri Erosion Experiment[a] *Compared to the Yearly Draft of an Average Field Crop*

Condition	N	P	K	Ca	Mg	S
Erosion Removal						
Corn grown continuously	66	18	605	220	87	17
Rotation: corn, wheat, and clover	26	8	214	85	29	6
Crop Removal						
Average for standard rotation	100	18	80	35	25	15

[a] These data are for two years only.

Erosion losses, even on a 4 per cent slope, may easily exceed the removal of nutrients by crops occupying the land. This seems to be true especially for calcium, magnesium, and potassium. The data in Table 9:9 emphasize once again the continual loss of valuable nutrients by the process of erosion. They also reemphasize the need to keep the soil covered and the value of close growing crops such as small grains or clovers in providing that cover. Removal of nutrients by crops is a necessary part of the production process; that by erosion loss is not.

9:12. SHEET AND RILL EROSION— METHODS OF CONTROL

One of the most important and at the same time the most under-rated means of erosion control is the maintenance of high soil fertility and productivity. The growing of bumper crops not only gives a maximum of ground cover but at the same time supplies sufficient organic matter to aid in the maintenance of this all-important soil constituent. The increased permeability of soils to water under such conditions is certainly a factor of major importance. Although not usually recognized as erosion control features, the wise use of fertilizers, lime, and manure may do more to prevent soil erosion, epecially sheet and rill, than some of the more obvious mechanical means of control.

MECHANICAL MEASURES.   In the growing of corn and similar crops, it is important that the cultivation be across the slope rather than with it. This is called *contour tillage*. On long slopes subject to sheet and rill erosion, the fields may be laid out in narrow strips across

Figure 9:12. Aerial photograph of fields in Kentucky where strip cropping is being practiced. (U.S. Soil Conservation Service photo.)

the incline, alternating the tilled crops such as corn and potatoes with hay and grain. Water cannot attain an undue velocity on the narrow strips of cultivated land, while the hay and grain tend to markedly check the runoff flow. Such a layout is called *strip cropping* and is the basis of much of the erosion control now advocated. (See Fig. 9:12.)

When the cross strips are laid out rather definitely on the contours, the system is called *contour strip cropping*. The width of the strips will depend primarily upon the degree of slope and upon the permeability of the land and its erodibility. Table 9:10 from Gustafson[10] gives some idea of the practicable widths. Contour strip cropping often is guarded by diversion ditches and waterways between fields. When their grade is high, they should be grass covered. This precaution is a number one rule in most erosion control.

Table 9:10. Suggested Strip Widths in Feet for Contour Strip Cropping

Slope Per Cent	Soil Conditions		
	Well-drained Erodibility Low	*Medium Drainage, Erodibility Moderate*	*Poor Drainage, Erodibility High*
5	125	100	75
10	100	75	50
15	75	50	—

However, when slopes are subject to very serious erosion, they should either be reforested or kept in permanent pasture, guarding always against incipient gullying. Even in permanent pastures and in young plantations *contour furrowing* at suitable intervals often is practical as it not only aids in stabilizing the soil but also provides more water for the crop. This is especially important on droughty slopes.

When the simpler methods of checking sheet erosion on cultivated lands are inadequate, it is often advisable to resort to *terraces* constructed across the slope. These catch the water and conduct it away at a gentle grade. Opportunity is thus given for more water to soak in. The *Mangum* terrace and its modifications are now largely in vogue. Such a terrace is generally a broad bank of earth with gently sloping sides, contouring the field at a grade from 6 to 8 inches to 100 feet. It is usually formed by

[10] A. F. Gustafson, *Soils and Soil Management* (New York: McGraw-Hill, 1941), p. 207.

back-furrowing and scraping. The interval between the successive embankments depends on the slope and erodibility of the land.

Since the terrace is low and broad, it may be cropped without difficulty and offers no obstacle to cultivating and harvesting machinery. It wastes little or no land, and is quite effective if properly maintained. Where necessary, waterways are sodded. Such terracing is really a more or less elaborate type of contour strip cropping.

9:13. GULLY EROSION AND ITS CONTROL

Small gullies, while at first insignificant, soon enlarge into unsightly ditches or ravines. They quickly eat into the land above, exposing its subsoil and increasing the sheet and rill erosion, already undesirably active. (See Fig. 9:11.) If small enough, such gullies may be plowed in and seeded down, using a nurse crop such as oats, barley, or wheat, which will check runoff until the grass obtains a start. Once the sod is established it may almost entirely stop the erosion.

When the gully erosion is too active to be thus checked and the ditch is still small, dams of rotted manure or straw at intervals of 15 or 20 feet are very effective. Such dams may be made more secure by strips or wire netting staked below them. After a time, the ditch may be plowed in and the site of the gully seeded and kept in sod permanently. It thus becomes a *grassed waterway,* an important feature of almost all successful erosion projects.

With moderately sized gullies, larger dams of various kinds may be utilized. These are built at intervals along the channels. If brush is used, it is piled in the gully at the desired location with the butt ends upstream. If the stakes are wired together before being driven down, the brush will be compressed and held firmly in place. Straw thrown above such dams will make them more effective in catching the eroded soil. Dams just as effective may be constructed from woven wire properly staked and secured. These are just a few of the details relating to this phase of water control.

With very large gullies, dams of earth, concrete, or stone are often successfully used. Most of the sediment is deposited above the dam and the gully is slowly filled. The use of semipermanent check dams, flumes, paved channels, and diversion ditches are also recommended on occasion. The only difficulty with engineering features at all extensive is that the cost may exceed the benefits derived or even the value of the land to be served. They thus may prove uneconomical.

9:14. WIND EROSION—
ITS IMPORTANCE AND CONTROL

The consideration of water erosion leads naturally to the question of the movement of soil by winds. This type of soil destruction, while most common in arid and semiarid regions, occurs to some extent in humid climates as well. It is essentially a dry-weather phenomenon and hence, in a sense, is a moisture problem. All kinds of soils and soil materials are affected and at times their more finely divided portions are carried to great heights and for hundreds of miles.

In the great dust storm of May 1934, which originated in western Kansas, Texas, Oklahoma, and contiguous portions of Colorado and New Mexico, clouds of powdery debris were caried eastward to the Atlantic seaboard and even hundreds of miles out over the ocean. Such aeolian activity is not a new phenomenon but has been common in all geologic ages. The wind energy that gave rise to the loessial deposits now so important agriculturally in the United States and other countries, belongs in this category (See Fig. 11:11).

The destructive effects of wind erosion are often very serious. Not only is the land robbed of its richest soils but crops are either blown away or left to die with roots exposed or they may be covered up by the drifting debris. Even though the blowing may not be great, the cutting and abrasive effects, especially of sand, upon tender crops often is disastrous. The area in the United States subject to greatest wind action is that broad expanse called the Great Plains. Here the mismanagement of plowed lands and the lowered holding power of the range grasses due to overgrazing, have greatly encouraged wind work. In dry years, as experience has shown, the results have been most deplorable.

AREAS OF EXCESSIVE WIND EROSION. Two great *dust bowls* (see Fig. 9:7) exist in the United States. One, the larger, occupies much of western Kansas, Oklahoma, and Texas, extending into southeastern Colorado and eastern New Mexico. The other, irregular and somewhat scattered, lies across the centers of three states—Nebraska and the two Dakotas. Eastern Montana is also affected. Curiously enough, areas of severe water erosion lie contiguous to these so-called dust bowls, while gully and sheet erosion, due to torrential rainfall, are not at all uncommon within their borders.

Possibly 12 per cent of continental United States is somewhat affected by wind erosion, 8 per cent moderately so, and perhaps 2 or 3 per cent badly. Although most of the damage is confined to regions of low rainfall, some serious wind erosion occurs in humid sections. Sand dune movement is a good example. More important agriculturally, sandy soils used for vegetables are often affected by the wind. This type of erosion is especially destructive on cultivated peats, particularly those that have been long and intensively cropped. The drying out of the cultivated and finely divided surface layers of sandy loams and peats leaves them both extremely susceptible to wind drift.

MECHANICS OF WIND EROSION. As was the case for water erosion, the loss of soil by wind movement involves two processes: (1) detachment, and (2) transportation. The abrasive action of the wind results in some detachment of tiny soil grains from the granules or clods of which they are a part. When the wind is laden with soil particles, however, its abrasive action is greatly increased. The impact of these rapidly moving grains dislodges other particles from soil clods and aggregates. These particles are now ready for movement.

The transportation of the particles once they are dislodged takes place in several ways. The first and most important is that of *saltation* or movement of soil by a short series of bounces along the surface of the ground. The particles remain fairly close to the ground as they bounce, seldom rising more than a foot or so. Depending on the conditions, this process may account for 50 to 75 per cent of the total movement.

Saltation also encourages *soil creep* or the rolling and sliding along the surface of the larger particles. The bouncing particles carried by saltation strike the larger aggregates and speed up their movement along the surface. Soil creep may account for 5 to 25 per cent of the total movement.

The most spectacular method of transporting soil particles is by movement in *suspension*. Here, dust particles of a fine-sand size and smaller are moved parallel to the ground surface and upward. Although some of them are carried at a height no greater than a few yards, the turbulent action of the wind results in others being carried miles upward into the atmosphere and hundreds of miles horizontally. They return to the earth only when the wind subsides and when precipitation washes them down. Although it is the most obvious manner of transportation, suspension movement generally accounts for no more than perhaps 3 to 40 per cent of the total movement.

FACTORS AFFECTING WIND EROSION. Susceptibility to wind erosion is related rather definitely to the moisture content of soils. Wet soils do not blow. The moisture content is generally lowered by hot dry winds to the wilting point and lower before wind erosion takes place. (Fig. 9:13.)

Other factors known to influence wind erosion are: (1) wind velocity, (2) soil surface condition, and (3) soil characteristics. Obviously, the rate of wind movement, especially gusts having greater than average velocity, will influence erosion. Wind turbulence will also influence the

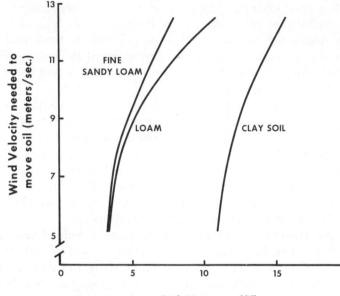

Soil Moisture (%)

Figure 9:13. The effect of soil moisture and soil texture on the wind velocity required to move soils. Soil moisture and soil texture play a highly significant role in determining the susceptibility of soils to wind erosion. (*Redrawn from F. Bisal and J. Hsiek, "Influence of moisture on erodibility of soil by wind,"* Soil Sci. 102:143–146, 1966.)

transporting capacity of the atmosphere. Although the wind itself has some direct influence in picking up fine soil, the impact of wind-carried particles on those not yet disengaged is probably more important.

Wind erosion is less severe where the soil surface is rough. This roughness can be obtained by proper tillage methods which leave large clods or ridges on the soil surface. Leaving stubble mulch is perhaps an even more effective way of reducing wind-borne soil losses.

In addition to moisture content, several other soil characteristics influencing wind erosion are: (1) mechanical stability of dry soil clods and aggregates; (2) the presence of a stable soil crust; and (3) bulk density and size of erodible soil fractions. The clods must be resistant to the abrasive action of wind-carried particles. If a soil crust resulting from a previous rain is present it too must be able to withstand impact without deteriorating. The importance of cementing agents here is quite apparent.

Soil particles of a given size and bulk density are apparently more susceptible to erosion than are others. Apparently those particles about 0.1 mm in diameter are most erodible, those larger or smaller in size being less susceptible to movement. Particles about 0.1 mm in size apparently are responsible to a degree for that movement of larger or smaller particles which does occur. By saltation, the most erodible particles bounce against larger particles causing surface creep and against the smaller dust particles resulting in movement in suspension.

CONTROL OF WIND EROSION. Factors just discussed give clues as to methods of reducing wind erosion. Obviously, if the soil can be kept moist there is little danger of wind erosion. A vegetative cover also discourages soil blowing, especially if the plant roots are well established. In dry-farming areas, however, sound moisture-conserving practices require summer fallow on some of the land and hot, dry winds reduce the moisture in the soil surface. Consequently, other means must be turned to on cultivated lands of these areas.

By roughening the soil surface, the wind velocity can be decreased and some of the moving particles trapped. Stubble mulch has proven to be effective in this manner. Tillage to provide for a cloddy surface condition should be at right angles to the prevailing winds. Likewise strip cropping and alternate strips of cropped and fallowed land should be perpendicular

Figure 9:14. Shrubs and trees make good wind breaks and add beauty to a North Dakota farm homestead. (Photo courtesy U.S. Soil Conservation Service.)

to the wind. Barriers such as tree shelterbelts (see Fig. 9:14) are effective in reducing wind velocities for short distances and for trapping drifting soil.

In the case of the blowing of sands, sandy loams, and cultivated peat soils in humid regions, various control devices are used. Windbreaks and tenacious grasses and shrubs are especially effective. (See Fig. 13:3 p. 375.) Picket fences and burlap screens, while less efficient as windbreaks than such trees as willows, are often preferred because they can be moved from place to place as crops and cropping practices are varied. Rye, planted in narrow strips across the field, is sometimes used on peat lands. All of these devices for wind-erosion control, whether applied in arid or humid regions and whether vegetative or purely mechanical, are, after all, but phases of the broader problem of soil moisture control.

9:15. SUMMARY OF SOIL MOISTURE REGULATION

In the effective control of soil water, four more or less closely related phases must be considered. They are: (1) weed transpiration, (2) surface evaporation, (3) percolation and leaching, and (4) runoff and erosion.

Weed transpiration and surface evaporation, by drawing on the available soil water, compete directly and seriously with the crop. Cultivation is the remedy commonly recommended for weeds, although herbicides are being utilized more and more in connection with a suitable rotation. Surface evaporation is subject to little control except through the use of organic mulches.

Percolation losses are serious because of the nutrients carried away, rather than because of the waste of the water. In fact, the removal of such water is necessary in order to promote soil aeration and encourage other desirable conditions. Keeping crops on the land as much as possible is the only practicable means of reducing leaching losses of nutrients.

The detrimental influence of runoff over the surface is due to the bodily removal of soil, as well as the loss of the water itself. Control measures involve organic matter maintenance to encourage infiltration, an effective vegetative cover, and mechanical practices such as contour strip cropping to allow an orderly removal of excess surface water.

Chapter 10

Soil Air and Soil Temperature

As was pointed out in Chapter 1, approximately one half the total volume of a representative mineral surface soil is occupied by solid materials. The remaining nonsolid or pore space is occupied by water and gases. The previous three chapters (7, 8, and 9) have placed major emphasis on the soil moisture phase. They have, nevertheless, constantly reminded the reader of the interrelationship of soil air and soil water. We cannot affect one without also changing the other.

In spite of the fact that this reciprocal relationship already has been duly stressed, there are certain aspects of soil aeration which deserve separate and special consideration. This is true particularly in respect to certain plant processes.

It is logical also to include in this chapter another important physical property—the temperature of the soils. Although subject to little direct control under field conditions, soil temperature is closely related to soil moisture and soil air and, of course, exerts a tremendous influence upon microorganisms and higher plants. Let us begin with the major problems of soil aeration.

10:1. SOIL AERATION DEFINED

Before considering the more detailed phases of soil aeration, it may be well to define, at least in a general way, what is meant by this particular soil property. In keeping with our edaphological viewpoint, soil aeration will be considered in relation to *plant growth*. Thus, we may look upon a well-aerated soil as *one in which gases are available to growing aerobic organisms (particularly higher plants) in sufficient quantities and in the proper proportions to encourage optimum rates of the essential metabolic processes of these organisms.*

A soil in which aeration is considered satisfactory must have at least two characteristics. *First*, sufficient space devoid of solids and water should be present. *Second*, there must be an ample opportunity for the ready movement of essential gases into and out of these spaces. Water relations largely control the *amount of air* space available, but the problem of adequate *air exchange* is probably a much more complicated feature. The supply of oxygen, a gas that is constantly being used in biological reactions,[1] must be continually renewed. At the same time the concentration of CO_2, the major product of these or similar reactions, must not be allowed to build up excessively in the air spaces.

10:2. SOIL AERATION PROBLEMS IN THE FIELD

Under actual field conditions there are in general two situations which may result in poor aeration in soils: (1) when the moisture content is excessively high, leaving little or no room for gases; and (2) when the exchange of gases with the atmosphere is not sufficiently rapid to keep the concentration of soil gases at desirable levels. The latter may often occur even when sufficient *total air space* is available.

---

[1] Two biological reactions largely account for the O_2 and CO_2 changes referred to above. They are (1) the respiration of higher-plant roots; and (2) the aerobic decomposition of incorporated organic residues by microorganisms. Although differing in many respects, these processes are surprisingly similar with regard to the gases involved. This similarity makes it possible to express both reactions in terms of the following very general equation:

$$[C] + O_2 \longrightarrow CO_2$$

Both processes result in the oxidation of carbonaceous compounds, oxygen being used up and CO_2 being evolved. Either a deficiency of O_2 or an excess of CO_2 would thus tend to cut down the rate of these reactions. In fact, both inhibitions commonly operate concurrently.

EXCESS MOISTURE. In the first case referred to above, essentially a waterlogged condition is established. This may be quite temporary, but, nevertheless, often seriously affects plant growth. Such a situation is frequently found on poorly drained, fine-textured soils which have a minimum of macropores through which water can move rapidly. It also occurs in soils that normally are fairly well drained if the rate of water supply to the soil surface is sufficiently rapid. A low spot in a field or even a flat area in which water tends to stand for a short while is a good example of this condition. Such complete saturation of the soil with water can be disastrous for certain plants in a short time, a matter of a few hours being critical in some cases. Plants which have previously been growing under conditions of good soil aeration are actually more susceptible to damage from flooding than are plants growing on soils where poor aeration has prevailed from the very start.

The prevention of this type of poor aeration requires the rapid removal of excess water either by land drainage or by controlled runoff. Because of the large volume of small capillary pores in some soils, even these precautions leave only a small portion of the soil volume filled with air soon after a rain. This often makes the artificial drainage of heavy soils surprisingly ineffective.

GASEOUS INTERCHANGE. The seriousness of inadequate *interchanges* of gases between the soil and the free atmosphere above it is dependent primarily on two factors: (1) the rate of biochemical reactions influencing the soil gases; and (2) the actual rate at which each gas is moving into or out of the soil. Obviously, the more rapid the usage of O_2 and the corresponding release of CO_2, the greater will be the necessity for the exchange of gases. Factors markedly affecting these biological reactions such as temperature, organic residues, etc., undoubtedly are of considerable importance in determining the air status of any particular soil. (See p. 247–248.)

The exchange of gases between the soil and the atmosphere above it is facilitated by two mechanisms: (1) *mass flow* and (2) *diffusion*. Mass flow of air is apparently due to pressure differences between the atmosphere and the soil air and is relatively unimportant in determining the total exchange that occurs. However, in the upper few inches of soil diurnal changes in soil temperature may result in mass flow of some significance. The extent of mass flow is determined by factors such as soil and air temperatures, barometric pressure, and wind movements.

Apparently most of the gaseous interchange in soils occurs by diffusion. Through this process each gas tends to move in a direction determined by its own partial pressure. (See Fig. 10:1.) The partial pressure of a gas in a mixture is simply the pressure this gas would exert if it alone were present in the volume occupied by the mixture. Thus, if the pressure

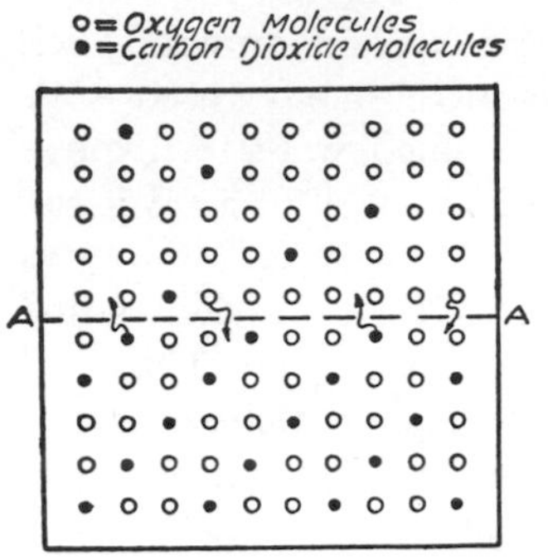

o = Oxygen Molecules
• = Carbon Dioxide Molecules

Figure 10:1. Diagram showing how the process of diffusion takes place. The total gas pressure is the same on both sides of boundary (A-A). The partial pressure of oxygen is greater, however, in the top portion of the container. Therefore, this gas tends to diffuse into the lower portion where fewer oxygen molecules are found. The CO_2 molecules, on the other hand, move in the opposite direction due to the higher partial pressure of this gas in the lower half. Eventually equilibrium will be established when the partial pressures of O_2 and CO_2 respectively are the same in both sides of the boundary.

of air is 1 atmosphere, the partial pressure of oxygen, which makes up about 21 per cent of the air by volume, is approximately 0.21 of an atmosphere.

Diffusion allows extensive movement from one area to another even though there is no over-all pressure gradient. Thus, even though the total soil-air pressure and that of the atmosphere may be the same, a higher concentration of O_2 in the atmosphere will result in a net movement of this particular gas into the soil. An opposite movement of CO_2 and water vapor is simultaneously taking place, since the partial pressures of these two gases are generally higher in the soil air than in the atmosphere. A representation of the principles involved in diffusion is given in Figure 10:1.

In addition to being effected by partial pressure differences, diffusion seems to be directly related to the volume of pore spaces filled wih air. On heavy-textured topsoils, especially if the structure is poor, and in compact subsoils the rate of gaseous movement is seriously slow. Moreover, such soils allow very slow penetration of water into the surface layer. This prevents the rapid replacement of air high in CO_2 and the subsequent inward movement of atmospheric air after a heavy rain or after irrigation.

OXYGEN DIFFUSION RATES.[2]   Perhaps the best measurement of aeration status of a soil is the oxygen diffusion rate (ODR). This determines the rate at which oxygen can be replenished if it is used by respiring plant roots or replaced by water.

In Figure 10:2 is a graph showing how ODR decreases with soil depth.

[2] For a review of this subject see L. H. Stolzy and J. Letey, "Characterizing soil oxygen conditions with a platinum electrode," *Advan. in Agron.*, 16:249–279, 1964.

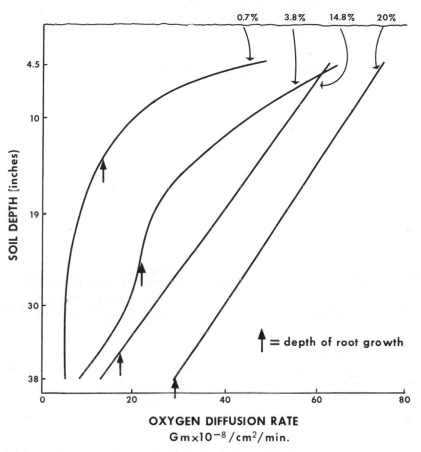

OXYGEN LEVEL AT SOIL SURFACE

OXYGEN DIFFUSION RATE
$Gm \times 10^{-8}/cm^2/min.$

Figure 10:2. The effect of soil depth and oxygen concentration at the surface on the oxygen diffusion rate (ODR). Arrows indicate snapdragon root pene-tration depth. Even with a 20% O_2 level at the surface the diffusion rate at 38 inches is less than half that at the surface. Note that when the ODR drops to about 20 gm x $10^{-8}/cm^2/min$ root growth ceases. (Redrawn from L. H. Stolsky et al., "Root Growth and Diffusion Rates As Functions of Oxygen Concentration," Soil Sci. Soc. Amer. Proc. 25:463–467, 1961.)

Even when atmospheric air with 21% O_2 was used, the ODR rate at 38 inches was less than half that at 4.5 inches. When a lower oxygen concen-tration was used, the ODR decreased even more rapidly with depth. Note that root growth ceased when the ODR dropped to about 20 g × $10^{-8}/cm^2/min$.

10:3. COMPOSITION OF SOIL AIR

In Table 10:1, data are given showing the composition of soil air at various locations as compared to that of the atmosphere itself. These

Table 10:1. The Composition of Soil Air at Various Locations Compared to That of the Atmosphere[a]

Location	Percentage by Volume		
	O_2	CO_2	N_2
Soil air:			
England	20.65	0.25	79.20
Iowa	20.40	0.20	79.40
New York	15.10	4.50	81.40
Atmospheric air:			
England	20.97	0.03	79.0

[a] These data were obtained from several sources. See T. L. Lyon; H. O. Buckman; and N. C. Brady, *The Nature and Properties of Soils* (New York: Macmillan, 1952), p. 278.

data are for topsoils only and consequently do not afford complete information as to the variabilities encountered, especially in the subsoil.[3] They do illustrate, however, the higher CO_2 concentration and lower O_2 content of soil air as compared to that of atmosphere. Also, there is a general inverse relationship between oxygen and carbon dioxide contents, that of O_2 decreasing as the CO_2 increases.

Although the actual differences in CO_2 contents are not impressive, comparatively speaking they are significant. Thus, when the soil air contains only 0.25 per cent CO_2 this gas is *more than 8 times* as concentrated as it is in the atmosphere. In cases where the CO_2 content becomes as high as 10 per cent, there is more than 300 times as much present as is found in the air above.

Compared to the atmosphere, soil air usually is much higher in water vapor, being essentially saturated except at or very near the surface of the soil. This fact has already been stressed in connection with the movement of water. Also the concentration of gases, such as methane and

[3] For example, under conditions of extremely poor aeration O_2 contents of soil air as low as 1 per cent have been found. See D. Boynton, *Soils in Relation to Fruit Growing in New York, Part XV. Seasonal and Soil Influences on Oxygen and Carbon Dioxide Levels of New York Orchard Soils*, Cornell Univ. Agr. Exp. Sta. Bul., 763, 1941.

hydrogen sulfide, which are formed by organic-matter decomposition is somewhat higher in soil air.

In addition to the free soil air already discussed, the small quantities of certain gases dissolved in the soil moisture must be considered. Also, the soil colloids are thought to hold at their surfaces small quantities of the various gases by physical adsorption. Undoubtedly, gases held in these two ways are of some importance and should not be disregarded in the study of soil aeration. Thus, oxygen so held may be utilized in oxidation reactions while dissolved carbon dioxide is of universal importance, especially in respect to soil pH and the solubility of soil minerals.

10:4. FACTORS AFFECTING THE COMPOSITION OF SOIL AIR

The composition of soil air is largely dependent upon the amount of *air space available* together with the rates of *biochemical reactions* and *gaseous interchange*.

The total porosity of soils is determined largely by the bulk density (see p. 55). This in turn is related to factors such as soil texture and structure and soil organic matter. Not all the pore space in field soils is filled with air, some being occupied by water. In poorly drained soils and in well drained soils, immediately after a heavy rain or irrigation a high proportion of the pore space is filled with water. If this situation persists for a period of time only small amounts of oxygen will be available for plants.

The concentrations of both O_2 and CO_2 are definitely related to the biological activity in the soil. Microbial composition of organic residues apparently accounts for the major portion of the CO_2 evolved. Incorporation of large quantities of manure, especially if moisture and temperature

Figure 10:3. The carbon dioxide content of soil air at four different sampling dates, showing the effects of manure and cropping. Air samples were taken from the topsoil only. An unaccountable variation occurred in the data of June 10, hence this sampling date was omitted. (From Russell and Appleyard.)

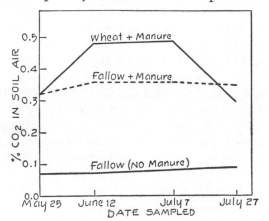

are optimum, will alter the soil-air composition appreciably. Respiration by higher plants as well as the continuous contribution of their roots to the organic mass by sloughage should not be disregarded. These influences are well illustrated by data from Russell and Appleyard[4] in Figure 10:3. The effects of a growing crop and especially that of organic manures are clearly shown.

SUBSOIL VS. TOPSOIL. As might be expected, subsoils are usually more deficient in oxygen than are topsoils. The total pore space as well as the average size of the pores is generally much less in the deeper horizons. Boynton,[5] working on orchard sites, determined the aeration status of several soils with depth. The average oxygen contents for the months of May and June in two of the soils studied are shown in Figure 10:4.

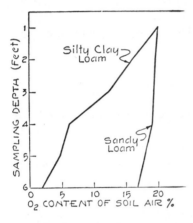

Figure 10:4. The average oxygen contents of two orchard soils during the months of May and June 1938. Normal root growth and functions would occur at much deeper levels on the sandy soil. (From D. Boynton.)

In both cases the oxygen percentage in the soil air decreased with depth, the rate of decrease being much more rapid with the heavier soil. Throughout the depth sampled, the lighter-textured sandy loam contained a much higher oxygen percentage. In both cases the decrease in O_2 content could be largely, but not entirely, accounted for by a corresponding increase in CO_2 content. For example, CO_2 percentages as high as 14.6 were recorded for the lower horizons of the heavier-textured soil.

SEASONAL DIFFERENCES. As would be expected, there is a marked seasonal variation in the composition of soil air. Most of this variation can be accounted for by soil-moisture and soil-temperature differences. High soil moisture tends to favor a low oxygen and high CO_2 level in the soil air. In temperate regions, this situation often prevails in the winter and late spring when the soil moisture is generally highest.

[4] E. J. Russell and A. Appleyard, "The Atmosphere of the Soil: Its Composition and the Causes of Variation," *Jour. Agr. Sci.*, 7:25–6, 1915.
[5] D. Boynton, *op. cit.*, pp. 26–43.

Because soils are normally drier during the summer months, opportunity for gaseous exchange is greatest during this period. This results in relatively high O_2 and low CO_2 levels. Some exceptions to this rule may be found, however. Since high summer temperatures also encourage rapid microbiological release of CO_2, a given soil containing easily decomposable organic matter may have higher CO_2 levels in the summer than in the winter. The dependence of soil-air composition on soil moisture and soil temperature cannot be over-emphasized.

10:5. EFFECTS OF SOIL AERATION ON BIOLOGICAL ACTIVITIES[6]

ON MICROORGANISMS. Perhaps the most apparent effect of poor soil aeration on microbiological processes is a decrease in the rate of organic-matter oxidation. This decrease seems to be associated more with a lack of O_2 than with an excess of CO_2. The slow rate of decay of plant residues in swampy areas is a somewhat exaggerated example of how a lack of oxygen prevents rapid organic-matter decomposition.

All aerobic organisms are unable to function properly in the absence of gaseous oxygen. For example, special purpose bacteria such as those responsible for the oxidation of the elements nitrogen and sulfur are relatively ineffective in poorly aerated soils. This is also true for the symbiotic nitrogen fixers and for some of the nonsymbiotic (*azotobacter*) groups. (See p. 457.)

The microorganism population, therefore, is drastically affected by soil aeration. Only the anaerobic and facultative organisms function properly under poor aeration conditions. They are able to do so because of their ability to utilize combined oxygen. Their activities consequently yield reduced forms of certain elements such as iron and manganese which are often toxic to higher plants. Organic toxins may also develop. Further attention will be given these effects in a subsequent section.

ON ACTIVITIES OF HIGHER PLANTS. Higher plants are adversely affected in at least four ways by conditions of poor aeration: (1) the growth of the plant, particularly the roots, is curtailed; (2) the absorption of nutrients and (3) also of water is generally lessened; and (4) the formation of certain inorganic compounds toxic to plant growth are favored by poor aeration. Since the last of these is considered in Section 10:6, only the first three phases will be discussed here.

PLANT GROWTH. The ability of different plant species to grow in soils with low soil-air porosity varies greatly. (See Fig. 10:5.)

---

[6] This subject was reviewed recently by A. R. Grable, "Soil Aeration & Plant Growth," *Advan. in Agron.* 18:57–106, 1966.

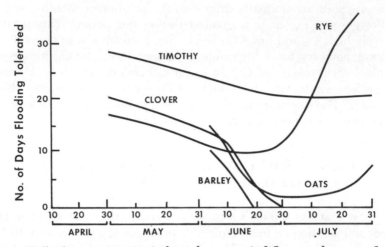

Figure 10:5. A comparison of the tolerance of different plants to flooding at different stages of plant growth under Finnish conditions. (*From: P. Sankko, "Investigation of the damage caused by excessive water on the lake shore lands at Saima." Maataloushall Vesitekn Tulkin 4 as redrawn in Drainage of Agricultural Lands* [Agronomy Vol. 7], *p. 535, The American Society of Agronomy, Madison, Wis. 1957.*)

Tomatoes, for example, require high air porosities (up to 20–30%) for best growth. In contrast, timothy, if well supplied with nitrogen, can grow with a very low air porosity and rice grows normally submerged in water. Furthermore, the tolerance of a given plant to low porosity may be different for seedlings than for rapidly growing plants. The tolerance of red pine to restricted drainage during its early development and its poor growth or even death on the same site at later stages is a case in point.

In spite of these wide variations in soil-air porosity limitation, soil physicists generally consider that if the soil porosity is reduced below 10–12 per cent, soil oxygen renewal is extremely slow and most plants are likely to suffer.

The abnormal effect of insufficient aeration on root development has been observed often. With root crops such as carrots and sugar beets the influence is most noticeable. Abnormally shaped roots of these plants are common on compact, poorly aerated soils. Even with sod crops the presence of an impervious soil layer generally results in restricted growth particularly of the smaller roots. An example of this is shown in Fig. 10:6, in which is pictured the root system of rape plants growing on a compacted soil. It is interesting to note the lack of extensive root penetra-

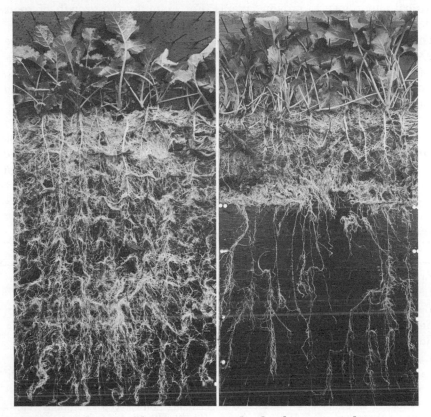

Figure 10:6. Effect of soil compaction on the development of the root system of the rape plant. Left, subsoil loosened before planting; Right, compacted layer at plow depth not loosened. (From work of H. C. de Roo, The Connecticut Agricultural Experiment Station.)

tion within the impervious layer. Such restricted root systems can hardly be expected to effectively absorb sufficient moisture and nutrients for normal plant growth.

Apparently, different levels of soil oxygen are required for the various functions of roots. For example, Boynton and co-workers[7] found that apple tree roots required at least 3 per cent of oxygen in the soil air to subsist, while 5 to 10 per cent was sufficient for the growth of existing roots. At least 12 per cent of O_2 was required for new root growth. Their results clearly emphasize the complexity of soil aeration problems.

Researchers have found that the *oxygen diffusion rate* (ODR) is of

[7] D. Boynton: J. E. DeVilliers; and W. Reuther, "Are there Different Critical Oxygen Concentrations for the Different Phases of Root Activity?" *Science,* 88:569–70, 1938.

critical importance to growing plants. For example, the growth of roots of most plants cease when the ODR drops to about 20 g × 10^{-8}/cm²/min. Top growth is generally satisfactory so long as the ODR remains above 30–40 g × 10^{-8}/cm²/min. In Table 10:2 are found some field measurements of ODR along with comments about the condition of the plants. Note the sensitivity of sugar beets to low ODR and the general tendency for trouble if the ODR gets below the above critical level.

Table 10:2. The Relationship Between Oxygen Diffusion Rates (ODR) and the Condition of Different Plants. When the ODR Drop Below About 40 g×10^{-8}/cm²/min the Plants Appear to Suffer. Sugar Beets Require High ODR Even at 30 cm Depth[a]

| | | ($g×10^{-8}$/cm²/min) | | | |
| | *Soil* | *Depth in cm* | | | |
Plant	*Type*	10	20	30	*Remarks*
Broccoli	Loam	53	31	38	Very Good Growth
Lettuce	Silt Loam	49	26	32	Good Growth
Beans	Loam	27	27	25	Chlorotic Plants
Sugar Beets	Loam	58	60	16	Stunted Tap Root
Strawberries	Sandy Loam	36	32	34	Chlorotic Plants
Cotton	Clay Loam	7	9	—	Chlorotic Plants
Citrus	Sandy Loam	64	45	39	Rapid Root Growth

[a] From L. H. Stolzy and J. Letey, "Characterizing Soil Oxygen Conditions With a Platinum Microelectrode," *Advan. in Agron.*, 16:249–279, 1964.

As might be expected, some plants are affected more by low ODR than are others. Grasses tend to be more tolerant of low diffusion rates than do legumes. Sugar beets and alfalfa require higher rates than does Ladino clover.

NUTRIENTS AND WATER. A deficiency of oxygen has been found to curtail nutrient and water absorption by plants. The exact reasons for the effects of aeration on these two processes are not well understood. However, these processes are known to be influenced quite markedly by the rate of root respiration. Apparently, the *energy* of respiration is utilized in bringing about at least part of the nutrient and water absorption. Since a supply of oxygen must be available if roots are to respire normally, a deficiency of this gas naturally results in sluggish nutrient and water uptake. It is surprising as well as ironical that an oversupply of water in the soil tends to reduce the amount of water which plants will absorb.

The effect of aeration on nutrient absorption is of considerable practical significance. Under poor aeration conditions, for example, plants exhibit nutrient-deficiency symptoms on soils fairly well supplied with available nutrient elements. Also, on certain soils, improper tillage may destroy the granulation leaving conditions that lead to inefficient nutrient utilization. The desirability of the frequent cultivation of heavy, poorly granulated soils when planted to row crops is undoubtedly related to this problem of nutrient uptake.

Soil aeration conditions in the field may vary drastically from day to day. Heavy rainfall, excessive irrigation or flooding may bring about a temporary but complete void of soil air. Plants will suffer depending on their stage of growth and their genetic tolerance (see Fig. 10:5).

SOIL COMPACTION AND AERATION. It may be well to point out that all ill effects of soil compaction are not due to poor aeration. Soil layers can become so dense as to impede the growth of roots even if adequate O_2 supply is available. For example, some compacted soil layers adversely affect cotton more by preventing root penetration than by lowering available oxygen content.

10:6. OTHER EFFECTS OF SOIL AERATION

As previously noted, anaerobic decomposition of organic materials is much slower than that occurring when ample gaseous oxygen is available. Moreover, the products of decomposition are entirely different. For example, the complete anaerobic decomposition of sugar occurs as follows:

$$C_6H_{12}O_6 \longrightarrow 3CO_2 + 3CH_4$$
$$\text{Sugar} \qquad\qquad \text{Methane}$$

Less complete decomposition yields other products such as organic acids, which under extreme conditions may accumulate in toxic quantities. Examples of acids occurring by anaerobic decay are lactic, butyric, and citric.

When decomposed anaerobically, organic nitrogen compounds usually yield amines and gaseous nitrogen compounds in addition to ammonia. Of course, these nitrogen compounds remain in reduced forms, not being subject to nitrification under anaerobic conditions. The absence of oxygen thus completely changes the nature of the decay processes as well as the rates at which they occur.

The chemical forms of certain elements found in soils in the oxidized and reduced states are shown in Table 10:3. In general, it can be stated that the oxidized forms are much more desirable for most of our common crops in humid regions. The advantages of the oxidized states of the

Table 10:3. Oxidized and Reduced Forms of Several Important Elements

Element	Normal Form in Well-Oxidized Soils	Reduced Form Found in Waterlogged Soils
Carbon	CO_2	CH_4
Nitro-gen	NO_3^-	N_2 and NH_4^+
Sulfur	SO_4^{--}	H_2S and S^-
Iron	Fe^{+++} (Ferric oxides)	Fe^{++} (Ferrous oxides)
Manga-nese	Mn^{+++} (Manganic oxides)	Mn^{++} (Manganous oxides)

nitrogen and sulfur compounds have already been discussed. (See p. 37–38.) The desirability of the higher-valent forms of iron and manganese is associated with the solubility of these elements at least in humid-region soils. The reduced states, being more soluble than the oxidized forms, are often present in such quantities as to be toxic. This is true especially if the poor aeration occurs in an acid soil. Lack of lime thus intensifies the adverse effects of poor aeration on iron and manganese toxicity.

The insolubility of the oxidized forms of iron and manganese under alkaline conditions may result in a deficiency of these elements. Consequently, the interrelation of soil pH and aeration is very important in determining whether an excess or a deficiency of iron and manganese is apt to occur.

In addition to the chemical aspect of these differences, *soil color* is markedly influenced by the oxidation status of iron and manganese. Colors such as red, yellow, and reddish brown are encouraged by well-oxidized conditions. More subdued shades such as grays and blues predominate if insufficient O_2 is present. These facts are made use of in field methods of determining the need for drainage. Imperfectly drained soils usually show a condition wherein alternate streaks of oxidized and reduced materials occur. This *mottled* condition indicates a zone of alternate good and poor aeration—a condition not conducive to proper plant growth.

10:7. AERATION IN RELATION TO
SOIL AND CROP MANAGEMENT

In view of the overwhelming importance of soil oxygen to the growth of most of the common crop plants, the question naturally arises as to the practical means of facilitating its supply. Interestingly enough, almost all methods employed for aeration control are concerned directly or indirectly with the management of soil water.

Measures that will encourage soil aeration logically fall into two categories: (1) those designed to remove excess soil moisture; and (2) those concerned with the aggregation and cultivation of the soil. Each of these will be considered briefly.

Both surface and under drainage is essential if one expects an aerobic soil environment. Since the nonsolid spaces in the soil are shared by air and water, the removal of excess quantities of the latter must take place if sufficient oxygen is to be supplied. The importance of surface runoff and tile drainage in this respect have already received attention and only need re-emphasis in connection with soil aeration. (For influence of drainage see p. 221.)

The maintenance of a stable soil structure should not be overlooked as a means of augmenting good aeration. Pores of macrosize, usually greatly encouraged by large stable aggregates, are soon freed of water following a rain, thus allowing gases to move into the soil from the atmosphere above. Organic-matter maintenance by the addition of farm manure and the growth of legumes is perhaps the most practical means of encouraging aggregate stability, which in turn will encourage good drainage and better aeration. These features have received adequate attention elsewhere. (See p. 62–63.)

In heavy soils, however, it is often impossible to maintain optimum aeration without resorting to the mechanical stirring of the soil by some type of cultivation. Thus, in addition to controlling weeds, cultivation in many cases has a second very important function—that of aiding soil aeration. Yields of row crops, especially those with large tap roots such as sugar beets and rutabagas, are often increased by frequent light cultivations that do not injure the fibrous roots. Part of this increase, undoubtedly, is due to aeration.

CROP-SOIL ADAPTATION. In addition to the direct methods of controlling soil aeration, one more phase of soil and crop management should be mentioned—that of crop-soil adaptation. The seriousness of oxygen deficiency depends to a large degree on the crop to be grown. Alfalfa, fruit and forest trees, and other deep-rooted plants, for example, require deep, well-aerated soils and are quite sensitive to a deficiency of oxygen, even in the lower soil horizons. Shallow-rooted plants such as grasses and alsike and ladino clovers, on the other hand, do very well on soils which tend to be poorly aerated, especially in the subsoil. These facts should not be overlooked in deciding what crops should be grown and how they are to be managed in areas where aeration problems are acute.

The dominating influence of moisture on the aeration of soils is everywhere apparent. And the control of the former means at least a partial control of the latter. This leads to a second important physical property that is at times influenced by soil water—that of soil temperature. Let us direct our attention first to some of the fundamentals concerned with this important physical characteristic.

10:8. SOIL TEMPERATURE [8]

The temperature of the soil affects markedly its usefulness to man. In cold soils chemical and biological rates are slow. Biological decomposition is at a near standstill, thereby limiting the rate at which nutrients such as N, P, S, and Ca are made available. For example, nitrification does not begin in the spring until the soil temperature reaches about 40°F, the most favorable limits being 80–90°F. Also, plant processes such as seed germination and root growth occur only above certain critical soil temperatures. Likewise, the absorption and transport of water and nutrient ions by higher plants is adversely affected by low temperatures.

Plants vary widely in the soil temperature at which they grow best. Likewise there is variability in the optimum temperature for different plant processes. For example, corn germination requires a soil temperature of 45–50°F and is optimum near 100°F. Dry matter production for corn is optimum when soil temperature is 80–85° F, although this is apparently altered under different conditions of air temperature and soil moisture. Potato tubers develop best when the soil temperature is between 60 and 70°F. Oats also grow best at about 70°F although the roots of this plant apparently do better when the soil temperature is about 60°F (see Fig. 10:7).

In addition to the direct influence of temperature on plant and animal life the effect of freezing and thawing must be considered. Frost action along with later thawing is responsible for some of the physical weathering which takes place in soils. As ice forms in rock crevices it forces the

[8] For a discussion on root temperature and plant growth, See K. F. Nielson and E. C. Humphries, "Effects of Root Temperature on Plant Growth," *Soils and Fertilizer*, 29:1–7, 1966.

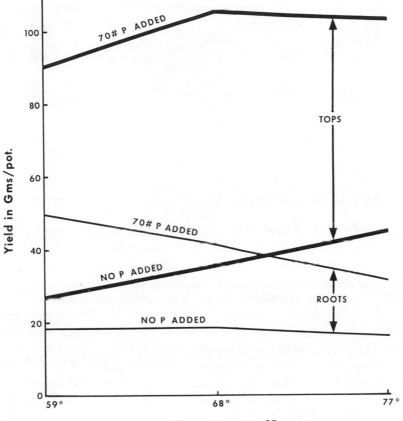

Soil Temperature °F.

Figure 10:7. The effect of soil temperature and phosphorus applications on the yield of oat roots and tops. Top yields were increased by increasing the soil temperature. The opposite was true for the roots when adequate P was present. (*From V. W. Case, N. C. Brady and D. J. Lathwell, "The influence of soil temperature and phosphorus fertilizers of different water-solubilities on the yield and phosphorus uptake by oats," Soil Sci. Soc. Amer. Proc. 28:409–412, 1964.*)

rocks apart causing them to disintegrate. Similarly, alternate freezing and thawing subjects the soil aggregates and clumps and rocks to pressures and thus alters the physical set up in the soil. Freezing and thawing of the upper layers of soil can also result in so-called *heaving* of perennial forage crops such as alfalfa. (See Fig. 10:8.) This action which is most severe on bare, imperfectly drained soils can drastically reduce the stand of alfalfa, some clovers, and trefoil. Changes in soil temperature have the

Figure 10:8. Alternate freezing and thawing of soils result in the "heaving" of perennial plants out of the ground. The above alfalfa crowns were exposed as a result of this type of action during the winter and spring months.

same effect on shallow house foundations and roads with fine material as a base. They show the effects of heaving in the spring.

The temperature of soils in the fields is dependent directly or indirectly upon at least three factors: (1) the net amount of heat the soil absorbs; (2) the heat energy required to bring about a given change in the temperature of a soil; and (3) the energy required for changes such as evaporation which are constantly occurring at or near the surface of soils. These phases will be considered in order.

10:9. ABSORPTION AND LOSS OF HEAT

The amount of heat absorbed by soils is determined primarily by the quantity of effective solar radiation reaching the earth. (See Fig. 10:10.) The latter in any particular locality depends fundamentally upon climate. But the amount of energy entering the soil is, in addition, affected by other factors such as: (1) the color; (2) the slope; and (3) the vegetative cover of the site under consideration. It is well known that dark soils will absorb more energy than light-colored ones[9] and that red and

---

[9] This does not imply that dark soils are always warmer. Actually the opposite may be true since dark soils usually are high in organic matter and consequently hold large amounts of water which must also be warmed.

yellow soils will show a more rapid temperature rise than will those that are white. Observation has also shown that the nearer the angle of incidence of the sun's rays approaches the perpendicular, the greater will be the absorption. (See Fig. 10:9.) As an example, a southerly slope of 20 degrees, a level soil, and a northerly slope of 20 degrees receive energy on June 21 at the 42nd parallel, north, in the proportion of 106, 100, and 81, respectively.

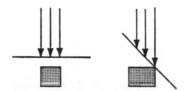

Figure 10:9. Diagram showing the area of soil warmed as affected by the angle at which the sun's rays strike the soil. If a given amount of radiation from the sun strikes the soil at right angles (left above), the radiation is concentrated in a relatively small area and the soil warms up quite rapidly. If the same amount of radiation strikes the soil at a 45° angle (right above), the area affected is larger, the radiation is not as concentrated and the soil warms up more slowly. This is one of the reasons why north slopes tend to have cooler soils than south slopes. It also accounts for the colder soils in winter as compared to summers.

The temperature of southward slopes varies with the time of year. For example, in the northern hemisphere the southeasterly inclination is generally warmest in the early season, the southerly slope during midseason, and the southwesterly slope in the fall. Southern or southeasterly slopes are often preferred by gardeners. Orchardists and foresters consider exposure an important factor not only in regard to the species or variety of tree to be grown but also in respect to sunscald and certain plant diseases.

Whether the soil is bare or covered with vegetation is another factor that markedly influences the amount of insolation received. The effect of a forest is universally recognized. Even an ordinary field crop, such as bluegrass, has a very noticeable influence, especially upon temperature fluctuations. Bare soils warm up more quickly and cool off more rapidly than those covered with vegetation, or with artificial mulches. Frost penetration during the winter is considerably greater in bare noninsolated land.

LOSS OF HEAT TO ATMOSPHERE. It should be pointed out that part of the solar radiation is not permanently retained by the soil but rather is lost directly to the atmosphere. The processes which are responsible for these losses are: (1) *conduction*[10] to the atmosphere, and (2) *radiation*[11] into outer space. (See Fig. 10:10.) While conduction no doubt is of considerable importance, especially if the air above the soil is in rapid movement, radiation probably accounts for a

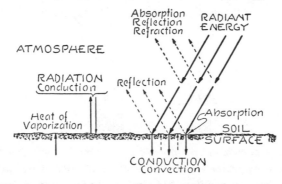

Figure 10:10. *A diagram showing the acquisition, loss, and movement of heat in soils.*

great loss of energy. Terrestrial bodies are continually giving off energy waves into the atmosphere. Since these rays are mostly of the infrared type and make no impression on the eye, they are often spoken of as *dark rays*. Suffice it to say, their energy capacity is high and, as their emission is continuous, much heat is lost in this way. This accounts in part, especially during clear weather, for rapid changes in surface-soil temperatures.

10:10. SPECIFIC HEAT OF SOILS

Another major factor affecting the temperature relations of a soil is its specific heat or its thermal capacity compared with that of water. Specific heat may be expressed as a ratio of the quantity of heat required to raise the temperature of a given substance from 15 to 16°C compared to that required for the same temperature rise of an equal weight of water. The importance of this property in soil-temperature control undoubtedly is great. The mere absorption of a given amount of heat by a soil does not necessarily assure a rapid rise in temperature. Everything else being equal, a soil with a high specific heat exhibits

---

[10] A molecular transfer of energy from one body to another when they are in contact or from one part of a particular body to another. The energy is conceived as communicated progressively from molecule to molecule.

[11] A transfer of energy through space by means of waves or pulsations which are transformed into heat values when they encounter an obstructing body.

much less rapid temperature changes than does one having a low specific heat.

Under actual field conditions the soil moisture content determines, more than any other factor, the energy required to raise the temperature of soils. For instance, the dry-weight specific heat of mineral soils, in spite of variations in texture and organic matter, is about 0.20. But if the moisture is advanced to 20 per cent, the specific heat of the wet mass becomes 0.33, while an increase of 30 per cent of moisture raises the wet-weight specific heat to 0.38.[12] Obviously, therefore, since moisture is one of the major factors in respect to the heat capacity of a soil, it has much to do with the rate of the warming up and the cooling off of soils.

10:11. HEAT OF VAPORIZATION

Soil moisture is also of major importance in determining the amount of heat used in the process of the evaporation of soil water. Vaporization is caused by an increased activity of the soil water molecules. This requires the expenditure of a certain amount of energy which results in a cooling effect especially at the surface where most of the evaporation occurs. It requires about 585 gram calories to evaporate 1 gram of water at 68°F. Similarly, 265 kilogram calories are required to evaporate 1 pound of water at the same temperature. This latter figure is sufficient to lower the temperature of a cubic foot of a representative mineral soil at optimum moisture about 28°F, providing that all of the energy of evaporation comes from the soil and its water. Such a figure is, of course, empirical as only a part of the heat of vaporization comes from the soil itself. Nevertheless, it indicates the tremendous cooling influence of evaporation.

The low temperature of a wet soil is due partially to evaporation and partially to high specific heat. The temperature of the upper few inches of a wet soil is commonly 6–12°F lower than that of a moist or dry soil.

---

[12] These figures can be easily verified. For example, consider the above soil at 20 per cent moisture content. Remembering that soil moisture is expressed as grams of water per 100 grams of soil solids, we have in this case 20 g of H_2O with each 100 g of soil. The number of calories required to raise the temperature of 20 g of water by 1° C is:

$$20 \text{ (g)} \times 1 \text{ (cal per g)} = 20 \text{ calories}$$

The corresponding figure for the 100 gms. of soil solids is:

$$100 \text{ (g)} \times 0.2 \text{ (cal per g)} = 20 \text{ calories}$$

Thus, a total of 40 calories are required to raise the temperature of 120 g of the moist soil by 1° C. Since the *specific heat* is the number of calories required to raise the temperature of one gram of wet soil by 1° C, in this case it is:

$$40/120 = 0.33 \text{ calories per gram}$$

Now verify the 0.38 figure for the soil with a 30 per cent moisture content.

This is a significant factor in the spring when a few degrees will make the difference between the germination or lack of germination of crop seeds. Stand failures are commonly due to wet cold soils.

SOIL COLOR AND TEMPERATURE. At this point it is appropriate again to call attention to the interrelationship of soil color and soil temperature. Although dark-colored soils absorb heat readily, such soils, due to their usually high organic-matter status, often have high moisture contents. Under such soil conditions, the evaporation and specific heat relationships become especially important. Consequently, a dark-colored soil, particularly if it happens to be somewhat poorly drained, may not warm up as quickly in the spring as will a well-drained light-colored soil nearby.

10:12. MOVEMENT OF HEAT IN SOILS

Before dealing with actual temperature data, let us consider briefly the movement of thermal energy in the soil. As already mentioned, much of the solar radiation is dissipated into the atmosphere. Some, however, slowly penetrates the profile largely by *conduction*. (See Fig. 10:10.) While this type of movement is influenced by a number of factors, the most important is probably the moisture content of the soil layers. Heat passes from soil to water about 150 times easier than from soil to air. As the water increases in a soil, the air decreases and the transfer resistance is lowered decidedly. When sufficient water is present to join most of the soil particles, further additions will have little effect on heat conduction. Here again the major role of soil moisture comes to the fore.

The significance of conduction in respect to field temperatures is not difficult to grasp. It provides a means of temperature adjustment but, because it is slow, the subsoil-changes tend to lag behind those to which the surface layers are subjected. More than this, the changes that do occur are always less in the subsoil. In temperate regions, we expect surface soils in general to be warmer in summer and cooler in winter than the subsoil, especially the lower horizons of the latter.

10:13. SOIL TEMPERATURE DATA

The temperature of the soil at any time depends on the ratio of the energy absorbed and that being lost. The constant change in this relationship is reflected in the *seasonal, monthly,* and *daily* temperatures. The accompanying data from College Station, Texas (Fig. 10:11) are

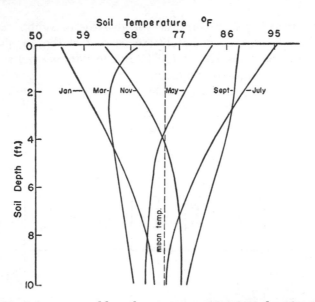

Figure 10:11. Average monthly soil temperatures for 6 of the 12 months of the year at different soil depths at College Station, Texas (1951–55). Note the lag in changes in soil temperature at the lower depths. (Reprinted from Fluker, B. J. "Soil Temperature," Soil Sci., 86:35–46, 1958.)

representative of average seasonal temperatures in relation to soil depth.

It is apparent from these figures that the seasonal variations of soil temperature are considerable even at the lower depths. The surface layers vary more or less in accord with the air temperature and, therefore, exhibit a greater fluctuation than the subsoil. On the average, the surface 6-inch layer of soil is warmer than the air at every season of the year, while the subsoil is warmer in autumn and winter but cooler in spring and summer due to its protected position and the lag in conduction.

This lag in temperature change in the subsoil is especially noticeable when the monthly march of soil temperature at Lincoln, Nebraska is considered. The monthly average temperatures, plotted in Fig. 10:12, show a greater annual range in temperature for the surface soil than for the air. Daily data would, of course, show the greatest range for the soil air. It must be kept in mind that changes in soil temperature, except at the very surface, are gradual while the air may vary many degrees in a very short time.

The daily and hourly temperatures of the atmospheric air and the soil in temperate zones may show considerable agreement or marked divergence according to conditions. Fluctuations are, of course, more rapid in the case of air temperatures, and in temperate regions usually are greater. It is well to remember, however, that the maximum temperature of a dry surface soil may definitely exceed that of the air, possibly approaching in some cases 125 or 130°F. But in winter even surface soils do not fall greatly below freezing.

With a solar control and a clear sky, the air temperature in temperate

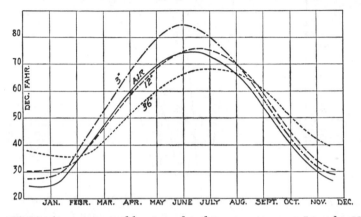

Figure 10:12. Average monthly air and soil temperatures at Lincoln, Nebraska (12 years). Note that the 3-inch soil layer is consistently warmer than the air above and that the 36-inch soil horizon is cooler in spring and summer, but warmer in the fall and winter than surface soil.

regions rises from morning to a maximum at about two o'clock. The surface soil, however, does not reach its maximum until later in the afternoon due to the usual lag (Fig. 10:13). This retardation is greater and

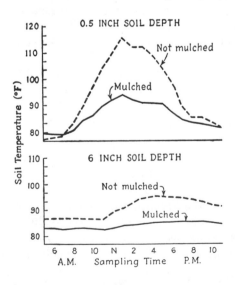

Figure 10:13. The effect of a sawdust mulch on the temperature at two depths of a Georgia soil on August 11. Note that the mulched area is cooler and is less subject to fluctuations than the area where no mulch was applied. (From A. W. White, Jr.; J. E. Giddens; and H. D. Morris, "The Effect of Sawdust on Crop Growth and Physical and Biological Properties of Cecil Soil," Proc. Soil Sci. Soc. Amer., 23:365–368, 1959.)

the temperature change is less as the depth increases. The lower subsoil shows little daily or weekly fluctuation, the variation, as already emphasized, being a slow monthly or seasonal change.

10:14. SOIL TEMPERATURE CONTROL

The temperature of field soils is subject to no radical human regulation. The use of organic mulches will give lower and more uniform surface-soil temperatures (Fig. 10:13). Such a practice has limited application, however, over large acreages and is used mostly for gardens and flower beds.

Soil-management methods, especially those that influence soil moisture, do provide for small but biologically vital modifications. Let us compare briefly the temperature relations of a well-drained and a poorly drained soil in a humid temperate region. The latter soil has a high specific heat. Therefore, large amounts of radiant energy must be absorbed to raise the soil temperature by those few extra degrees so badly needed in early spring. And since the excess water will not percolate through this soil, much of it must be removed by evaporation, another costly process in terms of heat dissipation. The low temperatures of poorly drained soils, especially in the spring, are well known. Experienced men expect a range from 6 to 12°F lower in the surface layer than in comparable well-drained areas. Drainage is, of course, the only practicable expedient.

Besides the control relations already mentioned, there is the influence of downward moving water on soil temperature. In general, it has a cooling effect except possibly in the early spring. Precipitation is usually cooler than the soil in temperate regions, especially in the summer. But even if rain water should be 10°F warmer than the soil, an improbable assumption, an average rain would raise the temperature of the surface 6 inches only slightly, and this would be quickly offset by the cooling effects of surface evaporation.

As was the case with soil air, the controlling influence of soil water on soil temperature is everywhere apparent. Whether it is a question of acquisition of insolation, loss of energy to the atmosphere, or the movement of heat to and fro within the soil, the percentage of water present is always important. Water regulation seems to be the key to what little practical temperature control it is possible to exert on field soils.

Chapter 11

The Origin, Nature, and
Classification of Parent Materials

The influence of weathering is evident on all sides. Nothing escapes it. It breaks up the country rocks, it modifies or destroys their physical and chemical characteristics, and carries away the soluble products and even some of the solids as well. The unconsolidated residues, *the regolith*, are left behind. But weathering goes further. It synthesizes a soil from the upper layers of this heterogeneous mass. Hence, the regolith, or at least its upper portions, may be designated as *parent material* of soils.[1]

Nor are these parent materials always allowed to remain undisturbed on the site of their development. Climatic agencies often shift them from place to place, with further grinding and leaching, until at last they are

---

[1] *Parent material* may be defined as "the unconsolidated and more or less chemically weathered mineral material from which soils may be synthesized." For a detailed discussion of weathering, see: M. L. Jackson and G. D. Sherman, "Chemical Weatheirng of Minerals in Soils," *Advan. in Agron.* 5:219–318, 1953.

allowed to rest long enough for soil profile development to take place. A study of weathering and of the parent materials that result is not only interesting in itself, but it is also a necessary introduction to soil formation and classification.

We shall begin the study of parent materials with a brief review of kinds of rocks from which the regolith and in turn the soils have formed.

11:1. CLASSIFICATION AND PROPERTIES OF ROCKS

The rocks found in the earth's crust are commonly classified as (1) igneous, (2) sedimentary, or (3) metamorphic. Those of igneous origin are formed from molten lava and include such common rocks as *granite* and *diorite* (Fig. 11:1). They are composed of primary miner-

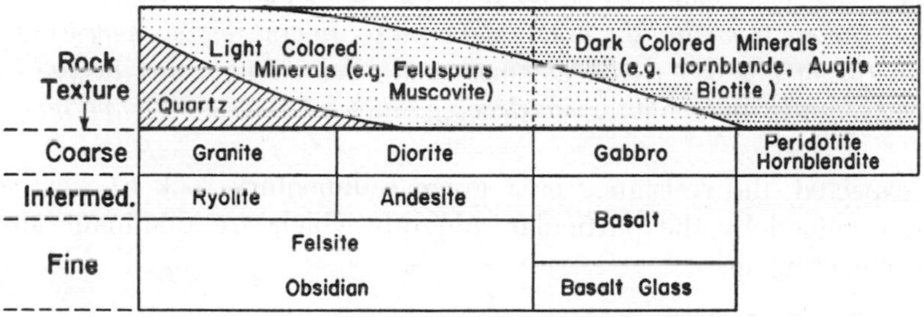

Rock Texture	Light Colored Minerals (e.g. Feldspars Muscovite) Quartz		Dark Colored Minerals (e.g. Hornblende, Augite Biotite)	
Coarse	Granite	Diorite	Gabbro	Peridotite Hornblendite
Intermed.	Ryolite	Andesite	Basalt	
Fine	Felsite			
	Obsidian		Basalt Glass	

Figure 11:1. Diagram showing the classification of some igneous rocks in relation to mineralogical composition and the size of mineral grains in the rock (rock texture). Light-colored minerals and quartz are generally more prominent than are the dark-colored minerals.

als such as (1) quartz, (2) the feldspars, and (3) the dark-colored minerals including biotite, augite, and hornblende. In general, gabbro and basalt (Fig. 11:2) which are high in the dark-colored, iron- and magnesium-containing minerals are more easily weathered than are the granites and other lighter colored rocks.

Sedimentary rocks have resulted from the deposition and recementation of weathering products of other rocks. For example, quartz sand weathered from a granite and deposited in the bottom of a prehistoric sea, may, through geological changes, have become cemented into a solid mass. This would be called a *sandstone*. Similarly, recemented clays are termed *shale*. Other important sedimentary rocks are shown in Table 11:1, along with a list of their dominant minerals. As might

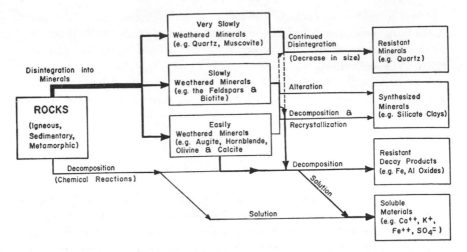

Figure 11:2. A generalized diagram showing trends in weathering which take place under acid conditions common in humid-temperate regions. One would expect climate to modify the exact relationships. In arid regions, physical breakdown (disintegration) would dominate and soluble ions would not be lost in large quantities. In humid regions decomposition becomes more important.

be expected, the resistance of a given sedimentary rock to weathering is determined by the particular minerals which are dominant and by the cementing agent.

Table 11:1. Some of the More Important Sedimentary and Metamorphic Rocks and the Minerals Commonly Dominant in Them

Sedimentary Rocks	Dominant Mineral	Metamorphic Rocks	Dominant Mineral
Limestone	Calcite ($CaCo_3$)	Gneiss	(Varies)[a]
Dolomite	Dolomite CaMg $(CO_3)_2$	Schist	(Varies)[a]
Sandstone	Quartz (SiO_2)	Quartzite	Quartz (SiO_2)
Shale	Clays	Slate	Clays
Conglomerate	(Varies)[b]	Marble	Calcite ($CaCO_3$)

[a] The minerals present are determined by the original rock which has been changed by metamorphism. Primary minerals present in the igneous rocks commonly dominate these rocks, although some secondary minerals are also present.

[b] Small stones of various mineralogical makeup will be cemented into conglomerate.

Metamorphic rocks are those which have formed by the metamorphism or change in form of other rocks. Igneous and sedimentary masses which have been subjected to tremendous pressures and high temperature have succumbed to metamorphism. Igneous rocks are commonly modified to form *gneisses* and *schists;* those of sedimentary origin such as sandstone and shale may be changed to *quartzite* and *slate,* respectively. Some of the common metamorphic rocks are shown in Table 11:1. As was the case with those of igneous and sedimentary origin, the particular mineral or minerals which dominate a given metamorphic rock will influence its resistance to weathering. (See Table 11:2 for a listing of the more common minerals.)

Table 11:2. The More Important Original and Secondary Minerals Found in Soils. (The original minerals are also found abundantly in igneous and metamorphic rocks. Secondary minerals are commonly found in sedimentary rocks.)

Original Minerals	
Name	*Formula*
Quartz	SiO_2
Microcline Orthoclase	$KAlSi_3O_8$
Na-plagioclase	$NaAlSi_3O_8$
Ca-plagioclase	$CaAl_2Si_2O_8$
Muscovite	$KAl_3Si_3O_{10}(OH)_2$
Biotite	$KAl(Mg \cdot Fe)_3Si_3O_{10}(OH)_2$
Hornblende[a]	$Ca_2Al_2Mg_2Fe_3, Si_6O_{22}(OH)_2$
Augite[a]	$Ca_2(Al \cdot Fe)_4(Mg \cdot Fe)_4Si_6O_{24}$

Secondary Minerals	
Name	*Formula*
Calcite	$CaCo_3$
Dolomite	$CaMg(CO3)_2$
Gypsum	$CaSO_4 \cdot 2H_2O$
Apatite	$Ca_5(PO_4)_3 \cdot (Cl, F)$
Limonite	$Fe_2O_3 \cdot 3H_2O$
Hematite	Fe_2O_3
Gibbsite	$Al_2O_3 \cdot 3H_2O$
Clay minerals	Al-silicates

[a] These are approximate formulas only since these minerals are so variable in their composition.

11 : 2. WEATHERING — A GENERAL CASE

Before we consider the various kinds of parent materials which develop from rocks, let us first examine the general trends of weathering responsible for the formation of the regolith and in turn, the soils. In a very general way some of the changes which take place during weathering are illustrated by the diagram in Fig. 11:2. Study it carefully, keeping in mind that it deals primarily with weathering as it occurs in temperate regions.

Weathering is basically a combination of destruction and synthesis. Rocks, which are the original starting point in the weathering process, are first broken down into smaller rocks and eventually into the individual minerals of which they are composed. Simultaneously, rock fragments and the minerals therein are attacked by weathering forces and are changed to new minerals either by minor modifications (alterations) or by complete chemical changes. These changes are accompanied by a continued decrease in particle size and by the release of soluble constituents, most of which are subject to loss in drainage waters.

The minerals which are synthesized are shown (Fig. 11:2) in two groups: (1) the silicate clays, and (2) the very resistant end products including iron and aluminum oxides. Along with the very resistant primary minerals such as quartz these two groups dominate temperate-region soils.

◥ THE PROCESSES. Two basic processes are concerned in the changes indicated in Fig. 11:2. These are mechanical and chemical. The former is often designated as *disintegration*, the latter as *decomposition*. Both are operative as you move from left to right in the weathering diagram. Forces responsible for disintegration bring about a decrease in size of rocks and minerals without appreciably affecting their composition. By decomposition, however, definite chemical changes take place, soluble materials are released, and new minerals are synthesized or are left as resistant end products. Mechanical and chemical processes may be outlined as follows:

1. Mechanical (disintegration)
   a. Temperature—differential expansion of minerals, frost action, and exfoliation.
   b. Erosion and deposition—by water, ice, and wind.
   c. Plant and animal influences.
2. Chemical (decomposition)

a. Hydrolysis.
b. Hydration.
c. Carbonation and related acidity processes.
d. Oxidation.
e. Solution.

11:3. MECHANICAL FORCES OF WEATHERING

TEMPERATURE EFFECTS. Variations of temperature, especially if sudden or wide, greatly influence the disintegration of rocks. During the day, rocks become heated and at night often cool much below the temperature of the air. This warming and cooling is particularly effective as a disintegrating agent. Rocks are aggregates of minerals which differ in their coefficients of expansion upon being heated. With every temperature change, therefore, differential stresses are set up which eventually must produce cracks and rifts, thus encouraging mechanical breakdown.

Due to slow heat conduction, the outer surface of a rock is often at a markedly different temperature than the inner and more protected portions. This differential heating and cooling tend to set up lateral stresses which, in time, may cause the surface layers to peel away from the parent mass. This phenomenon is spoken of as *exfoliation* and at times is markedly accelerated by the freezing of included water.

The presence of water, if freezing occurs, greatly increases the mechanical effects just mentioned. The force developed by the freezing of water is equivalent to about 150 tons to the square foot, an almost irresistible pressure.[2] It widens cracks in huge boulders and dislodges mineral grains from smaller fragments. Nor is this influence of temperature ended when rocks are reduced to fragments. It carries onward in the parent material and finally in the resultant soil. Freezing and thawing are of great practical importance in altering the physical condition of medium- and fine-textured soils.

INFLUENCE OF WATER, ICE, AND WIND. Rainwater beats down upon the land and then travels oceanward, continually shifting, sorting, and reworking unconsolidated materials of all kinds. When loaded with such sediments, water has a tremendous cutting power as is amply demonstrated by the gorges, ravines, and valleys the country

[2] This is equivalent to a pressure of about 142 atmospheres or over 4 times the negative tension exerted upon the water molecules at the liquid-air interface of a soil when its moisture content is at the hygroscopic coefficient.

over. The rounding of sand grains on an ocean beach is further evidence of the abrasion which accompanies water movement.

Ice is an erosive and transporting agency of tremendous capacity, and next to water is perhaps the most important and spectacular physical agent of weathering. One must visit Greenland or Alaska to realize its power. The abrasive action of glaciers as they move under their own weight disintegrates rocks and minerals alike. Not only do glaciers affect the underlying solid rock, but also they grind and mix unconsolidated materials which have been picked up as they move over the countryside. Even though they are not so extensive at the present time, glaciers in ages past have been responsible for the transportation and deposition of parent materials over millions of acres. The importance of ice as a mechanical agent is not to be minimized. (See p. 285 and ff.)

Wind has always been an important carrying agent and, when armed with fine debris, exerts an abrasive action also. Dust storms of almost continental extent have occurred in the past, with the result that tons of material have been filched from one section and transferred to another. As dust is transferred and deposited, abrasion of one particle against another occurs. The rounded rock remnants in some arid areas of the West are caused largely by wind action.

PLANTS. Simple plants, such as mosses and lichens, grow upon exposed rock, there to catch dust until a thin film of highly organic material accumulates. Higher plants sometimes exert a prying effect on rock which results in some disintegration. This is most noticeable in the case of tree roots in rocky sections. Such influences, as well as those exerted by animals, are, however, of little import in producing parent material when compared to the drastic physical effects of water, ice, wind, and temperature changes.

11:4. CHEMICAL PROCESSES OF WEATHERING

Scarcely has the disintegration of rock material begun when its decomposition usually is also apparent. This is especially noticeable in humid regions where chemical and physical processes are particularly active and markedly accelerate each other.

HYDROLYSIS. The reaction of minerals with water is perhaps the most important way by which chemical breakdown occurs. Hydrolysis, which is a decomposition reaction, is important in the weathering of a wide range of minerals including the feldspars and micas. The change may be indicated as follows, using microcline ($KAlSi_3O_8$) as the mineral undergoing hydrolysis:

$$KAlSi_3O_8 + HOH \longrightarrow HAlSi_3O_8 + KOH$$
$$2HAlSi_3O_8 + 8HOH \longrightarrow Al_2O_3 \cdot 3H_2O + 6H_2SiO_3$$

The potassium released by this reaction is soluble and can be adsorbed by the soil colloids, used by plants or removed in the drainage water. The aluminum and silicon compounds may recrystallize into a clay mineral such as kaolinite. If conditions are suitable, one or both may remain in the soil as their respective oxides, or they may be removed in the drainage.

HYDRATION. Hydration involves the rigid attachment of H and OH ions to the compound being attacked. In most cases, these ions become an integral part of the mineral crystal lattice. As micas become hydrated, some H and OH move in between the platelike layers. In so doing, they tend to expand the crystal and make it more porous, thus hastening other decomposition processes.

A good example of hydration is the development of limonite from hematite. It may be shown as follows:

$$2Fe_2O_3 + 3H_2O \longrightarrow 2Fe_2O_3 \cdot 3H_2O$$
Hematite (red)   Limonite (yellow)

When the products of hydration dry out due to varying weather conditions, dehydration may occur. Thus, limonite may readily be changed to hematite, with a noticeable change in color. Variations in the color of subsoils in the Southeastern states are due to a considerable extent to the reaction cited above.

CARBONATION AND OTHER ACIDIC PROCESSES. The disintegration and decomposition of mineral matter are greatly hastened by the presence of the hydrogen ion in percolating waters. Even that contained in carbonic acid is effective in this respect. For example, this acid is known to result in the chemical solution of calcite in limestone, the following reaction being illustrative of what takes place:

$$CaCO_3 + H_2CO_3 \longrightarrow Ca(HCO_3)_2$$
Calcite   Soluble Bicarbonate

Other acids much stronger than carbonic are also present in most humid region soils. They include very dilute inorganic acids such as HNO_3 and H_2SO_4 as well as some organic acids. Also present are the H ions associated with soil clays which are available for reaction with other soil minerals.

An example of the reaction of H ions with soil minerals is that of an acid clay with a feldspar such as anorthite.

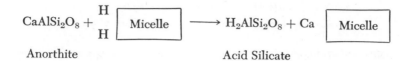

$$CaAlSi_2O_8 + \begin{array}{c} H \\ H \end{array} \boxed{Micelle} \longrightarrow H_2AlSi_2O_8 + Ca \boxed{Micelle}$$

Anorthite   Acid Silicate

The mechanism is simple, the H ions of the acid clays replacing the bases of the fresh minerals which they may closely contact. An acid silicate results which is subject to recrystallization, thus producing clay. Thus, "clay begets clay" by a mechanism that depends upon the removal of bases from the weathering mass of minerals by insoluble inorganic acids.[3]

OXIDATION. Of the various chemical changes due to weathering, oxidation is usually one of the first to be noticed. It is particularly manifest in rocks carrying iron, an element which is easily oxidized. In some minerals the iron is present in the reduced ferrous ($Fe++$) form. If the oxidation to the ferric ion takes place while the iron is still part of the crystal lattice, other ionic adjustments must be made since a 3-valent ion is replacing a 2-valent one. These adjustments result in a less stable crystal which is then subject to both disintegration and decomposition.

In other cases, the ferrous iron may be released from the crystal and almost simultaneously oxidized to the ferric form. An example of this is the hydration of olivine and the release of ferrous oxide which may be immediately oxidized to ferric oxide (hematite).

$$3MgFeSiO_4 + 2H_2O \longrightarrow H_4Mg_3Si_2O_9 + SiO_2 + 3FeO$$

Olivine   Serpentine   Ferrous Oxide

$$4FeO + O_2 \longrightarrow 2Fe_2O_3$$

Ferrous Oxide   Hematite

SOLUTION. The solvent action of water and the ions it carries as it moves through and around rocks and minerals furthers the weathering process. The solution effects of dissolved CO_2 and the H ions in water have already been mentioned. Also, the release of soluble potassium by hydrolysis or orthoclase has been cited. In each case, ions of the alkali metals (Na, K, etc.) or the alkaline earths (Ca, Mg, etc.) were represented as being solubilized rather readily. (See Table 11:3.) Less spectacular is the slower dissolution of some iron, silicon, and aluminum. These elements are subject to solution, the specific climatic conditions determining the extent to which it occurs.

[3] For a more detailed consideration of acid clays as weathering agents see: E. R. Graham and H. C. Turley, "Soil Development and Plant Nutrition: III. The Transfer of Potassium from the Nonavailable Form as Reflected by the Growth and Composition of Soybeans," *Proc. Soil Sci. Soc. Amer.*, 12:332–35, 1947.

Table 11:3. Comparative Loss of Mineral Constituents as Weathering Takes Place in a Granite and in a Limestone. (The losses are compared to that of aluminum which was considered in these cases to have remained constant during the weathering process.)[a]

| | Granite to Clay | | Limestone to Clay |
Constituent	Comparative Loss (%)	Constituent	Comparative Loss (%)
CaO	100.0	CaO	99.8
Na_2O	95.0	MgO	99.4
K_2O	83.5	Na_2O	76.0
MgO	74.7	K_2O	57.5
SiO_2	52.5	SiO_2	27.3
Fe_2O_3	14.4	Fe_2O_3	24.9
Al_2O_3	0.0	Al_2O_3	0.0

[a] The losses are given in per cent of that presumed to be present originally for each constituent. The granite data were taken from G. P. Merrill, *Weathering of Micaceous Gneiss*, Bul. 8, Geol. Soc. Amer., 1879, p. 100. Those for limestone are from J. S. Diller, *Educational Series of Rock Specimens*, Bul. 150, U.S. Geol. Survey, 1898, p. 385.

11:5. FACTORS AFFECTING WEATHERING OF MINERALS

Many factors influence the rate of weathering of minerals. Because of this, few generalizations can be made concerning the rate at which their breakdown will occur. It has been established, however, that certain general factors have a marked effect on the weathering process. For example, the following are known to be significant: (1) climatic conditions; (2) physical properties; and (3) chemical characteristics of the rocks and minerals. These will each be discussed briefly.

CLIMATIC CONDITIONS. If sufficient time is allowed, the climatic conditions, more than any other factor, will tend to control the kind and rate of weathering which take place. Only a few examples of the many effects of varied climatic factors will be cited.

Under conditions of low rainfall, there is a dominance of mechanical processes of weathering, which decrease particle size with little change in composition. The presence of more moisture encourages chemical as well as mechanical changes, new minerals and soluble products resulting. In humid-temperate regions, silicate clays are among the minerals synthesized. They account for much of the strong agricultural character of soils in these areas.

Weathering rates are generally more rapid in regions of high annual temperatures, especially if sufficient moisture is present to encourage chemical decomposition. Furthermore, the more resistant products of chemical weathering, such as the hydrous oxides of iron and aluminum, tend to be most prominent in the humid-tropical areas. This is due to the fact that less resistant minerals have succumbed to the intense weathering common to these areas. Even quartz, which is perhaps the most resistant of the common macro-grained primary minerals, disappears in time under these conditions.

Climate also largely controls the dominant types of vegetation present over wide areas. In this way it indirectly influences the biochemical reactions in soils and in turn their effect upon mineral weathering. For example, conifer trees, whose presence is often determined by climate, markedly influenced the kind and rate of weathering occurring in the soil or parent material. Needles of these plants are low in metallic cations and when decomposed they encourage very acid conditions. Other trees or grasses are generally less apt to effect weathering in this manner.

PHYSICAL CHARACTERISTICS. Particle size, hardness, and degree of cementation are three physical characteristics which influence weathering. In rocks, large crystals of different minerals encourage disintegration. This is due to the fact that there is some variation in the amount of expansion and contraction which take place with each mineral as temperatures change. The resulting stress helps to develop cracks and to break these rocks into their mineral components. Finer grained materials are apparently more resistant to mechanical breakdown.

Particle size also influences the chemical breakdown of minerals. In general, a given mineral is more susceptible to decomposition when present in fine particles than when in larger grains. The much larger surface area of finely divided material presents greater opportunity for chemical attack. Apparently, this greater ease of weathering of small particles is more pronounced with some minerals than with others. For example, quartz particles of sand-size are extremely resistant to chemical weathering. In contrast, clay-size quartz, although not subject to ready decomposition, is not as resistant as many of the other minerals of that size.

Hardness and cementation apparently influence weathering primarily by their effect on the rate of disintegration into particles small enough for decomposition. Thus, a dense quartzite or a sandstone cemented firmly by a slowly weathered mineral will resist mechanical breakdown and will present a small amount of total surface are for chemical activity.

Porous rocks such as volcanic ash or coarse limestones, on the other hand, are readily broken down into smaller particles. These have in total a larger surface area for chemical attack and are obviously more easily decomposed.

CHEMICAL AND STRUCTURAL CHARACTERISTICS. For minerals of a given particle size, chemical and crystalline characteristics determine the ease of decomposition. Minerals such as gypsum ($CaSO_4 \cdot 2H_2O$) which are sparingly soluble in water are quickly removed if there is adequate rainfall. Water charged with carbonic acid likewise dissolves less soluble minerals such as calcite and dolomite. (See p. 273.) Consequently, these minerals are seldom found in the surface of the regolith in areas with even moderate rainfall.

The dark-colored primary minerals, sometimes called ferromagnesian because of their iron and magnesium contents, are more susceptible to chemical weathering than are the feldspars and quartz. The presence of iron (and perhaps less tightness of crystal packing) helps account for the more rapid breakdown of the ferromagnesian minerals. The ease with which iron-containing minerals become "stained" with oxides of this element is well known. Iron is quite subject to oxidation and hydration. As it is pulled from the crystal lattice of the primary minerals, a breakdown, both chemical and physical occurs. Obviously, the presence of this element denotes a notable weakness in the stability of a mineral.

Tightness of packing of the ions in the crystal units of minerals is thought to influence their weathering rates.[4] For example, olivine and biotite which are relatively easily weathered have crystal units that are less tightly packed than zircon and muscovite, comparable minerals which are quite resistant to weathering.

Climatic and biotic conditions will likely determine the relative stability of the various soil forming minerals. Consequently, one cannot present a listing of minerals based on their resistance to weathering under all climatic conditions. However, studies of minerals remaining in the soil and the regolith under various environmental conditions have led to the following general order of weathering resistance of the sand- and silt-size particles of some common minerals; quartz (most resistant) >muscovite, K-feldspars > Na- and Ca-feldspars > biotite, hornblende and augite > olivine > dolomite and calcite > gypsum,[5] It is expected that this order would be changed slightly depending on the climatic and other environmental conditions. This listing accounts for the absence

[4] See a chapter on "Soil Development" by I. Barshad, in F. E. Bear, *Chemistry of the Soil* (New York: Reinhold, 1955), pp. 1–52.
[5] Clay-size particles include a large number of secondary minerals in addition to some of those listed here. Their resistance to weathering is given by Jackson and Sherman, *op. cit.*, p. 235.

of gypsum, calcite, and dolomite in soils of humid regions and for the predominance of quartz in the coarser fraction of most soils.

11:6. WEATHERING IN ACTION — GENESIS OF PARENT MATERIALS

A general understanding of the influences of the separate forces of weathering makes it possible to picture in a simple way the development of parent material from bedrock. A physical weakening, due usually to temperature changes, initiates the process, but it is accompanied and supplemented by certain chemical transformations. Such minerals as the feldspars, mica, hornblende, and the like, suffer hydrolysis and hydration, while part of the combined iron is oxidized and hydrated. The minerals soften, lose their lustre, and become more porous. If hematite or limonite is formed, the decomposing mass becomes definitely red or yellow. Otherwise, the colors are subdued.

Coincident with these changes, such active cations as calcium, magnesium, sodium, and potassium suffer carbonation and solution. Then, as the water present drains away, these constituents are removed, leaving a residue more or less bereft of its easily soluble bases. As the process goes on, all but the most resistant of the original minerals disappear, and their places are occupied by: (1) secondary hydrated silicates that tend to recrystallize into highly colloidal clay; and (2) more resistant products such as Fe and Al oxides. (See Fig. 11:2.)

Such a brief statement of rock weathering demands certain supplementary explanations. In the first place, it must be recognized that the intensity of the various agencies will fluctuate with climate. Under arid conditions, the physical forces will tend to dominate, and the resultant soil material will contain the less weathered minerals. Temperature changes, wind action, and water erosion will be accompanied by a minimum of chemical action.

In a humid region, however, the forces are more varied, and practically the full quota will be energetically at work. Vigorous chemical changes will accompany disintegration, and the result will be shown in the greater fineness of the product. Clayey materials will be more evident, and a higher colloidality can be expected. Moreover, the process is more likely to be hastened and intensified by decaying organic matter.

It must be remembered that the forces of weathering lose their intensity as one goes downward from the surface. Both the physical and chemical transformations are in general somewhat different. The lack of organic matter is a factor as well as the decrease in the porosity and

aeration of the under layers. This differentiation with depth is the fore-
runner of a profile development if and when soil genesis takes place.

11:7. GEOLOGIC CLASSIFICATION OF PARENT MATERIALS

In discussing weathering, it was tacitly assumed that parent
material could originate in a number of different ways. In addition, it
was suggested that this unconsolidated debris might lie in its original
position above bedrock for centuries or it might sooner or later be moved
to new positions by the mechanical forces of nature.

On this basis, two groups of inorganic parent materials, designated as

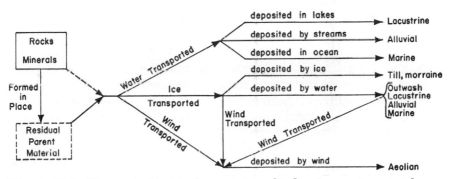

*Figure 11:3. Diagram showing how various kinds of parent material are
formed, transported, and deposited.*

sedentary and *transported,* are usually recognized. The latter may be
subdivided according to the agencies of transportation and deposition as
follows: (See also Fig. 11:3.)

1. Sedentary. Still at original site .... Residual

2. Transported.
   Gravity .... Colluvial
   Water .... Alluvial / Marine / Lacustrine
   Ice .... Glacial
   Wind .... Aeolian

While these terms relate only to the placement of the parent materials,
it has become customary to use them loosely in referring to the soils that

have been developed by the weathering of these deposits. Hence, much is heard of *glacial* soils, *alluvial* soils, *residual* soils, and the like. Such a grouping is very general, however, as a wide diversity is sure to occur within each soil group so recognized. This renders the terms of little specific significance.

11:8. RESIDUAL PARENT MATERIAL

This type of regolith develops in place from the country rock below and has suffered little transportation. If typically developed, it has usually suffered long and often intense weathering. In a warm, humid climate, it is likely to be thoroughly oxidized and well leached. Even though it may come from rocks such as limestone, it is often comparitively low in calcium due to the ready loss of this constituent. Red and yellow colors are characteristic when weathering has been intense, as may be demonstrated by a trip through the Piedmont Plateau of the eastern United States. In cooler, and especially in drier climates, residual weathering is much less drastic, and the oxidation and hydration of the iron may be hardly noticeable. Also, the lime content is higher and the colors of the debris subdued. Tremendous areas of this type of debris are found on the Great Plains and in other regions of western United States.

Residual materials are of wide distribution on all of the continents. In the United States, a glance at the physiographic map (Fig. 11:4) shows six great eastern and central provinces—the Piedmont Plateau, Appalachian Mountains and plateaus, the limestone valleys and ridges the limestone and sandstone uplands, and the Great Plains region. The first three groups alone encompass about 10 per cent of the area of the United States. In addition, great expanses of these sedentary accumulations are found west of the Rocky Mountains.

As might be expected, a great variety of soils occupy these regions covered by residual debris, since climate and vegetation, two of the determining factors in soil characterization, vary so radically over this great area. It has already been emphasized that the profile of a mature soil is largely a reflection of climate and its accompanying vegetation.

11:9. COLLUVIAL DEBRIS

Colluvial debris is made up of the fragments of rock detached from the heights above and carried down the slopes mostly by gravity. Frost action has much to do with the development of such deposits.

Figure 11:4. Generalized physiographic and regolith map of the United States. The regions located are as follows:

1. New England, mostly glaciated crystalline rocks.

2. Adirondacks, glaciated crystalline and sedimentary rocks.

3. Appalachian Mountains and Plateaus, shales and sandstones.

4. Limestone Valleys and Ridges, mostly limestone.

5. Blue Ridge Mountains, sandstones and shales.

6. Piedmont Plateau, crystalline rocks.

7. Atlantic Gulf and Coastal Plain, sands, clays, and limestones.

8. Mississippi Flood Plain and Delta, alluvium.

9. Limestone Uplands, mostly limestone and shale.

10. Sandstone Uplands, mostly sandstone and shale.

11. Central Lowlands, mostly glaciated sedimentary rocks of many kinds. Great areas are overlaid with loess, a wind deposit of great agricultural importance (see Fig. 11:11).

12. Superior Uplands, glaciated crystalline and sedimentary.

13. Great Plains Region, sedimentary rocks of many kinds.

14. Rocky Mountain Region, mountains, uplands, and valleys.

15. Northwest Intermountain, mostly igneous crystalline rock. Great areas in Columbia and Snake Rivers basins are covered by loess (see Fig. 11:8.)

16. Great Basin, gravels, sands, alluvial fans from various rocks.

17. Southwest Arid Region, gravel, sand and other debris of desert and mountain.

18. Sierra Nevada and Cascade Mountains, mountains, uplands, and valleys.

19. Pacific Coast Province, mountains and valleys, mostly sedimentary rocks.

20. Puget Sound Lowlands, glaciated sedimentary.

21. California central valley, alluvium and outwash.

Talus slopes, cliff detritus, and similar heterogeneous materials are good examples. Avalanches are made up largely of such accumulations.

Parent material developed from colluvial accumulation is usually coarse and stony, as physical rather than chemical weathering has been dominant. At the base of slopes in regions of medium to fine textured material such as loess some superior soils develop. In general, however, colluvial materials are not of great importance in the production of agricultural soils because of their small area, their inaccessibility, and their unfavorable physical and chemical characteristics.

11:10. ALLUVIAL STREAM DEPOSITS

There are three general classes of alluvial deposits: (1) flood plains, (2) alluvial fans, and (3) deltas. They will be considered in order.

FLOOD PLAINS. A stream on a gently inclined bed usually begins to swing from side to side in variable curves, depositing alluvial material on the inside of the curves and cutting on the opposite banks.

Figure 11:5. The flood plain and delta of the lower Mississippi River. This is the largest continuous area of alluvial soil in the United States.

This results in so-called *oxbows* and *lagoons*, which are ideal for the further deposition of alluvial matter and development of swamps. This state of meander naturally increases the probability of overflow at high water, a time when the stream is carrying much suspended matter. Part of this sediment is deposited over the flooded areas; the coarser near the channel, building up natural levees; the finer farther away in the lagoons and slack water. Thus, there are two distinct types of first-bottom deposits—*meander* and *flood*. As might be expected, flood-plain deposits are variable, ranging texturally from gravel and sands to silt and clay.

Due to a change in grade, a stream may cut down through its already well-formed alluvial deposits, leaving *terraces* on one or both sides. Often two, or even three, terraces of different heights may be detected along some valleys, marking a time when the stream was at these elevations.

Flood-plain deposits are found to a certain extent beside every stream, the greatest development in the United States occurring along the Mississippi. (See Fig. 11:5.) This area varies from 20 to 75 miles in width and from Cairo, Illinois, to the Gulf is over 500 miles long. The soils derived from such sediments usually are very rich, but if they are first bottoms, they may require drainage and protection from overflow.

ALLUVIAL FANS. Where streams descend from uplands, a sudden change in gradient sometimes occurs as the stream emerges at the lower level. A deposition of sediment is thereby forced, giving rise to *alluvial fans*. They differ from deltas in their location and in the character of their debris. Fan material often is gravelly and stony, more or less porous and, in general, well drained.

Alluvial-fan debris is found over wide areas in arid and semiarid regions. The soils therefrom, when irrigated and properly handled, often prove very productive. In humid regions, especially in certain glaciated sections, such deposits also occur in large enough areas to be of considerable agricultural importance.

DELTA DEPOSITS. Much of the finer sediment carried by streams is not deposited in the flood plain, but is discharged into the body of water to which the stream is tributary. Unless there is sufficient current and wave action, some of the suspended material accumulates, forming a delta. Such delta deposits are by no means universal, being found at the mouths of only a small proportion of the rivers of the world. A delta often is a continuation of a flood plain, its front so to speak, and is not only clayey in nature but is likely to be swampy as well. The deltas of the Nile and Po are good examples of this set of conditions.

Delta sediments, where they occur in any considerable acreage and are subject to flood control and drainage, become rather important agriculturally. The combination deltas and flood plains of the Mississippi,

Ganges, Po, Tigris, and Euphrates rivers are striking examples. Egypt, for centuries the granary of Rome, bespeaks the fertility and productivity of soils originating from such parent material.

11:11. MARINE SEDIMENTS

Much of the sediment carried away by stream action is eventually deposited in the oceans, seas, and gulfs, the coarser fragments near the shore, the finer particles at a distance. Also, considerable debris is wrenched from the shore line by the pounding of the waves and the undertow of the tides. If there have been changes in shore line, the alternation of beds will show no regular sequence and considerable variation in topography, depth, and texture. These deposits have been extensively raised above sea level along the Atlantic and Gulf coasts of the United States and elsewhere, and have given origin to large areas of valuable soils. (See Fig. 11:6.)

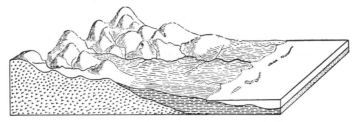

Figure 11:6. Block diagram showing the location of marine sediments and their relation to the uplands. The emerged coastal plain has already suffered some dissection from stream action.

Marine deposits have been worn and weathered by a number of agencies. First, the weathering and erosion necessary to throw them into stream-suspension were sustained. These were followed by the sorting and solvent action of the stream itself. Next, the sediment was swept into the ocean to be deposited and stratified, possibly after being pounded and eroded by the waves for years. At last came the emergence above the sea and the final action of the forces of weathering. The latter effects are of great moment, since they determine the topography and, to a considerable extent, the chemical and physical nature of the resultant parent material.

The marine sediments of the United States, although they have been subjected to weathering a shorter time than some of the residual debris, are generally more worn and usually carry less of the mineral nutrient elements. Their silica content is high, and they are often sandy, especially along the Atlantic seaboard. But in the Atlantic and Gulf coastal flat-woods and the interior pine lands of Alabama and Mississippi, clayey deposits are not uncommon. It is interesting to note that these marine clays may be dominated by kaolinite, illite, or montmorillonite.

In the continental United States, the marine deposits of the Atlantic and Gulf coastal provinces (see Fig. 11:4) occupy approximately 11 per cent of the country and are very diversified due to source of ma-terial, age, and the climatic conditions under which they now exist. Severe leaching as well as serious erosion occurs in times of heavy rain-fall. In spite of this, however, their soils support a great variety of crops when adequately supplied with organic matter, properly cultivated and carefully fertilized.

11:12. THE PLEISTOCENE ICE AGE

During the Pleistocene,[6] northern North America, as well as northern and central Europe and parts of northern Asia, were invaded by a succession of great ice sheets. Certain parts of South America as well as areas in New Zealand and Australia were similarly affected. And Antarctica undoubtedly was capped with ice much as it is today.[7]

In North America, the major centers of ice accumulation were in cen-tral Labrador and the western Hudson Bay region, with a minor con-centration in the Canadian Rockies. From the major centers, great continental glaciers pushed outward in all directions, but especially southward, covering, from time to time, most of what is now Canada and the northern part of the United States. The southernmost extension was down the Mississippi Valley, since here, due to the lower and smoother topography, the least resistance was met. (See Fig. 11:7.)

Central North America and Europe apparently sustained at least four[8] distinct ice invasions, separated, in each case, by long interglacial periods. So long, in fact, were these ice-free intervals that they are estimated to have covered in total a period considerably longer than the

---

[6] For supplementary reading as to the Great Ice Age and its influence, see: R. F. Flint, *Glacial Geology and the Pleistocene Epoch* (New York: Wiley, 1947).

[7] It is estimated that the Pleistocene ice at its maximum extension covered perhaps 20 per cent of the land area of the world. In this connection, it is surprising to learn that present-day glaciers, which we consider as mere remnants of the Great Ice Age, occupy almost half as much land surface. The respective amounts of ice, however, are not in the same proportion, since our living glaciers are comparatively thin and are definitely on the wane.

[8] The ice invasions of the central United States are recognized as four in number: Nebraskan, Kansan, Illinoian, and Wisconsin. The glacial debris of the eastern United States and Canada is practically all of Wisconsin age.

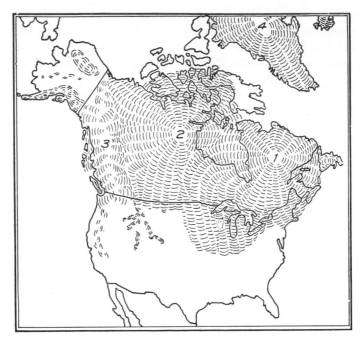

*Figure 11:7. Sketch map of North America showing the maximum develop-
ment of the continental glaciation. The three centers of ice accumulation are
numbered. Apparently eastern and central United States were invaded from
the Labradorian (1) and Hudson Bay (2) centers. Note the marked south-
ernly advance of the ice in the Mississippi Valley where topography offered
little resistance. To the eastward the Appalachian highlands more or less
blocked the ice invasion.*

time that it actually blanketed the country.[9] Some of the interglacial intervals evidently were times of warm or even semitropical climate in
regions that are now definitely temperate.

As the glacial ice was pushed forward, it conformed itself to the un-
evenness of the areas invaded. It rose over hills and often over mountains with surprising ease. Not only was the existing regolith with its

---

[9] The total length of the Pleistocene ice age is estimated at 700,000 to 1,000,000
years. According to recent studies using radioactive carbon (C^{14}), the glacial ice
disappeared from northern Iowa and central New York possibly only about 12,000
years ago. We may be now enjoying the mildness of another interglacial period.

Of the major interglacial periods, the first (Aftonian) persisted perhaps 200,000
years, the second (Yarmouth) may have lasted for 300,000 years, while the third
(Sangamon), which preceded the Wisconsin ice advance, possibly endured for 125,-
000 years. Assuming the Pleistocene age to have continued for not more than 1,000,-
000 years, it is obvious that glacial ice occupied what is now the north-central and
northeastern United States less than half of the period designated as the Great Ice
Age.

mantle of soil swept away, but also hills were rounded, valleys filled, and, in some cases, the underlying rocks were severely ground and gouged. Thus, the glacier became filled with rock wreckage, carrying much on its surface and pushing great masses ahead. Finally, when the ice melted away and the region again was free, a mantle of glacial drift remained—a new regolith and fresh parent material for soil formation.

The area covered by glaciers in North America is estimated as 4,000,-000 square miles, while perhaps 20 per cent of the United States is either directly or indirectly influenced by the deposits. An examination of the maps of Figs. 11:7 and 11:8 will make clear the magnitude of the ice invasion at maximum glaciation in this country.

11:13. GLACIAL TILL AND ASSOCIATED DEPOSITS

The materials deposited directly by the ice are commonly spoken of as glacial till. Till is a mixture of rock debris of great diversity, especially as to size of particles. Boulder clay, which is so common in glaciated regions, is typical of the physical heterogeneity to be expected.

Glacial till is found mostly as irregular deposits called *moraines* of which there are various kinds. *Terminal* moraines, for instance, mark the southernmost extension of the various glacial lobes when the ice margin was stationary long enough to permit an accumulation of debris.[10] (See Fig. 11:9.) Many other moraines of a *recessional* nature are found to the northward, marking points where the ice front became stationary for a time as it receded by melting. While moraines of this type are generally outstanding topographic features, they give rise to soils that are rather unimportant due to their small area and unfavorable physiography.

The *ground moraine*, a thinner and more level deposition laid down as the ice front retreated rather rapidly, is of much more importance. It has the widest extent of all glacial deposits and usually possesses a rather favorable agricultural topography. Associated with the moraine in certain places are such special features as *kames, eskers,* and *drumlins.*

An outstanding feature of glacial till materials discussed above is their variability. This is due to the diverse ways by which the debris was laid down, to differences in the chemical composition of the original materials, and to fluctuations in the grinding action of the ice. As might be expected, the soils derived from such soil material are most heterogeneous.

---

[10] The position of the front of a glacier is determined by the relationship between the forward movement of the ice and rate of melting. When the former is dominant, the ice front advances. When melting is dominant, the ice front recedes. When these two forces are balanced, conditions are favorable for a stand of the ice and the building of a moraine.

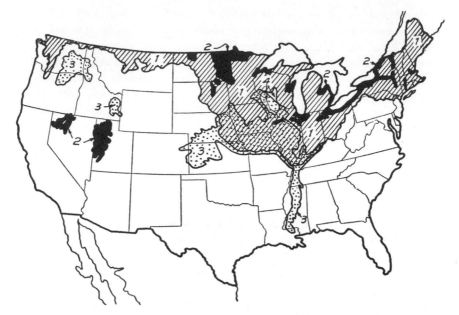

Figure 11:8. Areas in the United States covered by the continental ice sheet and the deposits either directly from, or associated with, the glacial ice. 1, till deposits of various kinds; 2, glacial-lacustrine deposits; 3, the loessial blanket—note that the loess overlies great areas of till in the Middle West; 4, an area, mostly in Wisconsin, that escaped glaciation. It is partially loess covered.

Such variations serve to indicate that the term "glacial soil" is of value only in suggesting the mode, in general, of deposition of the parent materials. It indicates practically nothing as to the characteristics of a soil so designated.

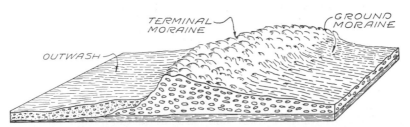

Figure 11:9. Diagram showing the relationships between a terminal moraine, its outwash, and its associated ground moraine. Note the differences in topography and in the general nature of the three deposits. The ground moraine is the most widely distributed.

11:14. GLACIAL OUTWASH AND LACUSTRINE SEDIMENTS

Great torrents of water were constantly gushing, especially during the summer, from the great Pleistocene ice sheet. The great loads of sediment carried by such streams were in part either dumped down immediately or carried to other areas for deposition. So long as the water had ready egress, it flowed rapidly away to deposit its load as outwash of various kinds.

OUTWASH PLAINS. A type of deposit of great importance is the *outwash* plain, formed by streams heavily laden with glacial sediment. (See Fig. 11:9.) This sediment is usually assorted and therefore variable in texture. Such deposits are particularly important in valleys and on plains where the glacial waters were able to flow away freely. Such valley fills are common in the United States, both north and south of the terminal moraine.

GLACIAL LAKE DEPOSITS. In many cases, however, the ice front came to a standstill where there was no such ready escape, for the water, and ponding due to the damming action of the ice occurred. (See Fig. 11:10.) Often, very large lakes were formed which existed for many years. Particularly prominent were those south of the Great Lakes in New York, Ohio, Indiana, Michigan, and in the Red River Valley. (See Fig. 11:8.) The latter lake, called Glacial Lake Agassiz, was perhaps 750 miles long and 250 miles wide at its maximum extension. The others, while individually much smaller, covered in total great stretches of country. Large lakes also occurred in the intermountain regions west of the Rockies as well as in the Connecticut Valley in New England and elsewhere.

Figure 11:10. When conditions of topography were favorable, the Wisconsin ice sheet acted as a great waning dam. The diagram shows a stage in the development of glacial lakes in Chicago (C) and Warren (W). (After Daly.)

With the glacial ice melting rapidly in the hills and higher valleys, these lakes were constantly fed by torrents from above which were laden with sediment derived not only directly from the ice but also from the unconsolidated till sheet over which they flowed. As a consequence, great deposits were made in these glacial lakes, ranging from coarse delta materials near the shore to fine silts and clay in the deeper and stiller waters. Such materials now cover large areas both in the United States and Canada, and their weathering has given rise to what are loosely designated as *glacial lake* soils.

The soils developed from these lake sediments are most heterogeneous. Weathering, due to climatic differences, has been variable, and profile contrasts are great. Extending westward from New England along the Great Lakes until the broad expanse of the Red River Valley is reached, these deposits have produced some of the most important soils of the Northern states. They also occur in the intermountain regions of the United States where they have given rise to agriculturally important soils especially when irrigated.

11:15. GLACIAL-AEOLIAN DEPOSITS

During the glaciation, much fine material was carried miles below the front of the ice sheets by streams that found their source within the glaciers. This sediment was deposited over wide areas by the overloaded rivers. The accumulations occurred below the ice front at all points, but in the United States seem to have reached their greatest development in what is now the Mississippi and Missouri valleys. Some of the debris found on the Great Plains probably had a similar origin, coming from glaciers debouching from the Rockies. All this, added to the great stretches of unconsolidated till in the glaciated regions and the residual material unclothed with vegetation on the Great Plains, presented unusually favorable conditions for wind erosion in dry weather.

ORIGIN AND LOCATION OF LOESS. It is generally agreed by glaciologists that a period of aridity, at least as far as the Great Plains and contiguous eastward areas were concerned, accompanied or immediately followed the retreat of the last ice sheet. The low rainfall of this period was accompanied by strong westerly winds which picked up and distributed fine material over wide areas on the Great Plains and particularly in the Mississippi, Ohio, and Missouri valleys. These deposits cover the original soils and parent materials, both residual and glacial in origin.

This wind-blown material, called *loess*,[11] is found over wide areas in

[11] Aeolian deposits, other than loess, occur, such as volcanic ash and sand dunes. Soils from volcanic ash occur in Montana, Idaho, Nebraska and Kansas. They are light and porous and not always of great agricultural value.

Sand dunes are of little value under any condition and become a menace to agriculture if they are moving. Examples of such deposits are found in the great Sahara and Arabian deserts. Smaller areas occur in this country in, for example, Nebraska, Colorado and New Mexico and along the Eastern Seaboard.

the United States, in most cases masking the unconsolidated materials
below. It covers eastern Nebraska and Kansas, southern and central Iowa
and Illinois, northern Missouri, and parts of southern Ohio and Indiana,
besides a wide band extending southward along the eastern border of the
Mississippi River. (See Figs. 11:8 and 11:11.) Extensive loessial deposits
also occur in the Palouse region in Washington and Idaho and other
areas of northwestern United States. In places, notably along the Missouri and Mississippi rivers, its accumulation has given rise to great bluffs
which bestow a characteristic topography to the region. Farther from the
rivers, the deposits, an upland type, are shallower and smoother in topography.

Figure 11:11. *Approximate distribution of loess in central United States. The
soil that has developed therefrom is generally a silt loam, often somewhat
sandy. Note especially the extension down the eastern side of the Mississippi
River and the irregularities of its northern extensions. Smaller areas of loess
occur in Washington, Oregon, and Idaho. (See Fig. 11:8.)*

NATURE OF LOESS. Loess is usually silty in character
and has a yellowish-buff color, unless it is very markedly weathered or
carries a large amount of humus. The larger particles are usually un-
weathered and angular. Quartz seems to predominate, but large quantities of feldspar, mica, hornblende, augite, and the like are found. The
vertical walls and escarpments formed when this deposit is deeply eroded
are one of its most striking physical characteristics.

In spite of the physical and chemical homogeneity of the loess as originally deposited, it has given rise in the central United States and elsewhere to soils of considerably diversity because of the climatic differences now existent in the various parts of the loessial area. A comparison of the loessial area of the Middle West (Fig. 11:11) with the map of the Great Soil Groups (Fig. 12:8) will show the presence of loess in six district soil regions. This situation, while indicating the probability of great differences in the fertility and productivity of loess soils, especially emphasizes the influence of climate as the final determinate of soil characteristics.

11:16. THE AGRICULTURAL SIGNIFICANCE OF THE GLACIATION

The Pleistocene glaciation, in most cases, has been a decided benefit, especially agriculturally. The leveling and filling actions, when drift was abundant, have given a smoother topography more suited to farming operations. The same can be said for the glacial lake sediments and loess deposits. Also, the parent materials thus supplied are geologically fresh, and the soils derived therefrom usually are, in general, not drastically leached. While it is difficult to show any consistent difference in total nutrients between the old residual and the younger glacial soils, it is generally admitted that glaciation has been a benefit to agriculture. Young soils generally are higher in available nutrients, and under comparable conditions they are superior in crop-producing power.

Chapter 12

Soil Formation,
Classification and Survey

To study satisfactorily any heterogeneous group in nature some sort of classification is necessary. This is especially true of soils. The value of experimental work of any kind is seriously restricted and may even be misleading unless the relation of one soil to another is known. The crop requirements in any region depend to a marked degree on the soils in question and on their profile similarities and differences.

In arriving at such an understanding three phases must be considered: (1) soil genesis or the evolution of a soil from its parent material; (2) soil classification, in this case especially as it applies to the United States; and (3) soil survey, its interpretation and utilization.

12:1. WEATHERING AND SOIL FORMATION

As shown in the last chapter, mineral soils have originated from the unconsolidated materials (the *regolith*) that mask the country rock.

293

The weathering processes of disintegration and decomposition which have given rise to this regolith are, in general, destructive processes. Thus, rocks and minerals are destroyed or altered. And soluble nutrients are subject to loss by leaching. It seems incongruous that these same seemingly destructive processes can promote the genesis of natural bodies we call soils and yet this is the case.

There are no distinct stages in the development of soils. Even if stages are identified, they seem to overlap and blend together to give a continuum of genetic processes. We can only identify a few of the obvious happenings as we move from solid rock or recently deposited soil material to a well-developed soil profile.

PRIME ELEMENTS IN PROFILE DEVELOPMENT. The process of disintegration of solid rock makes possible a foothold for living organisms. Decomposing minerals release nutrients which nourish simple plant and animal forms. Alteration of primary minerals to silicate and other clays destroys one mineral while giving birth to another. These clays hold reserves of nutrients and water, permitting plants to gain a foothold. Residues from the plants return to the weathering mass and are altered to humus, which exceeds even clay in its nutrient and water holding capacity.

Thus, *silicate clays, humus,* and *living organisms* together with life-giving *water* become prime elements in determining soil character. They affect markedly the kind and extent of layering or horizon differentiation that occurs. A general description as to how soil layers form will illustrate this point.

ORGANISMS AND ORGANIC MATTER. As soon as plants gain a foothold in a weathering rock or in recently deposited soil material, the development of a soil profile has begun. Residues of plants and animals remain on and in the soil material. As these decay and are mixed with mineral matter by living organisms, the first evidence of layering occurs. The upper part of the soil mass becomes slightly darker in color than the deeper layers. And it assumes structural stability due to the presence of the organic matter. Thereby, the surface A horizon begins to appear in the young soil.

The presence of decaying organic matter accelerates soil layering in other ways. Acids released from organic decomposition enhance the breakdown of base-containing minerals yielding soluble nutrients and secondary minerals such as the silicate clays and the oxides of iron and aluminum. These products may simply enrich the upper layers in which they are formed, or they may be moved downward by percolating waters, eventually to accumulate as layers at some lower depth in the developing soil. This downward movement and accumulation again dictates layer or horizon formation. Upper horizons may be depleted of nutrients and of

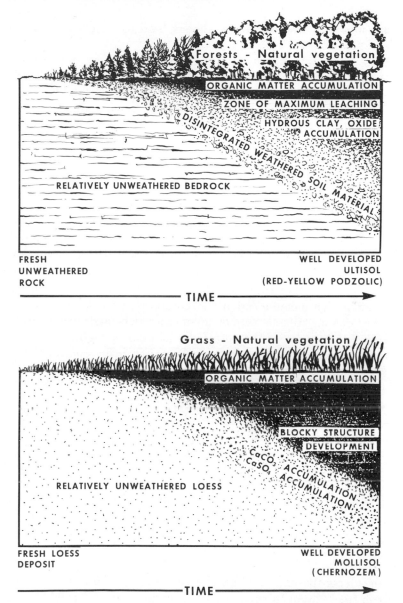

Figure 12:1. Diagrams show how two soil profiles may have developed from the weathering in place of solid rock (upper) and from the weathering of wind deposited loess (lower). Organic matter accumulation in the upper horizons occurs in time, the amount and distribution depending on the type of natural vegetation present. Clay and iron oxide accumulate and characteristic structures develop in the lower horizons. The end products differ markedly from the soil materials from which they form.

clay size minerals, whereas deeper layers tend to be enriched in these same constituents. (See Fig. 12:1.)

As these chemical and physical changes occur, living organisms continue to play a vital role. They physically manipulate, move and bind the soil particles and structural units, helping to provide stability of the horizons. At the same time, by burrowing or moving through the soil they help mix materials from adjacent horizons, thereby reversing the process of distinct horizon differentiation.

NUTRIENT RECYCLING. Living organisms team up with soil water to provide an important mechanism for stabilizing the acid-base ratio of the soil solution in given weathering situations. This is done by *recycling nutrients* through the soil. Soluble elements are absorbed by plants from the soil body, translocated to the upper plant parts, released again upon the death of the plant, and moved downward into the soil by percolating water ready to be recycled again. The nutrient content of the plant parts and the amount of rainfall thereby establish the ionic environment of the weathering soil. Plants high in mineral elements help to maintain a high metallic cation concentration in the soil solution. Low nutrient-containing plants cannot maintain such high concentrations, especially if they grow, as they often do, in areas of high rainfall and of high leaching potential. Nutrient recycling thus helps control the acid-base balance of the weathering solutions, and the ultimate horizons which develop.

WATER'S ROLE. Soil water is active from the very beginning in helping to enhance the development of soil layers. In the first place, its presence is essential for plant growth and for most of the chemical reactions whereby mineral breakdown occurs. Its movement in the regolith is of no less significance to soil development. This is shown by the nutrient recycling just described and by the downward movement of silicate clays, oxides of iron and aluminum, and salts of various kinds. In regions of low rainfall, upward movement and evaporation of water result in the accumulation of salts at the soil surface or at some point below the surface. Water is seen to be the principal transport within the soil body.

Water affects the nature of soil horizons in other important ways. If water can freely drain from the weathering area, aerobic conditions generally exist. The resulting soil is generally weathered to a considerable depth and contains oxidized minerals and nutrient elements. And root penetration is uninhibited by excess water.

Contrasting this situation is that found in wet areas. Oxidative weathering is minimized and undecomposed organic matter tends to accumulate at or near the mineral surface. Reduced conditions characterize the soil horizons which are exploited to only a limited extent by growing plants.

Horizon differentiation is indeed affected directly by presence of excess water.

ACQUIRED VS. INHERITED CHARACTERISTICS.
Each of these examples illustrates how, over a period of time, a natural layering begins to occur as weathering proceeds. This layering and the specific properties of the layers are new characteristics not formerly possessed by the parent material. These are *acquired*[1] characteristics in contrast to those *inherited* from the parent material. In the early stages of soil profile development, inherited soil properties dominate but as the soil develops, acquired characteristics become more prominent and eventually may become dominate.

SOIL MATURITY. The sequence of events leading to profile development leads one to a concept of soil maturity. Thus, soils with only the beginnings of horizon development are said to be *young* soils. In contrast, those with more fully expressed horizons eventually reach the stage where they seem to be in dynamic equilibrium with their environments. They are then thought to be *mature*.

Care must be taken to differentiate between *soil maturity* and *period of time of soil weathering*. Two soils may have been subjected to weathering forces for the same period of time but may differ markedly in their degree of maturity. For example, let us assume that acid leaching is a requisite for the development of a given kind of soil. The presence of either $CaCO_3$ or heavy clay would delay such development; coarse textured soil material from sandstone would encourage it. Obviously, soil maturity and length of weathering period are often quite unrelated.

12:2. FACTORS INFLUENCING SOIL FORMATION

Studies of soils throughout the world have shown that five major factors largely control the kinds of soil that develop. These are:

1. *Climate* (particularly temperature and precipitation)
2. *Living organisms* (especially the native vegetation)

---

[1] The presence of quartz is perhaps the most common example of an *inherited* characteristic, although the presence of any mineral, such as feldspar or mica, carried over unchanged into a soil, is a good illustration. Color also is often inherited, as in the case of a red parent sandstone or shale. Even clay, if originally a part of the parent material, may be rated as inherited.

Examples of *acquired* characteristics are as easily cited. Those due to organic matter, to clay formed as the soil developed, and to products of weathering such as red and yellow iron oxides are common. Certainly profile layering and the development of various structural forms within the various horizons are due largely to environmental influences.

3. *Nature of parent material* $\begin{cases} \text{Texture and structure} \\ \text{Chemical and mineralogical composition} \end{cases}$

4. *Topography of area*
5. *Time* that parent materials are subjected to soil formation.

CLIMATE. From an over-all standpoint, climate is perhaps the most influential factor. It determines in no small degree the nature of the weathering that occurs. For example, temperature and precipitation exert profound influences on the rates of chemical and physical processes—the essential means by which profile development is effected. Consequently, if allowed ample opportunity, climatic influences eventually tend to dominate the soil formation picture.

Climatic influences are also expressed through or in combination with the other factors. Thus, much of the influence of climate is due to the measure of control which it exercises over natural vegetation. In humid regions, plentiful rainfall provides an environment favorable for the growth of trees. In contrast, grasslands are the dominant native vegetation in semiarid regions. Climate exerts part of its influence through a second soil forming factor, the living organisms.

LIVING ORGANISMS. The major role of living organisms in profile differentiation has already been discussed (p. 294). Organic matter accumulation, profile mixing, nutrient cycling, and structural stability are all made possible by the presence of organisms in the soil. Also, nitrogen is added to the soil system by microorganisms alone or in association with plants. And vegetative cover reduces natural erosion rates, thereby slowing down the rate of mineral surface removal. It is obvious that the nature and number of organisms growing in and on the soil will play a vital role in the kind of soil that develops.

PARENT MATERIAL. The nature of the parent material, even in humid regions, may still profoundly influence the characteristics of even fully mature soils. For example, the downward movement of water is controlled quite largely by the texture of the soil. Its chemical and mineralogical compositions often not only determine the effectiveness of the weathering forces, but in some instances partially control the natural vegetation. For example, the presence of limestone in a humid region soil will delay the development of acidity, a process which the climate encourages. In addition, the species of trees usually found on limestone materials are relatively high in metallic cations or bases. By continually bringing these bases to the surface, the vegetation is responsible for a further delay in the process of acidification, or in this particular case, the progress of soil maturity.

TOPOGRAPHY. The topography of the land may be such as to hasten or delay the work of climatic forces. Thus, in smooth flat country the rapidity with which excess water is removed is much less than if the landscape were rolling. The latter topography encourages some natural erosion of the surface layers, which, if extensive enough, may eliminate the possibility of a deep soil. On the other hand, if water stands for part or all of the year on a given area, the climatic influences become relatively ineffective in regulating soil development. Topography, therefore, is significant not only as a modifier of climatic effects, but often as a major control in local areas.

TIME. The actual length of time that materials have been subjected to weathering plays a significant role in soil formation. Perhaps the best evidence of the importance of time may be obtained by a comparison of the soils of a glaciated region with those in a comparable area that was untouched by the ice sheet. As a general rule, the influence of parent material is much more apparent in the soils of glaciated regions. This is due primarily to the fact that in many cases insufficient time has lapsed since the disappearance of the ice to permit the changes in the composition of the glacial deposit that are necessary for full maturity of soils.

12:3. THE SOIL PROFILE

The layering or horizon development described in the previous sections eventually gives rise to natural bodies called soils. Each soil is characterized by a given sequence of these horizons. This sequence is termed a *soil profile*. Let us now turn our attention to the major horizons making up soil profiles and the terminology used to describe them.

SOIL HORIZONS. For convenience in study and description, the layers resulting from soil forming processes are grouped under four heads: O, A, B, and C. (See Fig. 12:2.) The subdivisions of these are called *horizons*. The O group are organic horizons which form above the mineral soil. They result from litter derived from dead plants and animals. The A group (eluvial)[2] are mineral horizons which lie at or near the surface and are characterized as a zone of maximum leaching. Beginning at the surface of the mineral matter, the horizons are designated as A_1, A_2, etc. (See Fig. 12:2.)

The B group (illuvial)[3] comes next and includes the layers in which

[2] Eluvial from *ex* or *e* meaning out and *luv* meaning washed.
[3] Illuvial from *il* or *in* meaning in and *luv* meaning washed. Although the B horizon is often referred to as the *subsoil*, this terminology may be technically incorrect. In some eroded soils and in soils with shallow A layers, the B horizon makes up at least part of the surface or plow layer. Also, since the A horizon of certain soils is deep (24 inches or more), the subsoil may include a part of A in addition to B.

deposition from above, or even from below, has taken place. It is the region of maximum accumulation of materials such as iron and aluminum oxides and the silicate clays. These materials may have washed downward from the surface layers or they may have formed in the B horizon. In arid regions calcium carbonate, calcium sulfate, and other salts may accumulate in the lower B. Its horizons are labeled in order downward as B_1, B_2, etc. The A and B horizons together are called the *solum*, that is, the portion of the profile developed by soil building processes as distinguished from the parent material immediately below.

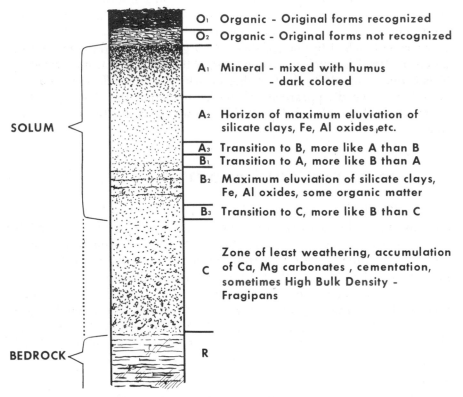

Figure 12:2. A theoretical mineral soil profile showing the major horizons which may be present. Any particular profile may exhibit only part of these illustrated. In addition, however, it may exhibit more detailed subhorizons than those indicated. The solum includes the A and B plus some fragipans and duripans of the C horizon.

Further details as follows:

$O_1 = $ *Organic horizon wherein the original forms of the plant and animal residues can be recognized by the naked eye.*

$O_2 = $ *Organic horizon in which the original plant and animal forms cannot be recognized by the naked eye. Organic horizons common in virgin forested areas, generally absent in grassland areas.*

A_1 = *Topmost mineral horizon, containing a strong admixture of humified organic matter which tends to import a darker color than that of lower horizons.*

A_2 = *Horizon of maximum eluviation of clay, iron, and aluminum oxides and organic matter. Loss of these constituents generally results in a concentration of quartz and other sand and silt size resistant minerals. Generally lighter in color than horizon above or below. Prominent in podzol soils.*

A_3 = *A transition layer between A and B with properties more nearly like those of the A, or A_2 above than the B below. Sometimes absent.*

B_1 = *A transition layer between A and B with properties more nearly like B than A. Sometimes absent.*

B_2 = *Zone of maximum accumulation of clays and iron and aluminum oxides. These may have moved down from upper horizons or may have formed in place. Organic matter content generally higher and color darker than that of the A_2 above. Maximum development of blocky or prismatic structure or both.*

B_3 = *Transition horizon between B and C with properties more like those of B_2 above than those of C below.*

C = *Horizon below the solum (A and B) relatively little affected by the solum-forming processes. It is outside the zone of major biological activity. If this horizon is similar to the material from which the A and B formed, it is designated as IC. If it is not the symbol IIC is used. It may contain accumulations of calcium and magnesium carbonates or even more soluble carbonates. It is sometimes characterized by cementation and the development of fragipans.*

R = *Underlying consolidated bedrock. It may or may not be like the parent rock from which the solum formed.*

The C horizon is the unconsolidated material underlying the solum. It may or may not be the same as the parent material from which the solum formed. It is noticeably less weathered than the solum and consequently as yet has not been subjected to major horizon differentiation. However, its upper layers will likely in time become a part of the solum as weathering and erosion continue. For further details of the profile see the notes accompanying Fig. 12:2.

HORIZONS IN A GIVEN PROFILE. It is at once evident that the profile of any one soil probably will not show all of the horizons that collectively are cited in Fig. 12:2. The profile may be immature or may be overly influenced by some local condition such as poor drainage, texture, or topography. Again some of the horizons are merely transitional and may at best be very indistinct. With so many factors involved in soil genesis, a slight change in their coordination may not encourage the development of some layers. As a result, we can be sure of finding in any well-drained and uneroded mature soil only certain horizons. They are: O_2, if the land is forested; A_1 or A_2 depending on circumstances; B_2; and C. (See Fig. 12:2.) Conditions of soil genesis will determine which others are present and their clarity of definition.

When a virgin soil is put under cultivation, the upper horizons become the furrow-slice. The cultivation, of course, destroys the original layered condition of this portion of the profile, and the furrow-slice becomes more or less homogeneous. In some soils the A horizons are of sufficient

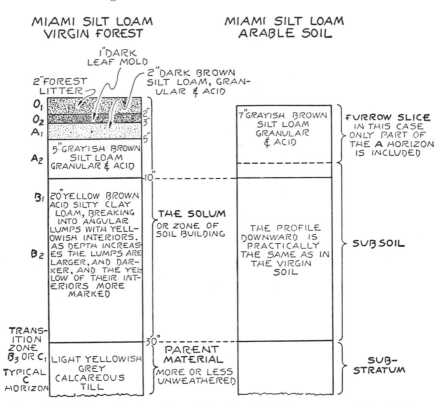

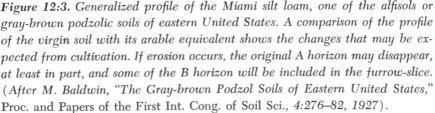

Figure 12:3. Generalized profile of the Miami silt loam, one of the alfisols or gray-brown podzolic soils of eastern United States. A comparison of the profile of the virgin soil with its arable equivalent shows the changes that may be expected from cultivation. If erosion occurs, the original A horizon may disappear, at least in part, and some of the B horizon will be included in the furrow-slice. (After M. Baldwin, "The Gray-brown Podzol Soils of Eastern United States," Proc. and Papers of the First Int. Cong. of Soil Sci., 4:276–82, 1927).

depth so that not all of the A is included in the furrow-slice (Fig. 12:3). In other cases where the A is quite thin, the plowline is just at the top of or even down in the B.

Many times, especially on cultivated land, serious erosion has occurred and as a result a *truncated* profile is encountered. As the surface soil was swept away, the plowline was gradually lowered in order to maintain a sufficiently thick furrow-slice. Hence the furrow, in many cases, is almost entirely within the B zone and the C horizon is correspondingly nearer the surface. Many farmers, especially in our Southern States, are today cultivating the subsoil without realizing the ravages of erosion. In profile study and description such a situation requires careful analysis.

12:4. THE CONCEPT OF INDIVIDUAL SOILS

Soils that have developed by the various processes discussed in this and the preceding chapter differ greatly from place to place. They vary in many profile characteristics, such as degree of horizon differentiation, depth, clay and organic matter contents, and wetness. These differences are noted, not only from continent to continent or region to region but from one part of a given field to another. In fact, notable differences sometimes occur within a matter of a few feet. Furthermore, the changes in soil properties occur gradually as one moves from one location to another.

To study intelligently the soil at different places in the earth's surface, and to communicate in an orderly manner information about it, man has developed systems of soil classification. These permit us to classify *the* soil into a large number of individual units or natural bodies which we call soils. We do this by taking two basic steps. First, we decide upon the kind and range of soil properties which are to characterize each soil unit. Second, we give each unit a name as for example, a Cecil clay, a Barnes loam, or a Miami silt loam. In this way, when a given soil unit is discussed by name its identity and characteristics are known by the soil scientist just as is the case for plants when botanists discuss them by their species names.

To develop a useful classification system and to establish the kinds and ranges of properties which are to characterize given soil units, the soil must be studied in the field. Even after tentative classes have been established they must be tested in the field to be certain of their utility in a classification scheme.

THE PEDON. It is obvious that we cannot study at one time the whole soil or even large areas of it. So we study small three-dimensional samples of the soil. Such a sampling unit is large enough so that the nature of its horizons can be studied and the range of its properties identified. It varies in size from about 1 to 10 square meters and is called a *pedon* (Gk. *pedon*, ground). It is the smallest volume that can be called "a soil."

Because of its very small size, a pedon obviously cannot be used as the basic unit for a workable field soil classification system. However, a group of pedons closely associated in the field and similar in their properties are of sufficient size to serve as a basic classification unit. Such a grouping approximates what in the United States has been called a *soil series*. More than 7,000 soil series have been characterized in this country. They are the basic units used in the field classification of the nation's soils.

We now have identified the two extremes in our concept of soils. One extreme is that of a natural body called *a* soil characterized by a three-dimensional sampling unit (pedon), related groups of which are termed a soil series. At the other extreme is *the* soil which is a collection of all these natural bodies and which is distinct from water, solid rock, and other natural parts of the earth's crust. These two extremes represent opposite ends of elaborate soil classification schemes which man has used to organize his knowledge of soils. We shall consider briefly two such schemes which have been or are being used in the United States.

12:5. SOIL CLASSIFICATION IN THE UNITED STATES

Soil classification in the United States is in a state of transition. The system generally in use between 1938 and 1960 was based to a marked extent on soil genesis—how soils formed or were thought to have formed. Although this system was useful in many ways, it had some weaknesses which prompted the development of a new comprehensive system based mostly on soil properties. The new system, still being developed and refined, is as yet incomplete. Even so it is now accepted in principle by most U.S. soil scientists and is receiving prominent recognition by many scientists throughout the world.

Since the literature dealing with soils contains references to both the old and new classification systems, each should be understood, at least in a general way by students of soil science. We shall consider first the newer classification scheme, because it will likely be most used as we look to the future. Then we shall refer to the older one, the terminology of which was used in most of the literature prior to the early 1960's.

12:6. SOIL CLASSIFICATION—NEW COMPREHENSIVE SYSTEM[4]

The classification system currently in use in the United States is that developed by the Soil Survey Staff of the U.S. Department of Agriculture. It is a relatively new system having been developed and evaluated through several stages or "approximations." The seventh approximation is now in use and is being further evaluated and tested.

The new system has many features to recommend it. However, there are two which students of soil science may find most useful. *First*, is the fact that the primary bases for identifying different classes in the system are the properties of soils as found in the field—properties which can be measured quantitatively. Furthermore, the measurements so obtained can be varified by others. This lessens the likelihood of controversy over the place of a given soil in the classification system. Such controversy is common when scientists deal with systems where genesis or presumed genesis is the basis for the classification.

The *second* significant feature of the new system is the nomenclature employed, especially for the broader classification categories. The names give a definite connotation of the major characteristics of the soils in question—a connotation easily understood in many languages since Latin or Greek root words are the bases for the names. Consideration will be given to the nomenclature used after brief reference is made to the major criteria for the system—soil properties.

BASES OF SOIL CLASSIFICATION. The new system is based on the properties of soils as they are found today. While one of the objectives of the system is to group soils similar in genesis, the specific criteria used to place soils in these groups are those of soil properties. The advantages of this system over that based primarily on soil genesis or presumed soil genesis are as follows:[5]

1. It permits classification of soils rather than soil-forming processes.
2. It focuses on the soil rather than related sciences such as geology and climatology.

[4] The publication used as a basis for much of this all-too-brief description of the new classification system is "Soil Classification—A Comprehensive System—7th Approximation," Soil Survey Staff, U.S. Department of Agriculture, August 1960. Also used was "Supplement to Soil Classification System (7th Approximation)," Soil Survey Staff, U.S. Department of Agriculture, March 1967.

[5] See G. D. Smith, "Objectives and Basic Assumptions of the New Soil Classification System," *Soil Science*, 96:6–16, 1963.

3. It permits the classification of soils of unknown genesis—only the knowledge of their soil properties is needed.
4. It permits greater uniformity of classification as applied by a large number of soil scientists. Differences in interpretation of how a soil was formed do not influence its classification under this scheme.

One should not gain the impression that the new comprehensive classification system ignores soil genesis. Since soil properties, the basis for the new system, are often related directly to soil genesis, one can hardly emphasize soil properties without at least indirectly emphasizing soil genesis as well.

It is not possible to generalize with respect to the kinds of soil properties used as criteria for soil classification. All of the chemical, physical and biological properties presented in this text are subject to use in this classification scheme. A few examples may be cited to illustrate the criteria that are used. The moisture, temperature, color, texture and structure of the soil are good examples. Chemical and mineral properties such as contents of organic matter, clay, and iron and aluminum oxides, and such as pH, percentage base saturation and the presence of salts may be cited. Soil depth is also an important criterion for classification.

Among the most significant of the properties used as a basis for classification is the presence or absence of certain soil horizons. Because of their prominence in helping to determine the place of a soil in the classification system, they will be given somewhat more detailed attention.

DIAGNOSTIC HORIZONS. To illustrate that soil properties are the primary criteria for classifying soils under the new system, brief mention will be made of certain *diagnostic* surface and subsurface horizons. The diagnostic surface horizons are called epipedons (Gr. *epi,* over; and *pedon,* soil). The epipedon includes the upper part of the soil darkened by organic matter, the upper eluvial horizons, or both. It may include part of the B horizon (see p. 299) if the latter is significantly darkened by organic matter. Six epipedons are recognized, but only four are of any importance in the soils of the United States.[6] The major features of these horizons are given in Table 12:1.

Many subsurface horizons characterize different soils in the system. Those that are considered diagnostic horizons are shown along with their major features in Table 12:1. In addition, there are a number of subsurface horizons in which materials have accumulated such as *gypsic* (gypsum), *calcic* (Ca, Mg carbonates), and *sodic* (soluble salts). Also, so-called pans (*duripans* and *fragipans*) are cemented layers which re-

───────

[6] The other two, called *Anthropic* and *Plaggen,* are the result of man's intensive use of soils. They are found in parts of Europe.

Table 12:1. The major features of diagnostic horizons used to differentiate at the higher levels of the comprehensive classification scheme.

Diagnostic Horizons	Major Feature
Surface Horizons (Epipedons)	
Mollic	Thick, dark colored, high base saturation, strong structure
Umbric	Same as Mollic except low base saturation
Ochric	Light colored, low organic content, may be hard and massive when dry
Histic	Very high in organic content, wet during some part of year
Subsurface Horizons	
Argillic	Silicate clay accumulation
Natric	Argillic, high in sodium, columnar or prismatic structure
Spodic	Organic matter, Fe and Al oxide accumulation
Cambic	Changed or altered by physical movement or by chemical reactions
Agric	Organic and clay accumulation just below plow layer
Oxic	Primarily mixture of Fe, Al oxides, and 1:1 type minerals

strict water movement and root penetration. Each of these layers can be used as a distinctive property to help place a soil in its proper class.

CATEGORIES OF THE SYSTEM. There are six categories of classification in the new system: (1) order (the broadest category); (2) suborder; (3) great group; (4) subgroup; (5) family; and (6) series (the most specific category). These categories may be compared with those used for the classification of plants. The comparison would be as shown on the next page using white clover (*trifolium repens*) and Miami silt loam as the examples of plants and soils, respectively.

Just as *Trifolium repens* identifies a specific kind of plant, the Miami silt loam identifies a specific kind of soil. The similarity is noted further as we move up the classification scale. Several soil types are grouped together in a single soil series, and a family is generally made up of groups of soil series just as the Leguminosae family of plants includes several genera in addition to the clovers. This same similarity between the soil and plant classification schemes can be followed to the highest categories—that of Phylum for plants and of Order for soils. With this general background, let us turn to a brief description of the six soil categories and to the nomenclature used in identifying them.

Plant Classification			Soil Classification
Phyllum—Pterophyta			Order—Alfisol
Class—Angiospermae			Suborder—Udalf
Subclass—Dicotyledoneae	Specificity	Increasing	Great Group—Hapludalf
Order—Rosales			Subgroup—Typic Hapludalf
Family—Leguminosae			Family—Fine loamy mixed mesic
Genus—*Trifolium*			Series—Miami
Species—*repens*			Type—Miami silt loam

The *order* category is based largely on morphology, but soil genesis is an underlying factor. A given order includes soils whose properties suggest that they are not too dissimilar in their genesis. As an example, soils developed under grassland vegetation have the same general sequence of horizons and are characterized by a thick dark, epipedon (surface horizon) high in bases. They are thought to have been formed by the same general genetic processes and are thereby mostly included in the same order, Mollisol.

Suborders are subdivisions of orders which emphasize genetic homogeneity. Thus, wetness, climatic environment, and vegetation are characteristics which help determine the suborder in which a given soil is found.

Diagnostic horizons (p. 306) are used to differentiate the *great groups* in a given suborder. Soils in a given great group are thought to have the same kind and arrangement of these horizons.

Subgroups are subdivisions of the great groups. The typical or central concept of a great group makes up one subgroup (Typic). Other subgroups may have characteristics that are intergrades between those of the central concept and those of another great group. (e.g., *Aquic Hapludult*).

The *family* category has not as yet been fully defined and awaits further testing. However, properties important to the growth of plants are used to differentiate families. This category permits the grouping of members of subgroups having in common similar characteristics such as texture, mineral content, pH, soil temperature and soil depth.

The *series* category is essentially the same as that which has been in use for years in the United States. It is defined as[7] "a collection of soil

[7] See "Soil Classification—A Comprehensive System—7th Approximation," Soil Survey Staff, U.S. Department of Agriculture, August, 1960.

individuals essentially uniform in differentiating characteristics and in arrangement of horizons." This category is given further attention later (see p. 323).

NOMENCLATURE. An important feature of the system is the nomenclature used to identify different soil classes. The names of the classification units are combinations of syllables, most of which are derived from the Latin or Greek, which are the root words in several modern languages. Since each part of a soil name conveys a concept of soil character or genesis, the name automatically describes the general kind of soil being classified. For example, soils of the order *Aridisol* (Latin *aridus*, dry and *solum*, soil) are characteristic of arid or dry places. Those of the order *Inceptisols* (L. *inceptum*, beginning and *solum*, soil) are soils with only the beginnings of profile development. Thus, the names of orders are combinations of (a) formative elements which generally define the characteristics of the soils and (b) the ending *sol*.

The names of suborders automatically identify the order of which they are a part. For example, soils of the suborder *Aquolls* are the wetter soils (L. *aqua*, water) of the Mollisol order. Likewise, the name of the great group identifies the suborder and order of which it is a part. *Argiaquolls* are Aquolls with clay or argillic (L. *argilla*, white clay) horizons.

The nomenclature as it relates to the different categories in the classification system might be illustrated as follows:

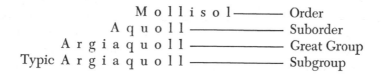

M o l l i s o l ——— Order
A q u o l l ——————— Suborder
A r g i a q u o l l ——————— Great Group
Typic A r g i a q u o l l ——————— Subgroup

Note that the three letters *oll* identify each of the lower categories as being in the Mollisol order. Likewise, the suborder name *aquoll* is included as part of the great group and subgroup name. If one were given only the subgroup name he would know automatically the great group, suborder and order to which the soil belonged.

Family names are still being developed and tested but in general they identify groups of soil series similar in texture and mineral composition and in soil temperature at 20 inch depths. Thus, the name *fine mixed mesic* applies to a family with a fine texture, mixed mineral content and mesic (8–15°C) soil temperature.

Soil series names have local significance since they normally identify the particular locale in which the soil is found. Thus, names such as Fort Collins, Cecil, Miami, Norfolk, and Ontario are used to identify the soil series. When the texture name of the surface horizon is added

Table 12:2. The Names of Soil Orders in the New Comprehensive Soil Classification System, Their Derivation, and Approximate Equivalents in the Old System.

| Name[b] | Formative -Element[a] | | Approximate Equivalents in the old system |
	Derivation	Pronunciation	
Entisol	Nonsense symbol	rec*ent*	Azonal, some Low-Humic Gley soils
Vertisol	L. *verto,* turn	in*vert*	Grumusols
Inceptisol	L. *inceptum,* beginning	in*cept*ion	Ando, Sol Brun Acide, some Brown Forest, Low-Humic Gley, and Humic Gley soils
Aridisol	L. *aridus,* dry	ar*id*	Desert, Reddish Desert, Sierozem, Solonchak, some Brown and Reddish Brown soils and associated Solonetz
Mollisol	L. *mollis,* soft	mo*lli*fy	Chestnut, Chernozem, Brunizem (Prairie), Rendzinas, some Brown, Brown Forest, and associated Solonetz, and Humic Gley soils
Spodosol	Gk. *Spodos,* wood ash	P*od*zol; odd	Podzols, Brown Podzolic soils, and Ground-water Podzols
Alfisol	Nonsense symbol	Ped*alf*er	Gray-Brown Podzolic. Gray Wooded, and Non-Calcic Brown soils, Degraded Chernozems, and associated Planosols and some Half-Bog soils
Ultisol	L. *ultimus,* last	*ult*imate	Red-Yellow Podzolic soils, Reddish-Brown Lateritic soils of the U.S., and associated Planosols and Half-Bog soils
Oxisol	F. *oxide,* oxide	*oxi*de	Laterite soils, Latosols
Histisol	Gk. *histos,* tissue	*histo*logy	Bog soils

[a] The italicized letters in the pronunciation column are used in the suborder and great group categories to identify the order to which they belong.
[b] Note that all orders end in sol (L. *solum,* soil).

to that of the series one has identified the soil type name. Fort Collins loam and Cecil clay are examples.

With this brief explanation of the nomenclature of the new system we now turn to a consideration of the order category of the system.

12:7. SOIL ORDERS

Ten orders are recognized. With the exception of one order (Entisols), which roughly corresponds to the azonal soils of the old system (see p. 343), the new orders show little resemblance to those formerly used. The names of these orders and their approximate equivalents in the old system are shown in Table 12:2. Note that all order names have a common ending *sol* from the Latin *solum* meaning soil.

ENTISOLS (RECENT SOILS). These are mineral soils without natural genetic horizons or with only the beginnings of such horizons. The central concept of this order are soils in deep regolith with no horizons except a plow layer. Included are the extremes of highly productive soils on recent alluvium, and infertile soils on barren sands. Shallow soils on bed rock are also included. The common characteristic of all entisols is lack of significant profile development.

Soils of this order are found under a wide variety of climatic conditions. For example, in the Rocky Mountain region and in southwest Texas, shallow, medium textured Entisols (Orthents) over hard rock are common. (Called lithosols in the old classification system). They are used mostly as range land. Sandy Entisols (Psamments) are found in Florida, Alabama and Georgia and typify the sand hill section of Nebraska. (See Fig. 12:4) Psamments are used mostly for grazing in the drier climates. They may be forested or used for cropland in humid areas. Some of the citrus, vegetable and peanut producing areas of the south are typified by Psamments (Regosols, old system).

Entisols are probably found under even more widely varied climatic conditions outside the United States. (See Fig. 12:5). Psamments are typical of the shifting sands of the Sahara Desert and Saudi Arabia. Large areas of Psamments dominate parts of southern Africa and of central and north central Australia. Entisols having medium to fine textures (Orthents) are found in northern Quebec and parts of Alaska, Siberia and Tibet. Orthents are typical of some mountain areas such as the Andes in South America and some of the uplands of an area extending from Turkey westward to Pakistan.

As might be expected, the agricultural productivity of the Entisols varies greatly depending on their location and properties. When ade-

PATTERNS OF SOIL ORDERS AND SUBORDERS OF THE UNITED STATES

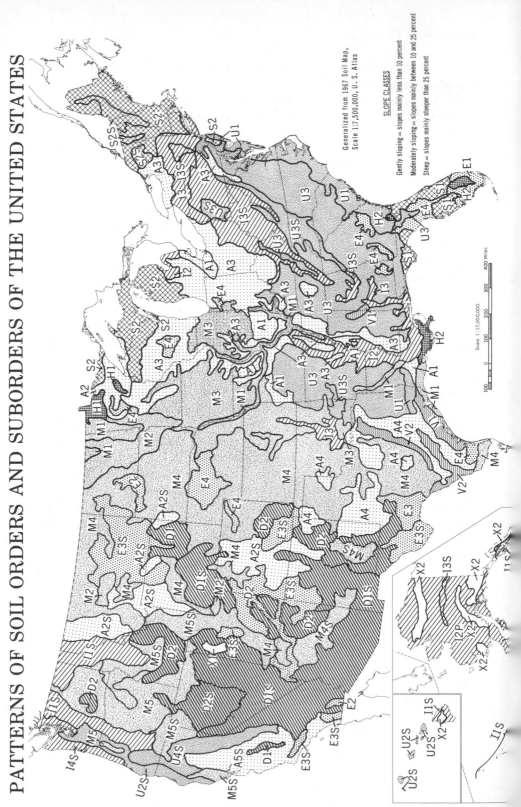

Generalized from 1967 Soil Map,
Scale 1:7,500,000, U. S. Atlas

SLOPE CLASSES

Gently sloping = slopes mainly less than 10 percent

Moderately sloping = slopes mainly between 10 and 25 percent

Steep = slopes mainly steeper than 25 percent

Scale 1:17,000,000

100   0   100   200   300   400 Miles

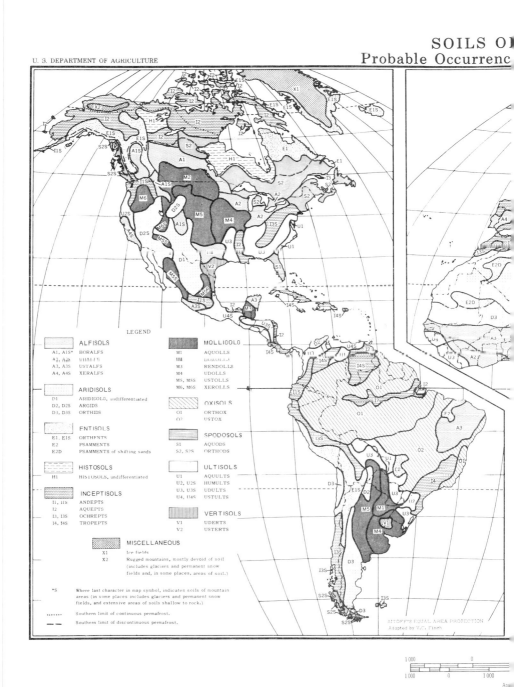

Figure 12:5. A generalized world soil map showing the probable occur comprehensive classification system. (Map courtesy Soil Survey Division

SOIL CONSERVATION SERVICE

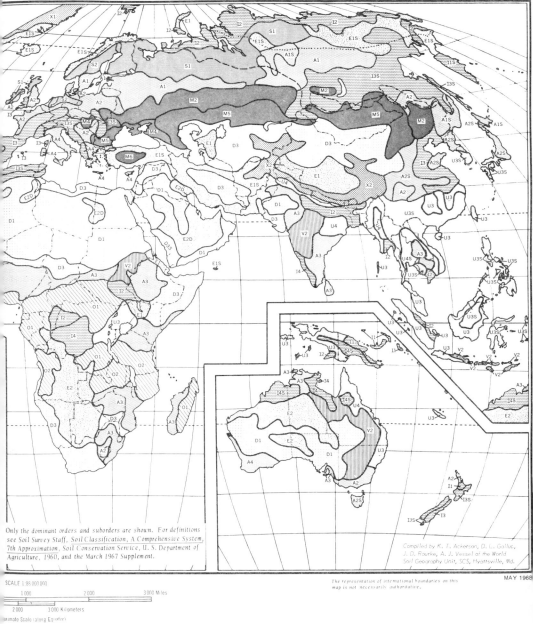

Only the dominant orders and suborders are shown. For definitions
see Soil Survey Staff, Soil Classification, A Comprehensive System,
7th Approximation, Soil Conservation Service, U. S. Department of
Agriculture, 1960, and the March 1967 Supplement.

Compiled by K. T. Ackerson, D. L. Gallut,
J. D. Rourke, A. J. Vessel of the World
Soil Geography Unit, SCS, Hyattsville, Md.

The representation of international boundaries on this
map is not necessarily authoritative.

MAY 1968

SCALE 1:88,000,000

1 000   2 000   3 000 Miles

2 000   3 000 Kilometers

ximate Scale (along Equator)

ence of orders and suborders according to the new
U.S. Soil Conservation Service.)

quately fertilized and when their water supply is controlled, some of these soils are quite productive. However, restrictions on their depth, clay content or water balance, limit the intensive use of large areas of these soils.

VERTISOLS (L. VERTO, TURN). This order of mineral soils is characterized by high content of swelling-type clays which in dry seasons cause the soils to develop deep, wide cracks. A significant amount of material from the upper part of the profile may slough off into the cracks, giving rise to a partial "inversion" of the soil. This accounts for the term *invert* which is used to characterize this order in a general way.

In the past, most of these soils have been called *Grumusols*. Because of their excessive shrinking, cracking, and shearing they are generally unstable and present problems when used for building foundations, highway bases and even for agricultural purposes.

There are several small but significant areas of Vertisols in the United States. (See Fig. 12:4). Two are located in humid areas, one in eastern Mississippi and western Alabama and the other along the southeast coast of Texas. The soils are of the Udert (L. *udus*, humid) suborder and, due to the moist climate, cracks do not persist for more than three months of the year.

Two Vertisol areas are found in east central and southern Texas where the climate is drier. Since cracks persist for more than 3 months of the year, the soils belong to the Ustert (L. *ustus*, burnt) suborder characteristic of areas with hot, dry summers.

In India, the Sudan and eastern Australia large areas of Vertisols are found. (See Fig. 12:5). These soils probably are of the Ustert suborder since dry weather persists long enough for the wide cracks to stay open for periods of three months or longer.

In each of the major Vertisol areas listed above some of the soils are used for crop production. Even so, their very fine texture and their marked shrinking and swelling characteristics make them less suitable for crop production than soils in the surrounding areas. They are sticky and plastic when wet and hard when dry. As they dry out following a rain, the period of time when they can be plowed or otherwise tilled is very short. This is a limiting factor even in the United States where powerful tractors and other mechanical equipment make it possible to plow, prepare seed beds, plant and cultivate very quickly. The limitation becomes even more severe in India and the Sudan where slow moving animals are used to till the soil. Not only can the cultivators not perform tillage operations on time, but they are limited to the use of small, near primitive tillage implements because their animals cannot pull larger equipment through the "heavy" soil.

In spite of their limitations, Vertisols are widely tilled, especially in India and in the Sudan. Sorghum, corn, millet and cotton are crops commonly grown. Unfortunately, the yields are generally low. Further research and timely soil management are essential if these large soil areas are to help produce the food crops these countries so badly need.

INCEPTISOLS (L. INCEPTUM, BEGINNING). Inceptisols may be termed young soils since their profiles contain horizons that are thought to form rather quickly and result mostly from alteration of parent materials. The horizons do not represent extreme weathering. Horizons of marked accumulation of clay and iron and aluminum oxides are absent in this order. The profile development of soils in this order is more advanced than that of the Entisol order, but less so than that of the other orders.

Soils formerly classified as Brown Forest, Ando, and Sols Brun Acide typify this order. Many agriculturally useful soils are included, along with others whose productivity is limited by factors such as imperfect drainage (see Table 12:2).

Inceptisols are found in several of the United States and in each of the Continents. (See Figs. 12:4 & 12:5). For example some Inceptisols called Andepts (productive soils developed from Volcanic ash) are found in a sizeable area of Oregon, Washington and Idaho, and in Ecuador and Columbia in South America. Some called Ochrepts (Gr. *Ochros*, pale) with thin, light colored surface horizons extend from southern New York through central and western Pennsylvania, West Virgina and eastern Ohio. Ochrepts dominate an area extending from southern Spain through central France to central Germany. They are also present in north Africa, eastern China and western Siberia.

Tropepts (Inceptisols of tropical regions) are found in northwestern Australia, central Africa, southwestern India and in southwestern Brazil. (See Fig. 12:5). Areas of wet Inceptisols or Aquepts (L. *Aqua,* water) are found along the Amazon and Ganges rivers.

As might be expected there is considerable variability in the natural productivity of Inceptisols. For example, those found in the Pacific Northwest are quite fertile and provide us with some of our best wheat lands. In contrast, some of the low-organic-containing Ochrepts in southern New York and northern Pennsylvania are not naturally productive. They have been allowed to reforest following earlier periods of crop production.

ARIDISOLS (L. ARIDUS, DRY). These mineral soils are found mostly in dry climates. Except where there is ground water or irrigation, the soil layers are dry throughout most of the year. Consequently, they have not been subjected to intensive leaching. They have an ochric epipedon which is generally light in color and low in organic matter. They may have a horizon of accumulation of calcium carbonate (calcic), gypsum (gypsic), or even more soluble salts (salic). If ground water is present, conductivity measurements show the presence of soluble salts.

Aridisols include most of the soils of the arid regions of the world such as those formerly designated as Desert, Reddish Desert, Sierozem, Reddish Brown, and Solonchak (see Table 12:2).

A large area of Aridisols called Argids (L. *Argilla,* white clay), which have a horizon of clay accumulation, occupies much of the southern parts of California, Nevada, Arizona, and central New Mexico. These Argids extend down into northern Mexico. Smaller areas of Orthids (Aridisols without clay accumulation) are found in several Western states.

Vast areas of Aridisols are present in the Sahara desert in Africa, the Gobi and Taklamakan deserts in China, and the Turkestan desert of the Soviet Union. Most of the soils of southern and central Australia are Aridisols as are those of southern Argentina, southwestern Africa, West Pakistan, and the Middle East countries.

Without irrigation, Aridisols are not suitable for growing cultivated crops. Some areas are used for sheep or goat grazing, but the production per unit area is low. Where irrigation water is available Aridisols can be made most productive. Irrigated valleys of the Western United States are among the most productive in the country.

M O L L I S O L S (L . M O L L I S , S O F T) . This order includes some of the world's most important agricultural soils. They are characterized by a so-called *mollic epipedon*[8] or surface horizon which is thick, dark, and dominated by divalent cations. They may have an argillic (clay), natric, albic, or cambic horizon but not an oxic or spodic one (See Table 12:1). The surface horizons generally have granular or crumb structures and are not hard when the soils are dry. This justifies the use of a name which implies softness.

Most of the Mollisols have developed under prairie vegetation. So-called grassland soils of the central part of the United States formerly classified as Chernozem, Brunizem (Prairie), Chestnut, and Reddish Prairie along with associated humic gley and Planosols make up the central core of this order. However, some soils developed under forest vegetation such as certain soils formerly classified as Brown Forest have a mollic epipedon and are included among the Mollisols. They, along with the grassland soils which dominate this order, are among the more productive cultivated soils in the world.

Mollisols are dominant in the Great Plain States. (See Fig. 12:4). Those in the eastern and more humid part of this region are called Udolls (L.

---

[8] An Epipedon (Gr. *epi,* over and *pedon,* soil, rhymes with head on) is a horizon that forms at the surface. It includes *upper eluvial* horizons, those darkened by organic matter, or both. (See p. 306.)

Udus, humid). A region extending from North Dakota to southern Texas is characterized by Ustolls (L. *Ustus*, burnt) which are intermittently dry during the summer. Further west in parts of Idaho, Utah, Washington, and Oregon are found sizeable areas of Xerolls (Gr. *Xeros*, dry) which are the driest of the Mollisols.

The largest area of Mollisols outside the United States is that stretching from east to west across the heartland of the Soviet Union. (See Fig. 12:5). Other sizeable areas are found in Mongolia and northern China, and in northern Argentina, Paraguay and Uruguay.

The native fertility of Mollisols dictates that they be rated among the world's best soils. When first cleared for cultivation, their high native organic matter released sufficient nitrogen and other nutrients to produce bumper crops even without fertilization. Yields on these soils were unsurpassed by other unirrigated areas. Even today when moderate to heavy fertilization gives a competitive advantage to less fertile soils in more humid areas, Mollisols still rate among the best.

SPODOSOLS (GK. SPODOS, WOOD ASH). These are mineral soils which have a spodic horizon, a subsurface horizon with an accumulation of organic matter and oxides of aluminum with or without iron oxides. This illuvial horizon usually occurs under an eluvial horizon, normally an albic horizon (light in color, hence justifying reference to "wood ash"). (See Table 12:1.)

These soils form mostly on coarse-textured, acid parent materials subject to ready leaching. They occur only in humid climates and are most common where it is cold and temperate. Forests are the natural vegetation under which most of these soils have developed.

Species low in metallic ion contents such as pine trees seem to encourage the development of Spodosols. As the litter from these low-base species decompose, strong acidity develops. Percolating water leaches acids down into the profile. The upper horizons succumb to this intense acid leaching. Most minerals except quartz are removed. In the lower horizons, oxides of aluminum and iron as well as organic matter precipitate, thus yielding the interesting Spodosol profiles.

Many of the soils in Northeastern United States, including those of northern Michigan and Wisconsin which were formerly classified as Podzol, Brown Podzolic and Ground Water Podzol belong to this order. (See Fig. 12:4) Most of them are Orthods, the "common" Spodosols described above. Some, however, are Aquods, since they are seasonally saturated with water and possess characteristics associated with this wetness such as very high surface organic accumulation, mottling in the albic horizon and the development of a hard pan (duripan) in the albic horizon. Important areas of Aquods occur in Florida.

The area of Spodosols in the Northeast extends up into Canada. Other large areas of this soil order are found in Northern Europe and Siberia. Smaller but important areas are found in the southern part of South America and in cool mountainous areas of temperate regions.

Spodosols are not naturally fertile. When properly fertilized, however, these soils can become quite productive. For example, the productive "Potato" soils of northern Maine are Spodosols as are some of the vegetable producing soils of Florida and of Michigan and Wisconsin. Even so, the low native fertility of most Spodosols makes them uncompetitive for tilled crops. They are covered mostly with forests, the vegetation under which they originally developed.

ALFISOLS. Typified by those soils called Gray-Brown Podzolic in the old system, Alfisols have gray to brown surface horizons, medium to high base status and contain an illuvial horizon in which silicate clays have accumulated. This horizon is termed *argillic* if only silicate clays are present and *natric* if, in addition to the clay, it is more than 15 per cent saturated with sodium and has prismatic or columnar structure. The clay horizon is generally more than 35 per cent base saturated. (See Table 12:1.)

The Alfisols appear to be more strongly weathered than the Inceptisols but less so than the Spodosols. They are formed mostly in humid-region areas under native deciduous forests, although grass is the native vegetation in some cases. In addition to the Gray-Brown Podzolic soils, Alfisols include most of those formerly called Noncalcic Brown and Gray Wooded soils and some of those called Planosols, Half Bog, and Solodized Solonetz.

Some of our best agricultural soils are in the Alfisol order. It is typified by Udalfs (L. *udus*, humid) in Ohio, Indiana, Michigan, Wisconsin, Minnesota, Pennsylvania and New York. It includes sizeable areas of Xeralfs (Gr. *Xeros*, dry) in central California, some cold-climate Boralfs (Gr. *Boreas*, northern) in the Rockies, Ustalfs (L. *Ustus*, burnt) in areas of hot summers including Texas and New Mexico, and wet Alfisols, Aqualfs, (L. *Aqua*, water) in parts of the Midwest.

Alfisols occur in other countries having climatic environments similar to those of areas cited above. (See Fig. 12:5) For example, a large area dominated by Boralfs is found in Northern Europe stretching from the Baltic States thru Western Russia. A second large area is found in Siberia. Ustalfs are prominent in the southern half of Africa, in Eastern Brazil, Eastern India, and in Southeast Asia. Large areas of Udalfs are found in Central China, in England, France and Central Europe, and Southeast Australia. Xeralfs are prominent in southwest Australia, Italy, and central Spain.

In general, Alfisols are quite productive soils. Their medium to high base status, generally favorable texture and location (except for some

Xeralfs) in humid and subhumid regions all favor good crop yields. In the United States, these soils rank favorably with the Mollisols and Ultisols in their productive capacity.

ULTISOLS. (L. *Ultimus* last) This order contains most soils which formerly were called Red-Yellow Podzolic and Reddish-Brown Lateritic soils and Rubrozems along with some called Humic Gley, Low Humic Gley, and Ground Water Laterite soils. They are usually moist soils and develop under warm to tropical climates. Ultisols are more highly weathered and acidic than the Alfisols but generally are not so acid as the Spodosols. They have argillic (clay) horizons with base saturations lower than 35 per cent. Except for the wetter members of the order, their subsurface horizons are commonly red or yellow in color evidence of accumulation of free oxides of iron. They still have some weatherable minerals, however, in contrast to the Oxisols (see below). Ultisols are formed on old land surfaces, generally under forest vegetation, although savannah or even swamp vegetation is common.

Most of the soils of the southeastern part of the United States fall in this order. The moist but not wet Ultisols, Udults, extend from the east coast (Maryland to Florida) to and beyond the Mississippi River Valley and are the most extensive of soils in the humid Southeast. Humults (high in organic matter) are found in Hawaii, eastern California, Oregon and Washington. Xerults (drier Ultisols) are common in southern Oregon and northern and western California.

Ultisols are prominent on the east and northeast coasts of Australia. Large areas of Udults are located in southeast Asia including southern China. Important areas are found in southern Brazil and Paraguay.

While Ultisols are not naturally as fertile as Alfisols or Mollisols, they respond well to good management. They are located mostly in regions of long growing seasons and of ample moisture for good crop production. Their clays are usually of the 1:1 type along with oxides of iron and aluminum. This assures ready workability. Where adequate chemical fertilizers are applied, these soils are quite productive. In the United States the better Ultisols compete well with Mollisols and Alfisols as first class agricultural soils.

OXISOLS (F. OXIDE, OXIDE). These are the most highly weathered soils in the classification system. Their most important diagnostic feature is the presence of a deep *oxic* subsurface horizon—a horizon generally very high in clay-size particles dominated by hydrous oxides of iron and aluminum. Weathering and intense leaching has removed a large part of the silica from silicate minerals in this horizon leaving a high proportion of the oxides of iron and aluminum. Some quartz and 1:1 type silicate clay minerals remain but the hydrous oxides are dominant. The clay content of these soils is very high, but the clays are of the non-sticky type. The depth of weathering in oxisols is much greater than for most of the other soils—fifty or more feet having been observed.

Those soils which in recent years have been termed latosols and some of those called Ground Water Laterites are included among the Oxisols. They occupy old land surfaces and occur mostly in the tropics. Relatively less is known of the Oxisols than of most of the other soil orders. They occur in large geographic areas, however, and millions of people in the tropics depend upon them for their food and fiber production. (See p. 336.)

The largest known areas of Oxisols occur in South America and Africa. (See Fig. 12:5). Orthox (normal Oxisols) occur in northern Brazil and neighboring countries. An area of Ustox (hot, dry summers) nearly as large occurs in Brazil to the south of the Orthox. Oxisols are found in the southern two-thirds of Africa, being located on old land surfaces of this area.

Relatively less is known about the management of Oxisols than of any other soil order. Most of them have not been cleared of their native vegetation nor used for modern cultivation. They are mostly either still covered with native vegetation or have been tilled by primitive methods. The few instances where modern farming techniques have been used have met with mixed success. Heavy fertilization, especially with phosphorus-rich materials, is required. Deficiencies of micronutrients have also been observed commonly. In some areas torrential rainfall makes practices which leave the soil bare extremely hazardous.

Although extensive research will be needed to better utilize these soils, experience up to now indicates that their potential for food and fiber production is far in excess of that currently being realized. In both Brazil and central Africa selected areas of these soils have been demonstrated to be high in productivity when they are properly managed.

HISTOSOLS. (G. HISTOS, TISSUE). The last of the soil orders includes the so-called organic soils (Bog soils) as well as some of the half-bog soils. These soils have developed in a water-saturated environment. They contain a minimum of 20 per cent organic matter if no clay is present and 30 per cent if the clay content is more than 50 per cent. In virgin areas, the organic matter retains much of the original plant tissue form. Upon drainage and cultivation of the area, the original plant tissue form tends to disappear.

Less progress has been made on the classification of these soils compared to those of the other orders. These soils are of great practical importance in local areas, however, being among the most productive especially for vegetable crops. Their characteristics are given more detailed consideration in chapter 13.

The soil map of the United States based on the comprehensive soil classification system in Figure 12:4 deserves careful study to identify regions in which the various soil orders and suborders are found. Likewise, the recently prepared generalized world soil map (Figure 12:5) shows the probable location of the different soil orders throughout the world. This too deserves careful attention as we turn now to further details of classification.

Table 12:3. Soil Orders and Suborders in the Comprehensive Soil Classification System. Note that the Ending of the Suborder Names Identifies the Order in which the Soils Are Found.

Order	Suborder	Order	Suborder
Entisol	Aquent	Mollisol	Alboll
	Arent		Aquoll
	Fluvent		Boroll
	Orthent		Rendoll
	Psamment		Udoll
			Ustoll
Vertisol	Torrert		Xeroll
	Udert		
	Ustert	Alfisol	Aqualf
	Xerert		Boralf
			Udalf
Inceptisol	Andept		Ustalf
	Aquept		Xeralf
	Ochrept		
	Plaggept	Ultisol	Aquult
	Tropept		Humult
	Umbrept		Udult
			Ustult
Aridisol	Agrid		Xerult
	Orthid		
		Oxisol	Aquox
Spodosol	Aquod		Humox
	Ferrod		Orthox
	Humod		Torrox
	Orthod		Ustox
		Histisol	Incomplete

Table 12:4. The Formative Elements in Names of Suborders (Comprehensive Soil Classification System)

Formative elements	Derivation of formative element	Connotation of formative element
alb	L. *albus*, white.	Presence of albic horizon (a bleached eluvial horizon).
and	Modified from Ando.	Ando-like.
aqu	L. *aqua*, water.	Characteristics associated with wetness.
ar	L. *arare*, to plow	Mixed horizons.
arg	Modified from argillic horizon; L. *argilla*, white clay.	Presence of argillic horizon (a horizon with illuvial clay).
bor	Gk. *boreas*, northern.	Cool.
ferr	L. *ferrum*, iron.	Presence of iron.
fibr	L. *fibra*, fiber.	Least decomposed stage.
fluv	L. *fluvius*, river.	Flood plains.
hem	Gk. *hemi*, half.	Intermediate stage of decomposition.
hum	L. *humus*, earth.	Presence of organic matter.
lept.	Gk. *leptos*, thin.	Thin horizon.
ochr	Gk. base of *ochros*, pale.	Presence of ochric epipedon (a light surface).
orth	Gk. *orthos*, true.	The common ones.
plag	Modified from Ger. *plaggen*, sod.	Presence of plaggen epipedon.
psamm	Gk. *psammos*, sand.	Sand textures.
rend	Modified from Rendzina.	Rendzina-like.
sapr	Gk. *sapros*, rotten.	Most decomposed stage.
torr	L. *torridus*, hot and dry.	Usually dry.
trop	Modified from Gk. *tropikos*, of the solstice.	Continually warm.
ud	L. *udus*, humid.	Of humid climates.
umbr	L. *umbra*, shade.	Presence of umbric epipedon (a dark surface).
ust	L. *ustus*, burnt.	Of dry climates, usually hot in summer.
xer	Gk. *xeros*, dry.	Annual dry season.

12:8. SUBORDERS AND GREAT GROUPS

The ten orders just described are subdivided into suborders as shown in Table 12:3. The characteristics used as a basis for subdividing into the suborders are those which give the class the greatest genetic homogeneity. Thus, soils formed under wet conditions are generally identified under separate suborders (e.g., Aquents, Aquerts, Aquept, etc.) as are the drier soils (e.g., Ustalfs and Ustults). This arrangement also provides a convenient devise for grouping soils outside the classification system (e.g., the *wet* and *dry* soils, etc.)

To determine the relationship between suborder names and soil characteristics, reference should be made to Table 12:4. Here the formative elements for suborder names are identified as is their connotation. Thus, the *Boroll* suborder (Gk. *Boreas,* Northern) (Table 12:3) is seen to include Mo*ll*isols that are found in cool climates. Likewise, soils in the *Udult* suborder (L. *Udus,* humid) are Ultisols of the more humid climates. Identification of the primary characteristics of each of the other suborders can be made by cross reference to Tables 12:3 and 12:4. Note that some of these suborder names were used in the previous section to identify classes of soil orders under discussion.

The *great groups* are subdivisions of suborders. They are defined "largely on the presence or absence of diagnostic horizons and the arrangements of those horizons." These horizon designations are included in the list of formative elements for the names of great groups shown in Table 12:5. Note that these formative elements refer to epipedons such as mollic and orchic (see Table 12:1), to subsurface horizons such as argillic and natric and to pans such as duripan and fragipan. Remember that the great group names are made up of these formative elements attached as prefixes to the names of suborders in which the great groups occur. Thus, a *Ustoll* with a *natric* horizon (high in sodium) belongs to the *Natrustoll* great group.

As one might expect, the number of great groups is high, nearly 200 having been identified. The names of great groups from five orders are given in Table 12:6. This list illustrates again the utility of the Comprehensive Soil Classification System and especially the nomenclature it employs. Note that the names tell us the suborder and order in which the great groups are found. Thus, Durargids are Aridisols of the Argid suborder characterized by the presence of a duripan. Cross reference to Table 12:5 identifies the specific characteristic which separates the great group classes from each other. Careful study of these two tables will show the utility of this classification system.

Table 12:5. The Formative Elements for Names of Great Groups and Their Connotation. (These formative elements combined with the appropriate suborder names give the great group names.)

Formative Element	Connotation	Formative Element	Connotation
acr	Extreme weathering	moll	Mollic epipedon
agr	Agric horizon	nadur	See *Natr* and *Dur*
alb	Albic horizon	natr	Natric horizon
and	Ando-like	ochr	Ochric epipedon
anthr	Anthropic epipedon	pale	Old development
aqu	Wetness	pell	Low chroma
arg	Argillic horizon	plac	Thin pan
calc	Calcic horizon	plag	Plaggen horizon
camb	Cambic horizon	plinth	Plinthite
chrom	High chroma	quartz	High quartz
cry	Cold	rend	Rendzina-like
dur	Duripan	rhod	Dark-red colors
dystr, dys	Low base saturation	sal	Salic horizon
eutr, eu	High base saturation	sider	Free iron oxides
ferr	Iron	sphangno	Sphagnum-moss
frag	Fragipan	torr	Usually dry
fragloss	See *frag* and *gloss*	trop	Continually warm
gibbs	Gibbsite	ud	Humid climates
gloss	Tongued	umbe	Umbric epipedon
hal	Salty	ust	Dry climate, usually hot in summer
hapl	Minimum horizon		
hum	Humus	verm	Wormy, or mixed by animals
hydr	Water	vitr	Glass
hyp	Hypnum moss	xer	Annual dry season
luo, lu	Illuvial	sombr	A dark horizon

12:9. FAMILY AND SERIES

The family category of classification is based on properties important to the growth or plants. The criteria used vary from one subgroup to another but include texture, thickness of horizons, mineralogy, pH, consistence, and permeability. Family categories are in the process of being developed and tested. The placement of soils into families will have to await this development and testing.

Families are subdivided into soil series, a category basically the same

Table 12:6. Names of Great Groups in the Aridisol, Mollisol, Spodosol,
Alfisol and Ultisol Orders (Comprehensive Soil Classification System). Note
that the suborder name is identified as the italicized portion of the great
group name. For the connotation of the formative element see Table 12:5.

Dur*argid*	Arg*iustoll*	Alb*aqualf*	Dur*ixeralf*
Hapl*argid*	Calc*iustoll*	Frag*iaqualf*	Haplo*xeralf*
Nadur*argid*	Dur*ustoll*	Glass*aqualf*	Natri*xeralf*
Natr*argid*	Hapl*ustoll*	Natr*aqualf*	Pale*xeralf*
Pale*argid*	Natr*ustoll*	Ochr*aqualf*	Plinth*oxeralf*
	Pale*ustoll*	Trop*aqualf*	Rhod*oxeralf*
Calci*orthid*	Verm*ustoll*	Umbr*aqualf*	
Camb*orthid*			Frag*iaquualt*
Dur*orthid*	Argi*xeroll*	Cryo*boralf*	Ochr*aquult*
Pale*orthid*	Calci*xeroll*	Eutro*boralf*	Plinth*aquult*
Sal*orthid*	Duri*xeroll*	Fragi*boralf*	Trop*aquult*
	Haplo*xeroll*	Glosso*boralf*	Umbr*aquult*
Argi*aboll*	Natri*xeroll*	Natri*boralf*	
Natr*alboll*	Pale*xeroll*	Pale*boralf*	Haplo*humult*
			Pale*humult*
Argi*aquoll*	Cry*aquod*	Arg*udalf*	Trop*ohumult*
Calci*aquoll*	Dur*aquod*	Ferr*udalf*	
Cry*aquoll*	Frag*iaquod*	Frag*iudalf*	Frag*iudult*
Dur*aquoll*	Hapl*aquod*	Gloss*udalf*	Hapl*udult*
Hapl*aquoll*	Plac*aquod*	Hapl*udalf*	Pale*udult*
Natr*aquoll*	Sider*aquod*	Natr*udalf*	Plinth*udult*
	Trop*aquod*	Pale*udalf*	Rhod*udult*
Argi*boroll*		Trop*udalf*	Trop*udult*
Calci*boroll*	Cryo*humod*		
Cryo*boroll*	Fragi*humod*	Dur*ustalf*	Hapl*ustult*
Haplo*boroll*	Haplo*humod*	Hapl*ustalf*	Pale*ustult*
Natri*boroll*	Plac*ohumod*	Natr*ustalf*	Plinth*ustult*
Pale*boroll*	Trop*ohumod*	Pale*ustalf*	Rhod*ustult*
Verm*iboroll*		Plinth*ustalf*	Trop*ustult*
	Cry*orthod*	Rhod*ustalf*	
Argi*udoll*	Fragi*orthod*		Haplo*xerult*
Hapl*udoll*	Hapl*orthod*		Pale*xerult*
Pale*udoll*	Plac*orthod*		
Verm*udoll*			

as that formerly in use. Profile characteristics below the plow layer are
the primary criteria for differentiating soil series which is the lowest

category of the new classification system. These will be considered in more detail later (p. 343) along with soil types.

12:10. SOIL CLASSIFICATION— OLD SYSTEM

The system of soil classification used in the United States prior to the acceptance of the new comprehensive system will now receive our attention. By means of this classification, soils are grouped in three orders: (1) zonal, (2) intrazonal, and (3) azonal (see Table 12:7). A brief description of each follows:

Table 12:7. A Classification of Soils into Orders, Suborders and Great Soil Groups. Each Great Soil Group is Subdivided into Numerous Soil Series and Soil Types. (See Sec. 12:24.)*

Order	Suborder	Great Soil Groups
Zonal Soils	1. Soils of the cold zone	Tundra
	2. Light-colored podzolized soils of timbered regions	Podzol Soils Brown Podzolic Soils Gray-Brown Podzolic Soils Red-Yellow Podzolic Soils Gray Podzolic or Gray Wooded Soils
	3. Soils of forested warm-temperate and tropical regions	A variety of Latosols are recognized. They await detailed classification
	4. Soils of the forest-grass-land transition	Degraded Chernozem Soils Noncalcic Brown or Shantung Brown Soils
	5. Dark-colored soils of semi-arid, subhumid, and humid grasslands	Prairie Soils (semipodzolic) Reddish Prairie Soils Chernozem Soils Chestnut Soils Reddish Chestnut Soils
	6. Light-colored soils of arid regions	Brown Soils Reddish-brown Soils Sierozem Soils Red Desert Soils

Table 12:7. (Continued)

Order	Suborder	Great Soil Groups
Intrazonal Soils	1. Hydromorphic soils of marshes, swamps, flats, and seepage areas	Humic-gley Soil (includes wiesenboden) Alpine Meadow Soils Bog Soils Half-bog Soils Low-humic Gley Soils Planosols Ground-water Podzols Ground-water Latosols
	2. Halomorphic (saline and alkali) soils of imperfectly drained arid regions, littoral deposits	Solonchak Soils (saline soils) Solonetz Soils (alkali soils) Soloth Soils
	3. Calcimorphic soils	Brown Forest Soils (Braunerde) Rendzina Soils
Azonal Soils	(No suborders)	Lithosols Regosols (includes dry sands) Alluvial

[a] Modified from J. Thorp and G. D. Smith, "Higher Categories of Soil Classification: Order, Suborder, and Great Soil Groups," *Soil Sci.*, 67:117–26, 1949.

The characteristics of *zonal* soils are determined primarily by the climate in which they have developed. Differences in rock formation and geological origin are largely masked, or have been rendered subordinate by dominating climate influences. Local features such as drainage and topography are such as to permit or even encourage the maximum influence of climate and vegetation. As the name *zonal* indicates these soils are of such wide expanse as to be thought of as more or less regional in extent.

Associated with zonal soils are the two other orders—*intrazonal* and *azonal.* The former includes those soils that, in spite of climate and vegetation, reflect the influence of some local condition such as poor drainage or alkali salts. Many of their properties are, of course, similar to those of the zonal soils with which they are associated, but the characteristics resulting from local conditions are dominant. Since such soils cross zonal boundaries, they are termed intrazonal. Azonal soils, in marked contrast, are those without horizon differentiation. Profile layers resulting from soil development are not apparent. Most soils developed on recent alluvial and colluvial deposits belong in this order.

12:11. ZONAL SOILS—A GENERAL SURVEY

As the classification of soils is followed still further, it seems logical to consider first the zonal soils because of their wide expanse and world importance. As seen in Table 12:7 the *order* of zonal soils is further broken down into *suborders* on the basis of specific climate and vegetative regions. Each of these suborders, in turn, is divided into *great soil groups* such as the podzol and prairie. These great soil groups, because they are an expression of more specific conditions, will be the subject of much of the discussion that follows.

The classification of zonal soils, outlined in Table 12:7, is presented somewhat more simply by the drawings in Fig. 12:6. Here the relationship among climate, vegetation, and some of the important zonal soils is illustrated. The diagrams are particularly helpful in the study of the soils of the United States since the general climatic differences shown in Fig. 12:6 approximate those found in this country when going from the Rocky Mountain area eastward. It would be advisable to observe this figure carefully before considering the specific properties of the zonal soils.

12:12. TUNDRA SOILS

In regions too cold for the growth of trees or grass and yet warm enough for some plant life, the vegetation which develops is known as *tundra*. (See Fig. 12:6.) This consists primarily of mosses, lichens, and shrubs. The tundra is found under both humid and arid conditions and the soils which develop are of little agricultural value except as pasturage for reindeer and caribou. Consequently, they deserve hardly more than passing mention in spite of their tremendous expanse in northern Europe, Asia, and North America. Roughly 40 per cent of the Soviet Union is thus covered, an area equal to that of the whole United States.

In tundra soils the accumulation of organic matter gives a peaty surface covering over a bluish-gray, sticky, compact subsoil. Since the substratum, and sometimes even the subsoil, of the tundra remains frozen most of the year, a poorly drained boggy condition exists at certain sea-

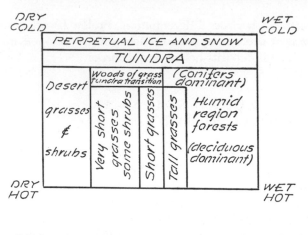

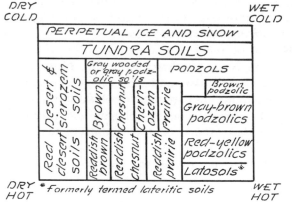

Figure 12:6. *Above—a simplified diagram showing how the natural vegetation varies with climate. Below—a similar diagram indicating the relationship of zonal soils to climate. Note that soil boundaries correspond rather closely to those of the natural vegetation.*

The right to left successions of soils and vegetation shown in the diagrams approximate those that will be encountered when travelling from the east coast of North America to the Sierra Nevada and Cascade Mountains. Typical desert conditions occur in the intermountain regions west of the Rockies.

sons. Much heaving takes place with the alternate freezing and thawing, and explosive blisters sometimes occur. With the tundra soils are associated the muskeg peats, often with perpetually frozen subhorizons.

12:13. PODZOLIZATION

Since, in addition to the true *podzols*, several of the other great soil groups are *podzolic* in nature, the process of podzolization should be thoroughly understood before proceeding further. This process is basically one of *acid leaching*. It occurs most intensively under forest vegetation where conditions favor the surface accumulation of organic matter. Fungi seem to be the dominant microorganisms. Earthworm activity is low or nonexistent. Organic acids are formed as the organic matter decays. These are leached downward through the profile by percolating waters. The process is speeded up if the parent material is loose and open.

As the acids are leached downward through the mineral layers, mineral salts, including the carbonates, are solubilized and move out of the solum. Weatherable minerals of the A horizon become unstable. Under the most acid conditions, iron and aluminum as well as organic matter are solubilized and move downward. Milder acidic leaching results in silicate clay formation and translocated to the lower horizons.

In the B horizons some of the materials leached from above accumulaate. In the true *podzol*, organic matter along with iron and aluminum oxides build up. Silicate clays, with or without these sesquioxides, accumulate under more mild acidic leaching which give rise to the so-called podzolic soils. A brief description of soils having been subjected to the process of podzolization follows.

12:14. PODZOLIC SOIL REGIONS OF THE UNITED STATES

Six podzolic soil regions may definitely be distinguished and are identified in Table 12:7.

TRUE PODZOLS. (Spodosols). The first drastically podzolized, is designated the region of typical podzol soils. A diagram of a profile of an uncultivated podzol is shown in Fig. 12:7. Note the acidic organic layers on the surface overlying a drastically leached and bleached A_2 horizon. Because of the ashy appearance of this horizon, the term podzol[9] has been applied to these soils. An accumulation of precipitated humus and of iron and aluminum oxides occurs in the B horizon.

These soils occur mostly in northern and northeastern United States. (See Fig. 12:8.) Their parent material is so drastically leached during soil formation and the upper layers are left so acidic, that such soils are rather low in agricultural value except in certain cases. Once the organic matter is gone, the slump in productivity is rapid. Most of these soils are best left in woodland. Only with certain crops, such as potatoes in Aroostock County, Maine, is their cultivation profitable.

BROWN PODZOLIC SOILS. (Spodosols). Just south of the typical podzols in New England, New York, and elsewhere in north-

[9] From the Russian *pod* meaning "under" and *zola* meaning "ash."

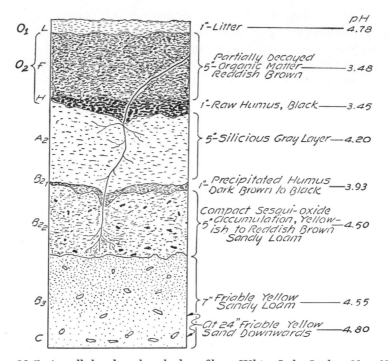

Figure 12:7. A well-developed podzol profile at White Lake Lodge, New York, on the southwestern edge of the Adirondack Mountains. The soil is a stony loam, forested with birch, hemlock, and spruce. Note the thickness of the organic layers (mor or duff), the depth of the gray silicious horizon (A_2), and the marked acidity of the whole profile, even the C_1. The layer of precipitated humus (B_2) is quite distinct. The letters L, F, and H refer to litter, zone of fermentation and humus layer.

ern United States is found a less drastically podzolized soil group of considerable importance in spite of its comparatively small area—*the brown podzolic.*

Most of the properties of these soils are such that they can be considered weak podzols. There is only a small amount of organic matter (O_2) on the surface of virgin soils. The infertile siliceous layer of the podzol (A_2) is absent or very faint. A thin A_1 (2–3 inches), which contains a considerable amount of organic matter, lies directly on the B horizon. Moreover, there is little evidence of cementation or clay accumulation in the B. Consequently, the brown podzolic soils are loose and well drained and, in spite of their acidity, are better suited for agriculture than are the typical podzols. They are a transitional group of great importance in New England and play an important role in the agriculture of this section.

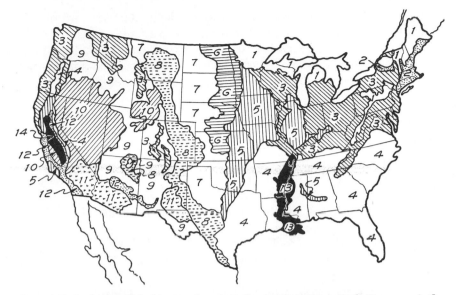

Figure 12:8. A simplified map showing the major Great Soil Groups of the United States. (After Marbut and Kellogg.) The poorly drained soils in most cases are included with their zonal associates. The regions located are as follows:

1. *Podzol.*
2. *Brown podzolic.*
3. *Gray-brown podzolic.*
4. *Red and yellow podzolic.*
5. *Prairie and reddish-prairie (Includes some Planosols & Rendzinas).*
6. *Chernozem.*
7. *Chestnut and reddish-chestnut.*
8. *Brown and reddish-brown.*
9. *Shallow soils (lithosols), mountain, upland, and valley.*
10. *Gray desert (Sierozem).*
11. *Reddish desert.*
12. *Non-calcic brown.*
13. *Mississippi alluvium.*
14. *Alluvium and outwash of the central valley, California.*

GRAY-BROWN PODZOLIC SOILS. (Alfisols). The gray-brown podzolic soils which lie still further southward (Fig. 12:8) are also mildly podzolized. Due to differences in climate, vegetation, and parent materials, however, they present a profile somewhat different from the brown podzolic. The organic matter, mostly from deciduous trees, becomes incorporated with the mineral soil (A_1) giving a *mull* layer several inches thick. The gray siliceous layer of the podzol is replaced by a gray or yellowish-brown horizon (A_2) from 5 to 12 inches thick. This eluvial horizon is characterized by a horizontal, platy structure. Considerable exchangeable calcium still occupies the colloidal complex and the layers, especially the A_1, are not excessively acid. Bacteria and actino-myces as well as fungi are active, and earthworms are numerous.

The B horizon of these soils shows some accumulation of silicate clays and often possesses a blocky structure. Oxides of iron and aluminum also accumulate in this horizon. For further profile details see Figs. 12:3 and 12:9.

All in all, the gray-brown podzolic soils constitute a zonal group of great agricultural value. Although their fertility is only medium, the climate under which they occur favors crops that assure stable agricul-tural conditions, especially in the United States. Opportunities for making a livelihood are such as to render the gray-brown podzolics, covering a great strip from the Middle Atlantic states westward to Iowa and Mis-souri (see Fig. 12:8), one of the bulwarks of American agriculture. Great areas of this soil group also occur in western Montana and northern Idaho. In addition, a wide belt extends down the coastal and valley regions of western Washington and Oregon and into California as far south as San Franscisco.

RED-YELLOW PODZOLIC SOILS. (Ultisols). The red-yellow podzolic soils of the Southern States have originated under a mild climate, an abundant rainfall, and a mixed forest, often markedly decidu-ous. As a result podzolic influences have been most genial.

Virgin soils of this group have a thin layer of unincorporated organic matter, underlain by 2 to 3 inches of A_1. The *red podzolic* soils have a yellowish-gray A_2 several inches thick over a red or brownish-red B horizon. Having developed under slightly greater effective moisture conditions, the iron oxides in the *yellow podzolics* are more highly hy-drated. Consequently, the colors are somewhat less brilliant. The A_2 is slightly yellow and is somewhat thicker than the corresponding horizon of the red podzolics. The heavy-textured B horizon is yellow to light yellow, an indication of the hydrated state of the iron.

These red and yellow soils have been developed from all sorts of parent materials. Yet they have many attributes in common. It is remark-able that climate and its accompanying vegetation has been able to mold them into such noticeable uniformity.

In eastern United States they stand next to the gray-brown podzolic in importance. But, because of their climate, they balance rather than com-pete with the latter in agricultural production.

PRAIRIE SOILS. (Mollisols). The fifth podzolic or perhaps semipodzolic soil region in the United States is that of the *prairie* whose soils are classified as dark-colored grasslands. (See Table 12:7 and Fig. 12:10.) Its climate is much the same as that operative in the gravy-brown podzolic soil region to the eastward. But because the native vegetation was tall grass instead of forest the soils are different. The leaching, while

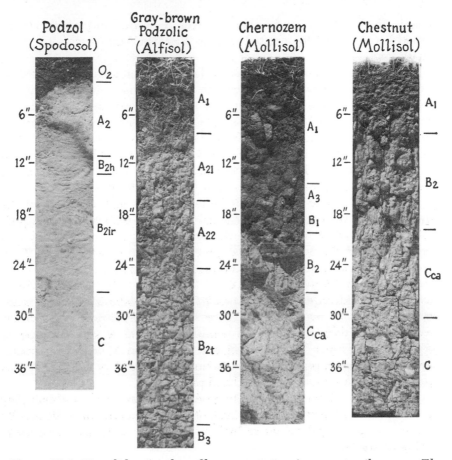

Figure 12:9. *Monoliths of soil profiles representing four great soil groups. The process of podzolization is more intense with the podzol than with the gray-brown podzolic soil even though both have developed under forest vegetation. Note the precipitated humus in the B_{2h} horizon of the podzol, below which iron and aluminum oxides have accumulated (B_{2ir}).*

In the case of the gray-brown podzolic soil, the A_2 is subdivided into two layers (A_{21} and A_{22}). Mild acid leaching has resulted in the formation of silicate clays which have accumulated in the B horizon (B_{2t}) of this soil.

The chernozem and chestnut have been subjected to calcification under grass vegetation. This accounts for the high organic content, noticeably present in the chernozem, and for the deep A_1 horizons. Note that the zone of $CaCO_3$ accumulation (C_{ca}) is found nearer the surface in the chestnut than in the chernozem.

sufficient to remove the calcium carbonate from the solum, has not seriously impaired the natural fertility. This is the only large area of such soils in the world. Just why they are free of woods and whether they would become partially forested in time if undisturbed by man are moot questions.

The abundant native grass cover of the prairie soil area has resulted in a deep, rich, dark-brown A horizon with a varied and active microorganic flora. Southward, the color changes to reddish brown and the soils are spoken of as *reddish prairie* soils. The structure of the surface soil is decidedly granular, due to the influence of the grass cover. The exchangeable calcium is high, in spite of the definite acidity, and little downward movement of iron and aluminum has occurred. In places the presence of clay indicates considerable translocation of clay to the B horizon.

This belt of prairie soils extends latitudinally through the heart of the country, with the chernozems on the one hand and with gray-brown podzolics on the other. They are uniformly fertile and, with the red and yellow soils of the South and the gray-brown forest soils of the East, control the agriculture of central and eastern United States.

GRAY WOODED SOILS. (Alfisols). The sixth podzolic soil to be considered is the *gray wooded* or *gray podzolic* group of western United States and Canada. These soils are developed under forest cover, and a cool, subhumid to semiarid climate. A semidecomposed organic matter layer (O_2) is found, and a very thin A_1 of mixed mineral and organic matter is present. The A_2 horizon like that of the gray-brown podzolic soils is somewhat leached and platy.

These soils, although definitely podzolized, are not so thoroughly leached as their humid region equivalents. Consequently, the soils usually are not as acidic, pH values as high as 7.0 in the B horizon frequently being encountered.

12:15. FORMATION OF LATOSOLS (OXISOLS)

Under the abundant rainfall and high temperatures of the tropics and semitropics, weathering forces work faster and carry their influence to greater extremes than in temperate regions. Thus weathering gives rise to Latosols, most of which would be classified as Oxisols in the new comprehensive classification system.

THE PROCESS AND ITS RESULTS. In the genesis of Latosols the rapid decay of organic residues and the immediate release of the bases from organic combination maintain a near neutral soil reaction. As a result, the solubility of the *silica* is encouraged and that of the *iron*, aluminum, and manganese retarded. If drainage is at all satisfactory, intense oxidation occurs. Thus, as weathering proceeds, red or yellow materials, high in the sesquioxide and low in silica, result. The extent of silicon removal and sesquioxide accumulation is remarkable. In Cuba, for example, a soil containing 1.8 per cent SiO_2 and 71.1 per cent Fe_2O_3 has developed from parent material showing 41.9 per cent SiO_2 and only 7.8 per cent Fe_2O_3.

Because of the intensity of tropical weathering, the regolith often becomes very deep. Original differences due to the character of the country rock are often practically eliminated by the vigor of the chemical processes.

Where drainage is restricted, soft deposits of iron and aluminum oxides often occur at or near the water table. In some countries these are cut out in conveniently sized blocks, which harden when dry and thus make excellent building material. These cemented horizons in certain Latosols are termed *laterites*. (See Fig. 21:2.)

12:16. CHARACTERISTICS OF LATOSOLS (OXISOLS)

It is not difficult to forecast some of the characteristics of a zonal, well-developed Latosol. A red or yellow color, especially in the B horizons, is a foregone conclusion. However, the surface soil, if uneroded, often is brown or gray. In other cases, the red or yellow color dominates the surface soil. This is likely to occur when the parent material was basaltic. Also, enough erosion may have occurred, especially on cultivated lands, to bring some of the bright red or yellowish subsoil into the furrow-slice.

Latosols have a characteristic granular condition which promotes excellent internal drainage. The hydrous oxide clays do not possess the plasticity and cohesion that characterize the silicate clays of temperate regions. This allows the cultivation of typical Latosols immediately after a heavy rain with little danger of generating an unsatisfactory physical state. In fact, Latosols are utilized for agriculture under a weight of rainfall that would render siliceous soils utterly unworkable.

Typical Latosols are low in cation-exchange capacity compared to representative temperate-region soils. This is due to their lack of organic matter and to the nature of their hydrous oxide clays. They are extremely deficient in exchangeable bases and in available nutrients in general. Virgin soils, unless precautions are taken, are soon depleted in fertility when put under cultivation. Such soils usually require liberal fertilization if plant culture is to be at all intensive.

It is not to be inferred, that all soils in the tropics are Latosols. Alluvial soils of all kinds occur as well as colluvial and fan debris. These may show very little latosolization. Moreover, at the higher elevations podzolization is often the dominant type of soil genesis.

In Europe, Latosols are found in southern France, Spain, Italy, and Greece. They also are typically developed in Central America, Mexico, Puerto Rico, Cuba, and other islands in the Caribbean Sea. In northern South America, India, Burma, Thailand, Java, Borneo, Sumatra, and contiguous regions, Latosols are common, and on the islands of the central Pacific, red earths are abundant. The Latosols of Hawii have received especially careful study. Originally forested, Latosols will grow many kinds of tropical and semitropical crops—sugar cane, rubber, coffee, bananas, and pineapples being common products.

12:17. FORMATION OF SOILS UNDER LOW MOISTURE CONDITIONS

In areas of lower rainfall, the acid leaching of podzolization does not occur. Climate and its resulting vegetation are largely responsible for this situation. (See Fig. 12:10.) The rainfall in these areas is insufficient to leach much of the calcium and other divalent cations from the soil profile. Only in the upper horizons are the soils even mildly affected in this way. Consequently the soils have high base saturations and are mildly acidic to basic in reaction.

Moreover, soluble constituents leached from the surface horizons are not removed from the profile. They are only moved to the lower horizons. Thus, a zone of accumulation of $CaCO_3$ occurs at a depth approximating the average penetration of the rain waters. On the drier soils, the more soluble calcium sulfate will also accumulate, usually below the zone of carbonate concentration. Even soluble salts of sodium and potassium may be present at the lower depths of the zonal soils of the arid regions.

The native vegetation, which ranges from grasses to desert shrubs, has contributed to the soil forming process. The grasses are particularly effective in returning bases to the surface of the soil. The extensive root systems of these plants also supply large amounts of organic matter. The humus that develops seems to be effective in stabilizing the soil colloids when adequate calcium is present. This prevents the downward movement of the finer materials, a process so characteristic of podzolization.

12:18. SOILS OF SEMIARID AND ARID REGIONS OF THE UNITED STATES

CHERNOZEMS MOLLISOLS. Moving westward from the prairie soils of the United States the first great soil group to be encountered is that of the *chernozems*. (See Figs. 12:6 and 12:10.) Here the rainfall ranges from 15 to 25 inches annually and the native vegetation is mixed grass. The precipitation is not heavy enough to leach through the profile. As a result, white spots or blotches of calcium carbonate accumulate in the upper C horizon. Under this lime accumulation lenses of gypsum are often found.

The A_1 horizon of a typical northern chernozem is black[10] due to the accumulation and decay of organic matter under scanty rainfall and hot dry summers. This horizon is surprisingly deep, often 12 to 15 inches. (See Fig. 12:9.) In reaction it usually is neutral to somewhat acid. Its granular structure is one of its outstanding physical characteristics. The amount of extremely black pigment present may be related to the high percentage base saturation.

A typical chernozem surface soil is surprisingly high in mineral nutrients as well as in nitrogen and sulfur. (See p. 24.) Chernozems are perhaps the most fertile soils of large area in the United States. Because of low uncertain rainfall, however, they do not consistently produce so much as the corresponding Prairie soils. The southern Chernozems are usually lower in organic matter, lighter in color, and have reddish or yellowish subsoils. (See Fig. 12:9 for contrast with a typical Podzol.)

CHESTNUT (MOLLISOLS) AND BROWN (SOME MOLLISOLS, SOME ARIDISOLS) SOILS. The *Chestnut* and *Brown* soil groups lie, in the order named, between the Chernozem belt and the Rocky Mountains. They are the principal soils of the Great Plains. (See Fig. 12:8.) With a rainfall of only 10 to 15 inches annually, the vegetation is mostly of a steppe type. Due to the scanty precipitation such soils are much lower in organic matter than are the Chernozems and the layer of carbonates is nearer the surface. Thus, the surface layers are neutral or even alkaline. Gypsum also is likely to be present in the subsoil. These soils, as well as the Chernozems, are used for cereal production but nonirrigated agriculture is hazardous because of the low and variable rainfall. The plowing of such soils has increased wind erosion. The dust bowls of Texas, Oklahoma, Colorado, and Kansas, and of the Dakotas and Nebraska lie in these soil regions. (See Fig. 9:7.) Much of this extensive area should be in range and again under the protection of native vegetation.

The comparative characteristics of the *Chestnut, Brown,* and *Chernozem* soils are illustrated in Fig. 12:10. All three great soil groups have developed under grasses. With decreasing rainfall, however, the shorter grasses dominate the vegetation. Profile development is less marked and organic matter content becomes more scanty as the annual precipitation

---

[10] *Chernozem* means black earth.

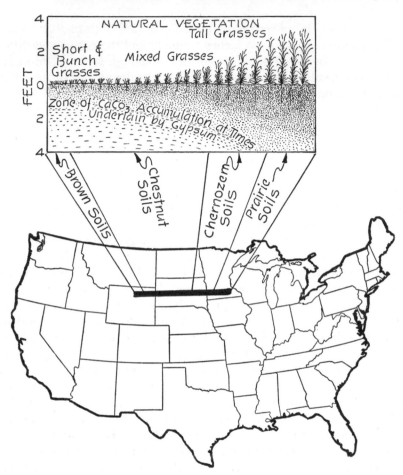

Figure 12:10. The correlation between natural vegetation and certain zonal soil groups is graphically shown for a strip of territory in north central United States. The control, of course, is climate. This figure is a field illustration of the concept carried by Figure 12:6. Note the greater organic content and deeper zone of calcium accumulation as one proceeds from the drier areas in the west toward the more humid region where prairie soils are found.

decreases. The depth at which carbonate accumulations are encountered is much less in the soils of arid regions. For a *Chestnut* profile see Fig. 12:9.

Under warmer conditions, the black and brown colors so common in the northern plain soils in this country give way to browns and reddish browns. The higher temperature apparently encourages the oxidation of iron and at the same time results in a lower organic matter content of the surface layers. The names associated with the great soil groups in these warmer regions—*Reddish-prairie, Reddish-chestnut,* and *Red-dish-brown* (see Fig. 12:6 and Table 12:7)—reflect this color change.

DESERT SOILS. (ARIDISOLS) When climatic conditions are so arid that grasses will not persist, desert shrubs become the natural vegetation. Under these conditions three zonal great soil groups are found: (1) *Sierozem* (Gray Desert), (2) *Desert,* and (3) *Red Desert.* The Sierozems develop under slightly higher moisture conditions than the Desert soils, and are found quite extensively in the intermountain region west of the Rockies. The vegetation on the Desert soils is even more scanty than that of the Sierozems and consequently much wind erosion occurs.

The *Red Desert* soils are found in southwestern United States under a warm to hot arid climate. As is the case with the Sierozem and Desert soils, there is a layer of $CaCO_3$ accumulation under the surface horizon. This $CaCO_3$ layer is frequently cemented, giving rise to a hardpan. Except when irrigated, such soils are of little agricultural value.

12:19. INTRAZONAL SOILS

Associated with each of the zonal soils already considered are those soils of the *intrazonal* order. (See Table 12:6.) The major characteristics of the latter are largely determined by some local feature rather than by climate. Three major suborders of intrazonal soils are recognized: (1) *Hydromorphic,* (2) *Halomorphic,* and (3) *Calcimorphic.* They will be considered in order.

12:20. HYDROMORPHIC SOILS

Hydromorphic soils are characterized by an excess of soil moisture. Drainage is usually poor either because of profile characteristics which prevent normal water filtration, or because the soil is located in a low-lying area. The *Ground Water Podzol, Half-Bog,* and *Bog* soils are typical examples of great soil groups belonging to this suborder in temperate forested regions.

These soils, in the order named, become progressively more poorly drained. The Ground Water Podzol has developed under a high water table. It has an exceptionally deep mat of undecomposed organic matter and is characterized by a cemented B_2 (ortstein). Progressing to the Half-Bog we find an increasingly high water table which in a Bog is at or very near the surface during most of the year. The latter soils include the peats and mucks so important in vegetable production when properly drained. (See Chapter 13.)

One characteristic common to many poorly drained mineral soils is the presence of so-called *gley* horizons. (See Fig. 12:12.) Due to alternate periods of dry and moist conditions these horizons have become mottled with irregular colorations. Red, yellow, and brown streaks or spots are indicative of the oxidized forms of iron and manganese. Mixed with these are blue and gray colors which are characteristic of reduced compounds. This mottled condition is looked for in the diagnosis of poorly drained soils.

Two hydromorphic soil groups found in *humid grasslands* are of special interest and importance. These are the *Wiesenboden*[11] and the *Planosol* groups. Although the Wiesenboden group is found only under grass or sedges, Planosols occur frequently in forested areas as well.

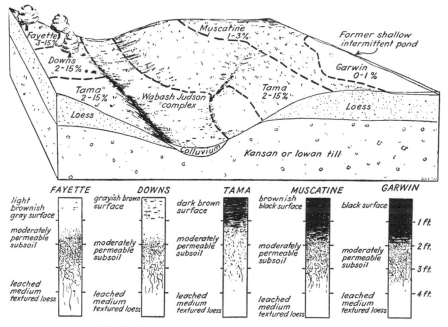

Figure 12:11. A block diagram showing an association of soils in Iowa. Note the relationship of soil type to (1) parent material, (2) vegetation, (3) topography, and (4) drainage. In this diagram two gray-brown podzolic (alfisol) soils (Fayette and Downs), two prairie (mollisol) soils (Tama and Muscatine), and a hydromorphic soil, also a mollisol, (Garwin) are shown. (From F. F. Riecken and G. D. Smith, "Principal Upland Soils of Iowa, Their Occurrence and Important Properties," Iowa Agr. Exp. Sta. Agron., 49, Revised.)

[11] These are included in the humic-gley soil group in Table 12:1 and are sometimes referred to as meadow soils.

The Wiesenboden group is encountered primarily in association with the zonal Prairie soils, which they resemble in many respects when properly drained. These soils occur in relatively flat areas of restricted drainage and have a dark colored surface horizon which is usually near neutrality. When drained, the productivity of the Wiesenbodens is high since their poor drainage is due to location rather than to clay pan development. The contrast between a Wiesenboden and a Prairie profile can be seen by referring to Fig. 12:11.

The *Planosols,* which are poorly drained upland soils, occupy great stretches of prairie in southern Illinois and Iowa and northern Missouri as well as scattered areas in humid forest regions. These soils have been subjected to podzolization and are characterized by a heavy clay pan. Their surface is strongly leached and, due to their profile restrictions, they are not nearly as productive, even when artificially drained, as are their zonal associates.

12:21. HALOMORPHIC SOILS[12]

Soils developed under imperfect drainage conditions in arid regions are often characterized by abnormal salt concentrations in the upper horizons. Because of the effects of salts on their properties, these soils are termed *halomorphic.* They are most generally found in association with the chernozems, chestnuts, browns, and desert soils, and as a group are commonly, though perhaps incorrectly, referred to as "alkali soils."

Solonchak or *saline* soils result when there is an accumulation of soluble salts of sodium, calcium, magnesium, and potassium in the upper horizon. The process operative is known as salinization. The anions found are mostly the chloride and sulfate with some carbonate and bicarbonate. The surface of a Solonchak often is irregularly covered with a white crust of salts. (See Fig. 14:10.) These salts have been carried upward by capillarity and have remained when the water evaporated. As a result, Solonchaks are commonly called "white alkali" soils.

Since the exchangeable ions of Solonchaks are dominantly calcium and magnesium with relatively low amounts of adsorbed sodium, these soils are only slightly alkaline, their pH seldom rising much above 8. Their high salt concentration prevents dispersion of the soil granules, giving

[12] The classification presented here is used by the United States Department of Agriculture, Soil Survey Division. A somewhat modified classification designed to evaluate soils in terms of plant response has been used by the United States Salinity Laboratory. This is discussed by H. E. Haward and C. H. Wadleigh, "Plant Growth on Saline and Alkali Soils," *Advan. in Agron.,* 1:1–38, 1949. This classification is discussed on page 405 and ff. of this textbook.

a physical condition that is not unfavorable for agricultural utilization. In spite of this, however, crop production on these soils is generally better where some drainage has been installed and the salt concentration lowered.

Under conditions which have allowed a high concentration of sodium to become associated with the colloids, a *Solonetz* soil is formed. The pH of this soil is high due to the adsorbed sodium and to the presence of sodium carbonate. The soil colloids, both inorganic and organic, become dispersed and tend to move slowly down the profile. The dark color of the salty surface crust that often is observed is due to the dissolved organic matter. This accounts for the common name "black alkali" applied to these soils. The process of the formation of Solonetz soils is aptly termed *solonization.*

The profile which develops as a result of this process is quite unique. Underneath a very thin friable surface horizon is found a dark horizon of hard clay. This zone has a characteristic columnar structure (see p. 58). and makes a Solonetz easy to identify. Solonetz soils are very unproductive due to their toxic chemical properties and poor physical condition. They can often be reclaimed, however, by proper management. (See p. 409–411).

If improved drainage is maintained in the case of a Solonetz it may eventually become leached thoroughly enough to allow the formation of a *Soloth.* This soil has an acid light-colored surface horizon over a heavy dark brown B. Moreover, the excess colloids have been removed from the A horizon. These soils can be used essentially in the same way as their zonal associates.

12:22. CALCIMORPHIC SOILS

The characteristics of *Calcimorphic* soils are largely due to the high lime content of their parent materials. *Brown Forest* soils of the humid east and their grassland equivalents, the *Rendzinas,* are the two soil groups commonly recognized. (See Table 12:1.) The surface soils of both are at least neutral if not alkaline. Brown Forest soils are dark brown in the surface and gradually grade into the gray calcareous parent material. There is little profile layering compared to zonal soils in the same region. Brown Forest soils apparently are of much greater importance in Europe than in America.

Rendzinas are rather thin dark-colored grassland soils developed from soft lime rocks. The blacklands of north central Texas is a well-known area of these soils in the United States. These soils are often subject to erosion damage, which is particularly serious due to their shallow depth.

12:23. AZONAL SOILS (ENTISOLS)

The characteristics of azonal soils are determined, not by the climate or any particular soil forming process but rather by the nature of their parent material. Three groups are commonly recognized—*Lithosols, Regosols,* and *Alluvial.* (See Table 12:7.) The first give rise to thin surface soils over bedrock. They are commonly found on steep slopes, show little soil development, and in general are not of significance agriculturally.

Regosols are also very young soils and are located on deep unconsolidated soft mineral deposits. They differ from Lithosols in that they are usually not stony. They are largely confined to areas of sand dunes, loess, and steeply sloping glacial drift.

Alluvial soils are of much greater agricultural importance than the azonal soils already mentioned. Large areas are found along rivers such as the Mississippi and Ohio wherever recent alluvium occurs. Valley bottoms throughout the country commonly contain alluvial soils. When properly drained such soils are very productive. The rich lands of the Mississippi delta and floodplain are good examples.

12:24. THE SUBDIVISION OF A SOIL GROUP[13] — SOIL SERIES

The great soil groups are subdivided into lesser groups called *series.* These units are quite distinct. The soils of any one series have similar profile characteristics except for the texture of the surface layer. In more precise terms, a *series* is a group of soils developed from the same kind of parent material, by the same genetic combination of processes, and whose horizons are quite similar in their arrangement and general characteristics. Ideally, the only differences of agricultural importance that should exist between the various soils of any given series are in the textures of the surface layer and even here the range should not be great.

DIFFERENTIATING AND NAMING OF SERIES. Series are of course established on the basis of profile characteristics. This requires a careful study of the various horizons as to number, order, thickness, texture, structure, color, organic content, and reaction (acid, neutral, or alkaline). Such features as hardpan at a certain distance be-

---

[13] Note that we have omitted consideration of the family. The grouping has never been well worked out and is of interest to the specialist only.

low the surface, a distinct zone of calcium carbonate accumulation at a
certain depth, or striking color characteristics greatly aid in series identification.

In the United States each series is given a name, usually from some
city, village, river, or county, such as Fargo, Muscatine, Cecil, Mohave,
Ontario, and the like. Members of the Ontario series include Ontario
sandy loam, Ontario fine sandy loam, and Ontario loam. These soils are
quite similar except for the texture of their A horizons.

12:25. SOIL TYPES, PHASES, AND CATENAS

The subdivision of the series on the basis of the texture of the
A horizon gives the soil *type*. It is well to emphasize, however, that differences in texture between the various soil types in any given series cannot
be great. For instance, a soil with a sandy surface layer could hardly have
the same profile otherwise that a soil with a clayey A horizon would
possess. A series generally consists of a dominant type or types with
several minor types varying somewhat as to the texture of the surface
horizons.

Any particular soil is designated for simplicity by the textural name
of its surface layer, such as sandy loam, gravelly loam, clay loam, and so
on. To this is prefixed the series name in designating the soil type. Mohave sandy loam, Carrington silt loam, Norfolk sandy loam, Miami silt
loam, Houston clay and Fort Collins loam are examples. The type name,
therefore, consists of two parts, the first designating the series, and the
second indicating the particular individual within the series.

All areas of the same soil type are alike within specified limits as to
profile characteristics, including the texture of the surface horizon, and
were originally similar in fertility. Methods of farming have, of course,
developed differences in immediate productivity. This sometimes leads
to confusion in comparing soils of different farms.

SOIL PHASE. A soil type is not quite the ultimate subdivision of a series since *phases* are often mapped within types. A *phase*
is a subdivision on the basis of some important deviation such as erosion,
slope, stoniness, or soluble salt content. It really marks a departure from
the normal, or key type, already established. Thus, a Cecil sandy loam,
eroded phase, or a Hagerstown silt loam, stony phase, are examples of
soils where distinctions are made in respect to the phase.

SOIL ASSOCIATION AND CATENAS. Before proceed-
ing with a consideration of soil survey methods, two more means of
classifying associated soils should be mentioned. In the field, soils of dif-

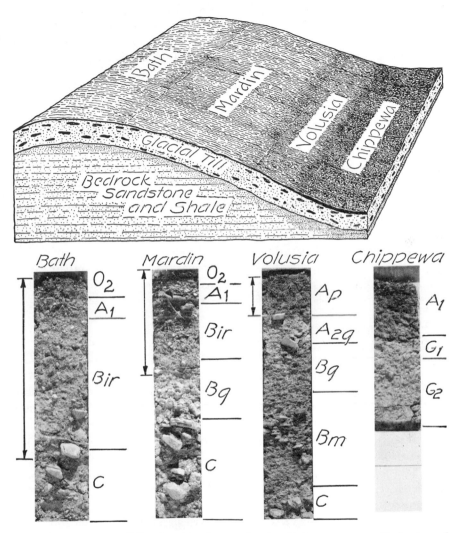

Figure 12:12. Monoliths showing four soils of a drainage catena (below) and
a diagram showing their topographic association in the field (above). Note
the decrease in the depth of the well aerated zone (indicated by arrows) from
the Bath soil (left) to the Chippewa (right). The latter remains poorly aerated
throughout the growing season. These soils are all developed from the same
parent material, differing only in drainage and topography. The Volusia soil
as pictured was cultivated (note Ap-plowed) while the others were located
on virgin sites. Other symbols are as follows: ir = iron; g and G = gleyed, a
mottled layer indicative of poor aeration, G being more intensely gleyed;
m = massive compact layer.

ferent kinds are commonly found together. Such an *association* of soils may consist of zonal soils, intrazonal soils, azonal soils, or a combination of members of one or more of these soil orders. Thus, a shallow regosol on steep uplands may be found alongside a well drained gray-brown podzolic or a soil developed from recent alluvium. The only requirement is that the soils be found together in the same area. Soil associations are important in a practical way since they help determine combinations of land-use patterns which must be used to support a profitable agriculture.

Zonal soils and imperfectly or poorly drained intrazonal soils, all of which have developed from the same parent materials under the same climatic conditions, are often found closely associated under field conditions. This association on the basis of drainage or of differences in relief is known as a *catena* and is very helpful in practical classification of soils in a given region. The relationship can be seen by referring to Fig. 12:12 where the Bath-Mardin-Volusia-Chippewa catena is shown. Although all four or five members of a catena are seldom found in given area, the diagram illustrates the relationship of drainage to topography.

12:26. SOIL SURVEY AND ITS UTILIZATION [14]

The classifications as outlined in the preceding pages are susceptible to enough detail and precision to make them valuable in soil survey. In fact, they were developed for just such a purpose. The function of a soil survey is to classify, locate on a base map, and describe the nature of soils as they occur in the field. The soils in the United States are classified into *series* and *types* on the basis of their profile characteristics. The field man, since his work is localized, concerns himself mostly with series and type separations, giving the broader regional distinctions only general consideration.

FIELD MAPPING. As the series and type identification progresses in the survey of any area, the location of each soil unit is shown on a suitable base map. The maps used in the United States are aerial base maps such as the one shown in Fig. 12:13. They have considerable advantage over the ordinary contour maps in that land cover and field boundaries show very clearly. Thus, the surveyor can quickly locate his position on the map and can indicate readily the soil boundaries. (See Fig. 12:14.)

---

[14] For an authoritative discussion of soil survey procedures and related features see "Soil Survey Manual," Agricultural Handbook No. 18, by Soil Survey Staff, Bur. of Plant Industry, Soils and Agr. Engineering, Wash., D.C., 1951. See also a series of articles on soil survey interpretation, *Proc. Soil Sci. Soc. Amer.* 22:152–70, 1958.

Figure 12:13. Soil survey maps are made using aerial photographs such as that above from Winneshiek County, Iowa. The field soil scientist is able to visualize quickly the topographic features of the section in which he is working. (Photo courtesy Soil Survey Division U.S. Soil Conservation Service.)

Using the procedure outlined above, a field map is thus obtained which not only gives the soil type and phase, but also often furnishes information as to slope and severity of erosion. Thus, the map becomes of even greater practical value.

The field map, after the separations have been carefully checked and correlated, is now ready for reproduction. In older maps this reproduction was made in color. For more recent maps a reproduction is made of the aerial photograph with the appropriate soil symbols shown on it. When published the map accompanies a bulletin containing a discussion of the topography, climate, agriculture, and soils of the area under consideration. Each soil type is minutely described as to profile and suggestions as to practical management are usually made. Such a field map is shown in Fig. 12:15 where the relationship of topography to soil associations can be seen readily.

Figure 12:14. Soil survey maps are prepared by soil scientists examining soils in the field (left) using a soil auger and other diagnostic tools. Mapping units are outlined on a topographic map (right) first in the field and finally more permanent in the map room. (Photo & map courtesy Soil Survey Division, U.S. Soil Conservation Service.)

USE OF SOIL SURVEYS. Soil-survey bulletins and maps are useful as a basis for other scientific work. Crop research of all kinds is facilitated if a soil survey has previously been made. Land evaluation

Figure 12:15. *Field examination makes possible the delineation of soil boundaries which are identified on the topographic map shown in Fig. 12:13, p. 347. The soil legend identifies the soil name (first two letters), the slope (second capital letter) and the degree of erosion (the number). Thus, OsC_2 is an Orwood silt loam (Os), with a 5–9% slope (C), and is moderately eroded (2). (Photo courtesy Soil Survey Division, U.S. Soil Conservation Service.)*

and appraisal, statistical studies, and sociological investigations are other
interests served.

There is a growing tendency to make use of soil survey maps and bulletins in a more practical way. The extension specialist and the county
agricultural agent find the survey maps and bulletins a guide in making
suggestions and recommendations. They afford information on the soils
and on the area surveyed that is impossible to obtain elsewhere.

In some cases simpler and more practical bulletins follow the rather
technical ones. The value of an illustrative means of showing the relationships among soil types within a given region can be seen by referring
to Fig. 12:11. A glance at this diagram shows the meaning and need for
classification. It also suggests that soil management must be accommodated to the soil type insofar as possible.

Engineers and hydrologists also use soil survey information in a practical way. Prospective road beds can be selected from soil survey maps.
Estimates of water runoff and infiltration can be made on the basis of
soil characteristics enumerated in soil-survey bulletins. Predictions can
be made of hydrologic changes in relation to modifications in land-use
patterns.

The soil survey in a practical way is perhaps of greatest value in land
classification for agricultural and other uses. The classification of most
concern to agriculturists is that in use by the United States Soil Conservation Service. Because of its widespread application it should be of
some interest.

12:27. LAND—CAPABILITY[15] CLASSIFICATION

Soil-survey maps and reports have become two of the bases for
a system of land-capability classification. This system requires that every
acre of land be used in accordance with its *capability* and *limitations*.
Land is classified according to the most suitable sustained use that can
be made of it while providing for adequate protection from erosion or
other means of deterioration. Thus, an area where the soils are deep,
well drained, and have a stable surface structure, and where the slope is

---

[15] At this point it may be well to point out the difference between *soil* and *land*.
Soil is the more restrictive term, referring to a collection of natural bodies with depth
as well as breadth, whose characteristics may be only indirectly related to their
current vegetation and use. Land is a broader term which includes among its characteristics, not only the soil, but other physical attributes such as water supply,
existing plant cover, and location with respect to cities, means of transportation, etc.
Thus, we have *forest land, bottom land,* and *grasslands* which may include a large
variety of soils.

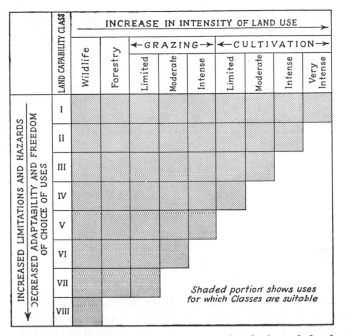

Figure 12:16. Diagram showing the intensity with which each land-capability class can be used with safety. Note the increasing limitations for which the land can be safely used as one moves from land-capability class I to class VIII. (Modified from R. D. Hackensmith, and J. G. Steele, "Recent Trends in the Use of the Land-Capability Classification," Proc. Soil Sci. Soc. Amer., 14; 383–88, 1949.)

only 1 to 2 per cent may be cropped intensively almost indefinitely with little danger of erosion or loss in productivity. Such an area has great capabilities and few limitations in the use to which it can be put. In contrast, an area on which shallow or poorly drained soils are found or wherein steep slopes are prevalent, has limited capabilities and many limitations as to its use. One can easily see how the characteristics of soils would be one of the criteria for identifying the best land use.

CAPABILITY CLASSES.[16]   Under the system set up by the United States Soil Conservation Service, eight land-capability classes are recognized. These classes are numbered from I to VIII. Soils having greatest capabilities for response to management and least limitations in the ways they can be used are in class I. Those with little capabilities and

---

[16] For a brief review of this subject see A. A. Klingebiel, "Soil Survey Interpretation—Capability Groupings," *Proc. Soil Sci., Soc. Amer.* 22:160–63, 1958. A somewhat more detailed discussion is given in *Administrator Memorandum SCS 136*, U.S. Dept. of Agric., May 19, 1958. These publications are the source of the descriptions of land capability classes used in this text.

great limitations are found in class VIII. (See Figs. 12:16 and 12:17.) A brief description of the characteristics and safe use of soils in each class follows:

CLASS I. Soils found in this land class have few limitations that restrict their use. They can be cropped intensively, used for pasture, range, woodlands, or even for wildlife preserves. The soils are deep, well drained and the land is nearly level. They are either naturally fertile, or have characteristics which encourage good response of crops to applications of fertilizer.

The water-holding capacity of soils in class I is high. In arid and semiarid areas soils having all the other favorable characteristics mentioned above may be in class I if they are irrigated by a permanent irrigation system.

The soils in class I need only ordinary crop-management practices to maintain their productivity. These include the use of fertilizer and lime and the return of manure and crop residues, including green manures. Crop rotations are also followed.

CLASS II. Soils in this class "have some limitations that reduce the choice of plants or require moderate conservation practices." These soils may be used for the same crops as class I. However, they are capable of sustaining less intensive cropping systems, or, with the same cropping systems, they require some conservation practices.

The use of soils in class II may be limited by one or more factors such as: (1) gentle slopes; (2) moderate erosion hazards; (3) inadequate soil depth; (4) less than ideal soil structure and workability; (5) slight to moderate alkali or saline conditions; and (6) somewhat restricted drainage.

The management practices that may be required for soils in class II include terracing, strip cropping, contour tillage, rotations involving grasses and legumes, and grassed waterways. In addition, those practices which are used on class I land are also generally required for soils in class II.

CLASS III. "Soils in class III have severe limitations that reduce the choice of plants or require special conservation practices or both." The same crops can be grown on class III land as on classes I and II. The amount of clean, cultivated land is restricted, however, as is the choice of the particular crop to be used. Crops which provide soil cover, such as grasses and legumes, must be more prominent in the rotations used.

Limitations in the use of soils in class III result from factors such as: (1) moderately steep slopes; (2) high erosion hazards; (3) very slow water permeability; (4) shallow depth and restricted root zone; (5) low

Figure 12:17. A photograph showing several land-capability classes in San Mateo County, California. A range is shown from the nearly level land in the foreground (class I) which can be cropped intensively, to that of the badly eroded hillsides (classes VII and VIII). Although topography and erosion hazards are emphasized here, it should be remembered that other factors such as drainage, stoniness, droughtiness, etc., also limit soil usage and help determine the land-capability class. (Photo by U.S. Soil Conservation Service.)

water-holding capacity; (6) low fertility; (7) moderate alkali or salinity; and (8) unstable soil structure.

Soils in class III often require special conservation practices. Those mentioned for class II land must be employed, frequently in combination with restrictions in kinds of crops. Tile or other drainage systems may also be needed.

CLASS IV. Soils in this class can be used for cultivation but there are very severe limitations on the choice of crops. Also, very careful management may be required. The alternative uses of these soils are more limited than for class III. Close-growing crops must be used extensively and row crops cannot be grown safely in most cases. The choice of crops may be limited by excess moisture as well as by erosion hazards.

The most limiting factors on these soils may be one or more of the following: (1) steep slopes; (2) severe erosion susceptibility; (3) severe past erosion; (4) shallow soils; (5) low water-holding capacity; (6) poor drainage; and (7) severe alkali or salinity. Soil conservation practices must be applied more frequently than on soils in class III. Also, they are usually combined with severe limitations in choice of crop.

CLASS V.   Soils in class V to VIII are generally not suited to cultivation. Those in class V are limited in their safe use by factors other than erosion hazards. Examples of such limitations follow: (1) subject to frequent stream overflow; (2) growing season too short for crop plants; (3) stony or rocky soils; and (4) ponded areas where drainage is not feasible. Oftentimes, pastures can be improved on this class of land.

CLASS VI.   Soils in this class have severe limitations that restrict their use largely to pasture or range, woodland, or wildlife. The limitations are the same as those for class IV land but they are more severe.

CLASS VII.   Soils in class VII have very severe limitations which restrict their use to grazing, woodland, or wildlife. The physical limitations are the same as VI except they are so severe that pasture improvement is impractical.

CLASS VIII.   In this land class are soils that should not be used for any kind of commercial plant production. Their use is restricted to "recreation, wildlife, water supply, or aesthetic purposes." Examples of kinds of soils or land forms included in class VIII are: sandy beaches, river wash, and rock outcrop.

SUBCLASSES.   In each of the land capability classes are *subclasses* which have the same kind of dominant limitations for agricultural use. The four kinds of limitations recognized in these subclasses are: risks of erosion (e), wetness, drainage, or overflow (w), root zone limitations (s), and climatic limitations (c). Thus, a soil may be found in class III (e), indicating that it is in class III because of risks of erosion.

This land-classification scheme illustrates the use which can be made of soil surveys in a practical way. The many soils delineated on a map by the soil surveyor are viewed in the light of their safest and best long-time use. The eight land capability classes have become the starting point in the development of farm plans so useful to thousands of American farmers.

Chapter 13

Organic Soils—Nature, Properties, and Utilization

On the basis of organic content, two general groups of soils are commonly recognized—mineral and organic. The so-called mineral soils vary in organic matter from a mere trace to as high as 15 or even 20 per cent. Those soils, the organic content of which ranges from 20 or 25 to as high in some cases as 90 or 95 per cent, are arbitrarily termed organic soils. For those that are cultivated, perhaps 80 per cent of organic matter is a good average figure.

Organic soils are by no means so extensive as are mineral soils, yet their acreage in the aggregate is quite large. Their use in favored localities for the intensive production of crops, particularly vegetables, has become very important. As the development of such lands goes on, more and more attention will be given to their investigation. In the past organic soils have not received the study that they deserve. As a result, less exact knowledge regarding their physical, chemical, and biological characteristics is available than for mineral soils. In general, however, the same edaphological principles hold in a broad way for both.

13:1. GENESIS OF ORGANIC DEPOSITS

Marshes, bogs, and swamps provide conditions suitable for the accumulation of organic deposits. The highly favorable environment in and adjacent to such areas has encouraged the growth of many plants, such as pondweed, cattails, sedges, reeds and other grasses, mosses, shrubs, and also trees. These plants in numberless generations thrive, die, and sink down to be covered by the water in which they grew. The water shuts out the air, prohibits rapid oxidation, and thus acts as a partial preservative. The decay that does go on is largely through the agency of fungi, anaerobic bacteria, algae, and certain types of microscopic aquatic animals. They break down the organic tissue, liberate gaseous constituents, and aid in the synthesis of humus.

As the process continues, the organic mass becomes brown or even black in color. If decomposition proceeds far enough, this mass of organic soil material acquires such profile characteristics as to justify its designation as a true organic soil. Apparently the humus now present is the result of ligno-protein unions and polyuronide formation much like the processes prevalent in mineral soils. (See p. 143.)

THE LAYERING OF PEAT BEDS. As one generation of plants follows another, layer after layer of organic residue is deposited in the swamp or marsh. The constitution of these successive layers changes as time goes on since a sequence of different plant life is likely to occur. Thus, deep-water plants may be supplanted by reeds and sedges, these by various mosses, and these in turn by shrubs, until finally forest trees, either hardwoods or conifers, with their characteristic undergrowth, may gain a foothold. The succession is by no means regular, or definite, as a slight change in climate or water level may alter the sequence entirely.

The profile of an organic deposit is, therefore, characterized by layers, differing not only as to their degree of decomposition but also as to the nature of the original plant tissue. In fact, these layers later may have become soil horizons. Their final character is determined in part by the nature of the original materials and in part by the type and degree of decomposition. Thus, the profile characteristics of organic soils, as with those dominantly mineral in nature, are in part inherited and in part acquired.

13:2. AREA AND DISTRIBUTION
OF PEAT ACCUMULATIONS

As might be expected, peat deposits are found all over the world wherever the conditions are favorable. But only in certain countries are these accumulations utilized in any intensive way. In Germany, Holland, Norway, Sweden, Russia, Poland, Ireland, England, and Scotland, economic use has long been made of peat and peat products. Organic deposits in Germany occupy perhaps 5,000,000 acres, in Sweden 12,000,000 and in Ireland 3,000,000 acres. Canada possesses approximately 12,000,-000 acres of peat, mostly undeveloped.

IN NONGLACIATED UNITED STATES. Organic deposits of the nature described occur in many parts of the United States. In Florida the Everglades, spread out over an extensive plain, contain considerably over 2,000,000 acres of saw-grass (sedge) accumulations. Along the Atlantic coastal plain great marsh deposits are found, especially in North Carolina. In California there are the tule-reed beds of the great central valley, approximately 300,000 acres in extent. Louisiana alone possesses about 3,000,000 acres of organic soils. All of these are southward and outside of the glaciated areas of the United States. They are related only indirectly to the glaciation through a change in climate and a rise in ocean level due to the melting of the ice.

IN GLACIATED UNITED STATES. Northward in the regions covered by glacial debris of various kinds, organic deposits are even more extended. In fact, about 75 per cent of the peat deposits of continental United States occur in the glaciated areas. Minnesota, Wisconsin, and Michigan are especially favored in this respect, their combined acreage running well above 12,000,000 acres. Washington, with about 2,000,000 acres, ranks highest of all the Western states. Indiana, Massachusetts, New York, and New Jersey fall into the 300,000- to 500,-000-acre class. Other states, especially Iowa, Illinois and Maine, contain smaller but often very important areas.

The total acreage of peat deposits in the United States proper is in the neighborhood of 25,000,000 acres. In Alaska and northern Canada, and in northern Asia and Europe as well, there occur great areas of peat derived from sedges and mosses called *muskeg*. In many cases the subhorizons of such accumulations are perpetually frozen. They are an important feature of the tundra soils that characterize these regions. (See p. 327.)

The Pleistocene glaciation by impeding drainage led to the formation of swamps and bogs. As the climate became milder and gradually attained its present status, conditions were ideal for swamp vegetation to flourish. As a result, certain parts of the glaciated region are liberally dotted with organic accumulations ranging from a few inches to 50 feet in depth. Some areas, a number of square miles in extent, are solidly occupied as in Minnesota, while in other localities the peat lies in isolated patches or in long ribbons as in southeastern Wisconsin and in central New York. Both of the latter accumulations are in many cases associated with drumlins. (See p. 287.) These long, cigar-shaped hills when parallel often alternate with narrow swamps several miles in length that are filled with organic matter in various stages of decay.

13:3. CLASSIFICATION OF PEAT— DESCRIPTION OF THE VARIOUS TYPES

Peat, regardless of its stage of decomposition, may conveniently be classified according to its parent materials and under three general heads as follows:

Classification of Peat[1]

1. Sedimentary peat ⎰ mixtures of water lilies, pondweed, hornwort, pollen, plankton, etc.

2. Fibrous peat ⎰ sedges of various kinds, mosses—sphagnum, hypnum, and others, reeds and other grasses, cattails, both latifolia and angustifolia ⎱ and their mixtures

3. Woody peat ⎰ deciduous and coniferous trees ⎱ and their undergrowth

SEDIMENTARY PEAT. Sedimentary peat usually accumulates in comparatively deep water and, therefore, generally is found well

---

[1] In Germany peats are classified in a general way into *high-moor* and *low-moor* in reference to the shape of the deposits. The high-moors are convex, that is, raised in the center; the low-moors are concave. The former is usually quite acid and low in calcium, the latter less acid and quite high in exchangeable calcium.

In England the corresponding terms are *moor* and *fen*. The term *heathland* refers to a shallow acid peat.

For a discussion of American peats and their classification, see A. P. Dachnowski-Stokes, and V. Auer, "American Peat Deposits," *Handbuch der Moorkunde*, Gebrüder Borntraeger, Berlin, 1933, Band 7.

down in the profile. Sometimes, however, it is intermixed with the other types of peat nearer the surface. Sedimentary peat seems to be derived from plant materials that humify rather freely and rather completely. Due to the nature of the original tissue and perhaps also to the type of decay, a highly colloidal and characteristically compact and *rubbery* substance develops. This material is unique and so different from the other types of peat commonly found in the profile that it always attracts considerable attention when encountered.

Not only is sedimentary peat rubbery in character but it is usually olive green when in its natural position. On exposure to the atmospheric air it darkens rapidly, sometimes becoming almost black. Due to its highly colloidal nature, its moisture capacity is high, perhaps four or five times its dry weight. Water thus imbibed is held tenaciously and therefore this peat dries out very slowly. The colloidal materials of sedimentary peat are largely irreversible—that is, when once dry, this peat absorbs water very slowly and persistently remains in a *hard* and *lumpy* condition.

Sedimentary peat is thus very undesirable as a soil, because its unfavorable physical condition renders it unsatisfactory for use in the growing of plants. Even small amounts in the furrow-slice lower the desirability of the peat for agricultural purposes. Fortunately, in most cases, it occurs well down in the profile and ordinarily does not appear above the plowline. Therefore, its presence usually is unnoticed or ignored unless it obstructs drainage or otherwise interferes with the agricultural utilization of the peat deposit.

FIBROUS PEAT. As indicated by the classification just presented, a number of fibrous peats occur, often in the same swamp deposit. They are all high in water-holding capacity, and may exhibit varying degrees of decomposition. They differ among themselves especially as to their filamentous or fibrous physical nature. Undecomposed moss and sedge are fine enough to be used in greenhouses and nurseries and as a source of organic matter for gardens and flower beds. Reed and cattails, however, are somewhat coarse, especially the latter.

All of the fibrous materials as they decay may make satisfactory field soils although their productivity will vary. Moss peats are almost invariably quite acid and relatively low in ash and nitrogen. The sedges are intermediate in these respects, while cattail peats are not so acid and have a better nutrient balance. Fibrous peats may occur at the surface of the organic accumulation of which they are a part or well down in the profile. They usually lie above the sedimentary deposit when this type of peat is present. Nevertheless, if just the right fluctuation of conditions has occurred a stratum of sedimentary peat may lie imbedded within the fibrous peat horizons and rather near the surface.

WOODY PEAT. Since trees are the vegetation present in many swamp deposits, woody peat is usually at the surface of the organic accumulation. This is not an invariable rule, however, since a rise in water level might kill the trees and so favor reed, sedge, or cattail as to give a layer of fibrous material over the woody accumulation. It is not particularly surprising, therefore, to find subhorizon layers of woody peat.

Woody peat is brown or black in color when wet, according to the degree of humidification. It is loose and open when dry or merely moist, and decidedly nonfibrous in character. Virgin deposits often are notably granular. It is thus easily distinguished from the other two types of peat unless the samples are unusually well disintegrated and decomposed.

Woody peat develops from the residues not only of deciduous and coniferous trees but also from the shrubs and other plants that occupy the forest floor of the swamp. Maple, elm, tamarack, hemlock, spruce, cedar, pine, and other trees occur as the climax vegetation in swamps of temperate regions. In spite of the great number of plants that contribute to its accumulation, woody peat is rather homogeneous unless it contains admixtures of fibrous materials.

The water capacity of woody peat is somewhat lower than that of sedge peats, which in turn is much less than that of moss peats. For that reason woody peat is less desirable than the others for use in greenhouses and nurseries where such materials are used as a means of moisture control and a compost conditioner. Woody residues produce a field soil, however, that is quite superior and much prized for the growing of vegetables and other crops. Such woody peats, unfortunately, are confined in general to Wisconsin, Michigan, and New York.

13:4. VARIOUS USES OF PEAT

NURSERIES, GREENHOUSES, AND LAWNS. Peat is utilized in a number of ways, depending on the nature of the material. In the United States, Canada, and Europe the more or less undecomposed products are very commonly employed as a source of organic matter. This is true of moss and sedge peat. When incorporated with mineral soil in sufficient quantities, peat not only insures a good physical condition but markedly increases the water capacity of the mixture. Soils for potting and other purposes are greatly benefited physically by its use. It is thus valuable in greenhouses, gardens, flower beds, and nurseries both as a soil amendment and as a mulch around growing plants of all kinds.

Peat is likewise useful in the preparation of lawn soils, of golf greens, and in numerous other ways where tilth and organic matter are important factors. While the undecayed materials are generally utilized for such purposes, the humified products are on occasion also employed. They are often just as satisfactory and in some instances even superior to the less decayed types.

AS BEDDING, LITTER, AND PACKING. Peat, especially the sedge and moss types, may be used in stables as bedding and litter. Such material readily absorbs and conserves the liquid manure, and when the mixture is applied to the soil, the peat contributes a considerable amount of slowly decomposing organic matter. However, the presence of the liquid and solid manure activates the organic matter of the peat and renders its decomposition more rapid than otherwise would be the case. Peat is likewise utilized in poultry houses as a litter under the roosts and in the runways. Sphagnum and other suitable forms of fibrous peats even serve as packing materials. They also are good insulating materials.

AS FUEL. In Holland, Germany, Belgium, Ireland, and other countries of Europe, peat is dug out in brickette form, dried thoroughly, and used as fuel. Thus, vast amounts of Dutch and German peat have not only been used locally, but also were shipped considerable distances for industrial purposes. In lands where wood is scarce and coal expensive, peat deposits are an exceedingly valuable natural resource. In Holland the excavation of peat has been so regulated as to leave the site well drained and in such a condition that field crops can be grown, aided by the portions of the organic matter that, by law, must be left behind. Some of the most productive agricultural areas in Holland lie on the site of these reclaimed and properly exploited bogs. Such soils must be heavily treated, of course, with commercial fertilizer.

FIELD SOILS. In the United States the most extensive use of peat is as a field soil, especially for vegetable production. Thousands of acres are now under cultivation, often producing two crops a year. In some respects the vegetable industry has been revolutionized by the exceedingly favorable nature of these organic soils when adequately drained and properly fertilized. Peats for such use should be well decomposed, the decay often having gone so far as to make it almost impossible to identify with certainty the various plants that have contributed to the accumulation. As the following pages indicate, the edaphological interest in peat relates mainly to its use as a natural soil and not as an artificial and commercial product for greenhouse, nursery, or factory consumption.

However, more and more of the processed peat is appearing on the market both in Canada and in the United States. Such material is mostly sedge and moss, undecomposed or only slightly decayed. With great quantities of suitable material available, there is no reason why the demand within the United States should not be met with a domestic product, rather than, as heretofore, with imports.

13:5. MUCK VERSUS PEAT— MUCK SOILS

Organic deposits are generally classified on the basis of their state of decomposition.[2] Those deposits that are slightly or nondecayed are termed *peat*, while those that are markedly decomposed are called *muck*. In peat deposits, one is able to differentiate the kinds of plants which were deposited, especially in the upper horizons. By contrast, muck is generally decomposed to the point where the original plant parts cannot be identified.

Peat may be quite coarse- or fine-structured depending on the nature of the deposited plant residues. Well-decomposed mucks on the other hand, are often quite fine since the original plant structure has broken down. When dry, they may be quite powdery and subject to wind erosion.

13:6. PEAT SOILS—THEIR CLASSIFICATION AND PROFILE SEQUENCE

Since the parent materials influence so definitely the physical and chemical properties of the resultant peat soils, any classification must take these original substances into account. The following grouping is simple and to anyone familiar with peat soils, very convenient as well. Since sedimentary peat is seldom near the surface on good peat land, and when so located is physically very undesirable, it is not included in the peat soil classification presented below:

Classification of Peat Soils
Based on Parent Materials

Fibrous peat soils
- (1) sedges of various kinds
- (2) mosses—sphagnum, hypnum and others
- (3) reeds and other grasses
- (4) cattails—latifolia and angustifolia

(5) and their mixtures

---

[2] In an earlier edition of this textbook, the distinction between muck and peat was on the basis of their content of mineral matter. Deposits containing from 20 to 50 per cent organic matter were called *muck;* those containing more than 50 per cent were classed as peats. Since the more dominant usage in the literature is as indicated above, the distinction based on degree of decomposition will be adhered to.

Woody peat soils { (1) deciduous and (2) coniferous trees and (3) undergrowth. In some cases, unfortunately, woody peats sometimes carry an admixture of rubbery material.

INHERITED VS. ACQUIRED CHARACTERISTICS. It is to be especially noted that the classification of peat soils is almost identical with the grouping of the original soil materials. (See p. 358.) This is because the parent substances so definitely determine the nature of the profile that no other scheme of classification is nearly so satisfactory. With mineral soils the situation is quite different. Although parent materials are very important, the profile characteristics of a well-developed zonal mineral soil are a reflection in large degree of climate. In other words, *acquired* characteristics rather than those *inherited* from the original materials dominate the profile (p. 297). The contrast presented by peat soils is noteworthy and of great practical significance.

It was found in the consideration of mineral soils that their genesis, their outstanding characteristics, and their plant relationship could not be clearly understood without some knowledge of their profiles. The same is true of peat soils. The next logical step, therefore, is to inquire into the profile sequence of organic soils.

PEAT PROFILES. Ideally, one might expect that the profile succession of peat soils would be rather definite for any region and especially for any particular bog. In many plots of Michigan, Wisconsin, and central New York, for instance, sedimentary peat is found mostly near the bottom of the profile, fibrous material of some kind comes next with woody peat, if the climax vegetation is attained, at the surface. (See Fig. 13:1.) These materials have been laid down through so-called *progressive* development under conditions of relatively stable water table. But if there have been radical changes in the water table, the succession ultimately attained may be quite different. Thus, woody peat is sometimes found below the surface of accumulation, covered by deposits that ideally should be encountered beneath. Admixing of the layers may further obscure the sequence. Hence, it sometimes is difficult to forecast, except in a broad way, the horizon order of the peat soil of any particular bog.

Again the profile may be immature, the possible succession of plants and their resultant accumulation having only well begun. Thus in New York, Michigan, and Wisconsin, the climax vegetation, as already suggested, is forest. Yet the surface peat in many beds may be derived from the decomposition of mosses or sedges or cattail or their intermixture, with a limited sequence or even no other organic horizons below. Thus, the arrangement of the profile layers in a peat bed are not always pre-

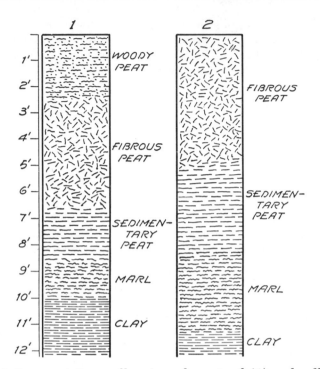

Figure 13:1. *Representative profiles of woody peat soil (1) and a fibrous peat soil (2). The woody peat is, of course, the more desirable as a field soil. Note the presence in both profiles of rubbery sedimentary peat and of marl. (After Wilson and Staker.)*

dictable. As a result, Figs. 13:1 and 13:2 only suggest in a tentative way what actually may be encountered under field conditions.

13:7. PHYSICAL CHARACTERISTICS OF FIELD PEAT SOILS

In spite of the many kinds of peat soils encountered in various parts of the United States, a generalized description will be ventured in respect to their outstanding physical characteristics. Such statements will apply merely to that portion of the organic accumulation that normally occurs in the furrow-slice of cultivated peats. This layer determines in part the suitability of the deposits for successful crop production. For a view of peat under cropping see Fig. 13:3.

COLOR.   The color of a typical cultivated peat soil, dark brown or intensely black when it is wet, is perhaps the first physical character-

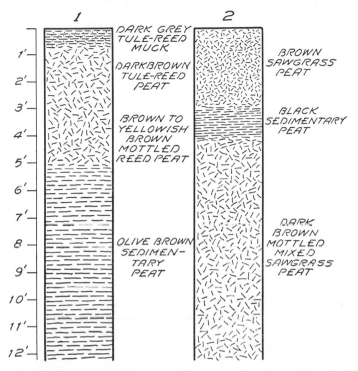

Figure 13:2. Generalized profiles of (1) San Joaquin tule-reed peat soil of the Mandeville type, and (2) Florida saw-grass peat soil of the Okeelanta type. (After Dacknowski-Stokes' description.)

istic that attracts the attention. Although the original materials may be gray, brown, or reddish-brown, dark humid compounds appear as decomposition advances. In general, the changes that the organic matter undergoes seem to be somewhat similar to those occurring to the organic residues of mineral soils in spite of the restricted aeration of the peat.

BULK DENSITY. The second outstanding characteristic is the light weight of the representative peat soil when dry. The bulk density (volume weight) compared with mineral surface soils is surprisingly low, 0.20 to 0.30 perhaps being a fair estimate. A cultivated surface mineral soil will usually fall within the limits of 1.25 to 1.45. A cubic foot of peat soil will contain from 8 to 20 pounds of dry matter, depending on its original source, the condition of the layer and the admixture of mineral materials. An acre-furrow-slice of the depth common in mineral soils, while variable, may be considered to weigh 400,000 or perhaps 500,000 pounds when dry. Compared with the 2,000,000 or 2,500,000 pounds ordinarily considered as the dry weight of an acre-furrow-slice of a representative mineral soil, such figures seem small indeed.

WATER CAPACITY. A third important property of peat soil is its high water-holding capacity, one of the characteristics of highly colloidal solids and especially developed by organic matter in such a state. While a dry mineral soil will adsorb and hold from one fifth to two fifths its weight of water, a peat soil will retain two or perhaps three or four times its dry weight of moisture, depending on conditions.[3] This water-holding capacity, possibly ten times greater by weight than that of mineral soils, is very important in the growing of vegetables. With such crops the presence of an abundant water supply is essential.

It must not be hastily assumed, however, that peats in the field greatly surpass mineral soils in their capacity to supply plants with water. Two conditions militate against the organic soils. In the first place, their amounts of unavailable water are much higher proportionately than that of mineral soils. Again, since the comparative figures quoted are on the basis of dry weight, the peat soils with their low bulk densities are at a considerable disadvantage. When considered on the volume basis, a given layer of peat soil at optimum moisture will supply somewhat more water to plants than a representative mineral soil also at optimum. But not in such excess as the figures quoted in the preceding paragraph might lead one to expect.

STRUCTURE. A fourth outstanding characteristic of a typical woody or fibrous peat soil is its almost invariably good physical condition. While decayed organic matter is, in large degree, colloidal and possesses high adsorptive powers, its cohesion and plasticity are rather low. A peat soil of good quality is therefore porous, open, and easy to cultivate. These characteristics make it especially desirable for vegetable production. However, during dry periods, the lightness and looseness of peat, the granular condition of which has been reduced by cultivation, may drift badly in a high wind and extensive crop damage may result. It may also become ignited when dry and support a smoldering fire to such an extent as greatly to decrease or even destroy its usefulness. Such a fire often is difficult to put out and may continue for several years.

In suggesting that the surface layer of an arable peat soil is likely to be granular, it is not to be inferred that the whole profile is in this structural condition also. Far from it. All sorts of physical arrangements are encountered in the subhorizons, such as laminated, vertical, fragmental, fibrous, and rubbery. The variability from horizon to horizon is determined not only by the character of the original materials, but also by the nature and degree of decomposition.

---

[3] Undecayed or only slightly decomposed moss or sedge peat in contrast with their soils have a much greater water-holding capacity. Not uncommonly such materials can hold water to the extent of 12, 15, or even 20 times their dry weights. This explains in part their value in greenhouse and nursery operations.

13:8. THE COLLOIDAL NATURE OF PEAT SOILS

Because of the very high content of organic matter and the particular type of humidification that occurs, the colloidality of peat soils is strikingly beyond that exhibited by most mineral soil colloids. Their surface area exceeds even that of montmorillonite clay perhaps two, three, or even four times, and cation-exchange capacities are correspondingly greater. However, in spite of differences as to original tissue and conditions of genesis, the humus of peat soils greatly resembles that of mineral soils except for the intensity of the colloidal properties. For instance, it has been suggested that the cation-exchange capacity of a mineral soil is enhanced approximately 2 milliequivalents for every gram increase in humus (p. 98.) The figure for peat soils, especially if they are woody in origin, is somewhat higher in general, perhaps in the neighborhood of 3 milliequivalents for every gram of dry organic matter.

FORMULA AND CALCIUM CONTENT. Not only can the same graphic formula employed for mineral soils— $\text{H} \begin{array}{c} \text{Ca} \\ \boxed{\text{Micelle}} \\ \text{B} \end{array}$ —

be used to represent the colloidal complex of peat, but it is noteworthy that the same metallic cations are adsorbed by the two types of soil, and in the same order of magnitude, namely, Ca > Mg > K or Na. (See pp. 92–93.) This important difference is to be noted, however. The amount of adsorbed calcium is very much greater than is the case with mineral soils. That this is likely to be true, whether the peat is comparatively low lime

Table 13:1. Cationic Condition of Two New York Woody-peat Soils—One Low and the Other High in Lime[a]

Exchange Characteristics	Ca	Mg	K	Na
Exch. metallic cations, m.e. 100 g:				
Low-lime peat	39.8	9.7	0.87	0.80
High-lime peat	159.7	12.0	1.16	0.87
Percentage of each cation in exchange- able condition:				
Low-lime peat	80	100	34	. . .
High-lime peat	75	51	27	. . .

[a] Calculated from B. D. Wilson and E. V. Staker, *Ionic Exchange of Peat Soils,* Memoir 172, Cornell Univ. Agr. Exp. Sta., 1935.

or high lime, is apparent from the data of Table 13:1. The two soils in question are New York woody peats. The total calcium content of the low-lime peat is 1.40 per cent of CaO and its cation exchange capacity is 184 milliequivalents. The corresponding figures for the high-lime soil are 6.00 per cent of CaO and 265 milliequivalents cation-exchange capacity.

The data of Table 13:1 show that most of the calcium present in peat soils and a very large proportion of the magnesium are in an exchangeable condition. Moreover, approximately one third of the total potassium is exchangeable. All this is strikingly in contrast with a mineral soil where usually less than 35 per cent of the calcium, less than 10 per cent of the magnesium, and less than 1 per cent of the total potassium are exchangeable. (See Fig. 2:3.)

STRENGTH OF ACIDS. The pH of peat soils, as with mineral soils, is controlled by the colloidal complex, its percentage base saturation being a major factor (p. 101). The ratio of the metallic cation and the nature of the micelle also exert an influence, the latter being especially important. In general, the colloidal complex of peat when saturated with hydrogen will develop a lower soil pH than will acid mineral clays similarly charged. In other words, the peat complex is the stronger acid. This means that at the same percentage base saturation peats will be somewhat more acid than mineral soils.

BUFFERING. Since the buffering of a soil is determined in large degree by the magnitude of its cation-exchange capacity, peat soils in general show an unusually marked resistance to a change in pH, much greater, of course, than do mineral soils. As a consequence, considerably more sulfur or lime is necessary to change the pH of a peat soil than to effect a similar modification in a mineral soil at a corresponding buffer level. However, the buffer curve obtained by plotting pH against percentage base saturation is of the same general order as that for mineral soils (p. 393), except that the pH at 50 per cent base saturation is somewhat less.

LIME LOSS. Because of the large amount of exchangeable calcium and magnesium in representative peat soils and the marked evolution of carbon dioxide if such soils are drained and under cultivation, cation exchange is even more active than in mineral soils. As a consequence, the drainage waters from peat swamps and bogs usually not only carry large amounts of lime, but they are likely to be alkaline also. However, the loss of lime from most peat bogs is not serious, because of the high initial content of this constituent. Moreover, a rise of the water table that often occurs in the spring may tend to restore somewhat the bases carried downward during the previous season. In general, the lime content of cultivated peat soils is reduced to the point where this constituent is critical only in special cases.

EXCHANGE DATA. In order that the cation-exchange prop-
erties may be visualized a little more concretely, further data are offered
about the two woody-peat surface soils already discussed, one comparatively low in lime, the other rather high. The exchange data, already
quoted on page 103, for a representative humid-region mineral soil, are
offered in contrast. (See Table 13:2.)

13:9. CHEMICAL COMPOSITION OF ORGANIC SOILS

While organic soils are even more variable chemically than mineral soils, as the data below[4] indicate, certain outstanding and fairly constant characteristics are in evidence. In order to present these more clearly,
a representative analysis of the surface layer of an arable peat soil is given
(Table 13:3), but with the understanding that it is merely suggestive.
The chemical analysis of the upper layer of a representative humid-
region mineral soil is cited for comparison and contrast.

NITROGEN AND ORGANIC MATTER. The high nitrogen
and organic content of peat soils are self-evident and need no further
emphasis here. But there are two interrelated features in respect to these
constituents that do justify further consideration. First, peat soils have
a wide carbon-nitrogen ratio, the minimum being in the neighborhood

[4] Chemical analyses of certain representative peat soils in percentage based on dry
matter are shown in the following table:

Source	Nature	Organic Matter	N	P_2O_5	K_2O	CaO
Minnesota	(low lime)	93.0	2.22	0.18	0.07	0.40
Minnesota	(high lime)	79.8	2.78	0.24	0.10	3.35
Michigan	(low lime)	77.5	2.10	0.26	...	0.16
Michigan	(high lime)	85.1	2.08	0.25	...	6.80
German	(low lime)	97.0	1.20	0.10	0.05	0.35
German	(high lime)	90.0	2.50	0.25	0.10	4.00
Austria	(low lime)	93.3	1.40	0.10	0.06	0.45
Austria	(high lime)	83.8	2.10	0.18	0.13	2.38
New York	(low lime)	94.2	1.26	0.15	0.10	0.60
New York	(high lime)	81.5	2.56	0.19	0.28	6.51
Minnesota	(low organic)	59.7	2.35	0.36	0.17	2.52
Minnesota	(high organic)	94.0	1.70	0.16	0.04	0.31
Florida	(sawgrass peat)	87.1	2.79	0.41	0.04	5.20
Canada	(peat soil)	74.3	2.19	0.20	0.16	...
Washington	(woody sedge peat)	89.2	3.52	0.43	0.09	1.29

These data were gathered from a number of sources. See T. L. Lyon; H. O. Buckman; and N. C. Brady, *The Nature and Properties of Soils* (New York: Macmillan,
1952), p. 381.

of 20. In contrast, this equilibrium ratio for a cropped mineral soil is usually around 10 to 12.

Table 13:2. Exchange Data for Two Woody-peat Surface Soils[a] and for a Representative Humid-region Mineral Surface Soil (Expressed in Milliequivalents per 100 G)

	Woody Peats		Humid-region
Exchange Characteristics	*Low Lime*	*High Lime*	*Mineral Soil*
Exchangeable Ca	39.8 m.e.	159.7 m.e.	6 to 9 m.e.
Other exch. bases, B	21.7 "	43.4 "	2 to 3 "
Exchangeable H	122.3 "	62.0 "	4 to 6 "
Total exch. capacity	183.8 "	265.1 "	12 to 18 "
Percentage base saturation	33.5	76.6	66.6
pH	4.0	5.1	5.6–5.8

[a] Calculated from B. D. Wilson and E. V. Staker, *Ionic Exchange of Peat Soils,* Memoir 172, Cornell Univ. Agr. Exp. Sta., 1935.

Second, peat soils, in spite of their wide carbon-nitrogen ratio, generally show exceedingly vigorous nitrification. In fact, the nitrate accumulation, even in a low-lime peat, is usually greater than that of a representative mineral soil. This can only be explained on the basis of the large amount of nitrogen carried by the peat, the presence of adequate calcium, and the inactivity of part of the carbon. Thus, the *effective* carbon-nitrogen ratio of peats may be as narrow as that of mineral soils. As a result, the multiplication of the competitive general-purpose heterotrophic organ-

Table 13:3. Suggested Analysis for a Representative Peat and a Mineral-surface Soil, Respectively, Expressed in Per Cent Based on Dry-matter

Constituent	*Peat Surface Soil*	*Mineral Surface Soil*
Organic matter	80.00	4.00
Nitrogen (N)	2.50	0.15
Phosphorus (P)	0.09	0.04
Pottassium (K)	0.08	1.70
Calcium (Ca)	2.80	0.40
Magnesium (Mg)	0.30	0.30
Sulfur (S)	0.60	0.04

isms is not excessively encouraged. The nitrifiers, therefore, are given ample opportunity to oxidize the ammoniacal nitrogen.

PHOSPHORUS AND POTASSIUM. The phosphorus and potassium of peat are both low, the latter exceedingly so in comparison with a mineral soil. Even the phosphoric acid is actually less in pounds per acre-furrow-slice. On this basis, the representative mineral soil is cited as containing 2,000 pounds of P_2O_5. An equivalent layer of peat soil (say 500,000 pounds) would furnish only 1,000 pounds of P_2O_5 or one-half as much. This explains why, in the growing of crops on a peat soil, phosphorus as well as potash must be applied in large amounts.

CALCIUM AND pH. The high calcium content of peat soil is easily explained. Much of the water entering swamps is from seepage and has had ample opportunity of dissolving lime in its passage through the subsoil and substratum of the surrounding uplands. Since decaying organic matter is highly adsorptive and calcium ions plentiful, the re- sultant peat horizons cannot avoid the presence of large amounts of exchangeable calcium ions. Nor is leaching, as with mineral soils, such an important factor in robbing the surface layers of lime. High lime, most of which is exchangeable, is an outstanding characteristic of many peat soils, especially those of woody origin.

In spite of this high lime content, the majority of peat soils are dis- tinctly acid, often very markedly so. For instance, the average pH of twelve woody-peat soils from Oswego County, New York, was 5.3 in spite of an average CaO content of 3.74 per cent.[5] So great are the cation adsorption capacities of peat soils that they may be at a low percentage base saturation and yet be carrying exceptionally large amounts of ex- changeable calcium. At the same time the percentage base saturation (see p. 368) is such as to assure a markedly acid condition.

MAGNESIUM AND SULFUR. The percentage of magne- sium in peat soil is usually no greater than that of a mineral soil. The actual amount, however, is much less due to the low dry-weight of peat by volume. (See p. 365.) The situation is thus much the same as that of phosphoric acid, although it is alleviated somewhat by the high pro- portion of the magnesium that is held in an exchangeable condition. Peat soils, long intensively cropped, may possibly develop a magnesia defi- ciency unless fertilizers carrying this constituent have been used. Since most peats are seldom limed, there is little chance of adding magnesium in this particular way.

The abundance of sulfur in peat soils is not at all surprising. Plant tissue always contains considerable sulfur, and as a consequence, organic deposits such as peat should be comparatively high in this constituent. When sulfur oxidation is vigorous, as is usually the case with arable peat soils, sulfates may accumulate. At times a white incrustation, probably

[5] B. D. Wilson, and E. V. Staker, *The Chemical Composition of the Muck Soils of New York,* Bulletin 537, Cornell Univ. Agr. Exp. Sta., 13, 1932.

calcium sulfate (gypsum), can be observed along ditches and at other places on the surface of peat deposits where the upward movement and the evaporation of moisture is taking place. Sulfur is abundant enough in most peat soils to reduce the possibility of this element being a limiting factor in plant growth.

ANOMALOUS FEATURES. Peat soils in comparison with mineral soils have been shown to exhibit three somewhat anomalous features. They are worthy of restatement. *First,* the representative peat soil possesses a wide carbon-nitrogen ratio and yet in spite of this it supports a very vigorous nitrification. *Second,* peat soils are usually comparatively high in lime and yet may be definitely acid, often highly so. And *third,* in the presence of a high H-ion concentration, nitrate accumulation takes place far beyond that common in mineral soils with the same low pH. This last feature indicates that in many peat soils the H-ion concentration does not impede, in itself, this very important biochemical transformation. Apparently, the high calcium content and the low content of iron, aluminum and manganese in peats account for this anomaly.

13:10. BOG LIME—ITS IMPORTANCE

In many cases peat soils are underlain at varying depths by a soft impure calcium carbonate called *bog lime* or *marl.*[6] Its probable position in the profile is indicated by Fig. 13:1. Such a deposit may come from the shells of certain of the Mollusca, which have inhabited the basin, or from aquatic plants, such as mosses, algae, and species of Chara. These organisms have the power of precipitating the calcium as insoluble calcium carbonate. It seems that these plants and animals occupied the basin before or in some cases during the formation of the peat, the marl resulting from the accumulation of their residues on the bottom of the basin or farther up in the profile.

Marl is a white or gray, soft, crumbly material, often full of shells. It effervesces freely with dilute hydrochloric acid which suggests that it is largely calcium carbonate. When the deposit is extensive enough and the presence of water or the thickness of the overburden do not interfere too much, marl may be dug out, dried and pulverized, and used as agricultural lime. In general, however, it cannot compete in price with ground limestone, although on the basis of calcium content it is often just as satisfactory a form of lime.

---

[6] Bog lime is usually spoken of agriculturally as *marl.* Marl, as correctly used by the geologist, refers to a calcareous clay of variable composition. Bog lime, when it contains numerous shells, is often termed *shell marl.*

In cases in which marl is present, it may not only supply calcium to the circulating waters, but if high in the profile, may actually become mixed with the surface peat. As a result, such peats are likely to be low in acidity or even alkaline. In general, an alkaline peat is not considered as highly desirable for intensive culture, especially the growing of vegetables, as are moderately acid peats.

13:11. FACTORS THAT DETERMINE THE VALUE OF PEAT AND MUCK SOILS

DRAINAGE AND WATER TABLE. The value of peat agriculturally will depend on a number of factors. Of first consideration is the possibility of drainage, that is, a more or less permanent lowering and control of the water table sufficient to allow an adequate aeration of the root zone during the growing season. Oftentimes, however, such drainage is expensive and may require the cooperation of a number of landowners, some of whom may have no interest in the utilization of the peat.

Moreover, it may be advantageous to raise or lower the water table of peat soils at various times during the season. For instance, celery at setting is benefited by plenty of moisture. As the crop develops, the water table should be gradually lowered to accommodate the root development. The probable cost of drainage and of the seasonal control of the moisture may be such as to make the reclamation of a peat bed economically unwise. Since peat is very often covered with a forest growth, the cost of clearing also must be reckoned with. In some cases this cost may be rather high.

DEPTH AND QUALITY. Peat settles considerably during the first few years after drainage and cultivation have become operative, and may continue to shrink appreciably in after years.[7] If a depth adequate for cropping does not remain, the expense of reclamation is more or less thrown away. Three or 4 feet of organic material are desirable, especially if calcareous clay or marl underlies the deposit.

The quality of the peat is of special importance, not only as to the degree of decay, but also as to the nature of the original plant materials. The presence of the rubbery sedimentary type in the furrow-slice is especially deplorable. (See p. 359.) Woody peat, on the other hand, is

7 See N. K. Ellis and R. Morris, "Preliminary Observations on the Relation of Yield of Crops Grown on Organic Soils with Controlled Water Table and the Area of Aeration in the Soil and Subsidence of the Soil," *Proc. Soil Sci. Soc. Amer.*, 10:282–83, 1945. These authors report a shrinkage in general of 1 inch in 10 years. See also J. E. Dawson, "Organic Soils," *Advan. in Agron.*, 8:378–401, 1956.

generally considered more desirable than that coming from cattails, reeds and other plants and it usually is highly prized wherever it occurs. Much of the United States acreage of this type of peat soil lies in Wisconsin, Michigan, and New York.

13:12. PREPARATION OF PEAT FOR CROPPING

Since peat soils are often forested or covered with shrubs and other plants, the first step is to clear the land. Drainage may then be facilitated further, and the water table lowered and brought under control. The utilization of the area as pasture for a few years is sometimes practiced. The roots and stumps are thus given time to decay, their removal being relatively easy when the land is finally fitted for cultivation.

If the peat area is burned over to remove the brush and other debris, it should be done early in the season while the land is wet and not likely to catch fire. Such a fire is often difficult to extinguish and may ruin the deposit by destroying the more fertile surface layer. Moreover, the acrid smoke may seriously impair the quality of certain neighboring crops. Tokay grapes in central California are a case in point. If, however, the surface soil is fibrous with a more desirable layer below, it may be of advantage to burn this part, the resultant ash serving to mineralize the newly exposed layers.

After breaking the peat soil, preferably with heavy plows drawn by a tractor powerful enough to mash down second growth brush or sapling trees, it is advisable to grow such crops as corn, oats, or rye for a year or two, as they do well on raw and uneven peat lands. Once the peat is adequately weathered, freed of roots and stumps, and all hummocks eliminated, it is ready for vegetable production. More thorough drainage is now required and is usually obtained by a system of ditches. Sometimes tile drains or even mole drains are used.

13:13. MANAGEMENT OF PEAT SOILS

All sorts of vegetable crops may be grown on peat soils— celery, lettuce, spinach, onions, potatoes, beets, carrots, asparagus, and cabbage perhaps being the most important as well as such specialized crops as peppermint. In some cases, peat is used for field crops, a more or less definite rotation being followed. Sugar beets, corn, oats, rye, buckwheat, flax, clover, timothy, and other field crops give good yields when suitable fertilization is provided. Moreover, certain nursery stocks do well on peat. In many cases, especially in Europe, peat soils are used extensively for pasture and meadows. In fact, almost any crop will grow on peat soil if properly managed. For a view of peat under cropping see Fig. 13:3.

STRUCTURAL MANAGEMENT. Plowing is ordinarily unnecessary every year, as the peat is porous and open, unless it contains considerable silt and clay. In fact, a cultivated peat soil generally needs packing rather than loosening. The longer a peat has been cropped the more important compaction is likely to be. Cultivation tends to destroy the original granular structure, leaving the soil in a powdery condition when dry. It is then susceptible to wind erosion, a very serious problem in some sections. (See Fig. 13:3).

Figure 13:3. Windbreaks such as these in Michigan help protect valuable muck land from blowing. The unprotected field in the lower left has been wetted by sprinkler to prevent its blowing. (Photo courtesy U.S. Soil Conservation Service.)

For this reason, a roller or packer is an important implement in the management of such land. The compacting of the peat allows the roots to come into closer contact with the soil and facilitates the rise of water from below. It also tends to reduce the blowing of the soil during dry weather, although a windbreak of some kind is much more effective. The cultivation of peat, while easier than for mineral soils, is carried on in much the same way and should be shallow, especially after the root development of the crop has begun.

USE OF LIME.   Lime, that so often must be used on mineral soils, ordinarily is less necessary on peat, since this soil, as already noted, usually is adequately supplied with calcium. On acid mucks containing appreciable quantities of inorganic matter, however, the situation is quite different. The highly acid conditions result in the dissolution of iron, aluminum, and manganese to the extent that they become present in toxic quantities. Under these conditions, large amounts of lime may be necessary to obtain normal plant growth.

COMMERCIAL FERTILIZERS.   Of much greater importance than lime are commercial fertilizers. In fact, complete reliance is placed on these materials in the production of most crops, especially vegetables. As organic soils are very low in phosphorus and potassium, these elements must by all means be added. Since vegetables usually are rapid-growing plants, succulence often being an essential quality, large amounts of readily available nitrogen are necessary. The nitrogen of newly broken peat is often available rapidly enough to supply this need, especially for oats, rye, corn, wheat, and similar crops. Such peat land, therefore, frequently requires at the beginning only a small amount of nitrogen with the phosphoric acid and potash. This is especially true of woody peats and is taken advantage of in the fertilization of such soils. After peat soils have been cropped for a few years, decay and nitrification are frequently too slow to meet the crop demand for nitrogen. Under such conditions this element is needed in larger amounts and a fertilizer containing nitrogen as well as phosphoric acid and potash is usually recommended. The amount of any given fertilizer applied will depend upon the kind of crop to be grown, the chemical and physical nature of the peat, its drainage, its previous fertilization and the length of time it has been under cultivation.

TRACE ELEMENTS.   Peat soils not only are in need of potassium, phosphorus, and nitrogen, but often some of the trace elements as well. Just what function the trace elements perform is not definitely known, but their fertilizer value is now well established on such soils, and they must be considered in any well-balanced fertilizer program. On New York woody peats, copper sulfate has given good results in the control of certain diseases of lettuce and has aided in the coloration of onions. In fact, the application of this salt at the rate of 100 to 200 pounds to the acre is becoming a recognized treatment for these soils when they are first put under cultivation.

In Florida and elsewhere not only copper sulfate, but salts of manganese and zinc, are used to better the physiological condition of both peat and muck soils. Boron deficiencies are also becoming evident. Michigan peats, in general, need both boron and copper, compounds of these trace elements being mixed with the ordinary fertilizer at the rate of 50 to 100 pounds of borax and 100 to 200 pounds of copper sulfate per ton of fertilizer. Common salt in addition seems to give good results on Michigan peats, especially for beets, celery and cabbage. Perhaps both the sodium and the chlorine play important roles in crop nutrition on these soils.

13:14. PEAT VS. MINERAL SOILS

In assigning peat soils to a separate chapter, one is encouraged to think of them as distinctly and even radically different from most mineral soils. In many respects this certainly is true. Yet, fundamentally, the same types of change occur in the two groups; nutrients become available in much the same way and their management is based upon the same principles of fertility. In recognition of this, peat appears in the world classification of soils (Table 12:1) as *bog* soils, subject, of course, to such subdivisions as best show their differences in agricultural value.

Chapter 14

The Soil Reaction;
Soil Acidity and Alkalinity

One of the outstanding physiological characteristics of the soil solution is its reaction. Since microorganisms and higher plants respond so markedly to their chemical environment, the importance of soil reaction, and of the factors associated with it, has long been recognized. Three conditions are, of course, possible: acidity, neutrality, and alkalinity.

Soil acidity is common in all regions where precipitation is high enough to leach appreciable amounts of exchangeable bases from the surface layers of soils. So widespread is its occurrence and so marked is its influence on plants that it has become one of the most discussed properties of soils. Because of the large area of arable acid soils the importance of soil acidity in a practical way surpasses that of soil alkalinity.

378

Alkalinity occurs when there is a comparatively high degree of base saturation. The presence of salts, especially calcium, magnesium, and sodium carbonates, also gives a preponderance of OH ions over H ions in the soil solution.[1] Under such conditions the soil is alkaline and sometimes, very strongly so, especially if sodium carbonate is present, a pH of 9 or 10 being not uncommon. Alkaline soils are, of course, characteristic of most arid and semiarid regions. Their discussion will follow that of acid soils.

14:1. SOURCE OF HYDROGEN IONS

As has been pointed out previously (p. 101), two adsorbed cations are largely responsible for soil acidity—hydrogen and aluminum. The mechanisms by which these two ions exert their influence differ, however. This difference is related to the source and nature of the charge to which each of these ions are attracted.

SOURCE OF NEGATIVE CHARGES. Two types of negative charges have been identified on soil colloidals: (1) permanent and (2) pH dependent. The first is associated primarily with the silicate clays. It is due to the electrostatic forces resulting from isomorphic substitutions within the clay crystals (see p. 86). The charge sites are located mostly on the internal surfaces. Cations are exchangeable at all pH levels at these permanent charge sites. Permanent charges are highest on the 2:1 type clay where ionic substitution is greatest.

The second type of charge is not permanent but is related directly to soil pH. The charge is low in very acid soils and increases as the pH rises. This charge is thought to have several sources. First, there are SiOH and AlOH groups at the broken edges and external surfaces of silicate clays (see p. 85). Also, there are carboxyl (COOH) and phenol (phenyl-OH) groups on the humus colloids (see p. 90). These groups each contain covalent bonded hydrogen which is not dissociated at low pH values. As the pH increases, however, the H dissociates leaving a negative charge on the colloid. In nature the hydrogen is replaced by metallic cations which are, in turn, exchangeable.

In acid soils, complex aluminum and iron hydroxy ions are tightly adsorbed within the crystal units of certain 2:1 type clays, particularly

---

[1] When salts of strong bases and weak acids, such as Na_2CO_3, K_2CO_3, and $MgCO_3$ go into solution they undergo hydrolysis and develop alkalinity. For Na_2CO_3 the reaction is as follows:

$$2Na^+ + CO_3^{--} + 2HOH \leftrightarrows 2Na^+ + 2OH^- + H_2CO_3$$

Since the dissociation of the NaOH is greater than that of the weak H_2CO_3, a domination of OH^- ions results.

vermiculites. These ions tend to block some of the negative charge sites of the colloid, thereby reducing its cation-exchange capacity. As the pH is raised, the complex ions are removed, forming insoluble $Al(OH)_3$ and $Fe(OH)_3$, thereby releasing the exchange sites. In this way the pH-dependent charge is increased. The relative proportion of permanent and pH-dependent charges will depend on the kind of colloid present. The 2:1 type clays are generally high in the permanent type charge, whereas humus is dominated by the pH-dependent types (see Fig. 4:9). Kaolinite is intermediate between these two.

STRONGLY ACID SOILS. Under very acid soil conditions much aluminum becomes soluble and is present in the form of aluminum or aluminum hydroxy cations. These become adsorbed even in preference to hydrogen by the so-called permanent electrostatic charges of clay minerals—charges that result from ionic substitutions within the crystal lattice (see p. 86).

The adsorbed aluminum is in equilibrium with Al ions in the soil solution. The latter contribute to soil acidity through their tendency to hydrolize. A simplified reaction may be used to illustrate how adsorbed aluminum can increase acidity in the soil solution.

$$\boxed{\text{Micelle}}\ \ Al \leftrightarrows Al^{+++}$$

Adsorbed   Soil Solution

The Al ions in the soil solution are then hydrolyzed in a manner such as the following:

$$Al^{+++} + H_2O \longrightarrow Al(OH)^{++} + H^+$$

The H ions thus released give a very low pH value in the soil solution and are perhaps the major source of hydrogen in most very acid soils.

Adsorbed hydrogen is a second source of H ions in very acid soils. However, under these conditions, much of the hydrogen[2] held by covalent bonds in the organic matter and on clay crystal edges is so tightly adsorbed that it contributes little to the soil solution. On only the strong acid groups of humus and some of the permanent charge exchange sites of the clays is the hydrogen held in an exchangeable form. This hydrogen is in equilibrium with the soil solution. A perhaps oversimplified equation to show the release of adsorbed hydrogen to the soil solution is as follows:

[2] In some very acid soils iron and especially aluminum are also thought to be held in this form. Since their ultimate effect on pH is the same as that of hydrogen, however, we will use only hydrogen in our discussion.

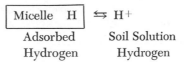

Thus, it can be seen that the effect of both adsorbed hydrogen and aluminum is to increase the H ion concentration in the soil solution.

MODERATELY ACID SOILS. Aluminum and hydrogen compounds also account for soil solution H ions in these soils, but again by different mechanisms. These soils have somewhat higher percentage base saturations and pH values. The aluminum can no longer exist as Al^{+++} ions but has been converted to Al-hydroxy ions by reactions such as these:[3]

$$Al^{+++} + OH^- \longrightarrow Al(OH)^{++}$$
$$Al(OH)^{++} + OH^- \longrightarrow Al(OH)_2^+$$
$$\textit{Al-hydroxy ions}$$

Some of the Al-hydroxy ions are adsorbed and act as exchangeable cations. As such, they are in equilibrium with the soil solution, just as was the Al^{+++} ion in very acid soils. In the soil solution, they are able to produce H ions by the following hydrolysis reactions, using again as examples the most simplified of the Al-hydroxy ions.

$$Al(OH)^{++} + H_2O \longrightarrow Al(OH)_2^+ + H^+$$
$$Al(OH)^+_2 + H_2O \longrightarrow Al(OH)_3 + H^+$$

In some 2:1 type clays, particularly vermiculite the Al-hydroxy ions (as well as iron hydroxy ions) play another role. They move in between the crystal units and become very tightly adsorbed. In this form they tend to prevent inter-crystal expansion and block some of the exchange sites. Their removal, which can be accomplished by raising the soil pH, results in the release of these exchange sites. In this way they are partly responsible for the so-called "pH-dependent" charge of soil colloids.

In moderately acid soils adsorbed hydrogen also makes a contribution to the soil solution H. The readily exchangeable hydrogen held by the permanent charges contributes in the same manner shown for very acid soils. In addition, with the rise in pH, some H ions which have been held tenaciously through covalent bonding by the organic matter and

[3] The actual Al-OH ions are likely much more complex than those shown. Formulas such as $[Al_6(OH)_{12}]^{6+}$, $[Al_{10}(OH)_{22}]^{8+}$ with the possibility of ring configurations have been postulated. See P. H. Hsu and T. F. Bates, "Fixation of Hydroxyl-aluminum Polymers by Vermiculite," *Soil Sci. Soc. Amer. Proc.*, 28:763–769, 1964.

clay are now subject to release. These are associated with the pH-dependent sites previously mentioned. Their contribution to the soil solution might be illustrated as follows:

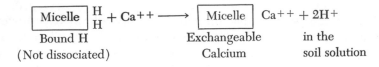

$$\boxed{\text{Micelle}} \begin{smallmatrix} H \\ H \end{smallmatrix} + Ca^{++} \longrightarrow \boxed{\text{Micelle}} \quad Ca^{++} + 2H^+$$

Bound H   Exchangeable   in the

(Not dissociated)   Calcium   soil solution

Again, the colloidal control of soil solution pH has been demonstrated as has the dominant role of the Ca and Al ions.

NEUTRAL TO ALKALINE SOILS. Soils that are neutral to alkaline in reaction are no longer dominated by either H or Al ions. The permanent charge exchange sites are now occupied primarily by exchangeable bases, both the H and Al-OH ions having been largely replaced. The aluminum hydroxy ions have been converted to gibbsite by reactions such as the following:

$$Al(OH)_2^+ + OH^- \longrightarrow Al(OH)_3$$
Insoluble
gibbsite

More of the pH-dependent charges have become available for cation exchange and the hydrogen released therefrom moves into the soil solution. Its place on the exchange complex is taken by Ca, Mg and other bases. The reaction is the same as that shown for the moderately acid soils.

Figure 14:1 presents diagrammatically the distribution of ions in a hypothetical soil as affected by pH. Study it carefully, keeping in mind that for any particular soil the distribution of ions might be quite different.

The effect of pH on the distribution of bases and of H and Al in a muck and in a soil dominated by 2:1 clays is shown in Fig. 14:2. Note that permanent charges dominate the exchange complex of the mineral soil, whereas the pH-dependent charges account for most of the adsorption in the muck soil. Kaolinite and related clays have a distribution intermediate between that of the two soils shown.

In Fig. 14:2 two forms of hydrogen are shown. That tightly held by the pH-dependent sites (covalent bonding) is termed *bound* hydrogen. The hydrogen ions associated with permanent electrostatic charges is exchangeable.

It is obvious that the factors responsible for soil acidity are far from

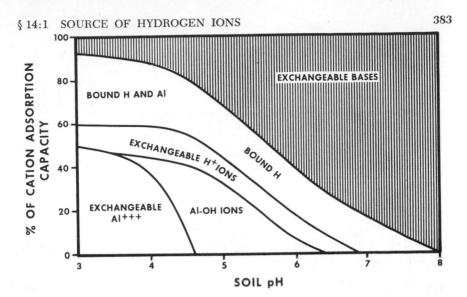

Figure 14:1. The general relationship between soil pH and the cations held by soil colloids. Under very acid conditions exchangeable aluminum ions and bound H and Al dominate. At higher pH values the exchangeable bases predominate, while at intermediate values aluminum-hydroxy ions are prominent. This diagram is for average conditions. Any particular soil would likely give a modified distribution.

simple. At the same time, there are two dominant groups of elements in control. Aluminum and hydrogen generate acidity, and most of the other cations combat it. This simple statement is worth remembering.

SOURCE OF OH IONS. If adsorbed hydrogen and aluminum are replaced from acid soils by cations such as Ca, Mg, and K, the H ion concentration in the soil solution will decrease. The concentration of OH ions will simultaneously increase since there is an inverse relationship between the H and OH ions. Thus, the so-called base-forming cations become sources of OH ions merely by replacing the adsorbed hydrogen.

The metallic cations such as Ca, Mg, and K also have a more direct effect on the OH ion concentration of the soil solution. A definite alkaline reaction results from the hydrolysis of colloids saturated with these cations. An example of such a reaction is as follows:

$$\text{Ca} \boxed{\text{Micelle}} + 2H_2O \;\rightleftharpoons\; {}^{H}_{H} \boxed{\text{Micelle}} + Ca^{++} + 2OH^-$$

In a Ca-saturated soil, the tendency for the metallic cations to encourage OH ion formation is obvious. In a soil containing H and Al as

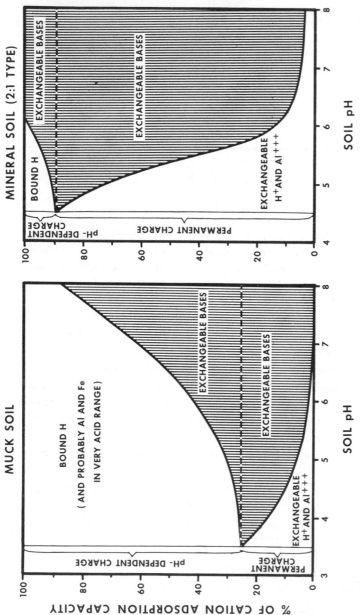

Figure 14:2. The relationship between soil pH and the proportion of the adsorptive complex satisfied by bases and by hydrogen and aluminum. The mineral soil (right) is of the White Store series in North Carolina. Its properties tend to be dominated by 2:1 type clays. The muck soil (left) is also from North Carolina. Note the dominance of the permanent charge in the mineral soil and the large pH-dependent charge in the muck. Soils dominated by 1:1 type colloids have distributions intermediate between these two extremes. (Redrawn from A. Mehlich, "Influence of sorbed hydroxyl and sulfate on neutralization of soil acidity." Soil Sci. Soc. Amer. Proc. 28:492–496, 1964.)

well as Ca ions the same tendency is there, but its effect is not so obvious because it is countered by the effect of the adsorbed H and Al ions. It should be kept in mind that under natural conditions the reactions to furnish H and OH ions to the soil solution occur simultaneously. That is, H and Al ions and the basic cations are held at one time by the same micelle. (See Fig. 14:1.) The pH of the soil solution, therefore, will depend upon the relative amounts of adsorbed hydrogen and aluminum compared to adsorbed metallic cations. Where the effect of the hydrogen and aluminum is dominant, acidity results. Excess bases yield alkalinity, whereas at just the right balance the pH of the soil solution will be 7. (See Fig. 2:5.)

14:2. COLLOIDAL CONTROL OF SOIL REACTION

PERCENTAGE BASE SATURATION. The relative proportions of the adsorbed hydrogen and aluminum and the exchangeable bases of a colloidal complex are shown by the *percentage base saturation*. (See p. 100.) Obviously, a low percentage base saturation means acidity, whereas a percentage base saturation approaching 100 will result in neutrality or alkalinity. In general, humid-region soils dominated by *silicate clays* and *humus* are acid if their percentage base saturation is much below 80. When such soils have a percentage base saturation of 80 or above they usually are neutral or alkaline. The exact pH value in any case, however, is determined by at least two other factors in addition to the percentage base saturation: (1) the nature of the micelle, and (2) the kind of adsorbed bases.

NATURE OF THE MICELLE. At the same percentage base saturation, different types of colloids will have different pH values. This is due to the fact that the various colloidal materials differ in their ability to furnish H ions to the soil solution. For example, the organic complex contains enough strong acid exchange sites to give very low pH values when the degree of base saturation is low. Even as bases are added the degree of H-ionization at the pH-dependent sites is sufficiently rapid to give lower pH values than are found commonly among mineral soils of comparable base saturation.

In contrast, the dissociation of the adsorbed hydrogen from the iron and aluminum hydrous oxides is relatively low. Consequently, soils dominated by this type of colloid have relatively high pH values for a given percentage base saturation. The dissociation of absorbed hydrogen from silicate clays is intermediate between that from humus and from the hydrous oxides.

The relative abilities to supply soil solution hydrogen can be seen by comparing the pH values found when the various colloids are about 50 per cent saturated with bases. The organic colloids would have pH values of 4.5 to 5.0, the silicate clays 5.2 to 5.8, and the hydrous oxides 6.0 to 7.0. These figures verify the importance of type of colloid in determining the pH of a soil.

It should be noted that the different acid silicate clays—the kaolinite, montmorillonite, and hydrous mica types—apparently supply hydrogen ions in somewhat different degrees, the kaolinite least and the montmorillonite greatest. (See p. 104.) Likewise, the organic colloids exhibit considerable variety among themselves. In spite of this, however, the organic group apparently has a lower pH value than any of the clays when at corresponding percentage base saturations.

KIND OF ADSORBED BASES. Another factor which influences the pH of a soil is the comparative amounts of the *particular* bases present in the colloidal complex. Sodium-saturated soils have much higher pH values than those dominated by Ca and Mg. Thus, at a percentage base saturation say of 90, the presence of Ca, Mg, K, and Na ions in the ratio of 10–3–1–1 would certainly result in a lower pH than if the ratio were 4–1–1–9. In the one case calcium is dominant, in the other we are dealing with a sodium-calcium complex dominated by sodium.

With the reaction of the soil solution influenced by three distinct and uncoordinated factors—percentage base saturation, nature of the micelle, and the ratio of the exchangeable bases—one would hardly expect to find a close correlation between percentage base saturation and pH when comparing soils at random. Yet with soils of similar origin, texture, and organic content, a rough correlation does exist.

14:3. MAJOR CHANGES IN SOIL pH

There are two major groups of factors which bring about large changes in soil pH: (1) those which result in increased adsorbed hydrogen and in turn aluminum, and (2) those which increase the content of adsorbed bases. Each group will be considered briefly.

ACID-FORMING FACTORS. In the process of organic matter decomposition, both organic and inorganic acids are formed. The simplest and perhaps the most widely found is carbonic acid (H_2CO_3) which results from the reaction of CO_2 and water. The solvent action of

H_2CO_3 on the mineral constituents of the soil is exemplified by its dissolution of limestone or calcium carbonate (p. 273). The long-time effects of this acid have been responsible for the removal of large quantities of bases by solution and leaching. Because carbonic acid is relatively weak, however, it cannot account for the low pH values found in many soils.

Inorganic acids such as H_2SO_4 and HNO_3 are potent suppliers of hydrogen ions in the soil. In fact, these acids along with the stronger organic acids account for the development of moderately and strongly acid conditions. Sulfuric and nitric acids are formed, not only by the organic decay processes but also from the microbial action on certain fertilizer materials such as sulfur and ammonium sulfate. In the latter case, both nitric and sulfuric acids are formed. (See p. 544.)

A good example of a process by which strong *organic* acids are formed is that of podzolization. The organic debris is attacked largely by fungi which have among their important metabolic end products relatively complex but strong organic acids. As these are leached into the mineral portion of the soil, they not only supply hydrogen for adsorption, but they also replace bases and encourage their solution from the soil minerals.

Leaching also encourages acidity. Thereby, bases which have been replaced from the colloidal complex or which have been dissolved by percolating acids are removed in the drainage waters. This process encourages the development of acidity in an indirect way by removing those metallic cations which might compete with hydrogen and aluminum on the exchange complex.

BASE-FORMING FACTORS. Any process which will encourage the maintenance or buildup of the exchangeable bases such as Ca, Mg, K, and Na will contribute toward a reduction in acidity and an increase in alkalinity. Of great significance are the weathering processes which release these exchangeable cations from minerals and make them available for adsorption. The addition of base-containing materials such as limestone is a common procedure which man uses to furnish metallic cations in order to augment nature's supply. Irrigation waters also frequently contain salts of various kinds, the cations of which are adsorbed by soil colloids. They may increase soil alkalinity, sometimes excessively so.

Conditions which permit the exchangeable bases to remain in the soil will encourage high pH values. This accounts for the relatively high pH of soils of the semiarid and arid regions. Leaching waters do not remove most of the metallic cations as they are weathered from soil minerals. Consequently, the percentage base saturation of these soils remains high. In general, this situation is favorable for crop production. Only when the pH is too high or when sodium is the dominant cation is plant growth unfavorably affected.

14:4. MINOR FLUCTUATIONS IN SOIL pH

Not only do soil solutions suffer major and often drastic changes in H ion concentration (as indicated above) but they also exhibit minor fluctuations. For instance, the drying of soils, especially above field temperatures, will often cause a noticeable increase in acidity. This is probably due to a change in the organization of the colloidal matter and should be kept in mind in preparing soil samples for pH determination.

The pH of mineral soils tends to decline during the summer, especially if under cultivation, due to acids produced by microorganisms. The activities of the roots of higher plants, especially with regard to acidic exudates, may also be a factor. In winter and spring an increase in pH often is noted, possibly because biotic activities during this time are considerably slower.

14:5. H-ION HETEROGENEITY OF THE SOIL SOLUTION

In considering the H-ion concentration of the soil solution, it is not to be inferred that one is dealing with an ordinary homogeneous solution. For example, differences in pH are noted from one portion of soil to that only a few inches away. This is due to local microbial action and to the uneven distribution of organic residues in the soil.

The variability of the soil solution is important in many respects. For example, it affords microorganisms and plant roots a great variety of solution environments. Organisms that are unfavorably influenced by a given H ion concentration may find, at an infinitesimal distance away, another that is more satisfactory. This may account in part for the many different floral species present in normal soils.

Even at a given location in the soil—in fact around a given micelle— there are marked differences in the distribution of H and Al ions (See Fig. 14:3). These cations are concentrated near the surfaces of the colloid and become less numerous as the distance from the micelle is increased. They are least concentrated in the soil solution. Furthermore, equilibrium conditions exist between the adsorbed and soil solution ions permitting the ready movement from one form to another.[4] This fact is of great practical importance since it provides the basis for the buffering capacity of soils.

14:6. ACTIVE VERSUS EXCHANGE ACIDITY

Figure 14:3 illustrates the presence in acid soils of two kinds of acidity. The H ion concentration of the soil solution is designated

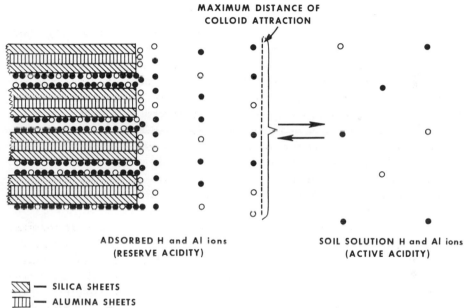

MAXIMUM DISTANCE OF
COLLOID ATTRACTION

ADSORBED H and Al ions
(RESERVE ACIDITY)

SOIL SOLUTION H and Al ions
(ACTIVE ACIDITY)

◪ — SILICA SHEETS
▥ — ALUMINA SHEETS
● — ALUMINUM ions
○ — HYDROGEN ions

Figure 14:3. Diagram showing the equilibrium relationship between reserve and active acidity on 2:1 type colloid. Note that the absorbed ions are much more numerous than those in the soil solution even when only a small portion of the clay crystal is shown. Remember that the aluminum ions, by hydrolysis, also supply H ions to the soil solution (see p. 380). It is obvious that neutralizing only the H and Al ions in the soil solution will be of little consequence. They will be quickly replaced by ions adsorbed by the colloid. This means high buffering capacity.

---

[4] The mechanisms by which adsorbed Al and H ions supply H^+ ions to the soil solution has already been discussed. See pp. 380–381.

active acidity. Those H and Al ions held on the soil colloids are referred to as the *reserve* or *exchange acidity* of the soil. This situation is shown graphically by Fig. 14:3 and by the following equation:

Adsorbed H and Al ions   ⇆   Soil solution H⁺ (and Al) ions
   (Reserve acidity)   (Active acidity)

Since the adsorbed hydrogen and aluminum tend to move outward and become active when the acidity of the soil solution is reduced, the term reserve is particularly significant. Distinct as the two groups apparently are, they grade into each other as progress outward from the colloidal interface is made.

AMOUNTS OF ACTIVE AND RESERVE ACIDITY. The relative magnitude of the two types of acidity—active vs. reserve—is not only interesting but also of vital practical importance. In referring to the acidity of a soil as high or very high, the impression may be given that the active acidity under certain conditions may be exceedingly great, even dangerously so. Actually, however, the reverse is true. For example, only about 1/50 of a *pound* of calcium carbonate would be required to neutralize the active acidity in an acre-furrow-slice of an average mineral soil having a pH of 6.[5] If the same soil should possess a pH of 5, 1/5 pound of calcium carbonate would be adequate; if the pH should be lowered to 4, two pounds would be ample. Thus, the *active* acidity is evidently ridiculously small even at its maximum.

Since limestone at the rate of 1, 2, or even 4 tons to the acre is often recommended, this neutralizing agent is obviously applied in amounts thousands of times in excess of the active acidity. The reason for such heavy applications is the magnitude of the reserve acidity. These adsorbed hydrogen and aluminum ions move into the soil solution when the H ion concentration becomes depleted. The reserve acidity thus must be depleted before the pH of the soil solution can be changed appreciably.

Conservative calculations indicate that the reserve acidity may be perhaps 1,000 times greater than the active acidity in the case of a sandy soil, and 50,000 or even 100,000 times greater for a clayey soil high in organic matter. The figure for a peat soil is likely to be even greater. The practical significance of this tremendous difference in magnitude of the active and reserve acidities of soils should be apparent after reading the next section.

---

[5] This assumes that the $CaCO_3$ could be brought in contact with the soil solution and that only the hydrogen ions actually in this solution would react with the $CaCO_3$. A soil moisture content of 20 per cent was assumed in making this calculation.

14:7. THE BUFFERING OF SOILS

As pointed out above, there is a distinct resistance to a change in the pH of the soil solution. This resistance, called *buffering*, can be explained very simply if we consider the equilibrium that exists between the active and reserve acidities. (See Fig. 14.4.) Removal of H ions from

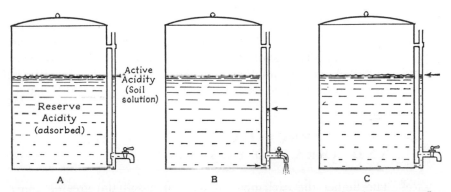

Figure 14:4. The buffering action of a soil can be likened to that of a coffee dispenser depicted above. A. The active acidity, which is represented by the coffee in the indicator tube on the outside of the urn, is small in quantity. B. When hydrogen ions are removed, this active acidity falls rapidly. C. The active acidity is quickly restored to near the original level by movement from the potential or absorbed acidity. By this process there is considerable resistance to the change of active acidity.

the soil solution results in their being largely replenished from the reserve acidity. The resistance to change in H ion concentration (pH) of the soil solution is thus established. This can be represented as before (see p. 381) as follows:

Adsorbed H (and Al) ions   ⇆   Soil solution H (and Al) ions
(Reserve acidity)   (Active acidity)

Now let us consider what would happen if we were to add just enough liming material to neutralize the H ions in the soil solution. Immediately the above reaction would be shifted to the right, resulting in more hydrogen ions moving out into the soil solution. As a consequence, the resulting pH rise would be negligibly small and would remain so until enough lime had been added to deplete appreciably the reserve acidity.

This resistance to pH change is equally important in preventing a rapid lowering of the pH of soils. For example, consider the case where H ions are added to a soil or where they result from certain biochemical changes. This would give a temporary increase in the H ions in the soil solution. In this case the equilibrium reaction above would immediately shift to the left and more H ions would become adsorbed on the micelle. Again, the resultant pH change, this time a lowering, in the soil solution would be very small.

These two examples point out rather clearly the principles involved in buffering. In addition, they show that the basis of buffer capacity lies in the adsorbed cations of the complex. Hydrogen and aluminum ions, together with the adsorbed metallic cations, not only indirectly control the pH of the soil solution, but also determine the quantity of lime or acidic constituents necessary to bring about a given pH change.

14:8. BUFFER CAPACITY OF SOILS AND RELATED PHASES

The higher the exchange capacity of a soil the greater, other factors being equal, will be its buffer capacity. This is because more reserve acidity must be neutralized to effect a given rise or lowering of the percentage base saturation. In practice this is fully recognized in that the heavier the texture of a soil and the higher its organic content, the larger must be the application of lime to force a given change in pH.

BUFFER CURVES. Another phase of buffering, less understood but equally important, logically presents itself at this point. Is the buffer capacity of soils the same throughout the percentage base saturation range? This is best answered by reference to an average theoretical titration curve presented by Peech[6] for a large number of Florida soils. (See Fig. 14:5.)

Three things are clearly obvious from the curve. *First,* there is a correlation, between the percentage base saturation of these soils and their pH. This has already been suggested (p. 101).

Second, the generalized curve indicates that the degree of buffering varies, being lowest at the extreme base saturation values. Between these extremes where the curve is flatter, the buffering reaches a maximum. Theoretically, the greatest buffering occurs at about 50 per cent base

[6] M. Peech, "Availability of Ions in Light Sandy Soils as Affected by Soil Reaction," *Soil Sci.*, 51:473–86, 1941. This author finds that the same type of composite curve also holds for New York mineral soils.

saturation. This situation is extremely important both technically and practically.

Third, the buffering, as indicated by the curve, is more or less uniform over a pH range of say 4.5 to 6.5. This is vitally significant as it indicates, for example, that under field conditions about the same amount of lime will be required to change the soil pH from 5.0 to 5.5 as from 5.5 to 6.0.

Before leaving this phase it is well to remark that the curve of Fig. 14:5 is a composite and represents the situation in respect to any particular soil only in a general way. That the titration curves for individual soils will deviate more or less widely is to be expected, since the colloidal complex of different soils varies with the kinds and amounts of clay and humus present.

VARIATION IN TITRATION CURVES. As an instance of the difference between the clay groups, Mehlich's[7] results are especially significant. He found the pH values of montmorillonite and the hydrous micas to lie between 4.5 and 5.0 when these clays were at 50 per cent

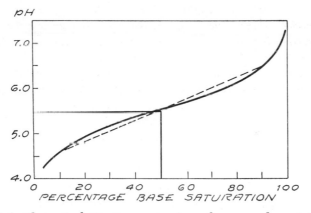

Figure 14:5. Theoretical titration curve for a large number of Florida soils. (After Peech.) The dotted line indicates the zone of greatest buffering. The maximum buffering should occur at approximately 50 per cent base saturation.

base saturation. The pH values of kaolinite and halloysite under comparable conditions were found in general to lie within a range of 6.0 to 6.5.

The influence of the different clays upon the titration curves of individual soils is nicely shown by the data in Fig. 14:6. Samples from the B horizon were used to avoid the complicating effects of organic

[7] A. Mehlich, "Base Unsaturation and pH in Relation to Soil Type," *Proc. Soil Sci. Soc. Amer.*, 6:150–56, 1941.

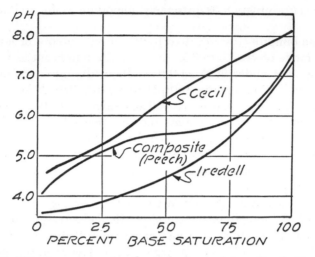

Figure 14:6. *Titration curves for the B horizon of two North Carolina soils. The Cecil is dominated by kaolinitic minerals (1 to 1 types) and the Iredell by montmorillonitic clays (2 to 1 types). Note the difference in the trends of the two curves and how they in turn differ from the composite ideal as set up by Peech (Fig. 14:5). This is to be expected.*

At 50 per cent base saturation, the Cecil shows a pH near 6.4. The corresponding figure for the Iredell is about 4.4. Obviously the Iredell presents a stronger acid and hence is more highly buffered. Since the samples from the two came from the subsoils, the trend of their curves is not influenced to any degree by humus. (The Cecil and Iredell curves are from Mehlich's paper cited on p. 393.)

matter. In light of the figures quoted from Mehlich in the preceding paragraph, it is easy to see from these curves that the Cecil subsoil with a pH of about 6.4 at 50 per cent base saturation must be highly kaolinitic. The corresponding pH for the Iredell is about 4.4, indicating that clays of the montmorillonite or similar types are dominant in this soil. Obviously, the clays of the Iredell develop stronger acids than those of the Cecil and, under comparable conditions, exhibit a higher buffer capacity.

14:9. IMPORTANCE OF BUFFERING

STABILIZATION OF SOIL PH. A marked change in pH undoubtedly indicates a radical modification in soil environment, especially in respect to the availability of plant nutrients. And if this environment should fluctuate too widely, higher plants and micro-organisms undoubtedly would suffer seriously before they could make adequate adjustments. Not only would they be affected directly by the change in H-ion concentration but the indirect influences on nutrient elements might prove to be exceedingly unsatisfactory. (See Fig. 14:7 and 14:8.) The stabilization of soil pH through buffering seems to be an effective guard against these difficulties.

QUANTITIES OF AMENDMENTS REQUIRED. Obviously, the greater the buffering capacity of a soil, the larger must be the amounts of lime or sulfur used to effect a given change in pH. Hence, in deciding the amount of lime to apply to a soil of known pH, texture and organic content are among the important soil factors to be considered. These properties give a rough idea of the adsorptive capacity of a soil and hence of its buffering. (See p. 99.) Chemical tests, such as a determination of cation-exchange capacity, are also helpful in a practical way.

14:10. SOIL-REACTION CORRELATIONS[8]

Certain correlations have been established in respect to soil pH that are of considerable practical as well as scientific interest. The interrelations between pH values and (1) exchangeability of *calcium* and *magnesium*, (2) the solubility of *aluminum* and of *iron* and other *trace elements*, (3) the availability of *phosphorus*, and (4) the activity of *soil microorganisms* are discussed in the following paragraphs.

EXCHANGEABLE CALCIUM AND MAGNESIUM. It has already been shown that as the exchangeable calcium and magnesium are lost by leaching, the acidity of the soil gradually increases. Consequently, in humid region soils there is a fairly definite correlation between the pH and the amounts of these two constituents present in exchangeable form. (See Fig. 14:7.) In arid regions, the same general relationships hold except under conditions where an appreciable amount of sodium is adsorbed. (See p. 405.)

ALUMINUM, AND THE TRACE ELEMENTS. The relationships between soil reaction and the activity of the micronutrients are shown in Fig. 14:7. When the pH of a mineral soil is low, appreciable amounts of these three constituents are soluble, so much so in fact that they may become extremely toxic to certain plants. However, as the pH is increased, precipitation takes place and the

---

[8] See N. A. Pettinger, *A Useful Chart for Teaching the Relation of Soil Reaction to the Availability of Plant Nutrients to Crops,* Bulletin 136, Va. Polytec. Inst., 1935; and E. Truog, "Lime in Relationship to Availability of Plant Nutrients," *Soil Sci.,* 65:1–7, 1948.

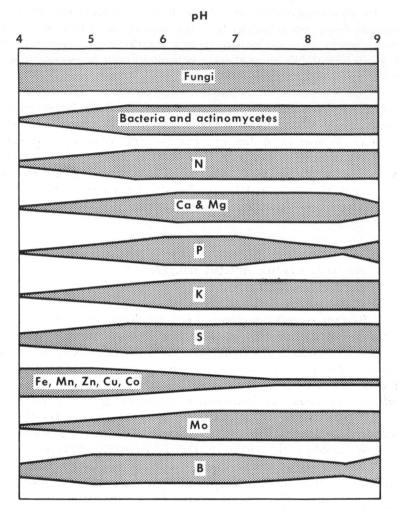

Figure 14:7. Diagram showing the relationships existing in mineral soils between pH on the one hand and the activity of microorganisms and the availability of plant nutrients on the other. The width of the bands indicate the zones of greatest microbial activity and the most ready availability of nutrients.

Considering the correlations as a whole, a pH range of approximately 6 to 7 seems to promote the most ready availability of plant nutrients. In short if soil pH is suitably adjusted for phosphorus, other plant nutrients, if present in adequate amounts, will be satisfactorily available in most cases.

amounts of these ions in solution become less and less until at neutrality or somewhat above certain plants may suffer from a lack of available manganese and iron. This is especially likely to be the case if a markedly acid sandy soil is suddenly brought to a neutral or alkaline condition by an over application of lime.

While deficiencies of manganese, and especially iron, are not widespread, they do occur in certain areas, particularly on overlimed sandy soils or alkaline arid region soils. If the soil reaction is held within a soil pH range of 6.0 to 7.0, the toxicity of the aluminum, iron, and manganese may satisfactorily be suppressed. At the same time their unavailability will be avoided unless these elements are decidedly lacking in the soil. Copper and zinc are affected in the same way by a rise in pH, the critical point being near 7 pH, above which their availability definitely declines. (See Fig. 14:7.)

With boron, the situation is somewhat different and probably is more complicated. Although neither the soil untreated nor the lime alone appreciably precipitate boron, some investigators feel that the two, when in combination, fix it markedly. Possibly also the excess of calcium hinders in some way the movement of boron into the plant, in spite of its solubility. Too much calcium in the plant cells might even interfere with boron metabolism even though plenty of the latter should be present. It has also been suggested that lime may create a serious competition for boron by a stimulation of soil microorganism activity.

Molybdenum availability is markedly dependent on pH. In strongly acid soils it is quite unavailable. As the pH is raised to 6 and above, its availability increases. The correlation between molybdenum availability and pH is so strong, that some researchers believe the main reason for liming is to increase the molybdenum supply.

AVAILABLE PHOSPHORUS. The kind of phosphate ion present varies with the pH of the soil solution. When the soil is alkaline, the HPO_4 ion apparently is the commonest form. As the pH is lowered, the soil becomes slightly to moderately acid, both the HPO_4 ion and the H_2PO_4 ion prevail. At higher acidities H_2PO_4 ions tend to dominate. Because of the formation of insoluble compounds, a soil reaction which yields a mixture of HPO_4 and H_2PO_4 ions is usually preferred.

The activity of the soil phosphorus is related to pH in another way, in this case indirectly. It has already been explained that as soil acidity increases there is an enhancement in the activity of the iron, aluminum, and manganese. Under such conditions soluble phosphates are markedly fixed as very complex and insoluble compounds of these elements. This fixation is most serious when the soil pH is below 5.0. The situation is shown graphically in Fig. 17:2.

If the pH of a mineral soil is raised much above 7, the phosphate nutrition of higher plants is disturbed in other ways. In the first place, at these high pH values, complex insoluble calcium phosphates are formed. Thus, the solubility of both the native and applied phosphorus may be very seriously impaired. Furthermore, at pH values above 7, the excess calcium may hinder phosphorus absorption and utilization of plants.

The correlation of phosphorus availability and soil reaction would be sadly incomplete without an examination of the situation in the intermediate pH range of mineral soils, say from 6 to 7. Between these two pH limits phosphorus fixation seems to be at a *minimum* and conversely phosphorus availability, as far as most plants are concerned, is at a maximum. (See Fig. 14:7.) In the regulation of the phosphorus nutrition of crops, it is rather important, therefore, that soil pH be kept within the conservative limits of 6 to 7 or very near thereto. Even then higher plants often do not absorb one half or even one third of the available phosphorus currently supplied by the application of superphosphate or other fertilizers carrying phosphorus. (For further consideration of phosphorus fixation and availability in soils, see Chapter 17, p. 480.)

SOIL ORGANISMS AND PH. It is well known that soil organisms are influenced by fluctuations in the reaction of the soil solution. This may be due in extreme cases to the H ion itself, but in most soils it must be ascribed to the factors correlated with soil pH and already discussed in the preceding paragraphs.

In general, it is recognized that bacteria and actinomycetes function better in mineral soils at intermediate and higher pH values, the activity being markedly curtailed when the pH drops below 5.5. Fungi, however, are particularly facultative, flourishing more or less satisfactorily at all soil reactions. In normal soils, therefore, fungi predominate at the lower pH values but at intermediate and higher ranges they meet strong competition from the bacteria and actinomycetes and, hence, must yield the field to some degree. (See Fig. 14:7.)

Nitrification and nitrogen fixation take place vigorously in mineral soils only at pH values well above 5.5. However, mineralization, although curtailed, will still proceed with considerable intensity at lower pH values because most fungi are able to effect these enzymic transfers at high acidities. This is, indeed, fortunate since higher plants growing on very acid soils are provided with at least ammoniacal nitrogen.

All in all, a soil in the intermediate pH range, say from 6 to 7, perhaps presents the most satisfactory biological regime. Here nutrient conditions are favorable without being extreme and phosphorus availability is at a maximum.

One very significant exception to the generalized correlation of bacteria with soil reaction should be mentioned. The organisms that oxidize sulfur to sulfuric acid (p. 469) seem to be markedly facultative. Apparently they not only function vigorously in soils at medium to higher pH values but under markedly acid conditions as well. This is extremely important as it is therefore possible to apply sulfur to soils and develop, through the activity of these bacteria, highly acid conditions. If these organisms were at all sensitive to low pH and its correlated factors, their activity would soon be retarded and finally brought to a halt by their own acidic products. Under such conditions sulfur would be relatively ineffective as a soil acidifier.

14:11. THE RELATION OF HIGHER PLANTS TO SOIL REACTION

Because of the many physiological factors involved, it is often difficult to correlate the optimum growth of plants on mineral soils with their pH. On the other hand, the general relationships of higher plants to strong acidity or alkalinity can be established and in a practical way are just as significant. With this relationship as a basis, some of the important plants are rated in Fig. 14:8.

CROP RATINGS. With such crops as alfalfa and sweet clover, calcium seems to be a very important factor. These plants are calcium-loving and are adjusted to the physiological conditions of a high-lime soil. Except under especially favorable conditions, humid-region mineral soils must, sooner or later, be limed in order to grow crops of this group satisfactorily.

Native rhododendrons and azaleas are at the other end of the scale and apparently require a considerable amount of iron. This constituent is copiously available only at low pH values and consequently at low percentage base saturations. Undoubtedly, highly acid soils also present other conditions physiologically favorable for this type of plant. Incidentally, soluble aluminum apparently is not detrimental as it is to certain plants higher up the scale. If the pH and the percentage base saturation are not low enough, plants of the low-lime type will show chlorosis and other symptoms indicative of an unsatisfactory nutritive condition.

As arable soils in a humid region are usually somewhat acid, it is indeed fortunate that most cultivated crop plants not only grow well on moderately to slightly acid soils but seem to prefer the physiological conditions therein. (See Fig. 14:8.) Since pasture grasses, many legumes, small grains, intertilled field crops, and a large number of vegetables are included in this broadly tolerant group, soil acidity is not such a calamity as it was once considered. In terms of pH, a range from 5.8 to 6.0 to slightly above 7.0 is most suitable for this group. (The significance of this as it relates to liming is presented in Chapter 15, pp. 431–32.

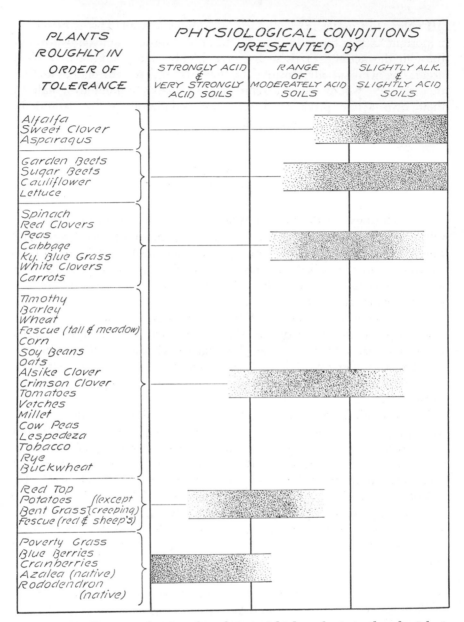

Figure 14:8. *Diagram showing the relation of higher plants to the physiological conditions presented by mineral soils of different reactions. Note that the correlations are very broad and are based on pH ranges. The fertility level will have much to do with what the relationship shall be in specific cases. Such a chart is of great value in deciding whether or not to add lime and the rate of application if any.*

Forest trees seem to grow well over a wide range of soil pH values. They are particularly tolerant, however, of acid soils. Many species, particularly the conifers, tend to intensify soil acidity. Forests exist as natural vegetation in regions of acid soils. This may not be a direct response to soil pH but rather to the climatic environment which incidentally encourages the development of acid soils. Even so, there are some isolated areas of high soil pH in humid regions where the natural vegetation is grass rather than trees. The so-called "black-belt" soil areas of Alabama and Mississippi are an example. These areas are surrounded by acid soils on which forests are the natural vegetation. This would indicate that the trees are better competitors on the more acid soil areas.

14:12. THE DETERMINATION OF SOIL pH

The importance of pH measurements as a tool in liming and similar problems should be obvious from the previous sections. In fact, pH is a diagnostic figure of unique value and as a result its determination has become one of the routine tests made on soils. Moreover, its determination in competent hands is easy and rapid.

ELECTROMETRIC METHOD. The most accurate method of determining soil pH is by means of a pH meter. In this electrometric method the H-ion concentration of the soil solution is balanced against a standard hydrogen electrode or an electrode that functions in a similar way. In the hands of a skilled operator the instrument gives very consistent results, but the mechanism is rather complicated. Hence, figures obtained by a person unable properly to check and standardize the apparatus may at times be questionable.

DYE METHODS. A second method, very simple and easy but somewhat less accurate than the electrometric, consists in the use of certain indicators. (See Fig. 14:9.) Many dyes change color with an increase or decrease of pH, making it possible, within the range of the indicator, to estimate the approximate H ion concentration of a solution. By using a number of dyes, either separately or mixed, a range of pH from 3 to 8 is easily covered. In making such a pH determination on soil, the sample is saturated with the dye and after standing in contact a few minutes a drop of the liquid is run out and its color observed in thin layer. By the use of a suitable color chart the approximate pH may be ascertained. When properly manipulated, the indicator method is accurate within about 0.2 of a pH unit.

LIMITATIONS OF pH VALUES. Because of the precision with which pH readings can be duplicated electrometrically, one

Figure 14:9. *The indicator method for determining pH is widely used in the field. It is simple and is accurate enough for most purposes. (Photo courtesy N.Y. State College of Agriculture, Cornell University.)*

may be led to interpretations which the pH measurement cannot justify. There are several reasons for this. In the first place, there is considerable variation in the pH as one goes from one spot in a given field to another. Even at a given location there are seasonal variations in pH. Localized effects of fertilizers may give sizeable pH variations within the space of a few inches. Lastly, the pH of a given soil sample will vary depending on the amount of water used in wetting the soil prior to the measurement. Obviously, standardization against field performance must be obtained.

In the light of such a situation, it might seem peculiar that so much reliance is placed on soil pH. In the first place, it is easily and quickly determined. More important, however, is its susceptibility to certain broad correlations that are of great practical significance (Figs. 14:7 and 14:8). Thus, a great deal may be inferred regarding the physiological condition of a soil from its pH value; much more, in fact, than from any other single analytical datum. Furthermore, the variations in pH value from one local soil area to another in a given field remind us that great accuracy in estimating soil acidity may not be so necessary from a practical point of view.

14:13. SOIL ACIDITY PROBLEMS

Other than the maintenance of fertility in general, two distinct procedures are often necessary on acid soils, especially those at intermediate pH values. One is the intensification of the acidity in order to encourage such plants as azaleas and rhododendrons. The other is the application of lime, usually in such amounts as to raise the pH at least to 6.0 or even to 6.5 or 7.0. This so modifies the physiological conditions as to favor alfalfa, sweet clover, red clover, and other lime-loving crops.

Since liming is such an important agricultural feature, its consideration will be reserved for a later and fuller discussion (Chapter 15). However, the methods of intensifying the acidity of the soil are briefly discussed in the following section.

14:14. METHODS OF INTENSIFYING SOIL ACIDITY

A reduction of the pH of soils is often desirable for several reasons. For example, this is done to favor such plants as rhododendrons and azaleas as suggested above, and also to discourage certain diseases, especially the actinomycetes that produce potato scab. In arid regions treatments are sometimes made to reduce the high pH of alkali soils sufficiently to allow common field plants to grow and to eliminate deficiencies of iron, manganese and zinc in other soils. (See p. 511.)

ACID ORGANIC MATTER. When dealing with ornamental plants mentioned above, acid organic matter may be mixed with the soil already at hand to lower the pH of the latter. Leafmold, pine needles, tanbark, sawdust, and moss peat, if highly acid, are quite satisfactory in preparing such a compost. Farm manure, however, may be alkaline and consequently should be used with caution for the purpose under consideration.

USE OF CHEMICALS. When the above methods are not feasible, chemicals may be used. For rhododendrons, azaleas, and other plants such as blueberries and cranberries that require considerable iron, ferrous sulfate[9] is sometimes recommended. This salt by hydrolysis de-

---

[9] Aluminum sulfate will acidify soil just as satisfactorily as the ferrous sulfate but it carries no iron. Moreover, the aluminum thereby introduced may be toxic to plants that might later occupy the soil.

velops sulfuric acid which drastically lowers the pH and liberates some of the iron already present in the soil. At the same time, soluble and available iron is being added. Such a chemical thus serves a double purpose in effecting a change in the physiological condition of a soil.

Another material that is even better in some respects is flowers of sulfur. This usually undergoes vigorous microbial oxidation in the soil (see p. 469) and under favorable conditions is four or five times more effective pound for pound in developing acidity than is ferrous sulfate. Moreover, it is comparatively inexpensive and easy to obtain, and is a material often used for other purposes on the farm.

No definite recommendation can be made as to the amounts of ferrous sulfate or sulfur that should be applied, since the buffering of soils and their original pH are so variable. With composted soils to be used in greenhouses, in nurseries, and around ornamental plants, the best way is to make several preliminary treatments using different amounts of the amendments with definite increments of the soil. After incubating at optimum temperature and moisture for several weeks, pH determinations may be made and an approximation may be made of the amounts of ferrous sulfate or sulfur that would give the desired results.

For rhododendrons and azaleas 1 to 2 pounds of sulfur per 100 square feet for each half a pH that a medium-textured soil is to be lowered, is perhaps not too much. The dosage must, of course, be varied according to the texture of the soil and its organic content. In any case the sulfur should be well mixed with the surface soil.

CONTROL OF POTATO SCAB. Sulfur is also effective in the control of potato scab since the actinomycetes that cause it are discouraged by acidity. Ordinarily when the pH is lowered to perhaps 5.3, their virulence is much reduced. In using sulfur to thus increase soil acidity, the management of the land, and especially the rotation, should be such that succeeding crops are not unfavorably affected.

The amount of sulfur to apply to control potato scab will vary depending on circumstances. The buffering capacity of the soil and the original soil pH will be the determining factors. The results of a given treatment both on the pH and the crop should be checked and succeeding applications changed to conform with the influence exerted by the previous dosage.

14:15. REACTION OF ZONAL SOILS OF ARID REGIONS

Arid region zonal soils occur in areas where the rainfall is seldom more than 20 inches yearly and usually is much less. Lack of extensive leaching leaves the base status of these soils high. In fact, a fully and normally developed zonal profile usually carries at some point in its profile (usually in the C horizon) a calcium carbonate accumulation greater than that of its parent material. The lower the rainfall the nearer the surface this layer will be. (See Fig. 12:10.)

As a result these soils may have alkaline subsoils and alkaline or neutral surface layers. When enough leaching has occurred to free the solum of calcium carbonate, a mild acidity may then develop in the surface horizons. Such a situation exists in the case of the chernozems. The genetic classification of zonal soils of arid regions with a pertinent description of each group has already been presented (pp. 341–342).

14:16. REACTION OF SALINE AND SODIC SOILS

When the drainage of arid region soils is impeded and the surface evaporation becomes excessive, soluble salts tend to accumulate in the surface horizon. Such intrazonal soils are designated halomorphic (see p. 341) and have been classified[10] under three headings: saline, saline sodic, and sodic.

SALINE SOILS.[11]   These soils contain a concentration of neutral soluble salts sufficient to seriously interfere with the growth of most plants. The electrical conductivity of a saturated extract (ECe) is greater than 4 mmho/cm. Less than 15 per cent of the cation-exchange capacity of these soils is occupied by sodium ions, and the pH usually is below 8.5. This is because the soluble salts present are mostly neutral and, due to their domination, only a small amount of exchangeable sodium is present.

Such soils are sometimes called *white alkali* soils because a surface incrustation, if present, is light in color (see Fig. 14:10). The excess soluble salts, which are mostly chlorides and sulfates of sodium, calcium, and magnesium, can readily be leached out of these soils with no appreciable rise in pH. This is a very important practical consideration in the management of these soils. Care must be taken, of course, to be certain that the leaching water is low in sodium.

SALINE-SODIC SOILS.   This group contains appreciable quantities of neutral soluble salts and enough adsorbed Na ions to seriously affect most plants. Although more than 15 per cent of the

10 L. A. Richards, ed., *Diagnosis and Improvement of Saline and Alkali Soils,* U.S. Regional Salinity Lab., 1947.
11 Salinization is the term used in reference to the natural processes that result in the accumulation of neutral soluble salts in soils.

Figure 14:10. Upper. *A white "alkali" spot in a field of alfalfa under irrigation. Because of upward capillarity and evaporation, salts have been brought to the surface where they have accumulated in amounts toxic to plants. (U.S. Soil Conservation Service photo.)* Lower. *A close-up photo showing the white salt crust on a saline soil from Colorado. The white salts are in contrast with the darker colored soil (left foreground) underneath. (Scale in inches is shown at the bottom of photo.)*

total exchange capacity of these soils is occupied by sodium, their pH, surprisingly enough, is likely to be below 8.5. This is because of the repressive influence of the neutral soluble salts, just as in the saline soils described above. The (ECe) is more than 4 mmho/cm.

But unlike the saline soils, leaching will markedly raise the pH of saline-sodic soils, unless calcium or magnesium salts concentrations are high in the soil or in the irrigation water. This is because the exchangeable sodium, once the neutral soluble salts are removed, readily hydrolyzes and thereby markedly increases the OH ion concentration of the soil solution. In practice, this is unfortunate as the Na ions disperse the mineral colloids, which then develop a tight, impervious soil structure. At the same time, sodium toxicity to plants is increased.

SODIC SOILS.[12]   These soils do not contain any great amount of neutral soluble salts, the detrimental effects on plants being largely due to the toxicity of the sodium as well as of the OH ions.[13] The exchangeable sodium, which occupies decidedly more than 15 per cent of the total exchange capacity of these soils, is free to hydrolyze, because the concentration of neutral soluble salts is rather low. The ECe is less than 4 mmho/cm. Consequently, the pH is above 8.5, often rising as high as 10.0. Due to the deflocculating influence of the sodium, such soils usually are in an unsatisfactory physical condition. As already stated, the leaching of a saline-sodic soil will readily change it to a characteristic sodic soil.

Because of the extreme alkalinity resulting from the Na_2CO_3 present, the surface of alkali soils usually is discolored by the dispersed humus carried upward by the capillary water—hence the name *black alkali* is frequently used. These soils are often located in small areas called *slick spots* surrounded by soils that are relatively productive.

14:17. GROWTH OF PLANTS ON HALOMORPHIC SOILS

Saline and saline-sodic soils with their relatively low pH (usually less than 8.5) detrimentally influence plants largely because of their high

---

[12] Alkalinization refers to the natural processes that give rise to soils with an undue accumulation of exchangeable sodium and a very high pH.

[13] The high pH is largely due to the hydrolysis of sodium carbonate which occurs as follows:

$$2Na^+ + CO_3^{--} + 2H_2O \rightleftharpoons 2Na^+ + 2OH^- + H_2CO_3$$

The OH ions resulting give pH values of 10 and above. Also, the sodium complex undergoes hydrolysis as follows:

$$Na \boxed{Micelle} + HOH \rightleftharpoons H \boxed{Micelle} + Na^+ + OH^-$$

soluble salt concentration. (See Fig. 14:10.) It is common knowledge that when a water solution containing a relatively large amount of dissolved salts is brought into contact with a plant cell it will cause a shrinkage of the protoplasmic lining. This action, called *plasmolysis,* increases with the concentration of the salt solution. The phenomenon is due to the osmotic movement of the water, which passes from the cell toward the more concentrated soil solution. The cell then collapses. The nature of the salt, the species, and even the individuality of the plant, as well as other factors, determine the concentration at which the individual succumbs. The adverse physical condition, especially of saline-sodic soils, may also be a factor.

Sodic soils, dominated as they are by active sodium, exert a detrimental effect on plants in three ways: (1) caustic influence of the high alkalinity induced by the sodium carbonate and bicarbonate, (2) toxicity of the bicarbonate and other anions, and (3) the adverse effects of the active sodium ions on plant metabolism and nutrition. As already suggested, the removal of the neutral salts from a saline-sodic soil will raise its pH and increase the activity of its adsorbed sodium to the point where it affects plants in the ways already described for sodic soils. Thus, uncontrolled leaching of saline-sodic soils may lead to their being rendered essentially useless.

14:18. TOLERANCE OF HIGHER PLANTS TO HALOMORPHIC SOILS

The capacity of higher plants to grow satisfactorily on salty soils depends on a number of interrelated factors. The physiological constitution of the plant, its stage of growth, and its rooting habits certainly are a part of the picture.[14] In respect to the soil we must consider the nature of the various salts, their proportionate amounts, their total concentration, and their distribution in the solum. The structure of the soil and its drainage and aeration are also of moment.

As a result, it is difficult to forecast accurately the tolerance of crops. Only carefully controlled trials will answer this question and even then with no great degree of certainty. Perhaps the best comparative data are those presented by Richards[15] (see Table 14:1), who stipulates that tolerance shall mean the ability to produce fairly satisfactory crop yields.

[14] It is interesting to note that old alfalfa is more tolerant than young alfalfa and that deep rooted legumes show a greater resistance than those with shallow rootage. For the salt tolerance of forage legumes and grasses see L. Bernstein, *Salt Tolerance of Grasses and Forage Legumes,* Agr. Inf. Bul. 194, U.S. Dept. of Agric., 1958.
[15] Richards, *op. cit.*

Table 14:1. Relative Tolerance of Certain Plants to Salty Soils. The Placings Are More or Less Tentative Due to the Number of Complicating Factors Involved

High Tolerance	Medium Tolerance	Low Tolerance
Alkali sacation	Alfalfa	Alsike clover
Bermuda grass	Barley	Apples
Canadian wild rye	Birdsfoot trefoil	Cabbage
Cotton	Carrots	Celery
Date palm	Figs	Ladino clover
Garden pea	Grapes	Lemon
Kale	Lettuce	Orange
Milo	Oats	Peach
Rape	Olives	Pear
Rescue grass	Onions	Peas
Rhodes grass	Rye	Plum
Salt grass	Sweet Clover	Potatoes
Sugar beets	Sudan grass	Red clover
Western wheat grass	Tomatoes	White clover

14:19. MANAGEMENT OF SALINE AND SODIC SOILS [16]

Ordinarily there are three general ways in which saline and alkali lands may be handled in order to avoid, at least partially, the injurious effects to plants. The first of these is *eradication;* the second is a *conversion* of some of the salts to less injurious forms; the third may be designated *control.* In the first two methods, an attempt is made actually to eliminate by various means some of the salts or to render them less toxic. In the third, soil-management procedures are employed which keep the salts so well distributed throughout the soil solum that there is no toxic concentration within the root zone.

ERADICATION. Of the methods used to free the soil, at least partially, of excess salts, the commonest are: (1) underdrainage, and (2) leaching or flushing. A combination of the two, flooding after tile drains have been installed, is the most thorough and satisfactory. When this method is used in irrigated regions, heavy and repeated applications of water can be made. The salts that become soluble are leached from

---

[16] See D. W. Thorne and H. B. Peterson, *Irrigated Soils* (Philadelphia and Toronto: Blakeston, 1954); and W. P. Kelley, *Alkali Soils, Their Formation Properties and Reclamation* (New York: Reinhold, 1951).

the solum and are drained off through the tile. The irrigation water used must, of course, be relatively free of silt and salts, especially those containing sodium.

The leaching method works especially well with pervious saline soils whose soluble salts are largely neutral and high in calcium and magnesium. Of course, little exchangeable sodium should be present. Leaching saline-sodic soils (and even sodic soils if the water will percolate) with waters very high in salt, but low in sodium may be effective. On the other hand, treating sodic and saline-sodic soils with low salt containing water may intensify their alkalinity because of the removal of the neutral soluble salts. This allows an increase in the per cent sodium saturation, thereby increasing the concentration of OH ions in the soil solution. This may be avoided, as explained below, by converting the toxic sodium carbonate and bicarbonate to sodium sulfate by first treating the soil with heavy applications of gypsum or sulfur. (For reaction see below.) Leaching will then render the soil more satisfactory for crops.

CONVERSION.[17]   The use of gypsum on sodic soils, as already suggested, is often recommended for the purpose of changing part of the caustic alkali carbonates into sulfates. Several tons of gypsum an acre are usually necessary. The soil must be kept moist, in order to hasten the reaction, and the gypsum should be cultivated into the surface, not plowed under. The treatment may be supplemented later by a thorough leaching of the soil with irrigation water in order to free it of some of its sodium sulfate. The gypsum reacts with both the Na_2CO_3 and the adsorbed sodium as follows:

$$Na_2CO_3 + CaSO_4 \leftrightarrows CaCO_3 + Na_2SO_4 \quad \downarrow$$
$$\text{leachable}$$

$$\begin{array}{c} Na \\ Na \end{array} \boxed{\text{Micelle}} + CaSO_4 \leftrightarrows Ca \boxed{\text{Micelle}} + Na_2SO_4 \downarrow$$
$$\text{leachable}$$

It is also recognized that sulfur can be used to advantage on salty lands, especially where sodium carbonate abounds. The sulfur upon oxidation yields sulfuric acid which not only changes the sodium carbonate to the less harmful sulfate but also tends to reduce the intense alkalinity. The reactions of the sulfuric acid with the compounds containing sodium may be shown as follows:

[17] See C. A. Bower, *Chemical Amendments for Improving Sodium Soils,* Agr. Inf. Bul. 195, U.S. Dept. of Agric., 1959.

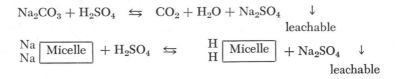

$$Na_2CO_3 + H_2SO_4 \leftrightarrows CO_2 + H_2O + Na_2SO_4 \quad \downarrow$$

leachable

leachable

It is to be noted that not only is the sodium carbonate changed to sodium sulfate, a mild neutral salt, but the carbonate radical is entirely eliminated. When gypsum is used, however, the carbonate remains as a calcium salt.

CONTROL. The retardation of evaporation is, of course, an important feature of salty soil control. This will not only save moisture, but also may retard the translocation upward of soluble salts into the root zone. As pointed out earlier, however, there are no inexpensive methods of reducing evaporation from large acreages. Consequently, other control practices must be turned to.

It is needless to say that, where irrigation is practiced, an excess of water should be avoided unless it is needed to free the soil of soluble salts. Frequent light irrigations are often necessary, however, to keep the salts sufficiently dilute to allow normal plant growth.

The timing of irrigation is extremely important on salty soils, particularly during the spring planting season. Since young seedlings are especially sensitive to salts, irrigation often precedes or follows planting to move the salts downward. After the plants are well established, their salt tolerance often is somewhat greater.

The use of salt-resistant crops is another important feature of the successful management of saline and alkali lands. Sugar beets, cotton, sorghum, barley, rye, sweet clover, and alfalfa are especially to be recommended. (See Table 14:1.) Moreover, a temporary alleviation of alkali will allow less-resistant crops to be established. Farm manure is especially useful in such an attempt. A crop, such as alfalfa, once it is growing vigorously, may maintain itself in spite of the salt concentrations that may develop later. The root action of tolerant plants is especially helpful in improving sodic soils which have a poor physical condition.

14:20. CONCLUSION

Although the discussion closes with pertinent suggestions regarding the management of saline and sodic soils, it must not be forgotten that the major theme of this chapter is soil reaction or, if you will, soil pH. And it is not difficult to see that as many, or even more, features of practical concern stem from soil reaction as from any other single soil characteristic. Material in the chapters that follow will emphasize this point even more decisively.

Chapter 15

Lime and Its Soil-Plant Relationships

Soil acidity and the nutritional conditions that accompany it result from a lack of exchangeable metallic cations. The quantity of these adsorbed cations controls the percentage base saturation and thereby indirectly determines the H ion concentration of the soil solution. Consequently, an increase in soil pH is attained by adding suitable quantities of certain compounds carrying one or more of these necessary metals. This narrows the problem, therefore, to that of choosing the compounds that will most suitably do the job.

The two metallic cations best suited for the alleviation of soil acidity are *calcium* and *magnesium*. They are cheap and plentiful and have favorable effects on the physical condition of soils. Moreover, their carbonates and even their oxides and hydroxides are comparatively mild and easy to handle. In humid region soils calcium and, to a lesser extent, magnesium are the metallic cations that, together with H and Al ions, normally predominate in the colloidal complexes. (See p. 92.) It is only natural, therefore, that on acid soils attempts are made to increase their concentration by artificial means.

The choice of these two cations, however, only partially solves the problem. The associated anion in the liming compounds must also be considered. For example, calcium and magnesium salts of strong acids are generally unsatisfactory. The reason is simple. When by cation exchange adsorbed hydrogen is replaced by the metallic cations of a salt such as $CaSO_4$, a strong acid is liberated in the soil solution. This may be shown as follows:

$$\begin{matrix} H \\ H \end{matrix} \boxed{\text{Micelle}} + CaSO_4 \rightleftharpoons Ca \boxed{\text{Micelle}} + 2\,H^+ + SO_4^{--}$$

Thus, even though the amount of active calcium has been increased, the pH of the soil solution may actually be reduced. Consequently, salts such as gypsum and calcium chloride are seldom recommended as liming materials. They are used only when large amounts of calcium are desired without an increase in pH.

15:1. FORMS OF LIME

With the elimination of salts of strong acids, two satisfactory groups of calcium and magnesium compounds remain. They are (1) the salts of weak acids such as the *carbonates,* and (2) basic compounds such as the *oxides* and *hydroxides.* These compounds of calcium and magnesium are commonly referred to as *agricultural limes*[1] and have the advantage, among other things, of leaving no residue of an objectionable nature in the soil. For example, the direct action of $CaCO_3$ and CaO with soil acids may be shown, perhaps oversimplified, as follows:

$$\begin{matrix} H \\ H \end{matrix} \boxed{\text{Micelle}} + CaCO_3 \rightleftharpoons Ca \boxed{\text{Micelle}} + CO_2 \uparrow + H_2O$$

$$\begin{matrix} H \\ H \end{matrix} \boxed{\text{Micelle}} + CaO \rightleftharpoons Ca \boxed{\text{Micelle}} + H_2O$$

Note that in both cases as the reaction goes to the right there is a neutralization or removal of H ions from the system and an increase in

---

[1] Lime from the strictly chemical standpoint refers to one and only one compound —calcium oxide. Agriculturally, however, the term has a broader meaning. Thus used, it includes all compounds of *calcium* and *magnesium* employed in a practical way to raise the pH of soils and to alleviate the nutritional factors associated with soil acidity.

exchangeable calcium. Consequently, an increase in percentage base saturation is effected while at the same time the pH of the soil solution is raised.

As is to be expected, liming materials do not appear on the market as single compounds of magnesium or calcium, nor are they by any means pure. The better grades of the oxides and hydroxides are generally used in the trades, the less pure materials being used as agricultural lime. The carbonated forms of lime have a number of different sources and vary to a marked degree in purity and fineness.[2]

15:2. OXIDE OF LIME

Commercial oxide of lime is commonly spoken of as *burned lime, quicklime,* or often simply as the *oxide.* Since it usually is a finely ground powder, it commonly is marketed in paper bags. Oxide of lime is quite caustic and often rather disagreeable to handle.

The devices for producing burned lime are various, ranging from small ovens to the large cylindrical kilns of commerce. In any case the general result is the same. The limestone with which the kiln is charged is decomposed by the heat. Carbon dioxide and other gases are driven off, and the impure calcium and magnesium oxides are left behind. The essential reactions that occur when calcium carbonate and dolomite are burned are as follows:

$$CaCO_3 + Heat \longrightarrow CaO + CO_2 \uparrow$$
$$CaMg(CO_3)_2 + Heat \longrightarrow CaO + MgO + 2\,CO_2 \uparrow$$

The purity of burned lime, as it is sold for agricultural purposes, is variable, ranging from 85 to 98 per cent. Perhaps a purity of 95 per cent is a suitable average figure. The impurities of burned lime consist of the original impurities of the limestone, such as chert, clay, and iron compounds etc.

A number of compounds are present in commercial oxide of lime. Calcium oxide and magnesium oxide are, of course, most prominent. With them are small amounts of the hydroxides since the oxides readily take up water from the air and slake to some extent even when bagged.

---

[2] Certain other compounds of calcium may at some future time be classed as agricultural lime if their use becomes common. For instance, by-product calcium silicates ($CaSiO_3$ and Ca_2SiO_4) have been successfully used in an experimental way. When an excess of this material is applied to soils, detrimental effects to higher plants, often obtained from overdoses of calcium carbonate, are not observed.

See W. H. MacIntire, *et al.,* "Nature and Liming Value of Quenched Calcium Silicate Slag," *Soil Sci.,* 50:219–32, 1940.

Also contact with the carbon dioxide of the atmosphere will tend to produce carbonates. Besides these, there are the inert impurities already mentioned.

15:3. HYDROXIDE OF LIME

This form of lime is commonly, and of course improperly, referred to as the *hydrate*. And since it is produced by adding water to burned lime, the hydroxides that result are often spoken of as *slaked lime*. The slaking reaction is as follows:

$$CaO + MgO + 2H_2O \longrightarrow Ca(OH)_2 + Mg(OH)_2$$

Hydroxide of lime appears on the market as a white powder, highly caustic and not at all pleasant to handle. And like the oxide it requires bagging. Representative samples generally show a purity of perhaps 95 or 96 per cent.

In order to maintain the concentration of this form of lime at a high point, the slaking often is not carried to completion. As a result, considerable amounts of the oxides are likely to remain. Moreover, hydroxide of lime carbonates rather readily.[3] This is likely to be the case if the bag is left open and the air is moist. Besides the impurities, six important lime compounds are usually present: the oxides, the hydroxides, and the carbonates of calcium and magnesium. The hydroxides, of course, greatly predominate.

15:4. CARBONATE OF LIME

A number of lime compounds are sold under the head of commercial carbonate of lime. Of these, pulverized or ground limestone is the most common. There are also bog lime or marl, oyster shells, and precipitated carbonates. Great deposits of marl occur under peat beds (p. 372), and when dredged out, dried, and crushed, make excellent lime. However, the cost usually is too high to allow successful competition with limestone. Also lime carbonates are by-products from certain industries. All of these forms of lime are variable in their content of calcium and magnesium.

[3] The carbonation of calcium and magnesium hydroxides occurs as follows:
$$Ca(OH)_2 + CO_2 \longrightarrow CaCO_3 + H_2O$$
$$Mg(OH)_2 + CO_2 \longrightarrow MgCO_3 + H_2O$$

The two important compounds carried by limestones are *calcium carbonate* ($CaCO_3$) and *dolomite* [$CaMg(CO_3)_2$]. These occur in varying proportions. When little or no dolomite is present, the limestone is spoken of as *calcic*. As the magnesium increases this grades into a *dolomitic limestone* and finally, if very little calcium carbonate is present and the stone is almost entirely made up of calcium-magnesium carbonate and impurities, the term *dolomite* is used. Most of the crushed limestone on the market is calcic and dolomitic, although ground dolomite is available in certain localities.

Ground limestone, which is used to a greater extent than all other forms of lime combined, varies in purity from approximately 75 to 99 per cent. The average purity of the representative crushed limestone may be put at perhaps 94 per cent.

15:5. CHEMICAL GUARANTEE OF LIMES

Since the various forms of lime are sold on the basis of their chemical composition, the commercial guarantees in this respect become a matter of great importance. The caustic forms, that is the oxide and hydroxide, may bear composition guarantees stated in one or more of the following ways—the *conventional oxide content*, the *calcium oxide equivalent*, the *neutralizing power*, and *percentages of calcium and magnesium*. In order to facilitate the explanation and comparison of the various methods of expression, composition figures for commercial burned and hydroxide of lime are drawn together in Table 15:1.

Table 15:1. Composition of a Representative Commercial Oxide and Hydroxide of Lime Expressed in Different Ways

Forms of Lime	Conventional Oxide Content Percentage	Calcium Oxide Equivalent	Neutralizing Power	Elemental, Percentage
Commercial oxide	CaO = 77 MgO = 18	102.0	182.1	Ca = 55.0 Mg = 10.8
Commercial hydroxide	CaO = 60 MgO = 12	76.7	136.9	Ca = 42.8 Mg = 7.2

CONVENTIONAL OXIDES AND CAO EQUIVALENT. Since the *oxide* form of expression is so commonly used, this type of guarantee is designated here as the *conventional* method. The *calcium oxide equivalent,* as the term implies, is a statement of the strength of the lime in one figure, namely, CaO. The magnesium oxide is expressed in terms of calcium oxide equivalent and this figure is added to the percentage of calcium oxide present. This may be conveniently done by means of conversion factors.[4] Thus, for the commercial oxide of Table 15:1, 18 per cent of MgO is equivalent to 25 per cent of CaO ($18 \times 1.389 = 25$) and $77 + 25 = 102$, the calcium oxide equivalent. This means that every 100 pounds of the impure burned lime is equivalent in neutralizing capacity to 102 pounds of *pure* calcium oxide.

NEUTRALIZING POWER AND ELEMENTAL EXPRESSION. The *neutralizing power,* as the term is arbitrarily used in respect to lime, is nothing more than a statement of its strength in terms of calcium carbonate—that is, its $CaCO_3$ *equivalent.* Thus, by multiplying by 1.786 in the case above, the calcium oxide equivalent of 102 becomes 182.1, the $CaCO_3$ equivalent. This means that every 100 pounds of the impure burned lime is equivalent in neutralizing capacity to 182.1 pounds of *pure* calcium carbonate.

The *elemental* method of expression, while not so common as the other modes of statement, is required by law in some states. It may be readily calculated from the conventional oxide guarantee. Or, if given alone, the other forms of statement may be derived from it.

Commercial caustic limes practically always carry the conventional oxide guarantee and sometimes the elemental. Thus, the amount of magnesium, as well as calcium, present is indicated. This is an important con-

---

[4] In order to express one lime in chemically equivalent amounts of another, simply multiply by the appropriate factor as given below:

MgO	to CaO	— 1.389	MgCO₃ to CaCO₃	— 1.186
CaCO₃	to CaO	— .560	MgCO₃ to Mg	— .288
CaO	to CaCO₃	— 1.786	CaCO₃ to Ca	— .400
MgCO₃	to CaO	— .664	MgO to Mg	— .602

CaO to Ca — .714

A thorough student should be able not only to derive the above factors but also to make the conversion without them, namely by the direct use of atomic and molecular weights. For example, we wish to express, say, 1 pound of pure MgO in chemically equivalent pounds of pure CaO. As the following reactions indicate, these two compounds, molecule per molecule, are equal in neutralizing power:

$$CaO + 2HCl \longrightarrow CaCl_2 + H_2O$$
$$MgO + 2HCl \longrightarrow MgCl_2 + H_2O$$

But the molecular weight of CaO is 56 ($40 + 16$) and that of MgO is 40.3 ($24.3 + 16$). Hence on the basis of weight it takes 56 lbs. of CaO to equal 40.3 lbs. of MgO. And if the pounds of CaO necessary to equal 1 pound of MgO are desired, the proportion would be:

$$40.3 : 56.0 : : 1 : x$$
$$40.3\, x = 56$$

$x = 1.389$ lbs. of CaO necessary to equal 1 lb. of MgO.

Here then is a factor that can be used to express pounds, or tons or per cents, etc., of MgO in chemically equivalent quantities of CaO.

sideration. In addition, one or even both of the other forms of guarantee may be given. The latter are especially desirable as they show the strength of the lime in one figure, thus making comparisons between different brands easy.

LIMESTONE GUARANTEES. The guarantees on ground limestone differ in two respects from those of the caustic forms of lime. Usually the separate percentages of calcium and magnesium carbonates are given. These are almost always accompanied by the percentage of total carbonates.[5] In addition, one or more of the other four modes of guarantee may be used. By way of illustration the six methods of expression are presented in Table 15:2 for a representative ground limestone.

Table 15:2. Composition of a Representative Commercial Ground Limestone Expressed in Different Ways

Separate Carbonates (Per Cent)	Total Carbonates (Per Cent)	Neutral- izing Power	Conventional Oxide (Per Cent)	Calcium Oxide Equivalent	Elemental (Per Cent)
$CaCO_3 = 80$			$CaO = 44.80$		$Ca = 32.00$
	94	96.6		54.10	
$MgCO_3 = 14$			$MgO = 6.70$		$Mg = 4.03$

TOTAL CARBONATES VS. NEUTRALIZING POWER. The total carbonate method of guarantee has many advocates because it is so simple and requires no chemical explanation. Furthermore, when the total neutralizing figure for a given limestone is higher than the total carbonates, it is usually due to the presence of dolomite in the limestone. Since this mineral reacts with the soil rather slowly (see Fig. 15:1), the advantage from the standpoint of total neutralizing power is questionable unless the lime is very finely ground. Consequently, the total carbonate method of expression is perhaps a truer indication of the comparative field value of limestones.

Those that favor the neutralizing-power method of expression stress its accuracy and the fact that it can be determined very easily and quickly. This is an important consideration in a control laboratory when many samples must be analyzed. Moreover, there is the advertising phase of the controversy. For instance, a dolomitic limestone containing 46 per cent

[5] It is well to remember that both of these methods of guarantee are in part conventional since only part of the calcium is present as $CaCO_3$. The remainder, as well as all the magnesium, is carried by the admixed dolomite [$CaMg(CO_3)_2$]. Magnesium carbonate, as such, is usually not present.

Figure 15:1. Alfalfa was seeded in this field trial. In the foreground the soil was unlimed (pH = 5.2). In the background 4 tons of limestone were applied before seeding.

of $CaCO_3$ and 43 per cent of $MgCO_3$[6] has a *neutralizing power* of 97 but its *total carbonate figure* is only 89. When competition is keen, such a difference may lead to much misunderstanding and controversy.

15:6. FINENESS GUARANTEE OF LIMESTONE

The application to the soil of two different liming materials in chemically equivalent quantities does not necessarily mean that equivalent results will be attained. This is especially true if the two materials are both limestones, since the particles contained therein are apt to be quite variable in size as well as hardness. The importance of this is apparent since it is well known that the finer the division of any material the more rapid is likely to be its solution and rate of reaction. The caustic limes usually appear on the market as almost impalpable powders; consequently their fineness is always satisfactory.

[6] This is only a conventional method of expressing the constituents in dolomitic limestone. Actually this material is composed of a mixture of $CaCO_3$ and dolomite $[CaMg(CO_3)_2]$. (See page 417.)

Therefore, in order to rate a limestone as to it probable effects in comparison with other limes, a *fineness guarantee* is desirable. This is usually one of the requirements of laws controlling the sale of agricultural limestone. A mechanical analysis is made by the use of screens of different mesh, a 10-mesh sieve, for example, having ten openings to the linear inch.[7] The proportion of the limestone that will pass through the various screens used constitutes the guarantee.

15:7. INTERPRETATION OF A FINENESS GUARANTEE

Before a statement can be made as to the degree of fineness a limestone should attain to be satisfactory, some of the experimental work available on the subject should be considered. White presents the following significant data (Table 15:3) as a result of certain laboratory and greenhouse studies at State College, Pennsylvania.

Table 15:3. A Comparison of Various Grades of Limestone When Applied at the Same Rates, Pennsylvania Agricultural Experiment Station[a]
(100-mesh material is taken as 100)

Conditions	100-mesh and Smaller	60–80-mesh	20–40-mesh	8–12-mesh
Solubility in carbonated water	100	57	45	28
Value in correcting acidity	100	57	27	18
Formation of nitrates	100	94	56	12
Plant Growth	100	69	22	5

[a] J. W. White, *The Value of Limestone of Different Degrees of Fineness*, Bulletin 149, Penn. Agr. Exp. Sta., 1917.

These figures show that the finer grades of limestone are much more rapidly effective. Further data by the same author indicate, that, while the coarser lime is less rapid in its action, it remains in the soil longer and its influence should be effective for a greater period of years. Other

[7] The diameter of the individual openings will, of course, be much less than 0.1 of an inch, the exact size depending on the wire used in making the sieve. Usually the diameter of the openings in inches is a little more than one-half of the quotient obtained by dividing 1 by the mesh rating. For instance, the openings of a 10-mesh screen are approximately .07 in. diameter; those of a 50-mesh, .0122 in.; and those of a 100-mesh screen, approximately .0058 in. Unfortunately there is no standardization of the sieves used for grading agricultural limestone.

investigators have published results that substantiate the above conclusions. The proportionate responses are somewhat different, however. This is to be expected, as limestones of different hardness applied to various soil types are sure to respond rather diversely.

FINE LIMESTONE. Everything considered, a pulverized limestone, *all of which will pass a 10-mesh screen, and at least 50 per cent of which will pass a 100-mesh sieve,* should give excellent results and yet be cheap enough to encourage its use. Such a lime is sufficiently pulverized to rate as a *fine* limestone.

Nevertheless, many limes are finer than this, 50 or 60 per cent sometimes passing a 200-mesh screen. However, because of the cost of grinding the stone to a very fine condition and the rapidity with which such material disappears from the soil, a medium ground lime such as specified above, seems to be a more desirable commercial product. Such material has enough of the finer particles to give quick results and yet a sufficient amount of the coarser fragments to make it last over the period of the rotation.

A limestone which does not approximate the fineness designated above should be discounted to the extent to which it falls short. It may be necessary, for example, to consider 3,000 pounds of one limestone as equal to 1 ton of another, even though their chemical analyses are the same. Considerable judgment in the interpretation of fineness guarantee is necessary in order that such an adjustment be made correctly. Much limestone that falls below the standard set above is now being used because, as a by-product, it is very cheap. When the amounts put on the land are properly adjusted, as good results may be expected from the coarser limes as from the finer limestones and the effects should last considerably longer.

15:8. CHANGES OF LIME ADDED TO THE SOIL

In considering the changes that lime undergoes when added to the soil two things must always be kept in mind: (1) that the calcium and magnesium compounds applied undergo solution under the influence of a variable partial pressure of carbon dioxide; and (2) that an acid colloidal complex will adsorb considerable amounts of calcium and magnesium ions.

REACTION WITH CO_2. When lime, whether the oxide, hydroxide, or the carbonate, is applied to an acid soil, the movement, as solution occurs, is toward the bicarbonate form. This is because the partial carbon dioxide pressure, usually several hundred times greater than that of the atmospheric air, generally is intense enough to prevent the existence of the hydroxide or even the carbonate. The reactions, written only for the purely calcium limes, are as follows:

$$CaO + H_2O \longrightarrow Ca(OH)_2$$
$$Ca(OH)_2 + 2\,H_2CO_3 \longrightarrow Ca(HCO_3)_2 + 2\,H_2O$$
$$CaCO_3 + H_2CO_3 \longrightarrow Ca(HCO_3)_2$$

REACTION WITH SOIL COLLOIDS. This, however, represents only the solution of the lime in carbonated water. The soil situation is not so simple as these reactions might lead one to assume. This is because the soil colloidal matter continually upsets the equilibrium tendencies by adsorbing the ions of calcium and magnesium. These ions may be taken from the soil solution proper or directly from the solid phase if the contact is sufficiently close. The adsorption in respect to calcium may be indicated as follows:

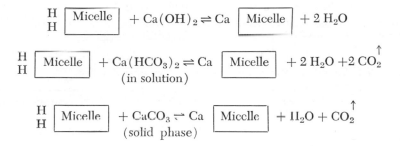

As the above reactions of limestone proceed, carbon dioxide is freely evolved. In addition, the adsorption of the calcium and magnesium raises the percentage base saturation of the colloidal complex and the pH of the soil solution is pushed up correspondingly. (See p. 385.)

DISTRIBUTION OF Ca AND Mg IN LIMED SOIL. Calcium and magnesium, if supplied by a limestone of average fineness, will exist in the soil, at least for a time, in three forms: (1) as solid calcium and calcium-magnesium carbonates; (2) as exchangeable bases adsorbed by the colloidal matter; and (3) as dissociated cations in the soil solution mostly in association with bicarbonate ions. When the calcium and calcium-magnesium carbonates have all dissolved, the system becomes somewhat simpler, involving only the exchangeable cations and those in soil solution.

DEPLETION OF Ca AND Mg. As time goes on the particles of the added lime carbonates gradually disappear and the colloidal complex loses part of its bases. This is affected by H ions generated by carbonic and other acids. In this way the so-called reserve lime, both carbonate and adsorbed, is gradually fed into the soil solution by cation exchange, there to be used in many different ways. The mechanism of these losses is fully explained on page 94.

As the soluble calcium and magnesium compounds are removed, the percentage base saturation and pH are gradually reduced and eventually another application of lime is necessary. This, then, is the type of cycle through which much of the calcium and magnesium added to arable soils swings in humid regions.

15:9. LOSS OF LIME FROM ARABLE SOILS

Calcium and magnesium are lost from soils in three ways: (1) by erosion, (2) by crop removal, and (3) by leaching. Since these three types of lime loss have already been discussed and evaluated in Chapter 9, it is a simple matter to draw such data together in tabular form (Table 15:4).

Table 15:4. Lime Losses from Soil in Pounds per Acre per Year

Manner of Removal	Calcium		Magnesium	
	CaO	CaCO$_3$	MgO	MgCO$_3$
By erosion, Missouri experiments, 4 per cent slope	120	214	48	100
By the average crop of a standard rotation	50	89	42	88
By leaching from a representative silt loam	125	223	30	63
Total		526		251

Although the values cited cannot be used as representing losses from soils in general, they are quite significant when used comparatively.

The data for erosion removals are for a silt loam in Missouri, cropped to a rotation of corn, wheat, and clover. (See Table 9:8.) The acre annual removal by crops was calculated for a standard and representative rotation assuming reasonable yields. (See Table 9:5.) The leaching losses are for a postulated representative silt loam under a rainfall of perhaps 36 to 40 inches and cropped to a standard farm rotation. (See Table 9:5.) All data are in pounds per acre per year expressed in the conventional *oxide* form and also in the more practical terms of *calcium* and *magnesium carbonates.*

The greater loss of calcium than magnesium, no doubt, is due to the fact that the soil colloidal matter almost always carries a much larger amount of the former in an exchangeable condition. And, since the average lime supplies several times more calcium than magnesium, this loss ratio will in general be maintained and even accentuated in arable lands as liming proceeds.

This does not mean, however, that the magnesium in lime is of minor importance. Far from it. In fact, judging from the figures of Table 15:4, there should always be at least one third as much magnesium as calcium in the lime applied in order to proportionately meet the outgo of the two constituents. Other things being equal, it is generally wise to select a magnesium-containing limestone.

The figures quoted in the above table indicate that 500 to 600 pounds of limestone per acre per year may be required to meet the loss from cropped soils in humid regions. This amounts to perhaps 1 to 1.5 tons of carbonate of lime during the period of the average rotation depending upon the kind of soil and other factors. Such a conclusion justifies the attention that is paid to lime in any scheme of fertility management in areas of medium to heavy rainfall.

15:10. THE EFFECTS OF LIME ON THE SOIL

It has already been emphasized that the changes of lime in the soil are many and complicated. Therefore, the discussion that follows must of necessity, rather than choice, be more or less general in nature. The better known effects of liming will be considered under three heads: (1) physical, (2) chemical, and (3) biological.

PHYSICAL EFFECTS. In heavy soils there is always a tendency for the fine particles to become too closely associated. Such a condition interferes with air and water movement and, therefore, granulation is highly desirable. A satisfactory crumb structure is somewhat encouraged in an acid soil by the addition of any form of lime, although the influence is largely indirect. For example, the effects of lime upon biotic forces are paramount, especially those that have to do with the decomposition of the soil organic matter and the synthesis of humus. The genesis of the latter as well as its persistence greatly encourages granulation. (See p. 60.) In this respect the stimulating effect of lime on deep rooted plants, especially legumes, should not be ignored.

CHEMICAL EFFECTS. If a soil at pH of 5.0 is limed to a more suitable pH value (say 6.5) a number of significant chemical changes occur. Many of these were stressed in Chapter 14 and will be merely outlined here to reemphasize their importance. For example:

1. The concentration of H ions will decrease.
2. The concentration of OH ions will increase.
3. The solubility of iron, aluminum, and manganese will decline.
4. The availability of phosphates and molybdates will be augmented.
5. The exchangeable calcium and magnesium will increase.
6. The percentage base saturation will increase.
7. The availability of potassium may be increased or decreased depending on conditions.

Of the specific chemical effects of lime mentioned, the reduction in acidity is one commonly uppermost in the popular mind. However, the indirect effects on nutrient availability and on the toxicity of certain elements are probably more important. Liming of acid soils enhances the availability and plant uptake of elements such as molybdenum, phosphorous, calcium, and magnesium. At the same time, it drastically reduces the concentration of iron, aluminum, and manganese which under very acid conditions are apt to be present in toxic quantities.

BIOLOGICAL EFFECTS. Lime stimulates the general-purpose, heterotrophic soil organisms, thereby increasing the activity of the organic matter and nitrogen of an acid soil. The rate of the turnover of these constituents often is more important than the actual amounts present. This stimulation of enzymic processes not only favors the formation of humus but also encourages the elimination of certain organic intermediate products that might be toxic to higher plants.

Most of the favorable soil organisms, as well as some of the unfavorable ones such as those that produce potato scab, are encouraged by liming. Aminization, ammonification, and sulfur oxidation are markedly speeded up by increasing the pH. The bacteria that fix nitrogen from the air, both nonsymbiotically and in the nodules of legumes, are especially stimulated by the application of lime.

Nitrification, a biological phenomenon of great importance, requires the presence of metallic cations. When lime is inadequate, this desirable transformation will not proceed rapidly. In fact, the successful growth of most soil microorganisms so definitely depends upon lime that satisfactory biological activities cannot be expected if soils fall below a given calcium and magnesium level.

15:11. CROP RESPONSE TO LIMING

The biological effects of lime will now be extended to include higher plants, obviously a consideration of great practical concern. Fig. 14:6 specifies in a general way the lime levels at which various plants seem to grow most satisfactorily, thereby indicating whether or not a particular crop is likely to be benefited by liming. Of the lime-loving plants, alfalfa, sweet clover, red clover, asparagus, cauliflower and lettuce are representative. However, a surprisingly large proportion of our crop plants is quite tolerant to the conditions presented by moderately acid soils. Such plants respond to lime, if at all, more or less indirectly due to its stimulating influence upon the legume preceding them in the rotation. And as a further examination of Fig. 14:6 will show, some plants, such as cranberries and native azaleas, grow much better when the content of exchangeable calcium and magnesium of soils is exceedingly low. The chart under consideration is worthy of careful study.

REASONS FOR RESPONSE. When plants are benefited by lime, a number of possible reasons may be suggested. These are listed as follows: (1) direct nutritive or regulatory action of the calcium and magnesium; (2) removal or neutralization of toxic compounds of either an organic or inorganic nature; (3) retardation of plant diseases; (4) an increased availability chemically of plant nutrients; and (5) an encouragement of microorganic activities favorable in a nutritive way. Since several of these factors undoubtedly function concurrently, crop response to liming is a complicated phenomenon and only the broadest conclusions may be drawn.

The growth of a number of plants is definitely retarded by liming, prominent among which are cranberries, blueberries, watermelons, laurel, and certain species of azaleas and rhododendrons. It is, therefore, advantageous not only to know the condition of the soil but also to understand the influence of lime on the crop to be grown. Lime is too often used as a cure-all, little attention being paid to the widely differing responses exhibited by various crops.

15:12. OVERLIMING

This brings us to the question of *overliming*, that is, the addition of lime until the pH of the soil is above that required for optimum plant growth on the soil in question. Under such conditions many crops that ordinarily respond to lime are detrimentally affected, especially during the first season following the application. With heavy soils and when farmers can afford to apply only moderate amounts of lime, the danger is negligible. But on sandy soils, low in organic matter and therefore lightly buffered, it is easy to injure certain crops even with a relatively moderate application of lime.

The detrimental influences of excess lime have been already mentioned. (See p. 397.) Consequently, they are merely outlined here for convenience:

1. Deficiencies of available iron, manganese, copper, or zinc may be induced.
2. Phosphate availability may decrease due to the formation of complex and insoluble calcium phosphates.
3. The absorption of phosphorus by plants and especially its metabolic use may be interfered with.
4. The uptake and utilization of boron may be hindered.
5. The drastic change in pH may, in itself, be detrimental.

With so many possibilities and with such complex, biocolloidal interrelations to deal with, it is easy to see why overliming injuries in many cases have not been satisfactorily explained.

15:13. PRACTICAL PROBLEMS RESPECTING LIME

The use of lime in a practical way raises three questions. If the first is answered in the affirmative, the other two present themselves in logical sequence. The three questions are: (1) Shall lime be applied? (2) Which form shall be used? (3) What shall be the rate of application? These queries will be considered in order.

15:14. SHALL LIME BE APPLIED?

The old idea respecting lime was that of a *cure-all*—that there would be no harm in trying it; and perhaps it might be beneficial. Such an attitude should now be a thing of the past as it may lead to a waste of money and in some cases to overliming. The use of lime must be based on measured soil acidity and on crop requirements.

SOIL pH AND CROPS TO BE GROWN. In determining the desirability of applying lime, the chemical condition of the soil itself should be examined. For this a pH determination commonly is made either by means of a glass electrode and potentiometer or by the less accurate indicator-dye method (p. 401). Representative subsoil as well as surface samples should be examined. The pH is correlated fairly closely with percentage base saturation and is an indicator of the probable activity of the calcium, magnesium, and other elements in the soil. Besides it is very easily and quickly determined. Here are two reasons why this test is one of the most popular and significant determinations that is now available for soil diagnosis.

Before a recommendation can be made, however, the lime needs in general of the crop or crops to be grown should be considered. The final decision rests upon the proper coordination of these two types of information. A grouping of crops such as that shown on page 400 (Fig. 14:8) will greatly aid in deciding whether or not to lime.

15:15. FORM OF LIME TO APPLY[8]

On the basis of the ideas already presented, it is evident that five major factors should be considered in deciding on a specific brand of lime to apply. These factors are as follows:

1. Chemical guarantees of the limes under consideration.
2. Cost per ton applied to the land.
3. Rate of reaction with soil.
4. Fineness of the limestone.
5. Miscellaneous considerations (handling, storage, bag, or bulk, etc.).

GUARANTEE AND COST RELATIONS. By a purely arithmetical calculation based on factors 1 and 2 above, the cost of equivalent amounts of lime as applied to the land can be determined. These factors will show which lime will furnish the greatest amount of neutralizing power in total for every dollar expended.

For instance, the *neutralizing power* ($CaCO_3$ equivalent) of two limes, a hydroxide and a ground limestone, are guaranteed at 135 and 95 respectively. The cost of applying a ton of each to the land (all charges, including trucking and spreading) for purposes of calculation will be

---

[8] It is well to remark at the outset that more than 95 per cent of the agricultural lime used in the United States is ground limestone, principally because it is cheaper than other forms. Handling and storage also are factors.

considered to be $15.00 in the case of the hydrate and $8.00 for the carbonate. Obviously, it will require only 95/135 or 0.7 of a ton of the hydroxide to equal 1 ton of the carbonate. The cost of equivalent amounts of neutralizing power, based on 1 ton of limestone, will therefore be $10.50 for the hydroxide of lime and $8.00 for the limestone. Unless a rapid rate of reaction were desired, the advantage in this case would definitely be with the limestone.

RATE OF REACTION WITH SOIL. Burned and hydrated limes react with the soil much more rapidly than do the carbonate forms. For this reason, these caustic materials may be preferred where immediate reaction with the soil is required. In time, however, this initial advantage is nullified due to the inevitable carbonation of the caustic forms of lime.

In comparing carbonate-containing materials, it should be remembered that highly dolomitic limestones generally react more slowly with the soil than do those which are highly calcic. This difference is due to the comparatively slow rate of reaction of dolomite, which is supplied along with calcite in dolomitic limestones. (See Fig. 15:1.) When rapid rate of reaction is not a factor, however, dolomitic limestone is often preferred due to the fact that significant quantities of magnesium are supplied by this material. Soils treated with highly calcic limestone have been known, over a period of two or three rotations, to develop a magnesium deficiency even though the pH was maintained near 7.

The fineness of the limestone under consideration is important especially if the material is high in dolomite. If it is not sufficiently pulverized to rate as a so-called *fine* lime (see rule on p. 422), allowance must be made for the lack of rapid acting material by increasing the rate of application.

MISCELLANEOUS FACTORS. Several miscellaneous factors may at times be important. The handling of the caustic limes, even when bagged, is somewhat more disagreeable than working with limestone. The necessity for storage also comes in, since sometimes it is desirable to carry lime from one season to another. The limestone has the advantage here, as it does not change in storage, as do the others.

The question of purchasing the lime, especially the limestone, in bags or in bulk, has become increasingly important in recent years. Spreading limestone in bulk by truck has greatly reduced the handling costs. (See Fig. 15:2.) This method, however, tends to limit the choice of when the material may be applied, since wet or plowed fields cannot be serviced by heavy machinery. The decision as to what method to use should not be finally approved, however, until the nature of the soil and the probable response of the crops have again been reviewed.

Figure 15:2. The relationship between particle size of calcite and dolomite respectively and the rate of reaction of these minerals with the soil. Note that calcite particles of a given size react more rapidly than do corresponding dolomite particles. The coarse fractions of both minerals neutralize the soil acidity very slowly. (These data were calculated from C. J. Schollenberger and R. M. Salter. "A Chart for Evaluating Agricultural Limestone" J. Amer. Soc. Agron. 35:955–66, 1943.)

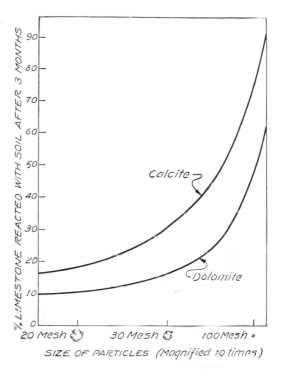

SIZE OF PARTICLES (Magnified 10 times)

15:16. AMOUNTS OF LIME TO APPLY

It is well to emphasize at the outset that all recommendations as to the amounts of lime to apply are only estimates. It is impossible to decide with accuracy and certainty. Too many factors are involved, among the more important is buffering. It must always be remembered that we are dealing with a colloidal complex, the buffering of which we are never quite sure of.

Moreover, the objective of the lime addition is to rectify properly the very indefinite nutritional condition of the soil. We are never quite certain what amounts of calcium and magnesium will accomplish this or just what pH should be temporarily established.

Another factor which must be considered is the cost of the liming material. Just as with fertilizers, the probable return from added crop yields must be sufficiently large to more than pay for the lime applied to the soil. Factors such as location of the limestone source may determine its cost. The crops to be grown may well determine the response obtained. Thus, economic returns, will be a deciding factor in determining the amount of lime to apply.

In arriving at a practical decision, a number of other factors should be considered. The principal ones are:

1. Soil
   Surface
     pH
     Texture and structure
     Amount of organic matter
   Subsoil: pH, texture, and structure
2. Crops to be grown
3. Length of the rotation
4. Kind of lime used and its chemical composition
5. Fineness of the limestone
6. Experience

SOIL CHARACTERISTICS. The pH test is invaluable in making decisions as it gives some idea of the percentage base saturation of the soil and the need for lime. The texture and organic matter also are important since they are indicative of the adsorptive capacity of the soil and the strength of buffering. Naturally the higher the buffer capacity of a soil the greater must be the amount of lime applied in order to attain a satisfactory change in pH.

The subsoil also should be tested for pH and examined as to texture and structure. A subsoil pH markedly above or below that of the furrow-slice may justify a reduction or an increase, as the case may be, in the acre-rate of lime application. Advice as to the cropping of any soil should not be given without a knowledge of subsoil conditions.

OTHER CONSIDERATIONS. The other factors listed above have already been discussed. Besides, their importance is self-evident. As to the kinds of lime, the three forms in respect to their effects on the soil are roughly in the ratio of 1 ton of representative finely ground limestone to 0.7 of a ton of commercial hydroxide to a little over 0.5 of a ton of representative oxide. The fineness of limestone is as important as chemical composition. The experience factor emphasizes the taking advantage of lime knowledge wherever it may be found.

SUGGESTED AMOUNTS. In ordinary practice it is seldom economical to apply more than 3 to 4 tons of finely ground limestone to the acre of mineral soil at any one time, unless it is very acid and the promise for increased crop yield exceptionally good. The data cited in Table 15:5 serve as guides in practical liming operations for a four- or five-year rotation with average mineral soils. It is assumed that a crop with a medium lime requirement is the principal legume of the rotation. The recommendations are in terms of finely ground limestone. If the lime is coarser than the minimum already quoted (see p. 422), or if an oxide or hydroxide is used, due allowance should be made.

Table 15:5. Suggested Total Amounts of Finely Ground Limestone That Should Be Applied per Acre-furrow-slice of Mineral Soil for Alfalfa in Rotation[a]

	Limestone, Pounds per Acre	
Need for Lime	*Sandy Loam*	*Silt Loam*
Moderate	2000–3000	3000–6000
High	3000–5000	6000–8000

[a] In calculating these rates, the assumption is made that the amounts suggested will be used as *initial* applications. After the pH of the soil has been raised to the desired level, smaller *maintenance* rates may be satisfactory.

15:17. METHODS OF APPLYING LIME AND ITS PLACE IN THE ROTATION

As already suggested, the activity of lime is greatly encouraged by contact. Hence, the more thoroughly it is mixed with the soil, the greater will be the number of active centers and the more rapid and effective will be the treatment.

METHODS OF APPLICATION. To obtain this quick action, lime is best applied to plowed land and worked into the soil as the seedbed is prepared. It should be mixed thoroughly with the surface half of the furrow-slice. Top-dressing with lime and leaving it on the surface is seldom recommended except on permanent meadows and pastures.

However, it is often much more convenient and in the long run just as effective to apply the lime on the surface and plow it under. The spreading is usually done in the fall on sod land that is to be turned later that autumn or the next spring. This practice provides a longer interval during which lime may be applied and usually results, in the case of a sod, in a minimum of soil packing if heavy machinery is used. It also makes possible the bulk spreading of lime, using large trucks. This is becoming increasingly popular. (See Fig. 15:3.)

The time of year at which lime is applied is immaterial, the system of farming, the type of rotation, and related considerations being the deciding factors. Winter application may even be practiced.

EQUIPMENT USED. A lime distributor should be used, especially if the amount to be applied is at all large. A manure spreader can be utilized and even an endgate seeder may be pressed into service. Small amounts of lime may be distributed by means of the fertilizer

Figure 15:3. The bulk application of limestone by trucks specially equipped is becoming more and more common. Because of the weight of such machinery much limestone is applied to sod land and plowed under. In some cases this same method is used to spread commercial fertilizers. (Photo courtesy Harold Sweet, Agway Inc., Syracuse, N.Y.)

attachment on a grain drill. Several types of distributors are available for the bulk spreading of limestone. The evenness of distribution is as important as the amount of lime used and should by no means be neglected.

The addition of small amounts of limestone, say 300 to 500 pounds an acre, often gives remarkable results, when drilled in with the crop that is being seeded. Even though the lime is not mixed thoroughly with the soil and there is little change in the pH of furrow-slice as a whole, the influence on the crop may be very favorable. Apparently the lime in this case is functioning more as a fertilizer and as a means of rectifying conditions within the crop and at its root-soil interfaces rather than as an amendment for the whole furrow-slice.

PLACE IN ROTATION. A discussion of the application of lime is never complete without some consideration being given to the place in the rotation at which the liming is best done. The rule is to apply the lime with or ahead of the crop that gives the most satisfactory response. Thus, in a rotation of corn, oats, fall wheat, and two years of alfalfa and timothy, the lime is often applied when the wheat is seeded in the fall. It can then be spread on the plowed ground and worked in as the seedbed is prepared. Its effect is thus especially favorable on the new legume seeding made in the wheat.

However, application to plowed land may result in some compaction of the soil if heavy machinery is used and certainly more power is necessary than for a soil in sod. For that reason spreading on sod land is often favored. In practice, the place of lime in the rotation is often determined, in part at least, by expediency, since the vital consideration is, after all, the application of lime regularly and in conjunction with a suitable rotation of some kind.

15:18. LIME AND SOIL FERTILITY MANAGEMENT

The influence of successively liming a soil over a period of years may tend to raise or lower its fertility, according to the system of management that accompanies the applications of the lime. (See Fig. 15:4.) The

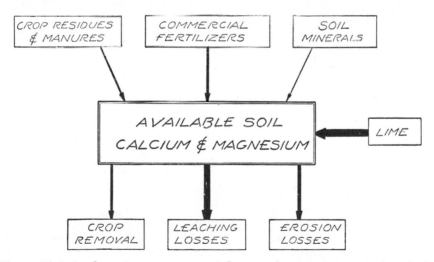

Figure 15:4. A schematic representation showing the important ways by which available calcium and magnesium are supplied to and removed from soils. The major losses are through leaching and erosion. These are largely replaced by lime and fertilizer applications. Additions in the latter form are much higher than is generally realized due to the large quantities of calcium contained in superphosphates.

use of lime alone may increase crop yields for a few years. Chemical reactions will be encouraged, soil organisms will be stimulated, and more nutrients will become available for crop use. Such stimulation, however, will soon wane and, if nothing is returned to the land, its productivity must ultimately drop back to even a lower level than before the lime applications began.

This being the case, farm manures, crop residues and legumes should be utilized to the fullest extent in connection with the lime. To help this combination keep up the fertility, fertilizers carrying nitrogen and potash as well as phosphates should be resorted to. Trace elements may be required in addition, especially boron. Lime improperly used exhausts the soil, but when rationally supplemented, it becomes one of the most important factors in the maintenance of the fertility and the productivity of acid soils.

Chapter 16
The Nitrogen and Sulfur
Economy of Soils

Of the various plant nutrients, nitrogen probably has been subjected to the greatest amount of study and even yet is receiving much attention. And there are very good reasons. The amount in the soil is small, while the quantity withdrawn annually by crops is comparatively large. At times, the soil nitrogen is too readily soluble and is lost in drainage; at times, it suffers volatilization; at other times, it is definitely unavailable to higher plants. Moreover, its effects on plants usually are very marked and rapid. Thus, overapplications sometimes occur which may be harmful.

Some plants such as the legumes have associated with their roots soil organisms which "fix" atmospheric nitrogen into forms which they can use. Others such as the grasses are largely dependent upon outside sources —either through nonsymbiotic fixation or through the addition of fertilizers or other combined forms of nitrogen. All in all, nitrogen is a potent nutrient element that should not only be conserved, but also carefully regulated.

16:1. THE INFLUENCE OF NITROGEN ON PLANT DEVELOPMENT

FAVORABLE EFFECTS. Of the macronutrients usually applied in commercial fertilizers, nitrogen seems to have the quickest and most pronounced effect. It tends primarily to encourage aboveground vegetative growth and to impart to the leaves deep green color. With cereals, it increases the plumpness of the grain and their percentage of protein. With all plants, nitrogen is a regulator in that it governs to a considerable degree the utilization of potassium, phosphorus, and other constituents. Moreover, its application tends to produce succulence, a quality particularly desirable in certain crops such as lettuce and radishes.

Plants receiving insufficient nitrogen are stunted in growth and possess restricted root systems. The leaves turn yellow or yellowish-green and tend to drop off. The addition of available nitrogen will cause a remarkable change, indicative of the unusual activity of this element within the plant.

OVERSUPPLY. Because of the immediate effect of nitrogen on plants, higher applications than are necessary are sometimes made. This is unfortunate, since nitrogen is expensive and is easily lost from the soil. Very dark green, soft, sappy leaves are an indication of an oversupply of nitrogen.

This oversupply may delay crop maturation by encouraging excessive vegetative growth. This results in the weakening of the stems and subsequent lodging of grains. An oversupply of nitrogen may adversely affect fruit and grain quality as in apples, peaches and barley. Also, resistance to some diseases is reduced by excess nitrogen.

It must not be inferred, however, that all plants are detrimentally affected by large amounts of nitrogen. Many crops such as the grasses and vegetables should have plenty of this element for their best and most normal development. With such crops the detrimental effects cited above are not to be expected unless exceedingly large quantities of nitrogen are applied. Nitrogenous fertilizers may be used freely in such cases, the cost of the materials in respect to the value of the crop increases being the major consideration.

16:2. FORMS OF SOIL NITROGEN

There are three major forms of nitrogen in mineral soils (1) organic nitrogen, associated with the soil humus; (2) ammonium nitrogen fixed by certain clay minerals; and (3) soluble inorganic ammonium and nitrate compounds.

Most of the nitrogen in soils is associated with the organic matter. In this form it is protected from rapid microbial release, only 2–3 per cent a year being mineralized under normal conditions. About half the organic nitrogen is known to be in the form of amino compounds. The form of the remainder is uncertain.

Some of the clay minerals have the ability to fix NH_4-nitrogen between their crystal units. The amount fixed varies depending on the nature and amount of clay present. Up to 8 per cent of the total nitrogen in surface soils and 40 per cent of that in subsoils has been found to be in the "clay-fixed" form. In most cases, however, both these figures would be considerably lower. Even so, the nitrogen so fixed is only slowly available to plants and microorganisms.

The amount of nitrogen in the form of soluble ammonium and nitrate compounds is seldom more than 1–2 per cent of the total present, except where large applications of inorganic nitrogen fertilizers have been made. This is fortunate since inorganic nitrogen is subject to loss from soils by leaching and volatilization. Only enough is needed to supply the daily requirements of the growing crops.

16:3. THE NITROGEN CYCLE[1]

In all soils there is considerable intake and outgo of nitrogen in the course of a year, accompanied by many complex transformations. Some of these changes may be controlled more or less by man, while others are beyond his command. This interlocking succession of largely biochemical reactions, constitutes what is known as the *nitrogen cycle*. (See Fig. 16:1.) It has attracted scientific study for years and its practical significance is beyond question.

The nitrogen income of arable soils is derived from such materials as commercial fertilizers, crop residues, green and farm manures, and ammonium and nitrate salts brought down by precipitation. In addition, there is the fixation of atmospheric nitrogen accomplished by certain microorganisms. The outgo is due to crop removal, to drainage, to erosion, and to loss in a gaseous condition.

Much of the nitrogen added to the soil undergoes many transformations before it is removed. The nitrogen in organic combination is sub-

---

[1] Most of the modifications made in this chapter from previous editions are based on the over-all and well-documented review of soil nitrogen. *Soil Nitrogen* (Agronomy, Vol. 10) edited by W. V. Bartholomew and F. E. Clark, Amer. Soc. of Agronomy, Madison, Wisconsin, 1965.

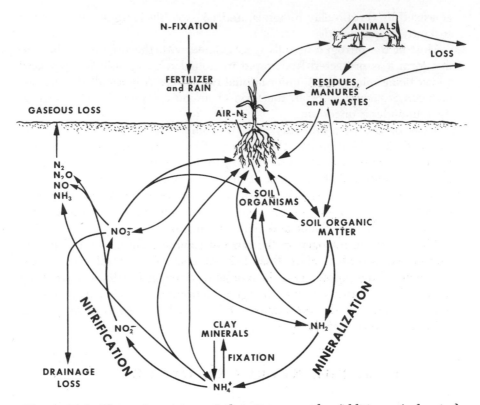

Figure 16:1. The main portions of the nitrogen cycle. Additions of chemical fertilizer make up an increasing important source of this element.

jected to especially complex changes. Proteins are converted into various decomposition products and finally some of the nitrogen appears in the nitrate form. Even then it is allowed no rest, as it is either appropriated by microorganisms and higher plants, or is removed in drainage, or is lost by volatilization. And so the cyclic transfer goes on and on. The mobility of nitrogen is remarkable, rivaling carbon in its ease of movement.

MAJOR DIVISIONS OF THE NITROGEN CYCLE.[2] At any one time, the great bulk of the nitrogen in a soil is in organic combinations protected from loss but largely unavailable to higher plants. For this reason much scientific effort has been devoted to the study of organic nitrogen, how it is stabilized, and how it may be re-

[2] The amount of nitrogen in mineral soils and its relationship to soil organic matter is dealt with on p. 151.

leased to forms useable by plants. The process of tying up nitrogen in organic forms is called *immobilization* and its slow release *mineralization*. (See Fig. 16:2)

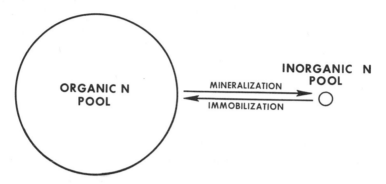

Figure 16:2. At any one time most of the nitrogen in soils is immobilized in organic combination and as such is not available for plant growth, leaching or gaseous loss. Through the process of mineralization microorganisms change a small amount of nitrogen each year to inorganic forms which higher plants can use.

IMMOBILIZATION. During the process of microbial decomposition of plant and animal residues, especially those low in nitrogen, much of the inorganic nitrogen is converted to organic forms. (See p. 148.) Initially the nitrogen is probably tied up in microbial tissue. If the residues are not sufficiently high in inorganic nitrogen, soil NO_3 and NH_4 ions will be assimilated. As the rate of microbial activity subsides, some of this immobilized nitrogen will be mineralized and ammonium and nitrate ions will again appear in the soil solution. However, much of the immobilized nitrogen remains in the organic form.

The mechanism by which simple nitrogen compounds are changed to organic combinations which resist breakdown is still obscure. (See p. 143.) Somehow the immobilized nitrogen in the microbial tissue becomes an integral part of the soil organic matter. In this form it is only slowly mineralized to compounds usable by higher plants. The process by which this occurs will now receive our attention.

MINERALIZATION. Tagged nitrogen experiments have demonstrated that only 2–3 per cent immobilized nitrogen may be expected to be mineralized annually. Even so, this release of nitrogen to inorganic forms has long supplied a significant portion of our crop needs.

Although the general term mineralization covers a whole series of reactions, the net effect can be rather simply visualized. Heterogenous soil organisms, both plant and animal attack the organic nitrogen compounds. As a result of enzymatic digestion the more complex proteins and allied compounds are simplified and hydrolyzed. The end product is ammonia. The enzymic process may be indicated as follows using an amino compound as an example of the nitrogen source.

$$\text{R-NH}_2 + \text{HOH} \xrightarrow[\text{Hydrolysis}]{\text{Enzymic}} \text{R-OH} + \text{NH}_3 + \text{Energy}$$

Amino combination

$$2\text{NH}_3 + \text{H}_2\text{CO}_3 \longrightarrow (\text{NH}_4)_2\text{CO}_3 \rightleftharpoons 2\,\text{NH}_4{}^+ + \text{CO}_3{}^-$$

Mineralization seems to proceed to the best advantage in well-drained aerated soils with plenty of basic cations present. It will take place to some extent under almost any conditions, however, due to the great number of different organisms capable of accomplishing such a change. This is one of the advantages of a general-purpose flora and fauna.

UTILIZATION OF AMMONIUM COMPOUNDS. The fate of the ammoniacal nitrogen (as shown in Fig. 16:1) is fourfold. *First,* considerable amounts are appropriated by organisms capable of using this type of compound. Mycorrhizal fungi (see p. 122), no doubt, are able to absorb ammoniacal nitrogen and pass it on some form to their host.

Second, higher plants are able to use this form of nitrogen, often very readily indeed. Young plants of almost all kinds are especially capable in this respect, although they seem to grow better if some nitrate nitrogen is also available. Azaleas, laurel, and other plants that require a low-lime soil are additional cases in point. Still other plants, such as lowland rice, for example, even prefer ammoniacal nitrogen instead of the nitrate.

Third, NH$_4$ ions are subject to fixation by some of the clay minerals and organic matter. In this fixed form, the nitrogen is not subject to rapid oxidation, although in time it may become available. This will receive attention in the next section.

Finally, when plant and animal syntheses temporarily are satisfied, the remaining ammonium nitrogen may go in a third direction. It is readily oxidized by certain special-purpose forms of bacteria that use it, not only as a source of nitrogen, but also as a source of energy. Thus, one arrives at a much talked of and perhaps comparatively over emphasized phase of biochemistry—*nitrification.* It is so named because its end product is nitrate nitrogen, and it will receive our attention following a consideration of ammonia fixation.

16:4. AMMONIA FIXATION

Both the organic and inorganic soil fractions have the ability to "fix" ammonia in forms relatively unavailable to higher plants or even microorganisms. Since different mechanisms and compounds are involved in these two types of fixation, they will be considered separately.

FIXATION BY CLAY MINERALS. Several clay minerals with a 2:1 type structure have the capacity to "fix" NH_4 and K ions. Vermiculite has the greatest capacity followed by illite and montmorillonite.

It will be remembered that these minerals have internal negative charges which attract cations to internal surfaces between crystal units. (See p. 77.) Most cations which satisfy these charges can move freely into and out of the crystal lattice. In other words, they are exchangeable. Ammonium and potassium ions, however, are apparently just the right size to fix into the "cavities" between crystal units thereby becoming fixed more or less as a rigid part of the crystal. (See Fig. 4:6 p. 78.) They prevent the normal expansion of the crystal lattice and, in turn, are held in a nonexchangeable form from which they are only slowly released to higher plants and microorganisms. The relationship of the various forms of ammonium might be represented as follows:

$$\begin{array}{ccccc} NH_4^+ & \xrightleftharpoons{\hspace{1.5cm}} & NH_4^+ & \xrightleftharpoons{\hspace{1.5cm}} & NH_4^+ \\ \text{soil solution} & & \text{exchangeable} & & \text{fixed} \end{array}$$

Ammonium fixation by clay minerals is generally greater in subsoils than in topsoil because of the higher clay content of the former. In some cases this fixation may be considered an advantage since it is a means of conserving soil nitrogen. In others, the rate of release of the fixed ammonium is too slow to be of much practical value.

FIXATION BY ORGANIC MATTER. Anhydrous ammonia or other fertilizers which contain free NH_3 or which form it when added to the soil can react with soil organic matter to form compounds which resist decomposition. In this sense the ammonia can be said to be "fixed" by the organic matter. The exact mechanism by which the fixation occurs is not known, although reactions with aromatic compounds and quinones are suspected.[3] The reaction takes place most readily in the presence of oxygen and at high pH values.

[3] See F. E. Broadbent, W. D. Burge, and T. Nakashima "Factors Influencing the Reaction Between Ammonia and Soil Organic Matter," *Trans. 7th Int Cong. Soil Sci.*, 2:509–516, 1961.

The practical significance of organic fixation depends upon the circumstances. In organic soils with a high fixing capacity it could be serious and would dictate the use of fertilizers other than those which supply free NH_3. In normal practice on mineral soils, however, organic fixation should not be too disadvantageous. In the first place the fertilizer is usually banded thereby contacting a relatively small portion of the entire soil mass and minimizing opportunities for fixation. Furthermore, the fixed ammonia is subject to subsequent slow release by mineralization.

16:5. NITRIFICATION[4]

Nitrification is a process of enzymic oxidation brought about by certain special-purpose bacteria. It seems to take place in two coordinated steps, two distinct groups of bacteria being involved. As shown below, the first step is the production of nitrous acid by one group of bacteria, apparently followed immediately by its oxidation to the nitrate form by another. (See Fig. 16:3 for this organism.) The enzymic changes are represented very simply as follows:

$$2NH_4^+ + 3O_2 \xrightarrow[\text{Oxidation}]{\text{Enzymic}} 2NO_2^- + 2H_2O + 4H^+ + \text{Energy}$$

$$2NO_2^- + O_2 \xrightarrow[\text{Oxidation}]{\text{Enzymic}} 2NO_3^- + \text{Energy}$$

Under most conditions favoring the two reactions, the second transformation is thought to follow so closely on the first as to preclude any great accumulation of the nitrite. This is fortunate, as this ion in any concentration is toxic to higher plants. In very alkaline soils or where large fertilizer ammonia applications have been made there is some evidence that the second reaction may be delayed until after the NH_4-ion concentration is reduced to a relatively low level. This may result in nitrite accumulation of sufficient magnitude to affect adversely plant growth or to encourage gaseous losses of nitrogen. (See p. 448.)

ORGANISMS CONCERNED. The organisms in this case are all special purpose and autotrophic (see p. 125), in contrast to the general purpose and heterotrophic organisms concerned with immobilization and mineralization. They obtain most of their energy by the oxidation of inorganic compounds. Like higher plants, they acquire carbon

[4] See M. Alexander; "Nitrification". A chapter in *Soil Nitrogen* (Agronomy, Vol. 10), Amer. Soc. of Agronomy, Madison, Wisconsin, 1965.

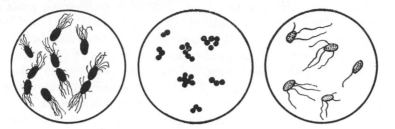

Figure 16:3. Some soil organisms especially important in the nitrogen cycle. Left to right, Azotobacter, *nitrate bacteria, and nodule organisms of alfalfa.*

from carbon dioxide, at the same time respiring quantities of this gas.

Collectively, the nitrifying organisms are called nitrobacteria. Of these the *nitrosomonas* are concerned in the conversion of ammonia into nitrites. The organisms having to do with the oxidation of nitrites to nitrates are generally designated *nitrobacter.* In common usage these two groups of bacteria are simply spoken of as nitrite and nitrate organisms.

It is necessary to remark in this connection that other soil organisms probably are able to produce nitrate by-products. A large number of heterotrophic bacteria, fungi, and actinomycetes have demonstrated abilities to oxidize nitrogen compounds. It is as yet uncertain however that these organisms contribute significantly to nitrate formation in soils. It is also possible that photochemical oxidation may take place in tropical soils. How extensive such forms of nitrification are cannot be stated. Apparently, however, the bilateral oxidation already sketched (reaction on p. 444) is the most important in a practical way.

RATE OF NITRIFICATION. Under ideal temperature, soil, and moisture conditions, nitrification occurs at a very rapid rate. Daily rates of from 6 to 22 pounds of nitrogen per 2 million pounds of soil have been found when 100 pounds of nitrogen in the ammonium form were added.[5] Much higher rates occurred when a larger application of ammonium compounds was made. Obviously, under ideal conditions the nitrifying organisms can supply nitrates at a rate which more than meets the needs of crop plants.

16:6. SOIL CONDITIONS AFFECTING NITRIFICATION

The nitrifying bacteria are extremely sensitive to their environment, much more so than most heterotrophic organisms. Consequently,

[5] See F. E. Broadbent and K. B. Tyler, "Nitrification of Ammoniacal Fertilizers in Some California Soils," *Hilgardia,* 27:247–67, 1957.

soil conditions that influence the vigor of nitrification deserve practical consideration. They are: (1) aeration, (2) temperature, (3) moisture, (4) active lime, (5) fertilizer salts, and (6) the nitrogen-carbon ratio.

AERATION. Since nitrification is a process of oxidation, any procedure that increases the aeration of the soil should, up to a certain point, encourage it. Plowing and cultivation, especially if granulation is not impaired, are recognized means of promoting nitrification.

TEMPERATURE. The temperature most favorable for the process of nitrification is from 80 to 90°F. At a temperature of 125°F, nitrification practically ceases. At freezing or below, nitrification will not take place, but at about 35 to 40°F it begins and slowly increases in intensity until the optimum temperature is reached. The lateness with which nitrification attains its full vigor in the spring is well known, application of fertilizer nitrogen being used to offset the delay.

MOISTURE. The rate with which nitrification proceeds in a soil is governed to a marked extent by the water content, the process being retarded by both very low and very high moisture conditions. In practice, it is safe to assume that the optimum moisture as recognized for higher plants is also optimum for nitrification. One reservation, however, must be made. Nitrification will progress appreciably at moisture contents at or even below the wilting coefficient for higher plants.

EXCHANGEABLE BASES. Nitrification requires an abundance of exchangeable bases. This accounts in part for the feeble nitrification in acid mineral soils and the seeming sensitiveness of the organisms to a low pH. As a matter of fact, however, acidity itself within reasonable limits seems to have little influence on nitrification when adequate bases are present. This is especially true of peat soils. At pH values even below 5 these soils may show remarkable accumulations of nitrates. (See p. 372.)

FERTILIZERS. Small amounts of many kinds of salts, even those of the trace elements, stimulate nitrification. A reasonable balance of N, P, and K has been found to be helpful. Apparently, the stimulation of the organisms is much the same as is that of higher plants.

Applications of large quantities of ammonium nitrogen to strongly alkaline soils have been found to depress the second step in the nitrification reaction. Apparently the ammonia is toxic to the nitrobacter under these conditions, but does not affect adversely the nitrosomonas. Consequently, nitrite accumulation may occur in toxic quantities when ammonium-containing compounds are added to soils very high in pH. Similarly, on such soils adverse effects may result from a compound such as urea which supplies NH_4 ions in the soil by hydrolysis.

CARBON-NITROGEN RATIO. The significance of the carbon-nitrogen ratio has already been rather fully considered (p. 148) so that the explanation here may be brief. When microbes decompose plant and animal residues with high C:N ratios, they incorporate into their bodies all the inorganic nitrogen. It is thereby immobilized. Nitrification is thus more or less at a standstill, because of a lack of ammoniacal nitrogen, this also having been swept up by the decay organisms. A serious competition with higher plants for nitrogen is thereby initiated.

After the carbonaceous matter has partially decomposed so that energizing material is no longer abundant some of the immobilized nitrogen will be mineralized and ammonium compounds will again appear in the soil. Conditions are now favorable for nitrification, and nitrates may again accumulate. Thus, the carbon-nitrogen ratio, through its selective influence on soil microorganisms, exerts a powerful control on nitrification and the presence of nitrate nitrogen in the soil. (See Fig. 6:4)

16:7. THE FATE OF NITRATE NITROGEN[6]

The nitrate nitrogen of the soil whether added in fertilizers or formed by nitrification may go in four directions (see Fig. 16:1). It may (1) be used by microorganisms, and (2) by higher plants, it may (3) be lost in drainage, and it may (4) escape from the nitrogen cycle in a gaseous condition.

USE BY SOIL ORGANISMS AND PLANTS.   Both plants and soil microorganisms readily assimilate nitrate nitrogen. However, if microbes have a ready food supply (e.g., carbonaceous organic residues) they utilize the nitrates more rapidly than do higher plants. Thus, the higher plants must be satisfied with what is left by the microorganisms or must await the subsequent release of the nitrogen when microbial activity slows down. (See p. 149.) This is one of the reasons why crops often are able during a growing season to recover only about half the fertilizer nitrogen added. Fortunately much of the immobilized nitrogen is released during the following growing seasons.

LEACHING AND GASEOUS LOSS.   The amount of nitrate nitrogen lost in drainage water depends upon the climate and cultural conditions. In arid and semiarid regions, such losses are minimal since water loss by leaching is low or nonexistent. In humid areas and where irrigation is practiced, losses of nitrate nitrogen by leaching are significant. Heavy nitrogen fertilization, especially for vegetables and other

[6] For an excellent review of this subject see F. E. Allison, "The Rate of Nitrogen Applied to Soils," *Advan. in Agron.*, 18:219–258, 1966.

cash crops grown on coarse-textured soils, accentuates loss by this means.

Under certain conditions, especially those of poor drainage and aeration, nitrate compounds in the soil may be *reduced*—their nitrogen, at least in part, escaping in gaseous form. The various phases of reduction will be considered in the next section.

16:8. THE GASEOUS LOSSES OF SOIL NITROGEN

The conditions under which the nitrates may be changed to gaseous forms are not well understood, but most authorities agree that this loss is greatly encouraged by poor drainage and lack of aeration. The maintenance of the soil in a bare condition and the presence of excessive amounts of mineral nitrogen compounds may also be important factors. The meager data available in respect to such volatilization indicate that this form of loss is of considerable magnitude even from well-managed cropped soils.

REDUCTION BY ORGANISMS. The biochemical reduction of nitrate nitrogen to gaseous compounds is called *denitrification* and is thought to be the most widespread type of volatilization. The microorganisms involved are common facultative anaerobic forms. They prefer elemental oxygen but under inadequate aeration can use the combined oxygen in nitrates and some of their reduced products. The exact mechanisms by which the reductions take place are not known. However, the general trend of the reactions may be represented as follows:

$$2HNO_3 \xrightarrow{-2[O]} 2HNO_2 \xrightarrow[-H_2O]{-2[O]} N_2O \xrightarrow{-[O]} N_2$$

Nitrates   Nitrites   Nitrous oxide   Elemental N

$$\xrightarrow{-O} 2NO$$
$$-H_2O \quad \text{Nitric oxide}$$

Under field conditions, nitrous oxide (N_2O) is the gas lost in largest quantities, although elemental nitrogen is a major gaseous form under some conditions. (See Fig. 16:4.) Nitric oxide loss is generally not great and apparently occurs most readily under acid conditions.

CHEMICAL REDUCTION. There are other ways by which nitrogen may be lost in the gaseous form. For instance, nitrites in a slightly acid solution will evolve gaseous nitrogen when brought in con-

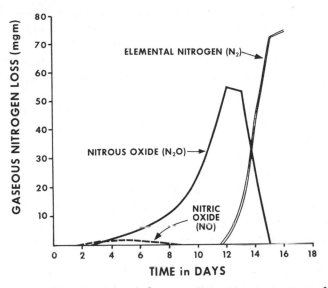

Figure 16:4. *Denitrification loss of three gaseous nitrogen compounds from an anaerobic acid Norfolk sandy loam at 12.5% moisture. A closed system was used. Apparently N_2 was formed from the reduction of N_2O. Under field conditions much of the N_2O would likely have gone off as a gas and would not have remained to produce elemental N_2. (From F. B. Cady and W. V. Bartholomew, "Sequential Products of Anaerobic Denitrification in Norfolk Soil Material," Soil Sci. Soc. Amer. Proc. 24:477–482, 1960.)*

tact with certain ammonium salts, with simple amines, such as urea, and even with non-nitrogenous sulfur compounds and carbohydrates. The following reaction is suggestive of what may occur to urea.

$$2HNO_2 + CO(NH_2) \longrightarrow CO_2 + 3H_2O + 2N_2 \uparrow$$
Nitrite   Urea

It is well to note that the type of gaseous loss pictured above is strictly chemical and does not require the presence of microorganisms or of adverse soil conditions. Its practical importance, of course, will depend upon the amount of nitrogen that thereby escapes from the soil.

Large, often rapid losses of gaseous nitrogen have been observed upon making heavy applications of urea or ammonium fertilizers. In cases where the fertilizers were applied on the surface, moved to the surface through capillarity, or were inadequately incorporated into the soil, losses as ammonia have occurred especially in alkaline soils. Even where proper soil coverage and contact was obtained losses as N_2 and N_2O have been found. Apparently a high concentration of ammonia is toxic to the second step of the nitrification process, resulting in an unusual build up of nitrites. Under acid conditions these nitrites are converted to gaseous N_2 or N_2O. The exact mechanism by which these losses take place is not known but they occur under conditions of good as well as poor drainage and are not always dependent upon microbiological activity.

QUANTITY OF N LOST IN GASEOUS FORM. Since gaseous nitrogen is unavailable to higher plants, any loss in this form is serious. As might be expected, the exact magnitude of the losses will depend upon the cultural and soil conditions. In well-drained humid-region soils that are not too heavily fertilized the gaseous losses are probably less than that from leaching. Where the drainage is restricted, and where large applications of ammonia and urea fertilizer are made, especially if they are not well incorporated, one might expect substantial losses—20 to 40 per cent of the nitrogen added not being too uncommon.

Lysimeter experiments[7] show a loss of 10–20 per cent of the nitrogen added while field experiments[8] in a dryland area showed even greater losses. If one were to take an average of all soil and cultural conditions, perhaps 10–15 per cent of the annual nitrogen additions might be a reasonable estimate of gaseous losses.

In general, these losses are largely unavoidable. Some control can be exerted by keeping a crop on the land, by providing for adequate drainage and tilth, and by avoiding an excess of fertilizer nitrogen.

The part of the nitrogen cycle, yet to be considered, concerns itself with the acquisition by the soil of nitrogen from various sources. Four ways of addition are recognized in arable soils: (1) nitrogen fixation by legume bacteria; (2) free fixation or azofication; (3) additions in rain water and snow; and (4) application of nitrogen in fertilizers, farm manure, and green manures. They will be considered in order.

16:9. FIXATION OF ATMOSPHERIC NITROGEN BY LEGUME BACTERIA

It has been recognized for centuries that certain crops, such as the clovers, alfalfa, peas, beans, and others, improve the soil in some way, making it possible to grow larger yields of cereals after these plants have occupied the land. Within the last century the benefit has been

---

[7] See F. E. Allison, "The Enigma of Soil Nitrogen Balance Sheets," *Advan. in Agron.*, 7:213–50, 1955.
[8] A. F. Bracken and J. E. Greaves, "Losses of Nitrogen and Organic Matter from Dry-land Soils," *Soil Sci.*, 51:1–15, 1941.

traced to the fixation of nitrogen through the agency of bacteria contained in nodules on the roots of certain host plants. Most of the specific plants so affected belong to the family of legumes although a significant number of nonlegume species are nodulated. (See p. 455.)

NODULE FORMATION. The legume organisms live in the root nodules, take free nitrogen from the soil air, and synthesize it into complex forms. The nodules evidently are the result of an irritation of the root surface, much as a gall is caused to develop on a leaf or on a branch of a tree by an insect. The entrance of the organisms normally is effected through the hairs. The infection tube ultimately extends the entire length of the root hair and into the cortex cells of the rootlets, where the growth of the nodule starts and where the fixation of nitrogen occurs. (See Figs. 16:3 and 16:5.)

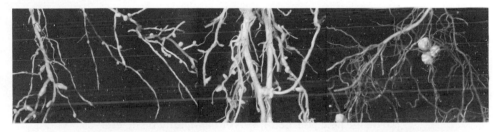

Figure 16:5. Nodules on the roots of legumes. Left to right, *red clover, alfalfa, and beans. Although the nitrogen fixing bacteria are segregated in the nodules, they apparently freely use the juices of the host plant as a source of energy. The nitrogen fixed may go in three directions—(1) appropriated by the host, (2) used by nonlegumes growing in close association, and (3) left in the soil when the nodules slough off and decompose.*

How the plant absorbs this nitrogen after it has been secured by the bacteria is not well understood; nor is it known in exactly what form the nitrogen is at first fixed, although amino and amide forms very soon appear. It seems likely that some of the nitrogen compounds produced within the bacterial cells are diffused through the cell wall and absorbed by the host plant.

ORGANISMS INVOLVED. Since the plants are able to use some of the nitrogen fixed by the microbes, the relationship thus established is often spoken of as *symbiotic.* The organism is a *rhizobium* and there are a number of strains, depending on the host plants. They may, therefore, be classified according to the host as *Rhizobium meliloti* for those of alfalfa and sweet clover, *Rhizobium trifolii* for the clovers, *Rhizobium japonicum* for soybeans, and so on. As a group, they are often referred to as the *nodule* or *legume organisms* instead of by the more technical terms.

The organisms from one species of legumes are not necessarily well adapted to the ready production of effective nodules on other leguminous species. Certain cross-inoculations are successful in practice, however. For example, the organisms seem to be readily interchangeable within the clovers, the vetches, and the beans. Those from sweet clover and bur clover will inoculate alfalfa, and the bacteria may be transferred from vetch to field pea or from cowpea to velvet bean.[9] The part played by the plant is doubtless to furnish the carbohydrates that supply energy to the nitrogen-assimilating bacteria.

A partial listing of the groups within which cross inoculation may easily be made follows:

Group 1. (Alfalfa group) Alfalfa, bur clovers, white, yellow and hubam sweet clovers, fenugreek, yellow trefoil, and others.

Group 2. (Clover group) Mammoth and red clover, alsike clover, crimson clover, hop clover, white clover, zigzag clover, ladino clover, and others.

Group 3. (Cowpea group) Lespedezas, acacia, kudzu, cowpea, peanut, partridge pea, jack bean, velvet bean, lima bean, etc.

Group 4. (Pea and vetch group) Garden pea, sweet pea, horse bean, lentil, Canada field pea, hairy vetch, common vetch, purple vetch, etc.

Group 5. (Soybean group) All varieties of soybeans.

Group 6. (Bean group) Garden bean (numerous varieties), pinto bean, and scarlet runner.

Group 7. (Lupine group) Lupine, serradella, blue lupine, yellow lupine and white lupine.

THE EFFECT OF INOCULATION. The influence of inoculation upon the crop yield and percentage of nitrogen in the legume is very striking. Data bearing upon the latter phase are shown in Table 16:1. Analyses are given for both the tops and roots of sweet clover and alfalfa grown on soil inoculated and not inoculated. The soil originally was not known to carry the legume organisms.

NUTRITIONAL REQUIREMENTS. It is difficult to separate requirements of symbiotic nitrogen fixers from those of the host plants. However, a few generalizations can be made.

[9] L. W. Erdman, *Legume Inoculations: What it is—What it does,* Farmers Bulletin 2003, U.S. Dept. of Agric. 1959.

Table 16:1. Effect of Inoculation with the Legume Organisms on the Nitrogen Content of Sweet Clover and Alfalfa[a]
(Calculated as percentages based on dry matter)

Soil Treatment	Sweet Clover		Alfalfa	
	Tops	Roots	Tops	Roots
Inoculated	2.29	2.01	2.56	2.14
Not inoculated	1.37	0.88	1.51	0.71

[a] A. C. Arny and R. W. Thatcher, "The Effect of Different Methods of Inoculation on the Yield and Protein Content of Alfalfa and Sweet Clover," *Jour. Amer. Soc. Agron.*, 9:127–37, 1917.

1. The organisms are sensitive to an excess of H^+ ions, although there is considerable variation among groups of organisms in their tolerance to acidity.
2. Apart from any effect on soil acidity, calcium affects favorably nodule formation and possibly fixation.
3. The organisms apparently require phosphorus, potassium, and sulfur for normal functioning.
4. The micronutrients molybdenum, boron, cobalt, and perhaps iron seem to play specific roles in the fixation process.
5. Nitrogen from combined sources (e.g., nitrates and ammonia) tends to reduce both nodule formation and nitrogen fixation.

16:10. AMOUNT OF NITROGEN FIXED BY LEGUME BACTERIA

The amount of nitrogen fixed by the legume bacteria depends on many factors. The conditions of the soil, especially aeration, drainage, moisture, pH and the amount of active calcium, are of prime importance. The sensitivity of legumes to soil acidity is largely attributed to the failure of nodule bacteria to function under these conditions. Even when the above factors are favorable, a large amount of readily available nitrogen in the soil will discourage nodulation and thereby reduce fixation. (See Fig. 16:6.)

Some legume field crops, such as alfalfa and sweet clover, facilitate a fixation of large amounts of nitrogen. The clovers are less effective, and some legumes can be credited with but a scanty acquisition. Lyon and Bizzell[10] in a ten-year experiment at Ithaca, New York, report the following magnitude of fixation in pounds per acre per year:

[10] T. L. Lyon and J. A. Bizzell, "A Comparison of Several Legumes with Respect to Nitrogen Secretion," *Jour. Amer. Soc. Agron.*, 26:651–56, 1934.

Alfalfa	251	Soybeans	105
Sweet Clover	168	Hairy Vetch	68
Red Clover	151	Field Beans	58
Alsike Clover	141	Field Peas	48

A fixation ranging from 188 to 260 pounds per acre per year was recorded by Collison[11] at Geneva, New York, for alfalfa. Perhaps for an average

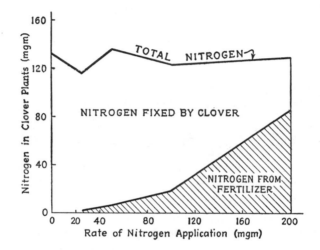

Figure 16:6. *The influence of added inorganic nitrogen on the total nitrogen in clover plants, the proportion supplied by the fertilizer and that fixed by the clover. Increasing the rate of nitrogen application decreased the amount of nitrogen fixed by the clover. (From T. W. Walker, et al., "Fate of Labeled Nitrate and Ammonium Nitrogen When Applied to Grass and Clover Grown Separately and Together," Soil Sci., 81:339–52, 1956.)*

crop of alfalfa, 200 to 250 pounds of nitrogen an acre would be a conservative figure for the first, and possibly the second, year. The corresponding estimate for red clover might well be 100 to 150 pounds per acre.

16:11. FATE OF THE NITROGEN FIXED BY LEGUME BACTERIA

The nitrogen fixed by the nodule organisms may go in three directions. *First*, it may be used by the host plant, the latter benefiting greatly by the symbiosis. *Second*, the nitrogen may pass into the soil itself,

[11] R. C. Collison, H. C. Beattie, and J. D. Harlan, *Lysimeter Investigations. III. Mineral and Water Relations and Final Nitrogen Balance in Legume and Nonlegume Crop Rotations for a Period of 16 Years*, Bulletin 212, N.Y. State Agr. Exp. Sta., 1933.

either by excretion or more probably by the sloughing off of the roots and especially of their nodules. The crop in association with the legume may thereby benefit. This influence is a matter of common observation. The vigorous development of a bluegrass lawn in association with clover is a well-known example.

Third, when a legume sod is turned under, some of the nitrogen becomes available to the succeeding crop. Because of the narrow carbon-nitrogen ratio of such residues, some of their nitrogen may swing through the nitrogen cycle with remarkable ease and may quickly appear in the ammoniacal and nitrate forms.

16:12. DO LEGUMES ALWAYS INCREASE THE SOIL NITROGEN?

Some people assume that legumes always leave the soil on which they have been growing definitely richer in nitrogen. As a matter of fact, the result can be just the opposite, especially when the soil already is high in nitrogen or the tops are harvested and removed from the land. Beans and peas in particular are likely to leave the land depleted, because they support a low nitrogen fixation. Moreover, their roots often are partially removed in harvesting.

In general, however, the net draft of legumes on the soil nitrogen is less than that of nonlegumes, and, as a consequence, their use is to be encouraged in a rotation where the maintenance of soil nitrogen is important. Legumes are usually so economical in their use of soil nitrogen that a high protein crop may often be harvested with little depletion of the land in respect to this element. Thus, they are nitrogen *savers*. This is an important fertility axiom.

16:13. FIXATION BY ORGANISMS IN SYMBIOSIS WITH NONLEGUMES[12]

A small but significant number of nonlegume species are known to develop nodules and the bacteria existing therein are proven nitrogen fixers. The species are mostly angio-sperms (see Table 16:2) and are often found in nature under conditions of low soil nitrogen. Since these are not cultivated crop plants, they have not been studied extensively. Consequently, relatively little is known species by species about their annual fixation rate, mode of organism infection, etc. From the meager data

---

[12] See F. J. Stevenson, "Origin and Distribution of Nitrogen in Soil." A chapter in *Soil Nitrogen* (Agronomy, Vol. 70), Amer. Soc. of Agronomy, Madison, Wisconsin, 1965.

Table 16:2. The Number and Distribution of Nodulated Nonlegume Species.[a]
(*In comparison there are nearly 9000 legume species*)

Family	Genus	Species nodulated	Geographical distribution
Betulaceae	Alnus	15	Cool regions of the northern hemisphere
Elaeagnaceae	Elaeagnus	9	Asia, Europe, North America
	Hippophae	1	Asia and Europe, from Himalayas to Arctic Circle
	Shepherdia	2	Confined to North America
Myricaceae	Myrica	7	Temperate regions of both hemispheres
Coriariaceae	Coriaria	3	Widely separated regions, chiefly Japan, New Zealand, Central and South America, and the Mediterranean region
Rhamnaceae	Ceanothus	7	Confined to North America
Casuarinaceae	Casuarina	12	Tropics and subtropics, extending from East Africa to the Indian Archipelago, Pacific Islands, and Australia

[a] From F. J. Stevenson, "Origin and Distribution of Nitrogen in Soil." A chapter in *Soil Nitrogen* (Agronomy, Vol. 10); Amer. Soc. of Agronomy, Madison, Wisconsin, 1965.

available, however, rates of fixation comparable to those of legume bacteria have been observed.

16:14. NONSYMBIOTIC FIXATION OF ATMOSPHERIC NITROGEN

There exist in soils and water certain free-living microorganisms that are able to fix elemental nitrogen from the soil air into their body tissue. Since these organisms are not directly associated with higher plants, as are the legume bacteria, the transformation is often spoken of as *non-symbiotic* or *free fixation*.

SPECIFIC ORGANISMS INVOLVED.[13] Several different groups of bacteria, blue-green algae, and fungi are able to acquire

[13] A recent review of this subject was made by H. L. Jensen, "Nonsymbiotic Nitrogen Fixation." A chapter in *Soil Nitrogen* (Agronomy, Vol. 10), Amer. Soc. of Agronomy, Madison, Wisconsin, 1965.

atmospheric nitrogen nonsymbiotically. In upland mineral soils the major fixation apparently is brought about by two groups of heterotrophic bacteria. One of these is the aerobic *Azotobacter* and related bacteria such as the *Beijerinckia* (common in tropical soils). (See Fig. 16:3.) The other is an anaerobic, or perhaps a faculative, bacterium called *Clostridium butyricum*. Because of pockets of low oxygen supply in most soils even when they are in the best of tilth, these two groups of bacteria probably work side by side in the fixation of the nitrogen of the soil air.

The *Azotobacter* and *Clostridium butyricum* do not acquire all of their nitrogen from atmospheric sources. Ammoniacal and nitrate nitrogen are readily used by these organisms. In fact, in a soil high in such available nitrogen, it is doubtful whether a great deal of free fixation takes place.

Where soils are used for lowland rice culture, nitrogen fixation by *blue-green algae* may occur. These organisms carry on photosynthesis and thus require no outside source of organic matter. Their ability to fix nitrogen seems to be enhanced by the presence of growing rice plants.

Blue-green algae are also known to grow in association with lichens. In desert areas and in the initial stages of rock disintegration, these algae fix nitrogen which ultimately can become available to higher plants.

FACTORS INFLUENCING NONSYMBIOTIC NITRO-GEN FIXATION. The heterotrophic fixers are encouraged by low available soil nitrogen and organic matter which supplies ready energy. Sod land presents almost ideal conditions.

Azotobacter are notably sensitive to soil pH, being most active at a neutral reaction. In mineral soils the free fixation of nitrogen often begins to lag noticeably at pH 5.6 and at pH values below 5.0 becomes more or less negligible.

Clostridium are more tolerant of acid conditions, although they too perform best at a near neutral reaction. *Beijerinckia,* common in tropical soils, seem to be tolerant of a wide range of pH levels.

The blue-green algae require light and a high moisture level or even water logging. They do best at a neutral to slightly alkaline reaction and fix nitrogen only in the absence of nitrate or ammonia nitrogen.

16:15. AMOUNT OF NITROGEN FIXED BY NONSYMBIOSIS

It is difficult to determine accurately the exact amount of nitrogen fixed by nonsymbiosis in soils because of the other processes involving nitrogen that are taking place simultaneously. However, estimates indicate that considerable quantities of nitrogen are fixed annually in this manner. For example, experiments in several areas indicate that 20 to 100 pounds of nitrogen per acre per year may be fixed by nonsymbiotic organisms. (See Table 16:3.) In these experiments carbonaceous plant residues were generally returned to the soil. One would expect fixation to have been at a maximum under these conditions.

Table 16:3. Nitrogen Gains Attributed to Non-Symbiotic Fixation (Field Experiments)[a]

Location	Period (Years)	Description	Nitrogen Gain (lbs. per acre per year)
Utah	11	Irrigated Soil and Manure	44
Missouri	8	Bluegrass Sod	102
California	10	Lysimeter Experiment	48
California	60	Pinus Ponderosa Stand	56
United Kingdom	20	Monoculture Tree Stands	52
Australia	3	Solonized Soil	22
Nigeria	3	Latosolic Soil	80
Michigan	7	Straw Mulch	50

[a] These data from various sources were summarized by A. W. Moore, "Non-Symbiotic Nitrogen Fixation in Soil and Soil-Plant Systems," *Soils and Fertilizers,* 29: 113–128, 1966.

Research with isotopic forms of nitrogen have shown wide variations in the amount of nitrogen fixed by free-living organisms.[14] The range in values found is from a few pounds to perhaps 60 pounds per acre per year. In most cases, evidence indicates that one would not expect more than about 25 pounds of nitrogen to be added in this manner, and that the amount may be much less.

16:16. THE ADDITION OF NITROGEN TO SOIL IN PRECIPITATION — MAGNITUDE

Nitrogen occurring in rain and snow generally is in the nitrate and ammoniacal forms and, consequently, is readily available to plants. The amounts thus brought down are variable, usually fluctuating markedly

[14] For a review of this subject see C. C. Delwiche and J. Wyler, "Nonsymbiotic Nitrogen Fixation in Soils," *Plant and Soil,* 7:113–29, 1956.

with season and location. It is well known that the additions are greater
in the tropics than in humid-temperate regions and larger in the latter
than under semiarid climates. In Table 16:4 will be found some of the
more important data regarding the amounts of nitrogen thus added to
the soil in various parts of the world. It will be noted that the figures are,
for the most part, from temperate regions.

Table 16:4. Amounts of Nitrogen Brought Down in Precipitation[a]

Location	Years of Record	Rainfall in inches	Pounds per Acre per Year	
			Ammoniacal Nitrogen	Nitrate Nitrogen
Harpenden, England	28	28.8	2.64	1.33
Garford, England	3	26.9	6.43	1.93
Flahult, Sweden	1	32.5	3.32	1.30
Groningen, Holland	. . .	27.6	4.54	1.46
Bloemfontein and Durban, South Africa	2	. . .	4.02	1.39
Ottawa, Canada	10	23.4	4.42	2.16
Ithaca, New York	11	29.5	3.65	0.69

[a] These data were obtained from a number of sources, see T. L. Lyon; H. O.
Buckman; and N. C. Brady, *The Nature and Properties of Soils* (New York: Macmillan, 1952), p. 467.

Apparently the ammoniacal nitrogen added to the soil in precipitation
is, at least in temperate regions, always larger in amount than that in the
nitrate form. The nitrate nitrogen is about the same for most locations,
but the ammonium form shows wide variations. The figures in Table 16:4,
suggest that under a humid-temperate climate, an average of about 4½
pounds of ammoniacal and 1½ pounds of nitrate nitrogen fall on every
acre of land yearly in rain and snow. Allowing for some loss in runoff,
perhaps 5 pounds of nitrogen an acre actually enter the soil each year.
This annual acquisition of nitrogen in a readily available form to each
acre of land affords some aid in the maintenance of soil fertility.

16:17 REACTIONS OF NITROGEN FERTILIZERS

Nitrogen applied in fertilizers undergoes the same kinds of reactions as does nitrogen released by biochemical processes from plant

residues. Most of the fertilizer nitrogen will be present in one or more of three forms: (1) nitrate, (2) ammonia, and (3) urea. The fate of each of these forms has already been discussed briefly. Thus, urea nitrogen is subject to ammonification, nitrification, and utilization by microbes and higher plants. Ammonium fertilizers can be oxidized to nitrates, fixed by the soil solids, or, they can be utilized without change by higher plants or microorganisms. And nitrate salts can be lost by volatilization or leaching or they too can be absorbed by plants or microorganisms.

HIGH CONCENTRATIONS. One important fact should be remembered when dealing with the reaction of fertilizer nitrogen. The added fertilizer salts will almost invariably be localized and in higher concentrations than one would expect to find in unfertilized soils. For this reason, the usual reactions are sometimes subject to modification. A few examples will be cited.

When anhydrous ammonia, ammonium-containing salts, or even urea are added to highly alkaline soils there is a possibility of some nitrogen loss in the form of free ammonia. Also, under these conditions, the nitrification process is inhibited, only the first step proceeding normally. Nitrites may thus accumulate in this situation until essentially all the ammonium form has been oxidized. Only then will the second step, that of nitrate formation, take place at normal speed.

The addition of large amounts of nitrate-containing fertilizers may effect the processes of free fixation and gaseous nitrogen loss. In general, fixation by free living organisms is depressed by adequate mineral nitrogen. Gaseous losses, on the other hand, are often encouraged by abundant nitrates. Heavy nitrate fertilization would thus tend to increase losses of nitrogen from the soil.

In most soil situations the effects of higher localized concentrations of fertilizer materials on nitrogen transformations are not serious. Except for a few situations such as these cited, we can assume that fertilizer nitrogen will be changed in soils in a manner very similar to that of nitrogen released by biological transformations.

SOIL ACIDITY. Ammonium-containing fertilizers and those which form ammonia upon reacting in the soil have a tendency to increase soil acidity. (See p. 544 for a more thorough discussion of this.) The process of nitrification (see equations on p. 444) releases hydrogen ions which become adsorbed on the soil colloids. Continued and substantial use of acid-forming fertilizers in humid regions must be accompanied by applications of lime for best crop growth.

The nitrate component of fertilizers does not increase soil acidity. In fact nitrate fertilizers containing cations in the molecule (e.g., $NaNO_3$) have a slight alkalizing effect.

16:18. PRACTICAL MANAGEMENT OF SOIL NITROGEN

The problem of nitrogen control is twofold: (1) the maintenance of an adequate supply in the soil; and (2) the regulation of the turnover to assure a ready availability to meet crop demands.

NITROGEN BALANCE SHEET. Major gains and losses of available soil nitrogen are diagrammed in Fig. 16:7. While the relative additions and losses by various mechanisms will vary greatly from soil to soil, the principles illustrated in the diagram are valid.

The major loss of nitrogen from most soils is that removed in crop plants. A good crop of wheat or cotton may remove only 125 pounds per acre, nearly half of which may be returned to the soil in the stalks or straw. A bumper silage corn crop in contrast may contain over 200 pounds per acre and a good yield of alfalfa or of well-fertilized grass hay more than 300 pounds. It is obvious that modern yield levels require nutrient inputs far in excess of those of a generation ago.

Erosion, leaching, and volatilization losses are determined to no small degree by water management practices. Their magnitudes are so dependent upon specific situations that generalizations are difficult. However, soil and crop management practices which give optimum crop yields will likely hold these sources of nitrogen loss to a satisfactory minimum.

MEETING THE DEFICIT. In practice, nitrogen deficits are met in four ways—crop residues, farm manure, legumes, and commercial fertilizers. On dairy farms and beef ranches, much of the deficit will be met by the first three methods, fertilizers being used as a supplementary source. On most other types of farms, however, fertilizers will play a major role. Where vegetables and other cash crops with high nutrient requirements are grown, the nitrogen deficit will be met almost entirely with commercial fertilizers. Even with the general field crops, modern yield levels can be maintained only through the extensive use of fertilizers.

TURNOVER REGULATIONS. By all odds, the more difficult of the two general problems of nitrogen control is the regulation of this element after it enters the soil. Availability at the proper time and in suitable amounts, with a minimum of loss, is the ideal. Even where commercial fertilizers are used to supply much of the nitrogen, maintaining an adequate, but not excessive, quantity of available nitrogen is not an easy task.

Soils under any given climate tend to assume what may be called a *normal* or *equilibrium content* of nitrogen. Thus, under ordinary methods

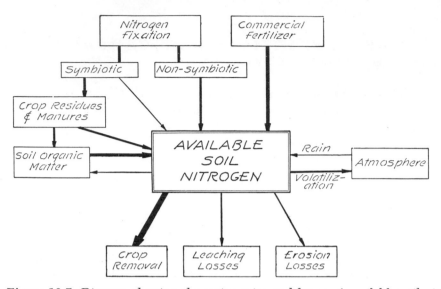

Figure 16:7. Diagram showing the major gains and losses of available soil nitrogen. The width of the arrows indicates roughly the magnitude of the losses and the addition often encountered. It should be emphasized that the diagram represents average conditions only and that much variability is to be expected in the actual and relative quantities of nitrogen involved.

of cropping and manuring, any attempt to raise the nitrogen content to a point materially higher than this normal will be attended by an unnecessary waste due to drainage and other losses. At the same time, the nitrogen should be kept suitably active by the use of legumes and other organic materials with a narrow C:N ratio and by the applications of lime and commercial fertilizers.

This is essentially the recommendation already made for soil organic matter (p. 159), and it is known to be both economical and effective. In short, the practical problem is to supply adequate nitrogen to the soil, to keep it mobile, and at the same time to protect it from excessive losses due to leaching, volatilization, and erosion.

16:19. IMPORTANCE OF SULFUR

Sulfur has long been known to be essential for plant and animal growth. Although much is yet to be learned about the functions of this element, it is already known to be essential for many reactions in every living cell. Sulfur is a constituent of the amino acids, methionine and cystine, deficiencies of which result in serious human malnutrition. The vitamins biotin and thiamine contain sulfur, and the structure of proteins is determined to a considerable extent by sulfur groups. The properties of certain protein enzymes are thought to be due to the type of sulfur linkages present. As with the other essential elements, sulfur plays a unique role in plant and animal metabolism.

Plants that are sulfur deficient are characteristically small and spindly. The younger leaves are light green to yellowish and in the case of legumes, nodulation of the roots is reduced. The maturity of fruits and seeds is delayed in the absence of adequate sulfur.

DEFICIENCIES OF SULFUR. It is only in recent years that deficiencies of sulfur have become common. Since it was first manufactured in 1840, sulfur-bearing superphosphate has helped supply the needs for this element. Likewise, ammonium sulfate, long a significant constituent of fertilizers, has been an important sulfur source. Atmospheric sulfur dioxide (SO_2), a by-product of the combustion of sulfur-rich coals and residual fuel oils, has supplied large quantities of this element to both plants and soils. Thus, by seemingly incidental means the sulfur needs of crops in the past have been largely satisfied, especially in areas near industrial centers.

In recent years, the trend to the use of high-analysis fertilizers has forced manufacturers to use alternatives to superphosphate and ammonium sulfate. (See Table 16:5.) As a result, many sulfur-free fertilizers are on the market and the average sulfur content of fertilizers has decreased. Even sulfur-containing pesticides so commonly used a few years ago have been replaced largely by organic materials free of sulfur.

The replacement of wood and coal for domestic heating by natural gas, electricity, and low-sulfur fuel oil has affected the amount and distribution of SO_2 in the atmosphere. Intensified efforts in the United States to reduce air pollution in and around cities and industrial areas will likely further reduce the quantity of sulfur in the atmosphere. The

Table 16:5. Changes in the production and use of two important sulfur containing fertilizers[a]

Item	1953–54	1962–63
1. Per cent of the world's phosphorus fertilizer production from super-phosphate	66	47
2. Per cent of U.S. nitrogen fertilizer consumption from ammonium sulfate	17	8

[a] Data quoted by Russell Coleman, "The Importance of Sulfur as a Plant Nutrient in World Crop Production," *Soil Science,* 101: 230–239, 1966.

recognition that clean air is a laudable goal will necessitate finding alternative means of supplying sulfur for plant growth.

Coupled with these reductions in the supply of sulfur to soils and plants is the greater removal of this element in harvested crops. Yields have increased markedly during the past 10–15 years and much of the nutrients removed in crops have not been returned. The quantity of sulfur thus removed is about the same as that of phosphorus. It is not surprising, therefore, that increased attention is being given to sulfur.

AREAS OF DEFICIENCY. In the United States, deficiencies of sulfur are most common in the Southeast, the Northwest, California, and the Great Plains. In the Northeast and in other areas with heavy industry and large cities, sulfur deficiencies do not seem to be widespread. (See Fig. 16:8.)

Crops vary in their sulfur requirements. Legume crops such as alfalfa, the clovers, and soybeans have high sulfur requirements as do cotton, sorghum, sugar beets, cabbage, turnips, and onions. Grasses and cereals generally have lower sulfur requirements, although wheat in the Northwest is often quite responsive to sulfur applications.

16:20. NATURAL SOURCES OF SULFUR

There are three major natural sources from which plants can be supplied with available sulfur: (1) soil minerals; (2) sulfur gases in the atmosphere; and (3) organically bound sulfur. These will be considered in order.

SOIL MINERALS. There are several soil minerals in which sulfur is combined and from which it may be released for growing plants. For example, sulfides of iron, nickel, and copper are found in many soils, especially those with restricted drainage. They are quite abundant in soils of tidal marsh areas. Upon oxidation, the sulfides are changed to sulfates which are quickly available for plant use.

In regions of low rainfall, sulfate minerals are common in soils. Accumulations of gypsum in the lower horizons of Mollisols and Aridisols (see p. 338) are examples. Accumulations of soluble salts, including sulfates, in the surface layers are characteristic of saline soils (see p. 341) of arid and semiarid regions. When the soils are dry, the salt accumulations are visible.

The accumulation of sulfates in subsoils is not limited to areas of low rainfall. For example, in the Southeast, higher sulfate contents are often found in the subsoils as compared to topsoils. Apparently, the sulfates

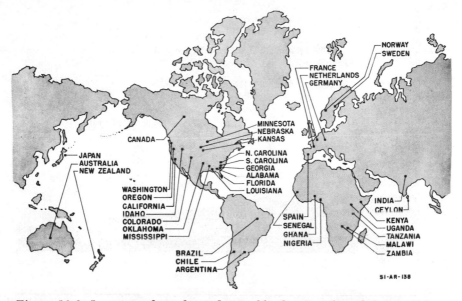

Figure 16:8. *Locations throughout the world wherein sulfur deficiencies have been reported. Other sulfur deficient areas undoubtedly exist but have as yet not been identified. (Photo courtesy The Sulphur Institute.)*

are absorbed by the clays which are usually present in larger quantities in the subsoil.

ATMOSPHERIC SULFUR. The combustion of fuels, especially coal, releases sulfur dioxide and other sulfur compounds into the atmosphere. In fact, the content of sulfur in the air is often directly related to the distance from industrial centers. (See Figure 16:8.) Except near seashores where salt spray adds sulfur in significant quantities and near marshes which are sources of hydrogen sulfide, the combustion of coal is the most significant source of atmospheric sulfur.

Atmospheric sulfur becomes part of the soil-plant system in three ways. Some of it is absorbed directly from the atmosphere by growing plants. A considerable quantity is absorbed directly by the soil from the atmosphere, and a like amount is added with precipitation.

The quantity of sulfur absorbed directly by plants from the atmosphere will vary with atmospheric and soil conditions. Experiments have shown that even plants supplied with adequate soil sulfate can absorb 25–35 per cent of their sulfur from the atmosphere. If the soil sulfur is low and the atmospheric sulfur high, most of the plant sulfur can come from the atmosphere.

Data presented graphically in Fig. 16:9 show a comparison of direct

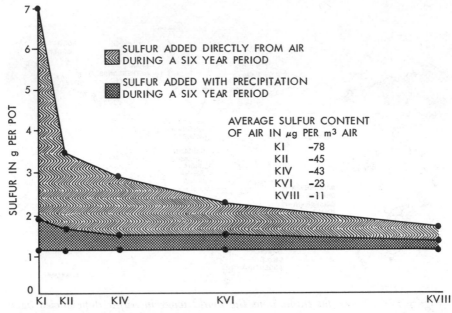

Figure 16:9. *Sulfur added to soils as affected by distance from an oil burning industrial plant in Sweden. Note the rapid dropoff in sulfur added directly from the air. (From O. Johannson, "On sulfur problems in Swedish agriculture," Kgl. Landbr. Ann. 25:57–169, 1960.)*

soil absorption of sulfur and the addition of this element in precipitation. At least in this instance the quantity directly absorbed from the soil was somewhat greater than that coming down in the precipitation.

The quantity of sulfur added in precipitation or absorbed directly varies according to the content of this element in the atmosphere. Samplings for sulfur in precipitation show variations in annual accretions from less than 1 lb per acre to more than 100.[15]

It is not surprising that soils absorb atmospheric sulfur directly or that this element moves in through rain and snow. The sulfur dioxide (SO_2) forms sulfurous acid (H_2SO_3) when in contact with water or with water vapor. Any sulfur trioxide present would form sulfuric acid by the same process. These strong acids are readily absorbed by soils.

ORGANIC BOUND SULFUR. In most humid-region surface soils, a major portion of the sulfur is in the organic form. Just as is the case with nitrogen, however, all too little is known of the specific organic sulfur compounds present. The sulfur added in plant residues is

[15] For data from a number of sources, see D. C. Whitehead, "Soil and Plant-Nutrition Aspects of the Sulfur Cycle," *Soils and Fertilizers*, 27, No. 1:1–8, 1964.

mostly in the form of proteins which are normally subject to rather ready microbial attack. In some manner the sulfur (along with the nitrogen) is stabilized during humus formation. In this stable form, or forms, it is protected from rapid release and thus cannot be lost or taken up by higher plants. The similarity between the general behavior of organic nitrogen and sulfur fractions is indeed remarkable.

Although the amount of specific sulfur compounds associated with soil organic matter is not known, the presence of some forms is strongly suspected. For example, amino acids and other compounds with direct C-S linkages are thought to be present as are organic sulfates.

FORMS OF SULFUR. Our discussion has identified three major forms of sulfur in soils and fertilizers, *sulfides, sulfates,* and *organic forms.* To these must be added the fourth important form, *elemental sulfur,* the starting point of most of the manmade chemical sulfur compounds. The following sections will show relationships among these forms.

16:21. SULFUR CYCLE

The major transformations which sulfur undergoes in soils is shown in Fig. 16:10. The inner circle shows the relationships among the four major forms of this element in soils and in fertilizers. The outer portions show the most important sources of sulfur and how this element is lost from the system.

Note some similarity between the sulfur and nitrogen cycles. (See p. 440.) In each case, the atmosphere is an important source of the element in question. Each is held largely in the organic fraction of the soil and each is dependent to a considerable extent upon microbial action for its various transformations.

Figure 16:9 should be referred to frequently as we take a more detailed look at sulfur in plants and soils beginning with the behavior of this element in soils.

16:22. BEHAVIOR OF SULFUR COMPOUNDS IN SOILS

MINERALIZATION AND IMMOBILIZATION. It is not surprising that sulfur behaves much like nitrogen as it is absorbed by plants and microorganisms and moves through the sulfur cycle. The organic forms of sulfur must be mineralized by soil organisms if the sulfur is to be used by plants. The rate at which this occurs is dependent

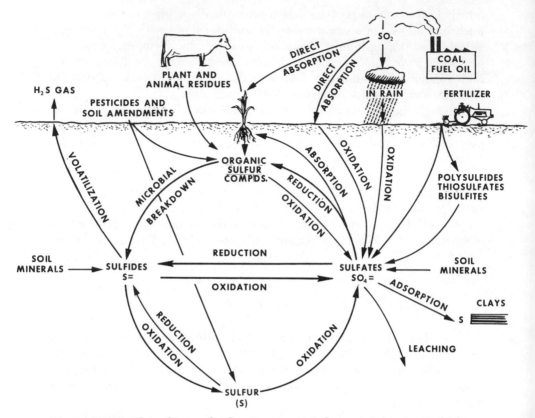

*Figure 16:10. The sulfur cycle showing some of the transformations which oc-
cur as this element changes form in soils, plants and animals. It is well to keep
in mind that except for certain soils in arid areas, the great bulk of the sulfur
is in the form of organic compounds.*

upon the same environmental factors as affect nitrogen mineralization
including moisture, aeration, temperature, and pH. When conditions are
proper for general microbial activity sulfur mineralization occurs. The
mineralization reaction might be expressed as follows:

$$\text{Organic Sulfur} \longrightarrow \text{Decay Products} \longrightarrow \text{Sulfates}$$

$$\begin{pmatrix}\text{Proteins and}\\ \text{other organic}\\ \text{combinations}\end{pmatrix} \quad \begin{pmatrix}\text{Of which } H_2S \text{ and}\\ \text{other sulfides are}\\ \text{simple examples}\end{pmatrix}$$

Immobilization of inorganic forms of sulfur occurs when low-sulfur,
energy-rich organic materials are added to soils not plentifully supplied
with inorganic sulfur. The mechanism is thought to be the same as for

nitrogen. The energy-rich material stimulates microbial growth, and the inorganic sulfur is synthesized into microbial tissue. Only when the microbial activity subsides does the inorganic sulfate form again appear in the soil solution.

These facts suggest that, like nitrogen, sulfur in soil organic matter may be associated with organic carbon in a reasonably constant ratio. The ratio among carbon, nitrogen, and sulfur for a number of soils on three different continents is given in Table 16:6. There appears to be some definite relationship among the contents of these three elements, a relationship which is in accord with their behavior in soils.

Table 16:6. Mean ratios of carbon to nitrogen to sulfur in a variety of soils throughout the world[a]

Location	Description and Number of Soils	Ratio C:N:S
North Scotland	Agricultural, non-calcareous (40)	147:10:1.4
Minnesota	Chernozems (6)	114:10:1.55
Minnesota	Podzolic soils (24)	132:10:1.22
Oregon	Agricultural, varied (10)	145:10:1.01
Eastern Australia	Acid soils (128)	152:10:1.21
Eastern Australia	Alkaline soils (27)	140.10.1.52

[a] These data were summarized from several sources by D. C. Whitehead, *op. cit.*, p. 2.

SULFUR OXIDATION AND REDUCTION. During the microbial decomposition of organic sulfur compounds, sulfides are formed along with other incompletely oxidized substances such as elemental sulfur, thiosulfates, and polythionates. These reduced substances are subject to oxidation just as are the ammonium compounds formed when nitrogenous materials are decomposed. The oxidation reactions may be illustrated as follows, using hydrogen sulfide and elemental sulfur as examples of the sulfur substances which are oxidized:

$$H_2S + 2O_2 \longrightarrow H_2SO_4$$
$$2S + 3O_2 + 2H_2O \longrightarrow 2H_2SO_4$$

The oxidation of some sulfur compounds such as sulfites (SO_3^{--}) and sulfides (S^{--}) can take place by strict chemical reactions. However, most of the sulfur oxidation occurring in soils is thought to be *biochemical* in nature. It is accomplished by a number of autotrophic

bacteria of the genus *Thiobacillus,* five species of which have been characterized. Since the environmental requirement and tolerances of these
five species varies considerably, the process of sulfur oxidation occurs
over a wide range of soil conditions. For example, it occurs at pH values
ranging from less than 2 to higher than 9. This is in contrast to the comparable nitrogen oxidation process, nitrification, where a rather narrow
pH range near neutral is desired.

Like nitrates, sulfates tend to be unstable in anaerobic environments.
They are reduced to sulfides by a number of bacteria of two genera
Desulfovibro (5 species) and *Desulfotomaculum* (3 species). The or-
ganisms use the combined oxygen in sulfate to oxidize organic materials.
A representative reaction follows:

$$2(R \cdot CH_2OH) + SO_4^{--} \longrightarrow 2(R \cdot COOH) + 2H_2O + S^{--}$$

organic alcohol   sulfate   organic acid   sulfide

In soils, the sulfide ion would likely react immediately with iron,
which in anaerobic conditions would be present in the ferrous form.
This reaction might be represented as follows:

$$Fe^{++} + S^{--} \longrightarrow FeS$$

Iron sulfide

Sulfur reduction takes place with compounds other than sulfates. For
example, sulfites(SO_3^{--}), thiosulfates ($S_2O_3^{--}$) and elemental sulfur
(S) are rather easily reduced to the sulfide form by bacteria and other
organisms.

The oxidation and reduction of inorganic sulfur compounds is of
marked significance to growing plants. In the first place, these reactions
determine to a considerable extent the quantity of sulfate present in soils
at any one time. Since this is the form taken up by plants, the nutrient
significance of sulfur oxidation and reduction is obvious. Secondly, the
state of sulfur oxidation determines to a marked degree the acidity of a
soil, a fact which will be considered further in the next section.

SULFUR OXIDATION AND ACIDITY. Sulfur oxidation
is an acidifying process. The reactions on p. 469 illustrate this point.
For every sulfur atom oxidized two hydrogen ions result. Advantage is
taken of this effect by adding sulfur to reduce the extreme alkalinity of
certain alkali soils of arid regions and to reduce the pH of certain soils
for the control of diseases such as potato scab (see p. 404).

The acidifying effect of sulfur oxidation can bring about extremely
acid soil conditions. For example, this has been known to occur when
land is drained after it has been submerged for some time under brack-

ish water or sea water. During the submerged period sulfates in the water are reduced to sulfides in which form they are stabilized generally as iron sulfides. Since there is a continuous supply of sulfates under these conditions, high levels of sulfides are built up. If there are periods of partial drying elemental sulfur can form by partial oxidation of the sulfides. The sulfide and elemental contents are hundreds of times higher than one would find in comparable upland soils.

When these areas are drained, the sulfides and/or elemental sulfur are quickly oxidized forming sulfuric acid. The soil pH may drop to levels as low as 1 or 2—levels unknown in normal upland soils. Obviously plant growth cannot occur under these conditions. Furthermore, the quantity of limestone needed to neutralize the acidity is so high as to make this remedy completely uneconomical.

Sizeable areas of these kinds of soils, called *cat-clays*, are found in southeast Asia. They also occur in the tideland areas along the coasts of several other areas including the southeastern part of the United States as well as the West Coast.

So long as these soils are kept submerged, the soil reaction does not drop prohibitively. Consequently, paddy rice production is sometimes possible under these conditions.

SULFATE RETENTION. Most soils will retain sulfate, although the quantity held is generally small and its strength of retention is low compared to that of phosphate. The retentive capacity is generally higher in the subsoil than in the surface layers. This is due to the high sulfate retentive capacity of certain compounds which tend to accumulate in the lower horizons. These include hydrous oxides of iron and aluminum and silicate clays, especially those high in kaolinite. Soils of the Southeast are commonly high in these sulfate-retaining substances. Consequently, sulfate retention in soils of this region is likewise high.

The mechanism of absorbing sulfate is thought to involve OH groups in the hydrous oxide and silicate clays. Hydroxyl groups held by aluminum ions in the oxides or silicates are replaced by sulfate or acid sulfate ions. A generalized equation such as the following illustrates how this may occur.

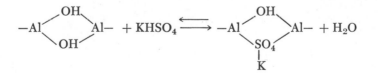

The addition of OH ions (increasing pH) would tend to drive the above reaction to the left, releasing the absorbed sulfate. For this reason, sulfate retention is generally lowered by the liming of acid soils.

16:23. SULFUR AND SOIL FERTILITY MAINTENANCE

The problem of maintaining adequate quantities of sulfur for minerals is decidedly less than is that of phosphorus. This element is added to soils through adsorption from the atmosphere and as an incidental component of many fertilizers. All in all, chances for widespread sulfur deficiencies are generally less than for the three so called "fertilizer" elements.

Even though areas of sulfur deficiency are not widespread, situations wherein crops respond to sulfur applications are becoming more and more common. Less "incidental" fertilizer sulfur is being added in some areas and additions of this element from the atmosphere will likely decrease as air pollution abatement efforts are pressed. Furthermore, steadily increasing crop yields are removing proportionately larger quantities of this and other elements. While crop residues and farmyard manures can help replenish the sulfur removed, greater and greater dependence must be placed on fertilizer additions. Already regular sulfur applications are necessary for good crop yields in large areas of the Southeast and Northwest and in parts of the Great Plains far removed from industrial plants. The future will likely see an increase in the size and frequency of sulfur responses.

Chapter 17

The Supply and Availability
of Phosphorus and Potassium

Considerable nitrogen can be added to soils through bio-chemical fixation brought about by microorganisms. If the proper legume is chosen, for example, the organisms will often fix this element from the air in quantities sufficient to temporarily increase the nitrogen already present. With other nutrient elements such as phosphorus and potassium, however, we have no such microbial aid. Consequently, other sources must be depended upon to meet the demands of plants.

There are at least four main sources of phosphorus and potassium from which we can draw in meeting these demands: (1) commercial fertilizer; (2) barnyard manures; (3) plant residues, including green manures; and (4) native compounds of these elements, both organic and inorganic, already present in the soil. Since the first three sources are to be considered in later chapters, our attention at present will be focused on the ways and means of utilizing the body of the soil as source of these mineral elements. We will begin with phosphorus.

17:1. IMPORTANCE OF PHOSPHORUS

With the possible exception of nitrogen, no other element has been as critical in the growth of plants in the field as has phosphorus. A lack of this element is doubly serious, since it may prevent other nutrients from being acquired by plants. For example, prior to the extensive usage of commercial fertilizers, most of our soil nitrogen was indirectly dependent upon the supply of phosphorus. This was due to the vital influence of the latter element on legume growth. Today the demand for phosphorus by nitrogen yielding legumes is still universally recognized.

The need of plants for phosphorus has been especially considered in the formulation of commercial fertilizers. This element, in the form of superphosphate, was the first to be supplied as a manufactured product. Until fairly recently the amount of "phosphoric acid" in mixed fertilizers almost invariably exceeded that of nitrogen or potash. Even today the total tonnage of phosphorus, expressed as P_2O_5, is exceeded only by that of nitrogen.

17:2. INFLUENCE OF PHOSPHORUS ON PLANTS

It is difficult to state in detail the functions of phosphorus in the economy of even the simplest plants. Only the more important functions will need be considered here. Phosphorus makes its contribution through its favorable effect on the following:

1. Cell division and fat and albumin formation.
2. Flowering and fruiting, including seed formation.
3. Crop maturation, thus counteracting the effects of excess nitrogen applications.
4. Root development, particularly of the lateral and fibrous rootlets.
5. Strength of straw in cereal crops, thus helping to prevent lodging.
6. Crop quality, especially of forages and of vegetables.
7. Resistance to certain diseases.

17:3. THE PHOSPHORUS PROBLEM

Although the amount of total phosphorus in an average mineral soil compares favorably with that of nitrogen, it is much lower than potassium, calcium, or magnesium. (See Table 2.3.) Of even greater importance, however, is the fact that most of the phosphorus present in soils is currently unavailable to plants. Also, when soluble sources of this element are supplied to soils in the form of fertilizers, their phosphorus is often "fixed" or rendered unavailable even under the most ideal field conditions. (See p. 480.)

Fertilizer practices in many areas exemplify the problem of phosphorus availability. As already emphasized, the tonnage of phosphorus-supplying materials used as fertilizers definitely exceeds all except the nitrogen carriers. The removal of phosphorus from soils by crops, however, is low compared to that of nitrogen and potassium, often being only 1/3 or 1/4 that of the latter elements. The necessity for high fertilizer dosage when relatively small quantities of phosphorus are being removed from soils indicates that much of the added phosphates become unavailable to growing plants.

The influence of this situation on fertilizer practice is clearly shown when we consider the additions of fertilizer phosphorus in comparison with crop removal.

Table 17:1. Nutrient Removal By Crops in The United States Compared to That Added in Fertilizers[a] (1965)

	Thousands of Tons		
	N	P	K
Removed in Crops	8,838	1,207	4,152
Added in Fertilizers	4,580	1,499	2,313
Addition as Per Cent of Removal	52	124	56

[a] Nutrient removal figures calculated from D. C. White, "1965 Harvest, USA," *Plant Food Review*, 11, No. 4: p. 16, 1965. Fertilizer additions from *Fertilizer Summary Data by States and Geographic Regions*, Tennessee Valley Authority, 1966.

In the United States, phosphorus added in fertilizers exceeds that removed by crops by more than 24 per cent. (See Table 17:1.) In some areas, notably the eastern seaboard states, additions of phosphorus more than triple the removal of this element by crops. Since phosphorus is lost only sparingly by leaching, the inefficiency of utilization of phosphate fertilizers is obvious.

Briefly then, the over-all phosphorus problem is threefold: (1) a small total amount present in soils; (2) the unavailability of such native phosphorus; and (3) a marked "fixation" of added soluble phosphates. Since crop removal of phosphorus is relatively low and world phosphate supplies are huge, problem (1), that of supplying sufficient total phosphorus, is not serious. Increasing the availability of native soil phosphorus and the retardation of fixation or reversion of added phosphates are, therefore, the problem of greatest importance. These two phases will be discussed following a brief review of the phosphorus compounds present in soils.

17:4. PHOSPHORUS COMPOUNDS IN SOILS[1]

Both inorganic and organic forms of phosphorus occur in soils and both are important to plants as sources of this element. There is a serious lack of information, however, on the relative amounts of these two forms in different soils. Data available from Oregon, Iowa, and Arizona (Table 17:2) give some idea of their relative proportions. Despite the variation which occurs, it is evident that a consideration of soil phosphorus would not be complete unless some attention were given to both forms. (See Fig. 17:1.)

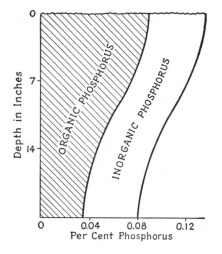

Figure 17:1. The distribution of organic and inorganic phosphorus with soil depth. Note that about ¾ the total phosphorus was in the organic form in the surface layer (0–7″) of these soils, while about half was in this form in the subsoil. (Average of 22 grassland soils calculated from T. W. Walker, and A. F. R. Adams, "Studies of Soil Organic Matter: I. Influence of Phosphorus Content of Parent Materials on Accumulations of Carbon, Nitrogen, Sulfur, and Organic Phosphorus in Grassland Soils," Soil Sci. 85:307–18, 1958.)

INORGANIC COMPOUNDS. Most inorganic phosphorus compounds in soils fall into one of two groups: (1) those containing *calcium* and (2) those containing *iron* and *aluminum*. The calcium compounds of most importance are listed in Table 17:3. Fluorapatite, the most insoluble and unavailable of the group, usually is an original mineral. It is found in even the more weathered soils, especially in their

---

[1] For a review of soil phosphorus see Sigurd Larsen, "Soil Phosphorus," *Advances in Agronomy,* 19:151–210, 1967.

Table 17:2. The Total Phosphorus Content in Parts per Million of Soils from Three States and the Percentage of the Total Phosphorus in the Organic Form

Soils	No. of Samples	Total P ppm	Organic Fraction %
Western Oregon Soils[a]			
Hill soils	4	357	65.9
Old valley—filling soils	4	1479	29.4
Recent valley soils	3	848	25.6
Iowa Soils[b]			
Prairie soils	2	613	41.6
Gray-brown podzolic soils	2	574	37.3
Planosols	2	495	52.7
Arizona Soils			
Surface soils	19	703	36.0
Subsoils	5	125	34.0

[a] From B. R. Bertramson and R. E. Stephenson, "Comparative Efficiency of Organic Phosphorus and of Superphosphate in the Nutrition of Plants," *Soil Sci.,* 53: 215–26, 1942.

[b] Iowa data from R. W. Pearson and R. W. Simonson, "Organic Phosphorus in Seven Iowa Profiles: Distribution and Amounts as Compared to Organic Carbon and Nitrogen," *Proc. Soil Sci. Soc. Amer.,* 4: 162–67, 1939. Arizona data from W. H. Fuller and W. T. McGeorge, "Phosphates in Calcareous Arizona Soils, II. Organic Phosphorus Content," *Soil Sci.,* 71: 45–50, 1951.

lower horizons. This fact is an indication of the extreme insolubility and consequent unavailability of the phosphorus contained therein. The simpler compounds of calcium such as mono- and dicalcium phosphate are readily available for plant growth. Except on recently fertilized soils, however, these compounds are present in extremely small quantities only, since they easily revert to the more insoluble forms.

Much less is known of the exact constitution of the iron and aluminum phosphates contained in soils. The compounds involved are probably hydroxy-phosphates such as dufrenite, wavellite, strengite, and variscite.[2] These compounds are most stable in acid soils and are extremely insoluble.

Many investigators have shown that phosphates react with certain iron or aluminum silicate minerals such as kaolinite. There is some uncertainty, however, as to the exact form in which this phosphorus is held in

[2] S. C. Chang and M. L. Jackson, "Fractionation of Soil Phosphorus," *Soil Science,* 84:133–44, 1957.

Table 17:3. Inorganic Calcium Compounds of Phosphorus Often Found in Soils

Compound	Formula	
Fluor-apatite	$3 Ca_3(PO_4)_2 \cdot CaF_2$	
Carbonate-apatite	$3 Ca_3(PO_4)_2 \cdot CaCO_3$	
Hydroxy-apatite	$3 Ca_3(PO_4)_2 \cdot Ca(OH)_2$	
Oxy-apatite	$3 Ca_3(PO_4)_2 \cdot CaO$	Solubility increases
Tricalcium phosphate	$Ca_3(PO_4)_2$	
Dicalcium phosphate	$CaHPO_4$	
Monocalcium phosphate	$Ca(H_2PO_4)_2$	

the soil. Most evidence indicates that it too is probably fixed as iron or aluminum phosphates such as those described in the preceding paragraph.

ORGANIC PHOSPHORUS COMPOUNDS. There has been relatively less work done on the organic phosphorus compounds in soils, in spite of the fact that this fraction in some cases comprises more than half of the total soil phosphorus. One of the reasons for lack of information on these compounds is the fact that they apparently are exceedingly complex. The meager data available, however, indicate that the three main groups of organic phosphorus compounds found in plants are also present in soils.[3] These are: (1) phytin and phytin derivatives, (2) nucleic acids, and (3) phospholipids. There are likely other organic phosphorus compounds present in soils; some investigators doubt that those listed account for all the organic phosphorus.

17:5. FACTORS THAT CONTROL THE AVAILABILITY OF INORGANIC SOIL PHOSPHORUS

The availability of inorganic phosphorus is largely determined by the following factors: (1) soil pH; (2) soluble iron, aluminum, and manganese; (3) presence of iron-, aluminum-, and manganese-containing minerals; (4) available calcium and calcium minerals; (5) amount and

[3] See C. A. Bower, "Separation and Identification of Phytin and Its Derivatives from Soils," *Soil Sci.*, 59:277–85, 1945.

Phytin is a calcium-magnesium salt of inositol phosphoric acid and is rather widely distributed in plants, especially in the seeds. Nucleic acids are found in both plants and animals and are even more complex than is phytin. They are apparently polymeric combinations of phosphoric acid, carbohydrates, and bases such as pyrimidine and purine.

decomposition of organic matter; and (6) activities of microorganisms. The first four of these factors are interrelated, because their effects are largely dependent upon soil pH.

17:6. pH AND PHOSPHATE IONS

It will be remembered from Chapter 14 (p. 397) that the availability of phosphorus to plants is determined to no small degree by the ionic form of this element. The ionic form in turn is determined by the pH of the solution in which the ion is found. Thus, in highly acid solutions only the H_2PO_4 ions are present. If the pH is increased, first the HPO_4 ions and finally PO_4 ions dominate. This situation is shown by means of the following equations:

$$\underset{\text{(Very Acid Solutions)}}{H_2PO_4^- } \overset{+OH^-}{\rightleftharpoons} H_2O + HPO_4^{--} \overset{+OH^-}{\rightleftharpoons} \underset{\text{(Very Alkaline Solutions)}}{H_2O + PO_4^{---}}$$

It should be remembered that at intermediate pH levels two of the phosphate ions may be present simultaneously. Thus, in solutions at pH 6.0 both H_2PO_4 and HPO_4 ions are found.

In general, the H_2PO_4 ion is considered somewhat more available to plants than is the HPO_4 ion. In soils, however, this relationship is complicated by the presence or absence of other compounds or ions. For example, the presence of soluble iron and aluminum under very acid conditions, or calcium at high pH values, will markedly affect the availability of the phosphorus. One can readily see, therefore, that the effect of soil pH on phosphorus availability is determined in no small degree by the various cations present. We will first discuss the effect of these ions in acid soils.

17:7. INORGANIC PHOSPHORUS AVAILABILITY IN ACID SOILS (SEE FIG. 17:2.)

Let us assume that we are working with either a nutrient solution or an organic soil very low in inorganic matter. Assume also that these media are acid in reaction but that they are low in iron, aluminum, and manganese. The H_2PO_4 ions, which would dominate under these

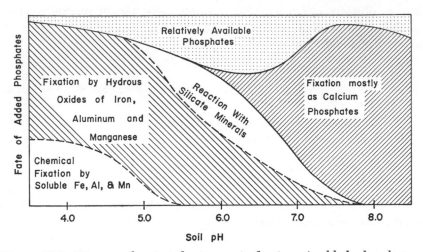

Figure 17:2. *Diagram showing the inorganic fixation of added phosphates at various soil pH values. Average conditions are postulated and it is not to be inferred that any particular soil would have exactly the above distribution. The actual proportion remaining in an available form will depend upon contact with the soil, time for reaction, and other factors. It should be kept in mind that some of the added phosphorus may be changed to an organic form in which it would be temporarily unavailable.*

conditions, would be readily available for plant growth. Normal phosphate absorption by plants woud be expected so long as the pH was not too low.

PRECIPITATION BY Fe, Al, AND Mn IONS. If the same degree of acidity should exist in a normal mineral soil, however, quite different results would be expected. Some soluble iron, aluminum, and manganese are usually found in strongly acid mineral soils. Reaction with the H_2PO_4 ions would immediately occur, rendering the phosphorus insoluble and also unavailable for plant growth.

The chemical reactions occurring between the soluble iron and aluminum and the H_2PO_4 ions probably result in the formation of so-called hydroxy-phosphates. This may be represented as follows, using the aluminum cation as an example[4]:

$$Al^{+++} + H_2PO_4{}^- + 2H_2O \leftrightharpoons 2H^+ + Al(OH)_2H_2PO_4$$

Soluble   Insoluble

[4] See C. V. Cole and M. L. Jackson, "Solubility Equilibrium Constant of Dihydroxy Aluminum Dihydrogen Phosphate Relating to a Mechanism of Phosphate Fixation in Soils," *Proc. Soil Sci. Soc. Amer.*, 15:84–9, 1950.

In most strongly acid soils the concentration of the Fe and Al ions greatly exceeds that of the H_2PO_4 ions. Consequently, the above reaction moves to the right forming the insoluble phosphate. This leaves only minute quantities of the H_2PO_4 ion immediately available for plants under these conditions.

An interesting series of reactions occur when fertilizers containing $Ca(H_2PO_4)_2$ are added to soils, even those relatively high in pH.[5] (See Fig. 17:3.) The $Ca(H_2PO_4)_2$ in the fertilizer granules attracts water from the soil and the following reaction occurs:

$$Ca(H_2PO_4)_2 \cdot H_2O + H_2O \longrightarrow CaHPO_4 \cdot 2H_2O + H_3PO_4$$

As more water is attracted, a H_3PO_4-laden solution with a pH of about 1.4 moves outward from the granule. This solution is sufficiently acid to dissolve and displace large quantities of Fe, Al, and Mn. These ions react with the phosphate to form complex compounds which later probably revert to the hydroxy-phosphates of Fe, Al, and Mn in acid soils and of calcium in neutral to alkaline soils. In any case, the immediate products of the addition to soils of a water-soluble compound ($Ca(H_2PO_4)_2 \cdot H_2O$) are a group of insoluble Fe, Al, Mn, and Ca compounds. Even so, the phosphorus in these compounds is released quite readily for plant growth. It is only after these freshly precipitated compounds are allowed to "age" or to revert to more insoluble forms that availability to plants is greatly reduced.

FIXATION BY HYDROUS OXIDES. It should be emphasized that the H_2PO_4 ion reacts not only with the soluble iron, aluminum, and manganese but also with insoluble hydrous oxides of these elements such as limonite and goethite. In fact, the actual quantity of phosphorus fixed by these minerals in acid soils quite likely exceeds that due to chemical precipitation by the soluble Fe, Al, and Mn cations. (See Fig. 17:2.)

The compounds formed as a result of fixation by iron and aluminum oxides are likely to be hydroxy-phosphates just as in the case of chemical precipitation described above.[6] Their formation can be illustrated by means of the following equation, if we represent the hydrous oxide of aluminum as aluminum hydroxide:

---

[5] See W. L. Lindsay and H. F. Stephenson, "Nature of the Reactions of Monocalcium Phosphate Monohydrate in Soils: I. The Solution That Reacts With the Soil; and II. Dissolution and Precipitation Reactions Involving Fe, Al, Mn and Ca," *Proc. Soil Sci. Soc. Amer.*, 23:12–22, 1959.

[6] J. A. Kittrick and M. L. Jackson, "Electron-microscope Observations of the Reaction of Phosphate with Minerals, Leading to a Unified Theory of Phosphate Fixation in Soils," *Soil Science*, 7:81–90, 1956.

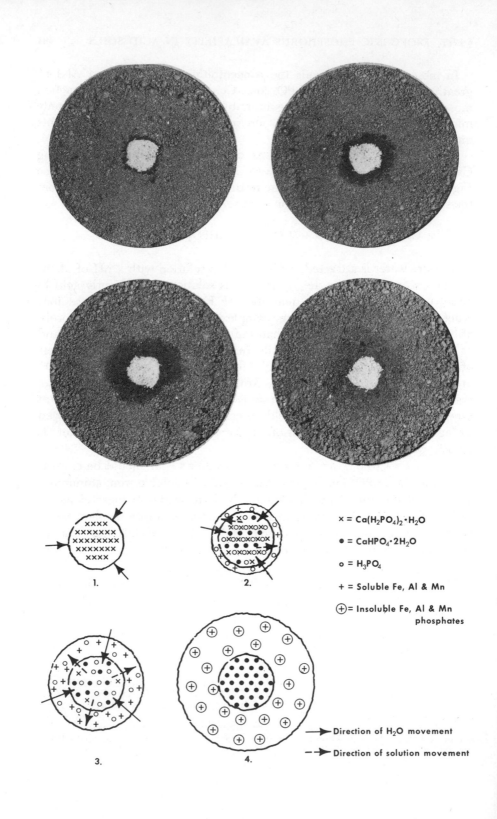

x = Ca(H₂PO₄)₂·H₂O

$x = Ca(H_2PO_4)_2 \cdot H_2O$

$\bullet = CaHPO_4 \cdot 2H_2O$

$o = H_3PO_4$

$+ = $ Soluble Fe, Al & Mn

$\oplus = $ Insoluble Fe, Al & Mn phosphates

1.

2.

3.

4.

⟶ Direction of H₂O movement

- -⟶ Direction of solution movement

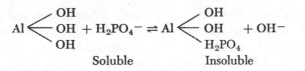

$$\text{Soluble} \qquad\qquad \text{Insoluble}$$

By means of this and similar reactions the formation of several basic-phosphate minerals, containing either iron or aluminum or both, is thought to occur. Since several such compounds are possible, fixation of phosphorus by this mechanism probably takes place over a relatively wide pH range. Also the large quantities of hydrous iron and aluminum oxides present in most soils make possible the fixation of tremendous amounts of phosphorus in total by this means.

Thus, as both of the above equations show, the acid condition which would make possible the presence of the readily available H_2PO_4 ion in mineral soils at the same time results in conditions conducive to the vigorous *fixation* or precipitation of the phosphorus by iron, aluminum, and manganese compounds. (See Fig. 17:2.)

   FIXATION BY SILICATE CLAYS. A third means of fixation of phosphorus under moderately acid conditions involves silicate minerals such as kaolinite, montmorillonite, and illite. Although there is some doubt about the actual mechanisms involved, the over-all effect is essentially the same as when phosphorus is fixed by simpler iron and aluminum compounds. Some workers visualize the fixation of phosphates by silicate minerals as a surface reaction between exposed OH-groups on the mineral crystal and the H_2PO_4 ions. Other investigators have evidence that aluminum and iron ions are removed from the edges of the silicate crystals forming hydroxy-phosphates of the same general formula as those already discussed. This type of reaction might be expressed as follows:

$$[Al] + H_2PO_4^- + 2H_2O \rightleftharpoons 2H^+ + Al(OH)_2H_2PO_4$$

In   Insoluble
silicate crystal

Figure 17:3. Illustrations of the reaction of $Ca(H_2PO_4)_2 \cdot H_2O$ granules with moist soils. Stage 1. The granule has just been added to the soil and is beginning to absorb water from it. Stage 2. In the moistened granule H_3PO_4 and $CaHPO_4 \cdot 2H_2O$ are being formed and more soil water is being absorbed. Stage 3. The H_3PO_4-laden solution moves into the soil, dissolving and displacing Fe, Al and Mn and leaving insoluble $CaHPO_4 \cdot 2H_2O$ in the granule. Stage 4. The Fe, Al and Mn ions have reacted with the phosphate to form insoluble compounds, which along with the residue of $CaHPO_4 \cdot 2H_2O$ are the primary reaction products. (Photos courtesy G. L. Terman and National Plant Food Institute.)

Thus, even though phosphates react with different ions and compounds in acid soils, apparently the same insoluble iron and aluminum compounds are formed in each case. Major differences from soil to soil are probably due to differences in rate of phosphate precipitation and in the surface area of the phosphates once reaction has occurred. This will receive attention later.

ANION EXCHANGE. Part of the phosphate which has reacted with iron and aluminum compounds and with silicate clays is subject to replacement by other anions such as the hydroxyl ion. Such replacement has been called *anion exchange*. It may be illustrated by a reverse of the reaction on p. 483. Thus,

$$Al(OH)_2H_2PO_4 + OH^- \rightleftharpoons Al(OH)_3 + H_2PO_4^-$$

One anion (OH) has been exchanged for another (H_2PO_4). This reaction shows how anion exchange can take place and illustrates the importance of liming in helping to maintain a higher level of available phosphates.

17:8. INORGANIC PHOSPHORUS AVAILABILITY AT HIGH pH VALUES (SEE FIG. 17:2)

In alkaline soils, phosphate precipitation is caused mostly by calcium compounds. Such soils are plentifully supplied with exchangeable calcium and in most cases with $CaCO_3$. Available phosphates will react with both the Ca ion and its carbonate. As an illustration, let us assume that concentrated superphosphate is added to a calcareous soil. The reactions would be as follows:

$$Ca(H_2PO_4)_2 + 2Ca^{++} \rightleftharpoons Ca_3(PO_4)_2 + 4H^+$$
(Soluble)   (Adsorbed)   (Insoluble)

$$Ca(H_2PO_4)_2 + 2CaCO_3 \rightleftharpoons Ca_3(PO_4)_2 + 2CO_2\uparrow + 2H_2O$$
(Soluble)   (Insoluble)

Although the $Ca_3(PO_4)_2$ thus formed is quite insoluble, it may be converted in the soil to even more insoluble compounds. The hydroxy-, oxy-, carbonate-, or even fluor-apatite compounds, may be formed if conditions are favorable and if sufficient time is allowed. (See Table 17:3.)

This type of reversion may occur in soils of the eastern United States which have been heavily limed. It is much more serious, however, in western soils due to the widespread presence of excess $CaCO_3$. The problem of utilizing phosphates in alkaline soils of the arid West is thus fully as serious as it is on highly acid soils in the East.

17:9. pH FOR MAXIMUM INORGANIC PHOSPHORUS AVAILABILITY

With insolubility of phosphorus occurring at both extremes of the soil pH range (see Fig. 17:2) the question arises as to the range in soil reaction in which minimum fixation occurs. The basic iron and aluminum phosphates have a minimum solubility around pH 3 to 4. At higher pH values some of the phosphorus is released and the fixing capacity somewhat reduced. Even at pH 6.5, however, much of the phosphorus is still probably chemically combined with iron and aluminum. As the pH approaches 6, precipitation as calcium compounds begins; at pII 6.5 the formation of insoluble calcium salts is a factor in rendering the phosophorus unavailable. Above pH 7.0, even more insoluble compounds such as apatites are formed.

These facts seem to indicate that maximum phosphate availability to plants is obtained when the soil pH is maintained in the range from 6.0 to 7.0. (See Fig. 17:2.) Even in this range, however, the fact should be emphasized that phosphate availability may still be very low and that added soluble phosphates are readily fixed by soils. The low recovery (perhaps 10 to 30 per cent) by plants of added phosphates in a given season is partially due to this fixation.

17:10. AVAILABILITY AND SURFACE AREA OF PHOSPHATES

Inorganic phosphate availability is determined primarily by two factors: (1) the nature of the phosphorus compounds present in soils; and (2) the surface area of these compounds. The first of these factors has been considered in the preceding section. We shall discuss briefly the second factor, that of surface area.

When soluble phosphates are added to soils two kinds of compounds form immediately: (1) fresh precipitates of Ca, or Fe and Al phosphates; and (2) similar compounds formed on the surfaces of either $CaCO_3$ or Fe and Al oxide particles. In each case, the total surface area of the phosphate is high and consequently the availability of the phosphorus contained therein is reasonably rapid. Thus, even though the water-soluble phosphorus in superphosphate may be precipitated in the soil in a matter of a few days, the freshly precipitated compounds will release much of their phosphorus to growing plants.

EFFECTS OF AGING. With time, changes take place in the reaction products of soluble phosphates and soils. These changes generally result in a reduction in surface area of the phosphates and a similar reduction in their availability. An increase in the crystal size of precipitated phosphates occurs in time. This decreases their surface area. Also, there is a penetration of the phosphorus held by $CaCO_3$ and Fe or Al oxide particles into the particle itself. (See Fig. 17:4.) This leaves less

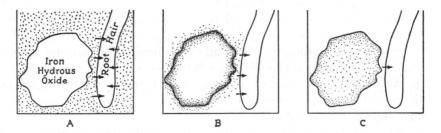

Figure 17:4. Diagrams showing how relatively soluble phosphates are rendered unavailable by compounds such as hydrous oxide. (A) The situation just after application of a soluble phosphate. The root hair and the crystal is surrounded by soluble phosphates. Within a very short time (B) most of the soluble phosphate has reacted with the surface of the iron oxide crystal. The phosphorus is still fairly readily available to the plant roots since most of it is located at the surface of the particle where exudates from the plant can encourage exchange. In time (C) the phosphorus penetrates the crystal and only a small portion is found near the surface. Under these conditions its availability is low.

of the phosphorus near the surface where it can be made available to growing plants. By these processes of aging, phosphate availability is reduced. Thus, the supply of available phosphorus to plants is determined not only by the kinds of compounds which form, but also by their surface areas. (See Fig. 17:5.)

17:11. PHOSPHORUS FIXING POWER OF SOILS

In light of the above discussion it is interesting to note the actual quantity of phosphorus which soils are capable of fixing. Data from three New Jersey soils presented in Table 17:4 emphasize the

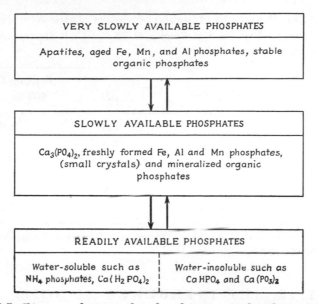

VERY SLOWLY AVAILABLE PHOSPHATES

Apatites, aged Fe, Mn, and Al phosphates, stable organic phosphates

SLOWLY AVAILABLE PHOSPHATES

$Ca_3(PO_4)_2$, freshly formed Fe, Al and Mn phosphates, (small crystals) and mineralized organic phosphates

READILY AVAILABLE PHOSPHATES

Water-soluble such as NH_4 phosphates, $Ca(H_2PO_4)_2$ | Water-insoluble such as $CaHPO_4$ and $Ca(PO_3)_2$

Figure 17:5. Diagram showing the classification of phosphate compounds in three major groups. Fertilizer phosphates are generally in the "readily available phosphate" group but are quickly converted to the slowly available forms. These can be utilized by plants at first but upon aging they are rendered less available and are then classed as very slowly available. At any one time perhaps 80–90 per cent of the soil phosphorus is in "very slowly available" forms. Most of the remainder is in the slowly available form since perhaps less than one per cent would be expected to be readily available.

tremendous power of certain soils in this respect. For example, to satisfy the phosphorus-fixing power of the unlimed Collington soil nearly 47 tons of superphosphate containing 20 per cent P_2O_5 would be required. Although liming definitely reduced the fixing capacity, the quantity of phosphorus fixed even on the limed soils is enormous. Thus, over 25 tons of superphosphate would be required to completely satisfy the phosphorus-fixing power of the limed Collington soil.

One Coastal Plain soil was reported[7] to have a phosphate-fixing capacity of 125 tons of 20 per cent superphosphate per acre-furrow-slice. Although such values are somewhat higher than usual because of the nature and amounts of the iron and aluminum compounds in the soils, they do not overemphasize the problem of phosphate fixation.

[7] F. E. Bear and S. J. Toth, "Phosphate Fixation in Soil and Its Practical Control," *Ind. and Eng. Chem.*, 34:49–52, 1942.

Table 17:4. The Phosphorus Adsorbing Power of Three New Jersey Soils Limed and Unlimed Expressed as Pounds of 20 Per Cent Superphosphate per Acre-Furrow-Slice[a]

Soil	Treatment	pH	P–fixing Power, Lbs 20% Super/A.F.S.
Sassafras	No lime	3.6	28,400
Sassafras	lime	6.5	13,916
Collington	No lime	3.2	93,720
Collington	lime	6.5	50,268
Dutchess	No lime	3.8	68,728
Dutchess	lime	6.5	44,020

[a] From S. J. Toth and F. E. Bear, "Phosphorus-Adsorbing Capacities of Some New Jersey Soils," *Soil Sci.*, 64:199–211, 1947.

17:12. THE INFLUENCE OF SOIL ORGANISMS AND ORGANIC MATTER ON THE AVAILABILITY OF INORGANIC PHOSPHORUS

In addition to pH and related factors, organic matter and microorganisms strikingly affect inorganic phosphorus availability. Just as was the case with nitrogen, the rapid decomposition of organic matter and consequent high microbial population results in the *temporary* tying up of inorganic phosphates in microbial tissue.

Moreover, products of organic decay, such as organic acids and humus, are thought to be effective in forming complexes with iron and aluminum compounds. This engagement of iron and aluminum reduces inorganic phosphate fixation to a remarkable degree. The exact importance of this effect has not as yet been completely ascertained. The ability of humus and lignin to reduce phosphate fixation, however, is shown in Fig. 17:6. Both materials were effective in releasing phosphorus after it had been fixed as basic iron phosphate. Thus, organic decomposition products undoubtedly play an important role in inorganic phosphorus availability.

17:13. THE AVAILABILITY OF ORGANIC PHOSPHORUS

Only meager information has been obtained on the factors affecting the availability to higher plants of organic phosphorus com-

Figure 17:6. The effect of added organic materials on the release of phosphorus previously fixed by iron compounds. Both humus and lignin are effective, the humus to the greater degree. These results suggest that mineral fixation of phosphorus may be lower in soils comparatively high in organic matter. (After Swenson, Cole and Sieling.)

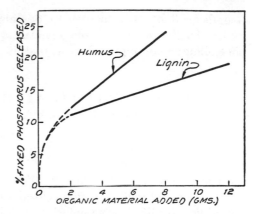

pounds. It has been established, however, that both *phytin* and *nucleic acids* can be utilized as sources of phosphorus.[8] Apparently the phytin is absorbed directly by the plants, while the nucleic acids probably are broken down by enzymes at the root surfaces and the phosphorus is absorbed in either the organic or inorganic form. In spite of the readiness with which these compounds may be assimilated, however, plants commonly suffer from phosphorus deficiency even in the presence of considerable quantities of organic forms of this element. Just as with the inorganic phosphates, the problem is one of availability.

Phytin behaves in the soil much as do the inorganic phosphates,[9] forming iron, aluminum, and calcium phytates. In acid soils the phytin is rendered insoluble and thus unavailable because of reaction with iron and aluminum. Under alkaline conditions calcium phytate is precipitated and the phosphorus carried is likewise rendered unavailable.

The fixation of nucleic acids involves an entirely different mechanism, but the end result—low phosphorus availability—is the same. Apparently nucleic acids are strongly adsorbed by clays, especially montmorillonite. This adsorption is particularly pronounced under acid conditions and results in a marked decrease in the rate of decomposition of the nucleic acids. Consequently, the available phosphorus supply from this source is low, especially in acid soils which contain appreciable amounts of montmorillonite.

The judicious application of lime to acid soils is thus fully as important in organic phosphorus nutrition as it is in rendering inorganic com-

[8] H. T. Rogers, R. W. Pearson, and W. H. Pierre, "Absorption of Organic Phosphorus by Corn and Tomato Plants and the Mineralizing Action of Exo-enzyme Systems of Growing Roots," *Proc. Soil Sci. Soc. Amer.*, 5:285–91, 1941.

[9] For a discussion of the factors affecting the availability of organic phosphorus compounds, see C. A. Bower, *Studies on the Forms and Availability of Soil Organic Phosphorus*, Iowa Agr. Exp. Sta. Res. Bul. 362, Aug. 1949.

pounds available. Whether we are dealing with inorganic soil phosphates, added fertilizers, or organic materials, the importance of lime as a controlling factor in phosphate availability is clearly evident.

17:14. PRACTICAL CONTROL OF PHOSPHORUS AVAILABILITY

From a practical standpoint, the phosphorus utilization picture is not too encouraging. The inefficient utilization of applied phosphates by plants has long been known. The experimental use of radioactive phosphorus materials has emphasized this point even more thoroughly. By adding fertilizers containing traceable phosphorus, it has been possible to determine the proportion of the applied phosphates absorbed during the year of application.

The results of experiments on corn, soybeans, and potatoes are shown in Table 17:5. Even though on some soils marked responses were obtained

Table 17:5. *The Recovery of Applied Fertilizer Phosphates During the First Crop Year*[a]

Soil	Crop	Percentage of Fertilizer Phosphorus Recovered the First Year
Bladen	Corn	11.8
Bladen	Potatoes	7.6
Bladen	Soybeans	18.2
Webster	Corn	6.5
Clarion	Corn	3.4

[a] Bladen data calculated from B. A. Krantz; W. L. Nelson; C. D. Welch; and N. S. Hall, "A Comparison of Phosphorus Utilization by Crops," *Soil Sci.*, 68:171–78, 1949. The other data are from G. Stanford and L. B. Nelson, "Utilization of Phosphorus as Affected by Placement: I. Corn in Iowa," *Soil Sci.*, 68:129–36, 1949.

from the addition of phosphate fertilizers, the efficiency of phosphorus utilization was very low. Apparently maximum yields were obtained only by supplying much more phosphorus than the plants absorbed in a given season.

LIMING AND PLACEMENT OF FERTILIZERS. The small amount of control that can be exerted over phosphate availability seems to be associated with *liming, fertilizer placement,* and *organic matter maintenance.* By holding the pH of soils between 6.0 and 7.0 the phosphate fixation can be kept at a minimum. (See Fig. 14:7 and 17:2.) In order to prevent rapid reaction of phosphate fertilizers with the soil these materials are commonly placed in localized bands. In addition, phosphatic fertilizers are quite often pelleted or aggregated to retard still more their contact with the soil. The effective utilization of phosphorus in combination with barn-yard manure is evidence of the importance of organic matter in increasing the availability of this element.

In spite of the above precautions, a major portion of the added phosphates still reverts to less available forms (see Fig. 17:7). It should be remembered, however, that the reverted phosphorus is not lost from the soil and through the years undoubtedly is slowly available to growing

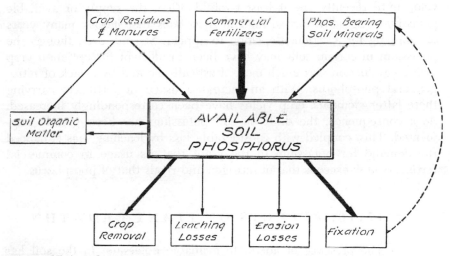

Figure 17:7. *A drawing showing how the* available *phosphorus level in a soil is depleted and replenished. Note that the two main features are the addition of phosphate fertilizers and the fixation of this element in insoluble forms. It should be remembered that the amount of available phosphorus in the soil at any one time is relatively small, especially when compared to that of calcium, magnesium, and potassium. For the availability of soil phosphorus, see Figure 17:2 on page 480.*

plants. This becomes an important factor especially in soils which have been heavily phosphated for years.

In summary, maintaining sufficient available phosphorus in a soil largely narrows down to a twofold program: (1) the addition of phosphorus-containing fertilizers; and (2) the regulation in some degree of the fixation in the soil of both the added and the native phosphates.

17:15. POTASSIUM—THE THIRD "FERTILIZER" ELEMENT

The history of fertilizer usage in the United States shows that nitrogen and phosphorus received most of the attention when commercial fertilizers first appeared on the market. Although the role played by potassium in plant nutrition has long been known, the importance of potash fertilization has received full recognition only in comparatively recent years.

The reasons that a widespread deficiency of this element did not develop until recently are at least twofold. First, the supply of available potassium originally was so high in most soils that it took many years of cropping for a serious depletion to appear. Second, even though the potassium in certain soils may have been insufficient for optimum crop yields, production was much more drastically limited by a lack of nitrogen and phosphorus. With an increased usage of fertilizers carrying these latter elements, crop yields have been correspondingly increased. As a consequence, the draft on soil potassium has been greatly augmented. This, coupled with considerable loss by leaching, has enhanced the demand for potassium to the point that its usage in commercial fertilizers now exceeds that of nitrogen and rivals that of phosphorus.

17:16. EFFECTS ON PLANT GROWTH[10]

The presence of adequate available potassium in the soil has much to do with the general tone and vigor of the plants grown. Moreover, by increasing crop resistance to certain diseases and by encouraging strong root systems, potassium tends to prevent the undersirable "lodging" of plants and to counteract the ill effects of too much nitrogen. In delaying maturity, potassium works against undue ripening influences of phosphorus. In a general way, it exerts a balancing effect on both nitrogen and phosphorus, and consequently is especially important in a mixed fertilizer.

Potassium is essential for starch formation and the translocation of sugars. It is necessary in the development of chlorophyll, although it does not, like magnesium, enter prominently into its molecular structure. This element is important to cereals in grain formation, giving plump

---

[10] Sodium has been found to partially take the place of potassium in the nutrition of certain plants. When there is a deficiency of potash, the native sodium of the soil, or that added in such fertilizers as nitrate of soda, may be very useful.

heavy kernels. Abundant available potassium also is absolutely necessary for tuber development. Consequently, the percentage of this element usually is comparatively high in mixed fertilizers recommended for potatoes. In fact, all root crops respond to liberal applications of potassium. As with phosphorus, it may be present in large quantities in the soil and yet exert no harmful effect on the crop.

The leaves of crops suffering from a potassium deficiency[11] appear dry and scorched at the edges, and the surfaces are irregularly chlorotic. In such plants as red and alsike clover, alfalfa, and sweet clover, these symptoms are preceded by the appearance of small dots arranged more or less regularly around the edges of the leaves. As a result of such deterioration photosynthesis is much impaired, and the synthesis of starch is practically brought to a standstill.

17:17. THE POTASSIUM PROBLEM

AVAILABILITY OF POTASSIUM. In contrast to the situation as regards phosphorus, most mineral soils, except those of a sandy nature, are comparatively high in *total* potassium. In fact, the total quantity of this element is generally greater than that of any other major nutrient element. Amounts as great as 40,000 to 60,000 pounds of K_2O per acre furrow-slice are not at all uncommon. (See p. 24.) Yet the quantity of potassium held in an easily exchangeable condition at any one time often is very small. Most of this element is held rigidly as part of the primary minerals or is fixed in forms that are at best only moderately available to plants. Also competition by microorganisms for this element contributes at least temporarily to its unavailability to higher plants. Thus, the situation in respect to potassium utilization parallels that of phosphorus and nitrogen in at least one respect. A very large proportion of all three of these elements in the soil is insoluble and relatively unavailable to growing plants.

LEACHING LOSSES. Unlike the situation in respect to nitrogen and particularly phosphorus, however, much potassium is lost by leaching. An examination of the drainage water from mineral soils on which rather liberal fertilizer applications have been made will usually show considerable quantities of potash. In extreme cases, the magnitude of this loss may approach that of potash removal by the crop. For example, heavily fertilized sandy soils on which crops such as vegetables or tobacco are grown may suffer serious losses by leaching. Even on a

---

[11] For the deficiency symptoms of potassium, see *Hunger Signs in Crops*, Third Edition, David McKay Co. Inc., N.Y., N.Y., 1964; and *If They Could Speak*, Chilean Nitrate Educational Bureau, New York, 1941.

representative humid region soil receiving only moderate rates of fertilizer, the annual loss of potash by leaching is usually about 20 pounds per acre. (See Table 9:5.)

CROP REMOVAL. The third phase of the potassium problem concerns the concentration of this element in plants, or in other words, its removal by growing crops. Under ordinary field conditions and with an adequate nutrient supply, potassium removal by crops is high, often being 3 to 4 times that of phosphorus and equaling that of nitrogen. The removal of 100 to 125 pounds K_2O per acre by a 20-ton silage corn crop is not at all unusual. Moreover, this situation is made even more critical by the fact that plants tend to take up soluble potassium far in excess of their needs if sufficiently large quantities are present. This tendency is termed *luxury consumption,* because the excess potassium absorbed apparently does not increase crop yields to any extent.

EXAMPLES OF LUXURY CONSUMPTION. The principles involved in luxury consumption are shown by the graph of Fig. 17:8. For many crops there is a more or less direct relationship between the available potassium in the soil and the removal of this element by

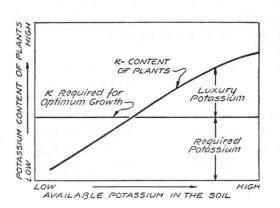

Figure 17:8. A schematic diagram showing the general relationship between the potassium content of plants and the available soil potassium. If excess quantities of potash fertilizers are applied to a soil, the plants will absorb potassium in excess of that required for optimum yields. This luxury consumption may be wasteful, especially if the crops are completely removed from the soil.

plants. The available potassium would, of course, include both that added and that already present. A certain amount of this element is needed for optimum yields and this is termed *required potassium.* All potassium above this critical level is considered a *luxury,* the removal of which is decidedly wasteful.

Under field conditions, luxury consumption becomes particularly serious. For example, to save labor a person may be tempted to supply potassium (1) only once in a 3- or 4-year rotation, or (2) during the first year of a 3- or 4-year perennial hay crop. Much of the potassium thus added is likely to be absorbed wastefully by the first crop of the rotation sequence, or in the case of the hay, even in the first cutting. Consequently, little of the added potassium would remain for subsequent crops.

In summary then the problem of potassium economy in its most general terms is at least threefold: (1) a very large proportion of this element at a given time is relatively unavailable to higher plants; (2) due to the solubility of its available forms, it is subject to wasteful leaching losses; and (3) the removal of potassium by crop plants is high, especially when luxury quantities of this element are supplied. With these ideas as a background let us now consider the various forms of potassium in soils and their availabilities.

17:18. FORMS AND AVAILABILITY OF POTASSIUM IN SOILS

For convenience, the various forms of potassium in soils can be classified on the basis of availability in three general groups: (1) *unavailable;* (2) *readily available;* and (3) *slowly available.* Although most of the soil potassium is in the first of these three forms, from an immediate practical standpoint the latter two are undoubtedly of greater significance.

The relationship among these three general categories is shown diagrammatically in Fig. 17:9. Equilibrium tendencies presented therein are of vital practical importance, especially when we are dealing with the slowly and readily available forms. A slow change from one form to another can and does occur. This makes possible a fixation and conservation of added soluble potassium and a subsequent slow release of this element when the readily available supply is reduced.

RELATIVELY UNAVAILABLE FORMS. By far the greatest part (perhaps 90 to 98 per cent) of all soil potassium in a mineral soil is in relatively unavailable forms. (See Fig. 17:9.) The compounds containing most of this form of potassium are the feldspars and the micas. These minerals are quite resistant to weathering and probably supply relatively insignificant quantities of potassium during a given growing season. However, their accumulative contribution from year to year to the over-all available potassium in the soil undoubtedly is of considerable importance. Potassium is gradually released to more available forms through the action of solvents such as carbonated water. Also, the presence of acid clay is of some significance in the breakdown of these primary minerals with the subsequent release of potassium and other bases. (See p. 31.)

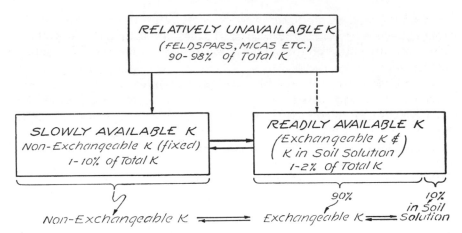

Figure 17:9. Diagram showing the relative proportions of the total soil potassium in unavailable, slowly available, and readily available forms respectively. Only 1 to 2 per cent is rated as readily available. Of this, approximately 90 per cent is exchangeable and only 10 per cent appears in the soil solution at any time.

Even higher values (11 to 18 per cent) have been obtained for so-called non-exchangeable colloid potassium. See L. K. Wood, and E. E. DeTurk, "The Absorption of Potassium in Soils in Nonreplaceable Forms," Proc. Soil Sci. Soc. Amer., 5:152–61, 1940.

The figures quoted are modified from O. J. Attoe and E. Truog, "Exchangeable and Acid Soluble Potassium as Regards Availability and Reciprocal Relationships," Proc. Soil Sci. Soc. Amer., 10:81–6, 1945.

READILY AVAILABLE FORMS. The readily available potassium constitutes only about 1 or 2 per cent of the total amount of this element in an average mineral soil. It exists in soils in two forms: (1) potassium in the soil solution, and (2) exchangeable potassium adsorbed on the soil colloidal surfaces. Although most of this available potassium is in the exchangeable form (approximately 90 per cent), soil solution potassium is somewhat more readily absorbed by higher plants and is, of course, subject to considerable leaching loss.

As represented in Fig. 17:9, these two forms of readily available potassium are in dynamic equilibrium. Such a situation is extremely important from a practical standpoint. To begin with, absorption of soil solution potassium by plants results in a temporary disruption of the equilibrium. Then to restore the balance, some of the exchangeable potassium immediately moves into the soil solution until the equilibrium is again established. On the other hand, when water-soluble fertilizers are added just the reverse of the above adjustment occurs.

It is not to be inferred from this, however, that it is necessary for an element to be in the soil solution before absorption by plants can take place. Direct absorption from the colloidal surfaces is also thought to occur and undoubtedly this plays a vital role in the nutrition of many plants.

SLOWLY AVAILABLE FORMS. In the presence of vermiculite, illite, and other 2:1 type minerals, the potassium of such fertilizers as muriate of potash not only become adsorbed as described above but also may become definitely "fixed" by the soil colloids. The potassium as well as ammonium ions (see p. 499) fit in between crystal units of these normally expanding clays and become an integral part of the crystal. Potassium in this form cannot be replaced by ordinary exchange methods and consequently is referred to as *nonexchangeable* potassium. As such, this element is not readily available to higher plants. This form is in equilibrium, however, with the available forms and consequently acts as an extremely important reservoir of slowly available potassium. The entire equilibrium may represented as follows. (See Fig. 17:9.)

$$\text{Nonexchangeable K} \rightleftharpoons \text{Exchangeable K} \rightleftharpoons \text{Soil solution K}$$

The importance of the adjustment shown above to practical agriculture should not be overlooked. It is of special value in the conservation of added potassium. For example, most potash-containing fertilizers are added at planting time and are usually applied in localized bands. Immediately upon dissolving, a large proportion of the soluble (soil solution) potassium becomes attached to the colloids. As a result, the above equilibria shift to the left and some exchangeable ions are converted to the nonexchangeable form. Although this renders more potassium at least temporarily unavailable, the over-all effect apparently is beneficial. In this form the potassium is not subject to leaching, and thus a significant conservation is attained. Also, since the fixed potassium is slowly reconverted to the available forms later, it is by no means completely lost to growing plants.

RELEASE OF FIXED POTASSIUM. The above reaction is perhaps of even greater practical importance in another way. The quantity of nonexchangeable or "fixed" potassium in some soils is quite large. (See legend of Fig. 17:9.) The fixed potassium in such soils is continually released to the exchangeable form in amounts large enough to be of great practical importance. For example, Bray and DeTurk[12] found a release of as much as 288 pounds of potassium per acre from an

[12] R. H. Bray, and E. E. DeTurk, "Release of Potassium from Nonreplaceable Forms in Illinois Soils," *Proc. Soil Sci. Soc. Amer.*, 3:101–06, 1939.

Table 17:6. Potassium Removal by Very Intensive Cropping and the Amount of This Element Coming from the Nonexchangeable Form

Soil	Total K Used by Crops (Lbs/A)	Percentage of the K Coming from Nonexchangeable Form
Wisconsin soils:[a]		
Carrington silt loam	119	75
Spencer silt loam	59	80
Plainfield sand	88	25
Mississippi soils:[b]		
Robinsonville f.s.l.	108	33
Houston clay	57	47
Ruston sandy loam	42	24

[a] Average of six consecutive cuttings of Ladino clover, from C. E. Evans and O. J. Attoe, "Potassium Supplying Power of Virgin and Cropped Soils," *Soil Sci.*, 66: 323–34, 1948.

[b] Average of eight consecutive crops of millet, from L. E. Gholston and C. D. Hoover, "The Release of Exchangeable and Nonexchangeable Potassium from Several Mississippi and Alabama Soils upon Continuous Cropping," *Proc. Soil Sci. Amer.*, 13: 116–21, 1948.

Illinois soil in a 6-month period. Other similar results have been observed. The data in Table 17:6 give an idea of the magnitude of the release of nonexchangeable potassium from certain soils. In several cases cited, the potassium removed by crops was supplied largely from nonexchangeable forms.

17:19. FACTORS AFFECTING POTASSIUM FIXATION IN SOILS

Although the exact mechanism or mechanisms that govern potassium fixation and release are not clearly understood, it is definitely known that several soil conditions markedly influence the amounts fixed. Among the factors are: (1) the nature of the soil colloids; (2) wetting and drying; (3) freezing and thawing; and (4) the presence of excess lime. These will be considered briefly in turn.

THE EFFECTS OF COLLOIDS, MOISTURE, AND TEMPERATURE. The ability of the various soil colloids to fix potassium varies widely. For example 1:1 type clays such as kaolinite and soils in which these clay minerals are dominant fix little potassium. On the other hand, clays of the 2:1 type such as vermiculite and illite fix potassium very readily and in large amounts.

The mechanisms for potassium fixation is probably the same as that for fixation of the ammonium ion (p. 443). These two ions are of such size as to fit snugly into the cavities which exist between the respective silica sheets of adjoining crystal units in 2:1 type clays. (See Fig. 17:10.) Because of this, these ions become trapped as a part of the rigid crystal structure, thereby preventing normal crystal lattice expansion, and reducing the cation-exchange capacity of the clay.

The potassium and ammonium ions are attracted between the crystal units by the same negative charges responsible for the internal adsorption of these and other cations. The tendency for fixation is greatest in minerals where the major source of negative charge is in the silica

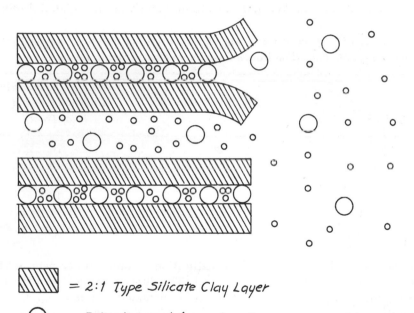

$\diagdown\diagdown$ = 2:1 Type Silicate Clay Layer

◯ = Potassium and Ammonium Ions

○ = Other Smaller Cations H^+, Na^+, Ca^{++} etc.

Figure 17:10. Clay minerals of the 2:1 type such as illite have the ability to fix ammonium and potassium ions. Smaller ions such as H^+, Na^+, and Ca^{++} can move in and out of the internal adsorption surface and are thus exchangeable. Potassium and ammonium ions are of such size as to fit snugly between crystals, thereby holding them together. At the same time, these larger ions are rendered at least temporarily non-exchangeable or fixed.

(tetrahedral) sheet. For that reason vermiculite and illite have fixing capacities which far exceed that of montmorillonite. (See Table 4:4, p. 88, for formulas for these minerals.)

Alternate freezing and thawing has been shown to result in the release of fixed potassium under certain conditions. Although the practical importance of this is recognized, the mechanism by means of which it occurs is not as yet understood.

INFLUENCE OF LIME. Applications of lime sometimes result in an increase in potassium fixation of soils. Under normal liming conditions this may be more beneficial than detrimental due to the conservation of the potassium so affected. Thus, potassium in well limed soils is not as likely to be leached out as drastically as is that in acid soils. This is illustrated by data in Table 17:7.

The sandy soil studied was limed to increase the base saturation from 28 to 72 per cent. When 6.2 inches of water were percolated through

Table 17:7. The Effect of Percentage Base Saturation on the Leaching Losses of Exchangeable Potassium from a Creedmore Coarse Sandy Loam[a]

Soil pH	Base Saturation (%)	Exchangeable Potassium Loss by Leaching (% of Total)
4.83	28	70
5.30	40	49
5.63	50	26
7.03	72	16

[a] From L. D. Baver, "Practical Applications of Potassium Interrelationships in Soils and Plants," *Soil Sci.*, 55: 121–26, 1943.

the original soil (28 per cent base saturation), about 70 per cent of the exchangeable potassium was removed. The limed sample (72 per cent base saturation) when similarly treated sustained a potassium loss of only 16 per cent. The effect of lime in preventing potash loss undoubtedly is of considerable practical importance in many cases.

There are conditions, however, under which the effects of lime on the availability of potash are so drastic as to become quite undesirable.[13] For example, in certain soils potassium deficiency is apparently due to the presence of excess calcium carbonate. The unavailability of potassium in such soils is thought to be due in some way to lime-induced fixation.

[13] See H. Allaway and W. H. Pierre, "Availability, Fixation and Liberation of Potassium in High-lime Soils," *Jour. Amer. Soc. Agron.*, 31:940–53, 1939.

17:20. PRACTICAL IMPLICATIONS IN RESPECT TO POTASSIUM

FREQUENCY OF APPLICATION. One very important suggestion that is evident from the facts thus far considered is that frequent light applications of potassium are usually superior to heavier and less frequent ones. Such a conclusion is reasonable when we consider the luxury consumption by crops, the ease with which this element is lost by leaching, and the fact that excess potassium is subject to fixation. Although the latter phenomenon has definite conserving features, these are in most cases entirely outweighed by the disadvantages of leaching and luxury consumption.

THE K SUPPLYING POWER OF SOILS. A second very important suggestion is that full advantage should be taken of the potash-supplying power of soils. The idea that each pound of potassium removed by plants or through leaching must be returned in fertilizers may not always be correct. In some soils the large quantities of moderately available forms already present can be utilized. Where slowly available forms are not found in significant quantities, however, supplementary additions are frequently necessary. Moreover, the importance of lime in reducing leaching losses of potassium should not be overlooked as a means of effectively utilizing the power of soils to furnish this element.

POTASSIUM LOSSES AND GAINS. The problem of maintaining soil potassium is outlined diagramatically in Fig. 17:11. Crop removal of potash generally exceeds that of the other essential elements with the possible exception of nitrogen. Annual losses from plant removal as great as 100 pounds K per acre are not uncommon, particularly if the crop is a legume and is cut several times for hay. As you might expect, therefore, the return crop residues and manures is very important in maintaining soil potash. As an example, ten tons of average barnyard manure supply about 100 pounds of K_2O, fully equal to the amount of nitrogen thus supplied.

The annual losses of available potassium by leaching and erosion greatly exceed those of nitrogen and phosphorus. They are generally not as great, however, as the corresponding losses of available calcium and magnesium. The available potassium depletion by erosion assumes considerable importance when we consider that total potassium removal in this manner generally exceeds that of any other major nutrient element. The loss of potential sources of available potassium (soil minerals) cannot but eventually be serious.

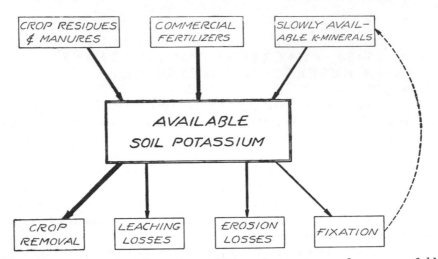

Figure 17:11. Gains and losses in available *soil potassium under average field conditions. The approximate magnitude of the changes is represented by the width of the arrows. For any specific case the actual amounts of potassium added or lost undoubtedly may vary considerably from the above representation.*

As was the case with nitrogen and phosphorus, it is well to note the increasing importance of commercial fertilizers in meeting crop demands. Also, it should be pointed out that the fixation and release by potash-bearing minerals will be much greater if soils contain appreciable quantities of minerals such as illite, a clay that is especially high in total and exchangeable potash. For the various forms of potassium in soils and their relative magnitude and relationships, see Figure 17:9 on page 496.

INCREASING USE OF POTASH FERTILIZERS.   In the past, potash in fertilizers was added to supplement that returned in crop residues and that obtained from the slowly available forms of potassium carried by soil minerals. Fertilizer potash is now depended upon to supply much of that needed for crop production. This is especially true in cash crop areas and in regions where sandy soils are prominent. Even in some heavier soils, the release of potassium from mineral form is much too slow to support maximum plant yields. Consequently, increased usage of commercial potash must be expected if yields are to be increased or even maintained.

In this chapter and the one preceding, the factors affecting the supplies of nitrogen, phosphorus, and potassium available to growing plants have been considered. We have dealt mostly with those reactions taking place within the soil which determine in part the amounts of these elements that plants have at their disposal. We are now ready to discuss means of supplementing the natural supply of these elements. This will be done in Chapter 19 which considers commercial fertilizers, our main outside source of these and other nutrient constituents.

Chapter 18

The Micronutrient Elements

Of the seventeen elements known to be essential for plant and microorganism growth, seven are required in such small quantities that they are called *micronutrients* or trace elements. These are iron, manganese, zinc, copper, boron, molybdenum, cobalt, and chlorine. Other elements such as silicon, vanadium, and sodium appear to be helpful for the growth of certain species. Still others such as iodine, and fluorrine have been shown to be essential for animal growth, but are apparently not required by plants. As better techniques of experimentation are developed and as purer salts are made available, it is likely that these or other elements may be added to the list of essential nutrients.

Micronutrients have become of more widespread concern during the past fifteen years than was the case earlier. (See Table 18:1.) The following have likely attributed to this situation: (1) crop removal of the trace elements has in some cases lowered their concentration in the soil below that required for normal growth; (2) improved crop varieties and macronutrient fertilizer practices have greatly increased the level of crop production and thereby the micronutrient removal; (3) the trend toward high analysis fertilizers has tended to eliminate the use of impure salts which formerly contained some micronutrients; and (4) man's increased knowledge of plant nutrition has helped in the diagnosis of trace element deficiencies which heretofore may have gone unnoticed. Demands for efficiency of crop production will undoubtedly continue to encourage attention to these elements.

18:1. DEFICIENCY VS. TOXICITY

One common characteristic of all the micronutrients is that they are required in very small amounts. (Fig. 18:1.) Also, they are all harm-

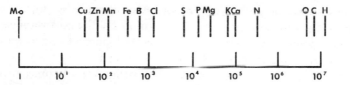

Figure 18:1. The relative number of atoms of the essential elements in alfalfa at bloom stage expressed logarithmically. Note that there are more than 10 million hydrogen atoms for each molybdenum atom. Even so, normal plant growth would not occur without molybdenum. Cobalt is generally present in even smaller quantities in plants than is molybdenum. (Modified from F. G. Viets, Jr., "The plants' need for and use of nitrogen." A chapter in Soil Nitrogen (Agronomy Vol. 10) Amer. Soc. of Agronomy, Madison, Wis. 1965.)

ful when the available forms are present in the soil in large quantities. Thus the range of concentration of these elements in which plants will grow satisfactorily is not too great. Molybdenum, for example, may be beneficial if added at rates as little as ½ to 1 *ounce* per acre, and applications of 3 or 4 pounds of available molybdenum per acre may be toxic to most plants. Even those quantities present under natural soil conditions are in some cases excessive for normal crop growth. Although somewhat larger amounts of the other micronutrients are required and can be tolerated by plants, control of the quantities added, especially in maintaining nutrient balance, is absolutely essential.

18:2. ROLE OF THE MICRONUTRIENTS[1]

As might be expected, the specific role of the various micronutrients in plant and microbial growth processes is not well understood. The meager information available, however, suggests that several trace elements are effective through certain *enzyme systems*. For example, copper, iron, and molybdenum are capable of acting as "electron carriers" in enzyme systems which bring about oxidation-reduction reactions in plants. Apparently such reactions, essential to plant development and reproduction, will not take place in the absence of these micronutrients. Zinc and manganese also function in enzyme systems which are necessary for important reactions in plant metabolism.

Molybdenum and manganese have been found to be essential for certain nitrogen transformations in microorganisms as well as in plants. Molybdenum is thought to be essential for the process of nitrogen fixation, both symbiotic and nonsymbiotic. Also, it must be present in plants if nitrates are to be metabolized into amino acids and proteins. In each case molybdenum apparently is an essential part of the respective enzyme system which facilitates the nitrogen change.

Zinc is thought to be concerned in the formation of some growth hormones and in the reproduction process of certain plants. Copper is involved in respiration and in the utilization of iron. A boron deficiency decreases the rate of water absorption and of translocation of sugars in plants—and iron is essential for chlorophyll formation and for the synthesis of proteins contained in the chloroplasts. It is obvious that the place of the trace elements in plant metabolism is a complicated one. As research uncovers new facts, the role of these micronutrients will be more fully understood and undoubtedly more adequately appreciated.

Chlorine and cobalt are the elements whose essentiality has been determined most recently. The role of chlorine is still somewhat obscure. However, both root and top growth seem to suffer if this element is absent.

Cobalt is essential for the symbiotic fixation of nitrogen (see Fig. 18:2). This element is a component of Vitamin B_{12} which is thought to be essential for the formation of a form of hemoglobin in N-fixing nodule tissue. Legumes and other plants are thought by some to

[1] See A. Nason, "The Functions of Metals in Enzyme Systems," *Soil Sci.*, 85:63–78:1958 and H. G. Gauch, "Mineral Nutrition of Plants," *Ann. Rev. of Pl. Phys.*, 8:31–64, 1957.

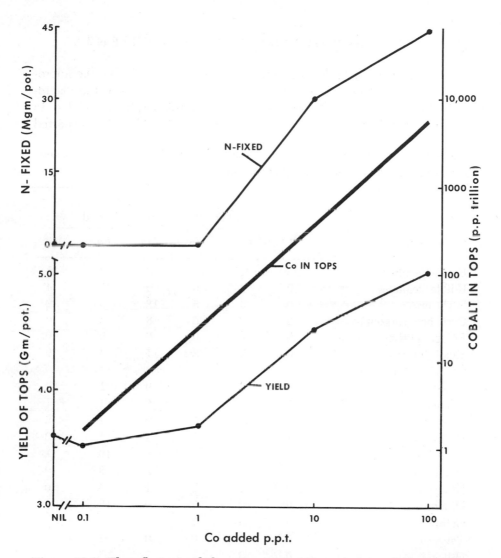

Figure 18:2. The effect of cobalt concentration in a nutrient solution (parts per thousand) on nitrogen fixation and on the yield and cobalt content of the tops of nodulated alfalfa plants. (Redrawn from D. O. Wilson and H. M. Reisenauer, "Cobalt requirement of symbiotically grown alfalfa." Plant and Soil *19:364–373, 1963.*)

have a cobalt requirement independent of N-fixation, although the amount required is small compared to that for the N-fixation process.

18:3. SOURCE OF MICRONUTRIENTS[2]

Parent materials tend to influence, in a practical way, the micronutrient contents of soils, perhaps even more so than that of the macronutrients. Deficiencies of trace elements can frequently be related to
low contents of the micronutrients in the parent rocks or transported

Table 18:1. *The number of states reporting field deficiencies of six micronu-*
trients in important crops of the United States[a]

Crop Group	B	Number of States in Which Deficiency Reported				
		Cu.	Zn	Mn	Fe	Mo
Forage legumes	36	1	1	2	2	15
Edible legumes	0	2	9	9	5	4
Soybeans	0	0	5	12	5	9
Corn and sorghum	3	5	26	8	8	0
Forage grasses	0	4	0	0	9	0
Small grains	0	4	3	11	4	0
Crucifers and various leafy vegetables	26	7	2	9	1	9
Solanaceous crops	6	3	1	6	1	1
Root and bulb crops	18	6	6	9	1	2
Cucurbits	1	0	0	4	1	2
Tree fruits	22	3	17	8	16	1
Small fruits	3	0	1	2	8	0
Nut crops	2	1	12	1	4	0
Ornamentals	0	0	2	0	18	1
Cotton	6	0	1	1	0	0
Tobacco	2	0	0	0	1	0
Other	0	3	4	1	5	0

[a] Data tabulated from two surveys reported as follows: "A survey of micronutrient deficiencies in the USA and means of correcting them" by the Soil Test Committee of the Soil Science Society of America, March 1965; and K. C. Berger
"Micronutrient deficiencies in the United States," *Jour. of Agricultural & Food Chemis-*
try 10: 178–181, 1962.

[2] For a recent review of this and other subjects relating to micronutrients see
J. F. Hodgson, "Chemistry of the Micronutrient Elements in Soils," *Advan. in Agron.,*
15:119–160, 1963.

parent material. Similarly, toxic quantities are commonly related to abnormally large amounts in the soil-forming rocks and minerals.

INORGANIC FORMS. As might be expected, the scant data available indicate that sources of the seven micronutrients vary markedly from area to area. Also, because of the extremely small quantities of some of these elements present in soils and in rocks, little is known about the specific compounds in which they are found. Except for iron and manganese, which are present in many soils in large total quantities, widespread accurate analyses for micronutrients in soils and rocks have not been made. (See Table 18:2.) For these reasons only generalizations can be drawn concerning micronutrient sources.

All of the micronutrients have been found in varying quantities in igneous rocks. Two of them, iron and manganese, have prominent struc-

Table 18:2. Major Natural Sources of the Seven Micronutrients and their Suggested Contents in a Representative Humid-region Surface Soil[a]

Element	Major Forms in Nature	Suggested Analysis of a Surface Soil[b] (p.p.m.)
1. Iron	oxides, sulfides, and silicates	25,000
2. Manganese	oxides, silicates, and sulfides	2,500
3. Zinc	sulfides, oxides, and silicates	100
4. Copper	sulfides, hydroxy-carbonates	50
5. Boron	boro-silicates, borates	50
6. Molybdenum	sulfides, molybdates	2
7. Chlorine	chlorides	50
8. Cobalt	silicates	8

[a] For a comprehensive discussion of the geochemistry of these and other elements see V. M. Goldschmidt, *Geochemistry* (London: Clarendon Press, 1954).

[b] Analysis of a given soil would likely give values severalfold higher or lower than those listed. Consequently these more or less average figures should be used with caution.

tural positions in certain of the original silicate minerals. Others such as cobalt and zinc may also occupy structural positions as minor replacements for the major constituents of silicate minerals including clays.

As mineral decomposition and soil formation occur, the mineral forms of the micronutrients are changed, just as was the case for macronutrients. Oxides, and, in some cases, sulfides of elements such as Fe, Mn, and Zn are formed. (See Table 18:2.) Secondary silicates, including the clay minerals, may contain considerable quantities of iron and manganese and smaller quantities of zinc and cobalt. The micronutrient cations that are released as weathering occurs are subject to colloidal adsorption just as are the Ca or H ions. Anions such as the borate and molybdate may suffer adsorption or reaction in soils similar to that of the phosphates. Chlorine, which is by far the most soluble of the group, is added to soils in considerable quantities each year through rain water. Its incidental addition in fertilizers and in other ways helps prevent the deficiency of chlorine under field conditions.

ORGANIC FORMS. Organic matter is an important secondary source of some of the trace elements. They seem to be held as complex combinations by the organic colloids. Copper is especially tightly held. In uncultivated profiles there is a somewhat greater concentration of micronutrients in the surface soil, much of it presumably in the organic fraction. Correlations between soil organic matter and Cu, Mo, and Zn have been noted. Although the elements thus held are not always readily available to plants, their release through decomposition is undoubtedly an important fertility factor.

18:4. GENERAL CONDITIONS CONDUCIVE TO MICRONUTRIENT DEFICIENCY[3]

Micronutrients are most apt to limit crop growth under the following conditions: (1) highly leached acid sandy soils; (2) muck soils; (3) soils very high in pH; and (4) soils which have been very intensively cropped and heavily fertilized with macronutrients only.

Strongly leached acid sandy soils are low in micronutrients for the same reasons that they are deficient in most of the macronutrients: (1) their parent materials were originally deficient in the elements; and (2) acid leaching has removed much of the small quantity of micronutrients originally present. In the case of molybdenum, acid soil conditions also have a marked depressing effect on availability.

The micronutrient contents of organic soils are dependent upon the extent of the washing or leaching of these elements into the bog area as the deposits formed. In most cases, this rate of movement was too slow to give deposits which are as high in micronutrients as are the surround-

---

[3] See A. A. Nikitin, "Technological Aspects of Trace Element Usage," *Adv. in Agron.*, 6:182–97, 1954.

ing mineral soils. Intensive cropping of muck soils and their ability to fix certain elements, notably copper, also accentuates trace element deficiencies. Much of the harvested crops, especially vegetables, are removed from the land. Eventually the micro- as well as macronutrients must be supplied in the form of fertilizers if good crop yields are to be maintained. Intensive cropping of heavily fertilized mineral soils can also hasten the onset of micronutrient shortage, especially if the soils are coarse in texture.

The soil pH and calcium content have a marked influence on the availability of all the micronutrients except chlorine. Under very acid conditions, molybdenum is rendered unavailable; at high pH values all the cations are unfavorably affected. Overliming or a naturally high pH is associated with deficiencies of iron, manganese, zinc, copper, and even boron. Such conditions occur in nature in many of the calcareous soils of the west.

18:5. FACTORS INFLUENCING THE AVAILABILITY OF THE MICRONUTRIENT CATIONS

Each of the five micronutrient cations (Fe, Mn, Zn, Cu, and Co) are influenced in a characteristic way by their soil environment. However, certain soil factors tend to have the same general effects on the availability of all of them. These factors will be given consideration first.

SOIL pH. The micronutrient cations are most soluble and available under acid conditions. In very acid soils there is a relative abundance of the ions of Fe, Mn, Zn, and Cu. In fact, under these conditions the concentrations of one or more of these elements is often sufficiently high to be toxic to common plants. As pointed out in Chapter 15 (p. 426), one of the primary reasons for liming acid soils is to reduce the concentration of these ions.

As the pH is increased, the ionic forms of the micronutrient cations are changed to the hydroxides or oxides. An example might be shown as follows, using the ferrous ion as typical of the group:

$$Fe^{++} + 2OH^- \longrightarrow Fe(OH)_2$$
(Soluble)   (Insoluble)

All of the hydroxides of the trace element cations are insoluble, some more so than others. The exact pH at which precipitation occurs varies from element to element and even between oxidation states of a given element. For example, the higher valent states of iron and manganese form hydroxides which are much more insoluble than their lower valent counterparts. In any case, however, the principle is the same—at low pH values the solubility of micronutrient cations is at a maximum and as the pH is raised, their solubility and availability to plants decrease. The desirability of maintaining an intermediate soil pH is obvious.

Zinc fixation at high pH values is favored by a second phenomenon only indirectly related to soil pH. Particles of lime, particularly if they contain dolomite as well as calcite, strongly adsorb the zinc ions. It is likely that zinc may react with the magnesium-containing lime, replacing the Mg ion in the mineral framework.

OXIDATION STATE AND pH. Three of the trace element cations are found in soils in more than one valence state. These are iron, manganese, and copper. The lower valence states are encouraged by conditions of low oxygen supply and relatively higher moisture level. They are responsible for the subdued subsoil colors, grays and blues, in contrast to the bright reds, browns, and yellows of well-drained mineral soils.

The changes from one valent state to another are in most cases brought about by microorganisms and organic matter. In some cases the organisms may obtain their energy directly from the inorganic reaction. For example, the oxidation of manganese from the two valent manganous form (Mn^{++}) to MnO_2 can be carried on by certain bacteria and fungi. (See Fig. 18:3.) In other cases, organic compounds formed by the microbes may be responsible for the oxidation or reduc-

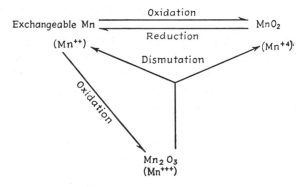

Figure 18:3. The relationship among the various forms of manganese in soils. Exchangeable Mn^{++} is available to plants but is subject to oxidation by microorganisms to the trivalent form (Mn_2O_3) or to the more insoluble 4 valent form (MnO_2). The Mn_2O_3 can be changed (dismutation) into Mn^{++} and MnO_2. High pH and good oxidation conditions encourage formation of MnO_2 and low manganese availability. (Modified from H. G. Dion, and P.J. G. Mann, Jour. Agr. Sci, 36:239–45, 1946.)

tion. In general, high pH values favor oxidation, whereas acid conditions are more conducive to reduction.

The oxidized states of Fe, Mn, and Cu are generally much less soluble at pH values common in soils than are the reduced states. The hydroxides (or hydrous oxides) of these high-valent forms precipitate at lower pH values and are extremely insoluble. For example, the hydroxide of trivalent ferric iron precipitates at pH values near 3.0, whereas ferrous hydroxide does not precipitate until a pH of 6.0 or higher is reached.

The interaction of soil acidity and aeration in determining micronutrient availability is of great practical importance. The micronutrient cations and molybdenum tend to be somewhat more available under conditions of restricted drainage. Flooded soils generally show higher availabilities than will aerated soils. Very acid soils that are somewhat poorly drained often supply toxic quantities of iron and manganese. Such toxicity is less apt to occur under well-drained conditions. At the high end of the soil pH range, good drainage and aeration often have the opposite effect. Well-oxidized, calcareous soils are sometimes deficient in available iron, zinc, or manganese even though there are adequate total quantities of these trace elements present. The hydroxides of the high-valent forms of these elements are too insoluble to supply the ions needed for plant growth. (See Fig. 18:3.)

OTHER INORGANIC REACTIONS. The application of large quantities of phosphate fertilizers can adversely affect the supply of some of the micronutrients. The uptake of both iron and zinc may be reduced in the presence of excess phosphates. From a practical standpoint, phosphate fertilizers should be used in only those quantities that are required for good plant growth.

Lime-induced chlorosis (iron deficiency) in fruit trees has been found to be encouraged by the presence of the bicarbonate ion. The chlorosis apparently results from iron deficiency on soils with high pH. In some way the bicarbonate ion interferes with iron metabolism.

Zinc, manganese, cobalt, and iron ions are found as integral elements in certain silicate clays, especially of the 2 to 1 type. Depending on conditions, these ions may be released from the clays or they may be fixed by them. Since the total quantities of iron and manganese in a soil are sufficiently large, the fixation of these elements by clays is apparently of little significance. Zinc and cobalt fixation is somewhat more serious, however, since the total amounts of these elements in soils are usually quite small. (See Table 18.2.)

ORGANIC COMBINATIONS. Each of the four micronutrient cations may be held in organic combination. Microorganisms also assimilate them as they are apparently required for many microbial transformations. The organic compounds in which these trace elements are combined undoubtedly vary considerably, but they include proteins, amino acids, and constituents of humus and acids such as citric and tartaric. Among the most important, are the so-called *organic complexes* which are a combination of the metallic cation and certain organic groups. These complexes may protect the micronutrients from certain harmful reactions such as the precipitation of iron by phosphates and vice versa. (See p. 488.) On the other hand, complex formation may reduce micronutrient availability below that necessary for normal plant needs.

On soils high in organic matter, complex formation by copper is thought to be responsible for the deficiency of this element. For example, copper appears to be bound very tightly by the organic matter in certain muck soils. Regular applications of copper-containing salts may be necessary for the normal production of vegetables on these high-organic-containing soils. Zinc deficiencies have also been attributed to reaction with organic matter. Advantage has been taken of the complex-forming tendencies of manganese, copper, zinc, and especially iron in the development of synthetic compounds called *chelates*. These compounds can be used to supply selected micronutrients in forms which protect the cations from some harmful inorganic reactions in soils. At the same time, the chelated nutrients can be utilized by growing plants. Chelates will be dealt with in the next section.

18:6. CHELATES[4]

Chelate is a term derived from a Greek word meaning "claw." As this term indicates, the chelates have a marked tendency to hold tightly certain cations that are attracted to them. Furthermore they tend to protect these cations, often to the benefit of growing plants.

A chelate is an organic compound which combines with and protects certain metallic cations including iron, manganese, zinc, and copper. The cation-chelate combinations make complex ring structures and the metals so bound essentially lose their usual ionic characteristics. (See Fig. 18:4.) They are less apt to take part in reactions with other soil constituents, which may be an advantage. For example, chelated metals remain in solution at much higher pH values than do the inorganic ionic forms. The protected cations are not so subject to precipitation as insoluble hydroxides.

[4] See A. Wallace (ed.), A *Decade of Synthetic Chelating Agents in Inorganic Plant Nutrition* (Los Angeles, Calif.: Arthur Wallace, 1962).

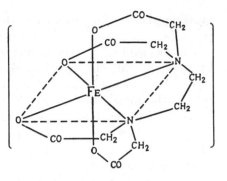

Figure 18:4. The structural formula for a common iron chelate, ferric ethylene-diaminetetraacetic acid (Fe-EDTA). The iron is protected and yet can be utilized by many plants.

In recent years primary attention has been given to synthetic chelates. However, the protection of heavy metal ions by naturally occurring organic complexes has been known for some time. The movement of iron, zinc, cobalt, and other heavy metals in soils is thought to be associated with the formation of organic chelates. For example, the downward movement of organic matter and of iron and aluminum during the process of podzolization is thought to involve chelates. These compounds protect the metal cations from reaction with materials which would otherwise render them insoluble.

Specific examples can be cited which show the protective action of chelating compounds. As pointed out in Section 18:5, inorganic iron salts added to a calcareous soil are precipitated and rendered unavailable for plant growth. If ferric sulfate were added, the reaction would occur as follows, assuming the hydroxyl ions to come from the soil solution:

$$Fe^{+++} + 3OH^- \rightleftarrows Fe(OH)_3$$
$$\text{(Soluble)} \qquad \text{(Insoluble)}$$

As the equilibrium arrows indicate, most of the ferric ion would be changed to the insoluble form.

If, instead of the sulfate salt of iron, an iron chelate were used, the ferric ion would be protected from precipitation. As shown in Fig. 18:4, the iron is part of a complex combination which supplies very few ferric ions. Consequently, there would be little opportunity for the above reaction to take place except where the soil pH is very high. One would expect the chelate to be a better source of iron than an inorganic salt where there is danger of reaction between the metallic cation (Fe^{+++}) and soil constituents.

Although chelated metals are protected against soil reactions, these forms of the micronutrients are apparently assimilated fairly readily by growing plants. Thus, so long as the nutrients remain in these combinations, they are considered as being in the available form.

The mechanism by which micronutrients from chelates are absorbed by plants is still obscure. The chelating agents in most cases are absorbed by growing plants but the rate of their absorption is lower than that of the metals they carry. Thus, it would appear that the primary function of the chelate is to keep the metals available in the soil. At the same time, there is evidence that some of the benefit from the chelating agents is through increased translocation of the metals once they are absorbed by the plants.[5]

STABILITY OF CHELATES.   The use of chelates to supply iron is quite successful so long as the soil pH is not too high. Application can be made to the soil or as a spray to the foliage. With some of the other nutrients, however, less consistent advantage has been shown for the chelates over other nutrient compounds. This may be due to the fact that for most of the chelates, iron is attracted more strongly by the organic compound than are the other micronutrients. Thus, if a zinc-containing chelate is added to a soil which has significant quantities of available iron the following reaction may occur:

$$Zn\ chelate + Fe^{++} \rightleftarrows Fe\ chelate + Zn^{++}$$

The iron chelate is more stable than its zinc counterpart, which explains the tendency of the reaction to go to the right. The released Zn ion is subject to reaction with the soil the same as is zinc from an inorganic salt such as $ZnSO_4$. It is obvious that the added metal-chelate combination must be stable within the soil if it is to have any lasting advantage.

It should not be inferred that only iron chelates are effective. The chelates of other micronutrients including zinc, manganese, and copper have been used successfully to supply these nutrients. Apparently, replacement by iron in the soil is sufficiently slow to permit absorption by plants of the added trace element. Also, since spray and banded applications are often used to supply zinc and manganese, the possibility of reaction of these elements with iron in the soil can be reduced or eliminated.

The use of chelates in the United States is substantial, approximately one million pounds being sold in 1954 for agricultural purposes.[6] More than half of this was used in meeting micronutrient deficiencies of citrus in Florida. Although chelates may not replace the more conventional

---

[5] See Arthur Wallace, "Micronutrient Deficiencies in Plants and Their Correction with Chelates," *Agr. Sci. Review*, 3:18–24, First Quarter 1965.
[6] See Wallace, *op. cit.*

methods of supplying most micronutrients, they do offer some possibilities in special cases. Agricultural and chemical research shall likely continue to increase the opportunities for their use.

The following specific synthetic chelating agents have been found to be effective for the indicated ions:

Fe, Zn, Mn, Cu	EDTA	Ethylenediamine tetraacetic acid
Fe	EDDHA	Ethylenediamedi- (O-hydroxy-phenylacetic acid)
Fe	DTPA	Diethylenetriamine pentaacetic acid
Zn	NTA	Nitrilotriacetic acid
Fe, Zn	HEDTA	Hydroxyethyl ethylenediamine tetraacetic acid

18:7. FACTORS INFLUENCING THE AVAILABILITY OF THE MICRONUTRIENT ANIONS

Unlike the cations needed in trace quantities by plants, the anions seem to have relatively little in common. Chlorine, molybdenum, and boron are quite different chemically so that one would expect little similarity in their reaction in soils.

CHLORINE. Chlorine has only recently been found to be essential for plant growth, in spite of the fact that it is used in larger quantities by most crop plants than any of the micronutrients except iron. Two reasons account for man's failure to recognize the essentiality of this nutrient earlier: (1) the wide occurrence of chlorine as an impurity in salts used for research work; and (2) the annual additions to soil of significant quantities of chlorine through precipitation.

Most of the chlorine in soils is in the form of simple, soluble chloride salts such as KCl. The chloride ions are not adsorbed by negatively charged clays and as a result are subject to movement with the water, both upward and downward in the profile. In humid regions, one would expect little chlorine to remain in the soil since it would be leached out. In semiarid and arid regions, a somewhat higher concentration might be expected, the amount reaching the point of salt toxicity in some of the poorly drained saline soils. In most well-drained areas, however, one would not expect a high chlorine content in the surface of arid-region soils.

Except under conditions where toxic quantities of chlorine are found in soils, there are apparently no common situations under field conditions which reduce the availability and utilization of this element. Accretions of chlorine from the atmosphere are believed to be in sufficient quantities to meet crop needs. Salt spray alongside ocean beaches evaporates, leaving NaCl dust which moves into the atmosphere to be returned later, dissolved in snow and rain. The amount added to the soil in this way varies tremendously, depending on the distance from the salty body of water and other factors. It is likely that a figure of about 10 pounds per acre per year is the minimum that can be expected in most situations. An average figure of perhaps 20 pounds would be more representative of the amount added. In any case, this form of accretion plus that commonly added as an incidental component of commercial fertilizers should largely prevent a field deficiency of chlorine.

BORON. The availability and utilization of boron is determined to a considerable extent by pH. Boron is most soluble under acid conditions. It apparently occurs in acid soils, in part at least, as boric acid (H_3BO_3) which is readily available to plants. In quite acid sandy soils, soluble boron fertilizers may be leached downward with comparative ease. Apparently, the element is not fixed under these conditions. In heavier soils, especially if they are not too acid, this rapid leaching does not occur.

At higher pH values, boron is less available. This may be due to lime-induced fixation of this element by clay and other minerals since the calcium and sodium borates are reasonably soluble. In any case, over-liming can, and often does, result in a deficiency of boron.

Boron is held in organic combinations from which it may be released for crop use. The content of this nutrient in the topsoil is generally higher than that in the subsoil. This may in part account for the noticeably greater boron deficiency in periods of dry weather. Apparently, during drouth periods plant roots are forced to exploit only the lower soil horizons where the boron content is quite low. When the rains come, plant roots again can absorb boron from the topsoil where its concentration is highest.

MOLYBDENUM. Soil conditions affect the availability of molybdenum much the same as they do that of phosphorus. For example, molybdenum is quite unavailable in strongly acid soils. (See Fig. 18:5.) Under these conditions, this element apparently reacts with soil minerals such as the silicates, and iron and aluminum compounds. The fixed molybdate ion (MoO_4^{---}) can be replaced by phosphates through anion exchange, indicating that the same soil compounds may be involved in molybdenum and phosphate fixation.

The liming of acid soils will usually increase the availability of molybdenum. The effect is so striking that some researchers, especially those

Figure 18:5. The effect of pH on the adsorption of molybdenum by an Australian soil. A given quantity of molybdenum was shaken with samples of soil at different pH values and the amount of Mo in solution was determined. (From Jones, L. H. P., "The Solubility of Molybdenum in Simplified Systems and Aqueous Soil Suspension," Jour. Soil Sci., 8:313–27, 1957.)

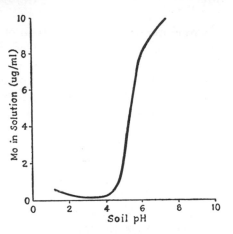

in Australia and New Zealand,[7] argue that the primary reason for liming very acid soils is to supply molybdenum. Furthermore, in some instances, an ounce or so of molybdenum added to acid soils has given about the same increase in the yield of legumes as has the application of several tons of lime. Although these general results have not been consistently verified by experiments in the United States, research has pointed to specific acid soil areas where economical responses can be obtained from molybdenum applications.

The utilization of phosphate by plants seems to favor that of molybdenum and vice versa. For this reason, molybdate salts are often applied along with superphosphate to molybdenum-deficient soils. This practice apparently encourages the uptake of both elements and is, of course, a convenient way to add the extremely small quantities of molybdenum required.

A second common anion, the sulfate, seems to have an effect on molybdenum absorption opposite to that of phosphorus. Sulfate has been found to reduce molybdenum uptake, although the specific mechanisms for this antagonism is not yet known.

18:8. NEED FOR NUTRIENT BALANCE

Nutrient balance among the trace elements is essential and is perhaps even more difficult to maintain than is that for the macronutrients. Some of the plant enzyme systems which are dependent upon

[7] See T. W. Walker, *et al.*, "The Effects and Interactions of Molybdenum, Lime, and Phosphate Treatments on the Yield and Composition of White Clover Grown on Acid, Molybdenum Responsive Soil," *Plant and Soil*, 6:201–20, 1955.

micronutrients require more than one element. For example, both manganese and molybdenum are needed for the assimilation of nitrates by plants.[8] The mutually beneficial effects of phosphates and molybdenum have already been discussed. Apparently, for some plants zinc and phosphorus are needed for optimum utilization of manganese. The utilization of boron and calcium is dependent upon the proper balance between these two nutrients. A similar relationship exists between potassium and copper, and between potassium and iron in the production of good quality potatoes. Copper utilization is favored by adequate manganese which in some plants is assimilated only if zinc is present in sufficient amounts. Of course, the effects of these and other nutrients will depend upon the specific plant being grown, but the complexity of the situation is seen from the examples cited.

ANTAGONISM. Some enzymatic and other biochemical reactions requiring a given micronutrient may be "poisoned" by the presence of a second trace element in toxic quantities. Examples of known antagonistic effects of elements on the absorption of micronutrients are as follows:

1. Excess copper or sulfate may adversely affect the utilization of molybdenum.
2. Iron deficiency is encouraged by an excess of zinc, manganese, and copper.
3. Excess phosphate may encourage a deficiency of zinc, iron and copper.
4. Heavy nitrogen fertilization intensifies copper deficiency.
5. Excess sodium or potassium may adversely affect manganese uptake.
6. Excess lime reduces boron uptake.
7. Iron, copper, and zinc may reduce the absorption of manganese.

Some of the antagonistic effects listed above may be taken advantage of in reducing toxicities of certain of the micronutients. For example, copper toxicity of citrus groves, caused by residual copper from insecticide sprays, may be reduced by adding iron and phosphate fertilizers. Sulfur additions to calcareous soils containing toxic quantities of soluble molybdenum may reduce the availability and hence the toxicity of the latter element.

These examples of nutrient interactions, both beneficial and detrimental, emphasize the highly complicated nature of the biological transformations in which micronutrients are involved. Luckily, the total acreage is small wherein unfavorable nutrient balances require special

[8] See E. G. Mulder and F. C. Gerretsen, "Soil Manganese in Relation to Plant Growth," *Advan. in Agron.*, 4:221–77,1952.

micronutrient treatment. This acreage is increasing, however, as man makes more intensive use of the soil and the crops grown thereon.

18:9. SOIL MANAGEMENT AND MICRONUTRIENT NEEDS

The needs for each of the micronutrients are just as specific as are those for the macronutrients. Because of the interactions just cited, they may be even more so. It is obvious, therefore, that any generalizations with respect to management practices involving all the trace elements should be used with caution. The advice of the expert should be sought in any specific case. He will be acquainted with the particular problem and will be prepared to suggest a solution. And he can point out the necessary precautions to prevent toxicities.

A review of factors determining micronutrient availability gives a clue as to how management practices might help keep these elements available at optimum levels. *First,* in ascertaining the cause of plant abnormalities one should keep in mind the conditions wherein micronutrient deficiencies or toxicities are apt to occur. Sandy soils, mucks, and soils having very high or very low pH values would be suspect. Areas of intensive cropping and heavy macronutrient fertilization may be deficient in the micronutrients.

Second, in thinking of remedies for a known deficiency or toxicity, soil pH changes should be considered. In very acid soils, one might expect toxicities of iron and manganese and deficiencies of phosphorus and molybdenum. These can be corrected by liming and by appropriate fertilizer additions. Calcareous alkaline soils may have deficiencies of iron, manganese, zinc, and copper, and in a few cases, a toxicity of molybdenum. The use of acidforming fertilizers or of sulfur may be resorted to in lowering the soil pH. High organic matter additions may not be desirable under these conditions since they encourage the oxidation of iron and manganese to the higher-valent and more insoluble forms.

No specific statement can be made concerning the pH value most suitable for all the elements. However, medium-textured soils generally supply adequate quantities of micronutrients when the soil pH is held between 6 and 7. In sandy soils, a somewhat more acid reaction may be justified since therein the total quantity of micronutrients is low, and even at pH 6.0 some deficiencies may occur.

Third, drainage and moisture control can influence micronutrient solubility in soils. Improving the drainage of acid soils will encourage the formation of the oxidized forms of iron and manganese. These are less soluble and, under acid conditions, less toxic than are the reduced forms.

Moisture control at high pH values can have the opposite effect. High moisture levels maintained by irrigation may result in the chemical reduction of high-valent compounds, the oxides of which are extremely insoluble. Flooding a soil will favor the reduced forms which are more available to growing plants.

The *fourth*, and perhaps the most common procedure is to add chemical nutrients to correct the deficiency or even toxicity. In some areas, this procedure has been used successfully for many years. Onion producers on the muck lands of some of the Northern states have added copper sulfate as a regular component of their fertilizer for many years. Citrus growers in California and especially Florida have supplied zinc as a spray for as many as 20 years and have used other micronutrients in their fertilizers for a like period of time. In wide areas throughout the country, boron is added as a regular component of fertilizer for alfalfa. It is also used for certain crops having high requirements for this element such as beets and celery.

Economic responses to micronutrients are becoming more widespread as intensity of cropping increases. For example, responses of fruits, vegetables, and field crops to zinc and iron applications have been noted in the Rocky Mountain area, the West Coast and the Northwest, and the Great Plain States. Even on acid soils of the South and of the East Coast deficiencies of the elements have been demonstrated. Molybdenum, which has been used for some time for cauliflower and other vegetables and for alfalfa, has received attention in recent years in soybean-growing areas, especially those of the South. Seed treatments of about ¼ ounce per acre have given good responses. These examples along with those from muck areas and sandy soils of the Southeast (particularly Florida) where micronutrients have been used for years illustrate the need for these elements if optimum yields are to be maintained.

Marked differences in crop needs for micronutrients make fertilization a problem where rotations are being followed. On general crop farms, vegetables are sometimes grown in rotation with small grains and forages. If the boron fertilization is adequaate for a vegetable crop such as red beets or even for alfalfa, the small grain crop grown in the rotation is apt to show toxicity damage. Such a situation occurs commonly in western New York. These facts emphasize the need for specificity in determining crop nutrient requirements and for care in meeting these needs. (See Table 18:3.)

Macronutrient deficiencies are more universally apparent than are those of the trace elements. For many years, applications of fertilizers containing nitrogen, phosphorus, and potash have been a means of supplying small quantities of the micronutrients. Superphosphate, for example, may contain up to about 20 parts per million of boron. Chilean

Table 18:3. Common Micronutrient Fertilizer Rates for Soil Application and Some Plants Having a High Requirement for these Nutrients

Micronutrient	Common Range in Fertilizer Rates[a] (lbs/acre)	Crops Having a High Requirement
1. Iron	15–50	Blueberries, cranberries, rhododendron, peaches, grapes, nut trees
2. Manganese	15–30	Oats, beans, soybeans, onions, potatoes, citrus
3. Zinc	5–50	Citrus and fruit trees, soybeans, corn, beans
4. Copper	2–50	Citrus and fruit trees, onions, small grains
5. Boron	5–30	Alfalfa, clovers, sugar beets, cauliflower, celery, apples and other fruits
6. Molybdenum	1 oz.–2 lbs.	Alfalfa, sweet clover, cauliflower, broccoli, celery

[a] These rates are in terms of the elements which are applied to the soil as soluble salts. Foliage-spray applications which are commonly made for zinc, manganese, molybdenum, and others, would, of course, be made at much smaller rates.

nitrate of soda supplies small quantities of several of the trace elements. These and other fertilizers will receive our attention in the chapter which follows.

Chapter 19
Fertilizers and
Fertilizer Management

Although the use of animal excrement on cultivated soils was common as far back as agricultural records can be traced, mineral salts have been systematically and extensively employed for the encouragement of crop growth hardly more than one hundred years. They are now an economic necessity on many soils. Any inorganic salt, such as ammonium nitrate, or an organic substance, such as sewage sludge, purchased and applied to the soil to promote crop development is considered to be a commercial fertilizer.

19:1. THE FERTILIZER ELEMENTS

There are at least thirteen essential nutrient elements that plants obtain from the soil. Two of these, calcium and magnesium, are applied as lime in regions where they are deficient. Although not usually rated as a fertilizer, lime does exert a profound nutritive effect. Sulfur is present in several commercial fertilizers and its influence is considered important, especially in certain localities. This leaves three elements other than the micronutrients—*nitrogen, phosphorus,* and *potassium.* And since they are so commonly applied in commercial fertilizers, they are often referred to as the *fertilizer elements.*

19:2. THE NUTRIENT BALANCE

Before taking up a discussion of the various fertilizing materials, one point should be emphasized most emphatically. The three fertilizer elements, when properly used, not only tend to check, balance, support, and supplement one another but the other nutrient elements as well. These relationships are very important in fertilizer practice, since they have much to do with the economy and effectiveness of fertilizers.

Ideally, the elements added should so supplement the nutrients already in the soil as to present to the plant just the correct proportion of available nitrogen, phosphorus, and potassium. At the same time, the amounts and availability of the other essential elements should be ideal. In short, the fertility balance as a whole should be such as to produce a large and normal crop growth.

In practice, however, such an ideal is difficult to attain. The soil is always more or less an unknown quantity as to the seasonal availability of its constituents. Moreover, it is difficult to forecast the reactions that will occur when the fertilizer contacts the soil. The influence of calcium, magnesium, manganese, iron, aluminum, and other elements upon the effectiveness of a fertilizer is always problematical.

19:3. THREE GROUPS OF FERTILIZER MATERIALS[1]

On the basis of the elements supplied, fertilizer materials automatically fall into three groups: (1) those that supply nitrogen; (2) those that serve as a source of phosphorus; and (3) those that carry water-soluble potash.

The classification, however, is not so simple as this grouping would imply, as several fertilizer materials carry two of the elements of nutrition. As examples of this overlapping, potassium nitrate and ammoniated

[1] For an excellent review of this subject see L. B. Nelson, "Advances in Fertilizer," *Advan. in Agron.* 17:1–84, 1965.

superphosphate may be cited. The situation will be fully apparent when the fertilizer tables presented later are examined and the compounding of mixed goods considered.

Because of the lack of space, it will only be possible to discuss each of the three groups in a general way, listing the various fertilizers of each, and mentioning the outstanding characteristics of the more important. Fortunately, detailed descriptions of the various fertilizers and their properties are available in published form if the reader cares to go further than these pages will carry him.

19:4. NITROGEN CARRIERS— TWO GROUPS

Nitrogen fertilizers may be divided for convenience into two groups: (1) *organic* and (2) *inorganic*. These groups are so different in both source and chemical and physical properties that they are best discussed separately. Let us begin first with the organic ammoniates.

19:5. ORGANIC NITROGEN CARRIERS

Because of their high cost per unit of nitrogen supplied, organic nitrogen carriers have been largely replaced as components of commercial fertilizers. However, some of them are still used as specialty fertilizers for lawns, flower gardens, and potted plants. Nitrogen is released slowly from these organic materials by microbiological action. This helps provide a continuing supply of the element during the warm summer months.

19:6. INORGANIC NITROGEN CARRIERS

GENERAL CONSIDERATION. Many inorganic carriers are used to supply nitrogen in mixed fertilizers. The most important of these, together with their compositions and sources, are listed in Table 19:1. Fortunately, there is a wide range in the nitrogen contents of the materials—from 3 per cent in ammoniated superphosphate to 82 per cent in anhydrous ammonia. Also, several chemical forms are represented, including ammonium and nitrate compounds as well as materials such as urea and cyanamid. Both of the latter upon hydrolysis in the soil yield NH_4 ions which can be taken up by plants or can be oxidized to nitrates. Although all the materials listed are used as nitrogen carriers, the am-

Table 19:1. Inorganic Nitrogen Carriers

Fertilizer	Chemical Form	Source	Approximate Per Cent Nitrogen
1. Sodium nitrate	$NaNO_3$	Chile saltpeter and synthetic	16
2. Ammonium sulfate	$(NH_4)_2SO_4$	By-product from coke and gas, and also synthetic	21
3. Ammonium nitrate[a]	NH_4NO_3	Synthetic	33
4. "Cal-nitro" and "A.N.L."	NH_4NO_3 & dolomite	"	20
5. Urea[b]	$CO(NH_2)_2$	"	42–45
6. Calcium cyanamide[c]	$CaCN_2$	"	22
7. Anhydrous ammonia[d]	Liquid NH_3	"	82
8. Ammonia liquor	Dilute NH_4OH	"	20–25
9. Nitrogen solutions	NH_4NO_3 in NH_4OH or Urea in NH_4OH	"	27–53
10. Ammo-phos[e]	$NH_4H_2PO_4$ and other ammonium salts	"	11 (48% P_2O_5)
11. Diammonium phosphate	$(NH_4)_2HPO_4$	"	21 (53% P_2O_5)

[a] Deliquescence controlled by surface coating materials or by mixing with dolomite, as in the case of "Cal-nitro" and "A.N.L." (trade names).

[b] The commercial compound is treated with a finely ground drier to control deliquescence.

[c] This fertilizer contains over 25 per cent $Ca(OH)_2$ and about 13 per cent carbon besides other ingredients such as $CaCO_3$, CaS, etc. The total amount of calcium expressed as CaO is approximately 53 per cent.

[d] The cheapest form of nitrogen for fertilizer use now available.

[e] Manufactured by treating ammonia with phosphoric acid
$$NH_3 + H_3PO_4 \longrightarrow NH_4H_2PO_4$$

monium and nitrate containing compounds are employed most widely.

The materials listed in Table 19:2 have one thing in common—they can all be produced synthetically starting with atmospheric nitrogen. This fact has far reaching significance, especially in respect to future nitrogen utilization. In the first place, it means that the quantity of nitrogen available to produce these compounds is limited only by the quantity present in the atmosphere.

Secondly, synthetic methods of supplying nitrogen have played a significant role in reducing the cost of this element, historically so much more expensive than either potassium or phosphorus. In addition, synthetic processes have yielded a wide variety of materials in large enough quantities to make their usage practical. Such a variety was not possible when natural deposits alone were depended upon.

As a result of these and other features, synthetic nitrogen carriers are assuming more and more importance. Considerably more than three fourths of the fertilizer nitrogen used in the United States today is carried by synthetics. Their methods of manufacture are worthy of brief consideration.

Table 19:2. The consumption of selected fertilizer materials in the United States in 1967 and quantities of plant nutrients supplied (expressed as N, P_2O_5 and K_2O)/[a]

Materials	Thousands of Tons of Nutrients
Nitrogen Carriers	(N)
Anhydrous ammonia[b]	9,747
Nitrogen solutions	1,340
Ammonium nitrate	1,686
Urea	1,016
Ammonium sulfate	545
Phosphorus Carriers	(P_2O_5)
Concentrated superphosphate	1,472
Ordinary superphosphate	1,183
Ammonium phosphates	1,655
Potassium Carriers	(K_2O)
Muriate of Potash	3,716
Sulfate of Potash	184

[a] Nitrogen and phosphorus data courtesy E. A. Harre, Tennessee Valley Authority. Potash data from American Potash Institute and include Canadian as well as American deliveries in the United States.

[b] About 1.7 million tons of anhydrous ammonia are applied directly. The remainder is used to manufacture other fertilizers.

AMMONIA AND ITS SOLUTIONS. Perhaps the most important of the synthetic processes is that in which ammonia gas is formed from the elements, hydrogen and nitrogen. This may be represented as follows:

$$N_2 + 3H_2 \longrightarrow 2NH_3$$

This reaction is extremely important since it yields a compound which is at the present time the least expensive per unit of nitrogen of any listed in Table 19:1. Furthermore, the consumption of this material in the United States far exceeds that of any other nitrogen carrier. (See Table 19:2.) Of equal importance is the fact that this is the first step in the formation of many other synthetic compounds.

The ammonia gas formed in the above reaction is utilized in at least three ways. First, it may be liquefied under pressure yielding anhydrous ammonia. (See Table 19:2.) This material is employed in the production of ammoniated superphosphate and mixed fertilizers, in addition to being used as a separate material for direct application. (See p. 553.) Second, ammonia gas may be dissolved in water yielding NH_4OH. This is often used alone (ammonia liquor) or more frequently as a solvent for other nitrogen carriers such as NH_4NO_3 and urea, to give the so-called "nitrogen solutions" (Fig. 19:1). In recent years, these solutions have become

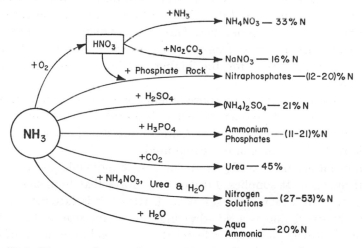

Figure 19:1. Diagram showing how various fertilizer materials may be synthesized from ammonia. This gas is obtained as a by-product of coke manufacture and, in even larger quantities, by direct synthesis from elemental nitrogen and hydrogen. In recent years, NH$_3$ and the other synthetic materials shown above have supplied most of our fertilizer nitrogen.

increasingly popular and now furnish a high proportion of the nitrogen in commerical fertilizers.

A third very important use of ammonia gas is in the manufacture of other inorganic nitrogen fertilizer materials. The reactions by means of which some fertilizer compounds are produced synthetically from ammonia are shown diagrammatically in Fig. 19:1. A careful study of this diagram will be very helpful in establishing the relationship beween ammonia and the materials derived synthetically from it. These substances will be considered briefly.

SULFATE OF AMMONIA. Sulfate of ammonia is produced synthetically as shown in Fig. 19:1.[2] This material has long been one of the most important nitrogen carriers, especially in the manufacture of mixed fertilizers. Its nitrogen is somewhat cheaper than that carried by nitrate of soda, but is more expensive than that of the liquid forms. Its use is most satisfactory on soils well supplied with lime since it has a residual acidifying effect. (See p. 544.)

SODIUM AND AMMONIUM NITRATES. Nitric acid, the manufacture of which is possible from oxidized ammonia, is used in making both ammonium and sodium nitrates. Ammonium nitrate, which has the advantages of supplying both NH_4 and NO_3 ions, has been employed in increasing quantities in the past few years. When used as a separate material, this salt is best supplied in the form of pellets which are suitably coated or otherwise treated to reduce its deliquescence. It must always be remembered that this fertilizer is a hazard in case of fire because of its explosive properties. The percentage of nitrogen in ammonium nitrate carriers ranges from 20 per cent for "Calnitro" and "A.N.L." to perhaps 33 per cent for the higher grades of ammonium nitrate (Table 19:2).

In addition to the synthetic source mentioned above, sodium nitrate is obtained as a natural product, saltpeter, from salt beds in Chile. In fact, before the coming of synthetics, Chilean nitrate of soda represented essentially the sole source of this compound.

Sodium nitrate has long been an important inorganic source of commercial nitrogen. It supplies nitrogen in a form that immediately stimulates many crops even if the soil is cold. Hence, it is extremely valuable early in the spring and as a side-dressing later in the season. Its high cost per unit of nitrogen, however, releases it to a secondary position of usage.

UREA. Another promising synthetic is urea, a fertilizer containing almost three times as much nitrogen as nitrate of soda. It readily

[2] Much of the NH_3 used in the production of $(NH_4)_2SO_4$ is a by-product of coke manufacture. Sulfate of ammonia obtained from this source is termed "by-product" in contrast to the "synthetic" cited in Figure 19:1.

undergoes hydrolysis in the soil, producing ammonium carbonate.[3] Thus, the immediate effect of this fertilizer is toward alkalinity, although its residual influence tends to lower soil pH. The ammonium carbonate produced is ideal for rapid nitrification, especially if exchangeable bases are present in adequate amounts. Urea thus ultimately presents both NH_4 ions and NO_3 ions for plant absorption. Its one serious objection, high deliquescence, has been largely overcome by coating its particles with dry powders.

AMMONIUM PHOSPHATES. Of the synthetics carrying phosphorus in addition to nitrogen, the ammonium phosphates are perhaps most important. Both mono- and diammonium phosphates are available. These compounds are made from phosphoric acid and ammonia. (See Fig. 19:1.) Since their phosphorus as well as their nitrogen is water soluble, these compounds are in demand where a high degree of water solubility is required.

Ammonium polyphosphates are beginning to find a place especially in liquid fertilizers. These materials are very high in phosphorus (58–61 per cent P_2O_5) and yet contain 12–15 per cent nitrogen.

OTHER SYNTHETIC NITROGEN CARRIERS. Calcium cyanamid, another synthetic product, has declined in importance in the United States in recent years due to its higher per unit cost of nitrogen. It continues to be used to a considerable extent in Europe, however. This product contains some $Ca(OH)_2$ which helps correct soil acidity. It changes rather readily in the soil to ammonium carbonate. Under certain conditions intermediate products are formed that may be harmful to crops.

By acidulating rock phosphate with nitric rarther than sulfuric or phosphoric acids, fertilizers containing so-called nitraphosphates are formed. They are apparently as effective as other materials in supplying nitrogen but are used primarily in the manufacture of complete fertilizers.

SLOW-RELEASE NITROGEN CARRIERS. For some purposes nitrates and to a lesser degree the other common nitrogen materials have the disadvantage of too ready availability. For example, the home owner wants a material which he can apply to his lawn in the spring with the expectation that it will keep his grass green throughout the summer. Materials have been developed which at least partially meet such slow-release requirements.

Urea-formaldehyde complexes were among the first slow-release synthetic compounds produced. They contain about 38 per cent nitrogen which is very slowly available. Other slow-release materials commercially available are floranid (crotonylideneduirea) which contains 28 per cent

[3] $CO(NH_2)_2 + 2H_2O \longrightarrow (NH_4)_2CO_3$

nitrogen and magnesium ammonium phosphate (8 per cent and 17.5 per cent P_2O_5). The rate of release of nitrogen with these materials is dependent primarily on particle size, making possible a wide range of rates of release. The major difficulty with these materials as well as experimental products such as oxamid $(CONH_2)_2$ produced by the Tennessee Valley Authority is their relatively high cost. This has up to now limited their use to specialty crops, lawns, and turfs.

Another approach to the problem of too rapid nitrogen release is that of coating conventional fertilizer with materials which slow down their rate of solution and microbial attack. Waxes, paraffin and acrylic resins, and elemental sulfur are among the materials which have been used with some success. They slow down the rate of moisture penetration of the granule and the outward movement of the soluble nitrogen.

Materials which delay and prevent nitrification have also been developed. Their purpose is to keep the nitrogen in the ammonium form so as to slow down its rate of assimilation by plants and its leaching from the soil. One product on the market is 2-chloro-6 (trichloromethyl)-pyridine ("N-Serve"). This is likely to be the first of several such compounds aimed at slowing down nitrification.

19:7. PHOSPHATIC FERTILIZER MATERIALS

SUPERPHOSPHATE. The principal phosphorus fertilizer material at the present time is superphosphate. (See Table 19:3.) The ordinary grades containing 16 to 21 per cent available P_2O_5 (7–9 per cent P) are made by treating raw rock phosphate with suitable amounts of sulfuric acid. (See Fig. 19:2.) A large proportion of the phosphorus is thus changed to the primary phosphate form $(Ca(H_2PO_4)_2)$, although some is left in the secondary condition $(CaHPO_4)$.[4] Much of the superphosphate now used is this ordinary grade, which consists of about 31 per cent phosphates, 50 per cent gypsum, and 19 per cent impurities of vari-

---

[4] By representing the complex raw rock by the simple formula $Ca_3(PO_4)_2$, the following conventional reactions may be used to show the changes that occur during the manufacture of ordinary 16 to 21 per cent superphosphate.

$$Ca_3(PO_4)_2 + 2H_2SO_4 \longrightarrow Ca(H_2PO_4)_2 + 2CaSO_4 + \text{impurities}$$
$$\text{(Insoluble)} \qquad\qquad\qquad \text{(Water Soluble)}$$

The acid is never added in amounts capable of completing this reaction. Consequently, some secondary phosphate—$CaHPO_4$, spoken of as *citrate soluble phosphoric acid*, is produced.

$$Ca_3(PO_4)_2 + H_2SO_4 \longrightarrow 2CaHPO_4 + CaSO_4 + \text{impurities}$$
$$\text{(Insoluble)}$$

Table 19:3. Phosphorus Carriers

Fertilizer	Chemical Form	Approximate Percentage of Available P_2O_5	% P
Superphosphates	$Ca(H_2PO_4)_2$ and $CaHPO_4$	16–50	7–22
Ammoniated superphosphate	$\left\{\begin{array}{l} NH_4H_2PO_4 \\ CaHPO_4 \\ Ca_3(PO_4)_2 \\ (NH_4)_2SO_4 \end{array}\right.$	16–18 (3–4%N)	7–8
Ammo-phos	$NH_4H_2PO_4$ mostly	48 (11% N)	21
Ammonium polyphosphates	$(NH_4)_4P_2O_7$ and others	58–60 (12–15% N)	
Diammonium phosphate	$(NH_4)_2HPO_4$	46–53 (21% N)	20–23
Basic slag[a]	$(CaO)_5 \cdot P_2O_5 \cdot SiO_2$	15–25	7–11
Steamed bone meal[b]	$Ca_3PO_4)_2$	23–30	10–13
Rock phosphate	Fluor- and Chlor-apatites	25–30	11–13
Calcium metaphosphate[c]	$Ca(PO_3)_2$	62–63	27–28
Phosphoric acid	H_3PO_4	54	24
Superphosphoric acid	H_3PO_4 and $H_4P_2O_7$	76	33

[a] The formula of this fertilizer is very uncertain. Basic slag is intensely alkaline because of the presence of large amounts of the hydroxide and carbonate of lime.

[b] The steamed bone meal is cooked under pressure and the fat and oil removed. The bone is left open and porous.

[c] Synthesized from rock phosphate or limestone and P2O5 Ca3(PO4)2 + 2P2O5 $\longrightarrow$ 3Ca(PO3)2 + impurities   or   CaCO3 + P2O5 $\longrightarrow$ Ca(PO3)2 + CO2 + impurities.

ous kinds. The total *phosphorus* to the hundred weight is rather low, ranging from 7 to 9 pounds, and the sulfur and calcium amount to about 12 and 18 pounds, respectively.

The high-analysis treble superphosphate contains 40 to 47 per cent available P_2O_5 (17–21 per cent P). It differs from the ordinary type principally in that it contains more phosphorus and no gypsum.[5] This

[5] The *treble* superphosphate is synthesized by treating a high grade phosphate rock with phosphoric acid:

Ca3(PO4)2 + 4H3PO4 $\longrightarrow$ 3Ca(H2PO4)2 + impurities

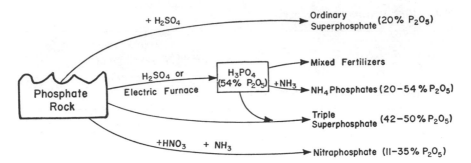

Figure 19:2. Diagram showing how several important phosphate fertilizers are manufactured. (This diagram is modified from one supplied the authors by Mr. Travis Hignett, Tennessee Valley Authority.)

material is becoming more and more widely used since higher analysis fertilizers have become accepted.

Of the two superphosphates, the ordinary grade, 16 to 21 per cent available P_2O_5 (7–9 per cent P), is still commonly used, although less so in recent years than the higher analyses. Since much of it goes into mixed fertilizers or is ammoniated, the finely ground superphosphate rather than the granulated materials are in demand. The former gives more uniform mixtures and does not segregate when handled as does the granulated. Moreover, it is contacted more readily by the ammonia when ammoniated superphosphate is made. But when superphosphate is to be applied separately to the soil or is used to reinforce farm manure (p. 571), the well-granulated type is preferable. This form does not revert as rapidly in the soil as do the finer grades and in addition is more pleasant to handle.

Since superphosphate gives a very acid reaction when tested with indicators, it is generally supposed that it must increase the acidity of soils to which it is added. As a matter of fact, it has practically no effect within the ordinary pH range. But at a low pH superphosphate tends to reduce acidity, whereas at a pH of 7.5 to 8.5 the modification is in the other direction. The slight influence of this fertilizer on soil reaction probably is due to the vigorous reversion that occurs as soon as it contacts the soil.

AMMONIATED PHOSPHATES. Ammoniated superphosphate contains from 3 to 4 per cent nitrogen and 16 to 18 per cent phosphoric acid. It affords a chance of easily changing ammonia to a suitable fertilizer form, at the same time improving the physical qualities of the superphosphate itself. It is usually made by treating superphosphate with ammonia liquor or nitrogen solutions.

Ammo-phos, which may analyze 11 per cent nitrogen and 48 per cent phosphoric acid, is also an economical fertilizer when a higher analysis is required. Diammonium phosphate is a more recently developed material containing up to 21 per cent N and 53 per cent P_2O_5 (23 per cent P). It is very valuable as one of the materials used in bulk blending (see p. 542) and as a constituent of high analyses fertilizers.

Ammonium polyphosphates made by ammoniating superphosphoric acid show great potential in manufacturing of liquid fertilizers. They help prevent the precipitation of iron and other impurities and keep most of the micronutrients in solution.

BASIC SLAG AND BONE MEAL. Basic slag, while commonly used in Europe, is on the market only to a limited extent in the United States. Because of the alkalinity and the rather ready availability of its phosphoric acid, it is a very desirable phosphatic fertilizer. It seems to be especially effective on acid soils apparently because of its high content of calcium hydroxide.

Bone meal is an expensive form of phosphoric acid. Moreover, it is rather slowly available in the soil. Bone meal can be applied in large amounts and yet produce no detrimental influence on crop growth.

ROCK PHOSPHATE. Raw rock phosphate, due to its insolubility, must be finely ground in order that it may react at all readily when applied to the soil. Its availability is markedly increased by the presence of decaying organic matter. For that reason it is often recommended as a reinforcement for farm manure, liberal amounts being used. Ordinarily it should not be applied alone unless the soil is rather well supplied with active organic matter.

Rock phosphate is the least available of the phosphatic fertilizers already mentioned, the order being: ammonium phosphates and superphosphate, basic slag, bone meal, and raw rock. Although its chemical formula is given conventionally as $Ca_3(PO_4)_2$, rock phosphate is much more complicated than this formula would suggest. It apparently approaches the fluorapatite $(3Ca_3(PO_4)_2 \cdot CaF_2)$ in its molecular make-up. (See p. 478.) This, no doubt, accounts in part for its slow availability.

Finely ground rock phosphate is most effective when added to soils high in organic matter. Because of its low solubility, however, its use will continue to be as a source for the manufacture of other and more soluble forms.

HIGH-ANALYSIS PHOSPHATES. Mention should be made of two very high-analysis phosphate fertilizers not as yet in general use—calcium metaphosphate $Ca(PO_3)_2$—62 to 63 per cent available P_2O_5 (27–28 per cent P) and superphosphoric acid containing 76 per cent P_2O_5 (33 per cent P). (See Table 19:3.) Both are more or less in the experimental stage but hold great promise as they seem to be as effective, when used in equivalent amounts, as superphosphate. Their concentrations make them extremely attractive when transportation is a factor.

The $Ca(PO_3)_2$, commonly called *meta-phos*, may be made by treating either phosphate rock or limestone with phosphorus pentoxide. (Table 19:3, note c.) The highly concentrated P_2O_5 can be produced at the mine, shipped to a point where limestone is cheaply available, and the meta-phos manufactured in the territory where it is to be used. Transportation costs are thus cut to a minimum.

Superphosphoric acid, a new synthetic product, is the highest phosphorus-containing material used in fertilizer manufacture today (Table 19:3). Its P_2O_5 content is 76 per cent (33 per cent P). It is made of a mixture of orthophosphoric, pyrophosphoric, and other polyphosphoric acids. This liquid can be used in the manufacture of other liquid fertilizers, or to make a high analysis superphosphate containing 54 per cent P_2O_5 (24 per cent P). In the formulation of liquid fertilizers, the polyphosphates help keep iron, aluminum, and micronutrients in solution.

CLASSIFICATION OF PHOSPHATE FERTILIZERS. For purpose of evaluation and sale the various phosphorus compounds present in phosphatic fertilizers are classified in an arbitrary yet rather satisfactory way in Table 19:4.

Table 19:4. Fertilizer Classification of Phosphates

1. *Water-soluble* $\begin{cases} Ca(H_2PO_4)_2 \\ NH_4H_2PO_4 \\ K \text{ phosphate} \end{cases}$	
2. *Citrate-soluble*	*Available phosphoric acid*[a]
In 15 per cent neutral ammonium citrate —$CaHPO_4$	
3. *Insoluble* Phosphate of bone and raw phosphate rock	*Unavailable phosphoric acid*[a]

[a] The various fertilizers studied are grouped as follows:
Available—superphosphate (all grades), ammoniated superphosphate, ammo-phos, basic slag, mono-calcium phosphate, meta-phos and dicalcium phosphate.
Mostly unavailable—rock phosphate and bone meal.

It is well to note that the classification of the phosphates is in some degree artificial as well as arbitrary. For instance, *available* phosphates, because of the reversion that occurs, are not strictly available once they contact the soil. The term *available* really refers to those phosphates

that readily stimulate plant growth. Those phosphates that are less
effective are rated as currently *unavailable*, yet in the soil they may
eventually supply a certain amount of phosphorus to crops. (See Fig.
19:3.)

Suppose in the case of ordinary superphosphate that the guarantee is
20 per cent available P_2O_5 (9 per cent P). The term available phosphoric
acid is here used in the sense explained above and includes both the
water-soluble $Ca(H_2PO_4)_2$ and the citrate-soluble $CaHPO_4$. With ammo-
phos (11 per cent total nitrogen and 48 per cent available P_2O_5) the

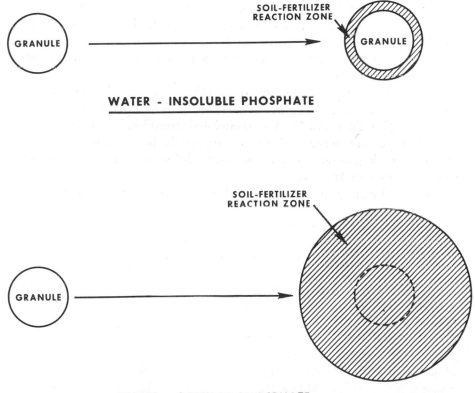

*Figure 19:3. Illustrations of the reaction of water soluble and water insoluble
phosphates with soil. The water insoluble granules react with only a small
volume of soil in their immediate vicinity. Soluble phosphates move into the
soil from water soluble granules reacting with iron, aluminum and manganese
in acid soils and calcium in alkaline soils. (From O. P. Engelstad, "Phosphate
fertilizers aren't all alike." Crops and Soils 17:14–15, Aug.–Sept. 1965.)*

available phosphoric acid is carried by the water-soluble $NH_4H_2PO_4$. Since phosphate fertilizers are guaranteed in the terms set forth above, it is absolutely necessary that a person be familiar with the distinctions noted. Otherwise, a correct interpretation of a guarantee is impossible.

19:8. FERTILIZER MATERIALS CARRYING POTASSIUM

One of the largest known deposits of potassium salts occurs in Germany, where there are extensive beds varying from 50 to 150 feet in thickness, lying under an area stretching from the Harz Mountains to the Elbe River. It is known as the Strassfurt deposits. Crude potash salts occur in other sections of Germany, in France, in the United States, in Canada, and elsewhere.

While potash deposits are found in other parts of the world, the French, German, and American mines are the ones operating most extensively. The First World War stimulated considerable investigation regarding possible sources of potash, especially in the United States. Domestic underground deposits and saline brines now furnish most of the potash used in America.

Kainit and manure salts (see Table 19:5) are the most common of the

Table 19:5. Potash Fertilizer Materials

Fertilizer	Chemical Form	Percentage Expressed as K_2O	K
Potassium chloride[a]	KCl	48–60	40–50
Potassium sulfate	K_2SO_4	48–50	40–42
Sulfate of potash-magnesia[b]	Double salt of K and Mg	25–30	19–25
Manure salts	KCl mostly	20–30	17–25
Kainit	KCl mostly	12–16	10–13
Potassium nitrate	KNO_3	44 (and 13% N)	37

[a] All of these fertilizers contain other potash salts than those listed.
[b] Contains 25 per cent of $MgSO_4$ and some chlorine.

crude potash sources. The high grade chloride and sulfate of potash originally imported from Germany and France are their refined equivalents. The potassium chloride, now used so extensively in the United

States, comes mostly from underground deposits, saline brines, and old lake beds found in this country.

All potash salts used as fertilizers are water-soluble and are therefore rated as readily available. Unlike nitrogen salts, most potassium fertilizers, even if employed in large amounts, have little or no effect on the soil pH. Some discrimination is made, however, against potassium chloride (muriate) in respect to potatoes and especially tobacco since large dosages are considered to lower the quality. Hence, when large amounts of potash are to be applied for the latter crop, the major part usually is preferred in the sulfate form.

Potassium-magnesium sulfate, although rather low in potash, has attained considerable usage in parts of this country where magnesium is likely to be deficient. In some respects it is a more desirable source of magnesium than is dolomitic limestone or dolomite.

19:9. SULFUR IN SOIL FERTILIZATION

In examining the sulfur problem in humid regions it will be found that for a representative farm soil the total loss of sulfur (erosion, leaching, and crop removal combined) perhaps falls within the range of 20 to 30 pounds an acre yearly. (See Tables 9:5 and 9:9) This deficiency is met in several ways.

Sulfur additions in rain and snow range from 2 or 3 pounds of combined sulfur an acre a year to perhaps over 100 pounds near industrial centers. Since the influence of industrial centers is extremely local, it is hardly safe in general to assume that this source will fully meet the deficit (20 to 30 pounds yearly per acre) already set up.

In general and dairy farming, the problem has been taken care of in the past in a more or less automatic way. Crop residues and commercial fertilizers, such as superphosphate, ammonium sulfate, and potassium sulfate, contain considerable amounts of sulfur. Also, the soil and higher plants can absorb some sulfur directly from the atmosphere.

In the light of the information available, it seems that the sulfur situation is not comparable with, nor so serious as that of phosphorus. With certain soils in eastern Washington and Oregon, in Minnesota, and in California, sulfur in some form undoubtedly must be added artificially, especially in the growing of alfalfa and sweet clover. However, as we increased the use of high-analysis fertilizers, often devoid of sulfur, and as crop yields increase in areas far from industrial centers, the need for sulfur additions is apt to increase. The supply of this element can no longer be taken for granted.

19:10. MICRONUTRIENTS

Micronutrient additions to fertilizers must be much more carefully controlled than is the case for the macronutrients. The difference between the amount of a given micronutrient present when deficiency occurs and when there is a toxicity is extremely small. Consequently, micronutrients should be added only when one is certain they are needed and when the amount required is known.

When a trace-element deficiency is to be corrected, especially if the case is urgent, a salt of the lacking nutrient often is added separately to the soil. (See Table 19:6.) Copper, manganese, iron, and zinc gen-

Table 19:6. Salts of Micronutrients Commonly Used in Fertilizers[a]

Compound	Formula	Nutrient Content
Copper sulfate	$CuSO_4$	25–35% Cu
Basic copper sulfate	$CuSO_4 \cdot 3Cu(OH)_2$	13–53% Cu
Copper carbonate (basic)	$CuCO_3 \cdot Cu(OH)_2$	57% Cu
Zinc sulfate	$ZnSO_4$	23–35% Zn
Zinc sulfate (basic)	$ZnSO_4 \cdot 4Zn(OH)_2$	55% Zn
Manganese sulfate	$MnSO_4$	23% Mn
Manganese sulfate (basic)	$2MnSO_4 \cdot MnO$	40–49% Mn
Sodium borate	$Na_2B_4O_7$	34–44% B_2O_3
Ferrous sulfate	$FeSO_4$	20% Fe
Ferric sulfate	$Fe_2(SO_4)_3$	17% Fe
Sodium molybdate	Na_2MoO_4	37–39% Mo

[a] Modified from A. A. Nikitin, "Technological Aspects of Trace Elements Usage," *Advan. in Agron.*, 6:183–97, 1954.

erally are usually supplied as the sulfate, and boron is applied as borax. Molybdenum is added as sodium molybdate. Iron and in some cases zinc may be supplied as a chelate. (See p. 514.) Iron, manganese, and zinc are sometimes sprayed in small quantities on the leaves rather than being applied directly to the soil. So called "fritted" silicate compounds of boron, manganese, iron, and zinc may also be used to supply these nutrients.

In recent years there has been an increase in the use of chelates to supply iron, zinc, manganese and copper (see p. 516.) These materials are especially useful on soils of high pH where mineral sources would be quickly rendered unavailable. Because of their high cost, however, these materials are often used as foliar sprays whereby the rate of application can be materially reduced.

The rate of application of micronutrients should be carefully regulated as an overdose can cause severe injury. For instance, 50 pounds of borax an acre are nearing the maximum for the average soil when its pH is near 7. A few ounces of molybdenum is often all that is required. Much, of course, depends upon the crop grown. In case of doubt as to the amounts to apply, expert advice should be sought.

In some cases trace elements, especially boron, are placed in ordinary commercial fertilizers and their presence therein stated in the guarantee. A stock mixture is compounded using some organic ammoniate as a base to which is added the desired trace-element salts. A few pounds of this mixture are included in each ton of the fertilizer.

The idea, of course, is to insure against a possible deficiency of the trace elements. One objection to such a practice is that not enough of any one trace element may be added to the soil to adequately meet a real deficiency should it occur. Furthermore, the amount of trace element applied varies with the dosage of the commercial fertilizer. Trace elements usually require a more careful regulation than can be attained in this way.

That the fertilization with trace elements is of great practical importance cannot be denied. Plant malnutritions, due to such deficiencies, are becoming more and more apparent. All kinds of plants are affected. The last few years have seen a tremendous development of this phase of fertility regulation.

19:11. MIXED FERTILIZERS

For years, fertilizer manufacturers have placed on the market mixtures of materials which contain at least two of the so-called "fertilizer elements," and usually all three. The former are designated *incomplete* fertilizers; the latter are spoken of as *complete*. In either case materials such as those discussed in previous sections are mixed in proper proportion to furnish the desired amount of the nutrient elements. For example, an ammonia solution, triple superphosphate, muriate of potash, and a very small amount of an organic might be used if a complete fertilizer is desired. Such fertilizers supply about two thirds of the total fertilizer nutrient consumption in the United States, the remainder coming from mixed goods.

PHYSICAL CONDITION. In addition to supplying nitrogen, phosphorus, and potassium in desired proportions, however, a commercial fertilizer should have certain other properties. Of utmost importance in this regard is the *physical condition* of the mixed goods. The fertilizer should be drillable when first purchased and should remain in this condition after storage. Mixtures of certain materials cannot be used because of their tendency to "set up" or harden. Of the fertilizer materials commonly found in mixed goods, ammonium nitrate, sulfate of ammonia, and potassium chloride are most likely to develop unsatisfactory physical conditions. Improperly cured superphosphate may also give trouble. The extreme deliquescence of some of the salts, especially ammonium nitrate, tends to make mixed fertilizers sticky and thus reduce the drillability.

METHODS OF INSURING FREE FLOWAGE. The free-flowing condition of a mixed fertilizer is maintained by important procedures: (1) Moisture-resistant bags are commonly used in distribution, (2) certain moisture-absorbing materials are usually included in the fertilizer mix, and (3) the mixed fertilizers may be granulated. In the past, organic materials such as castor pomace and tobacco stems were used commonly to improve the physical condition of fertilizers. Their high cost and low analysis has been to their disadvantage, however. Today only small quantities are used.

Another method of encouraging the free flowing of fertilizers is that of granulating the goods after mixing. Separate materials such as sodium and ammonium nitrates have been pelleted for several years to prevent caking. In recent years the granulation of mixed fertilizers has become commonplace in this country, more than half these fertilizers being sold in granular condition.

In addition to having free-flowing properties, granulated fertilizers present certain other advantages. For example, they are less disagreeable to handle since they are comparatively free of small dustlike particles. The granulation also prevents the fertilizer from being carried by the wind, thus permitting more uniform spreading. Also, granulation tends to reduce the rate of reaction with large volumes of soil.

BULK BLENDING. In the past, essentially all mixed fertilizers were bagged at the manufacturing plant and then shipped to distribution points where they were sold to farmers. The farmers applied the fertilizers usually at the same time other operations such as planting or plowing were done.

In recent years, the bulk handling and blending of fertilizers has become more and more common, especially in the North Central States. Granular materials are shipped in bulk to a blending plant located within a 25–30 mile radius of the intended use of the fertilizer. (See Fig. 19:4.) The fertilizers are mixed to the customer's order and move directly to the farm where they are field spread. Frequently the

Figure 19:4. A bulk blending fertilizer plant and bulk spreading trucks. *Different fertilizer analyses can be mixed to order and spread by truck on a
custom basis. (Photo Courtesy Harold Sweet, Agway Inc.)*

spreader trucks are owned and operated on a custom basis by the
blending plant.

The most obvious advantage of bulk blending and handling is as a
labor saving process. Furthermore, costs of storing, production, transportation, and spreading are all lower at least for the medium to large
sized farms than the conventional means of handling fertilizers. Also, the
fertilizers are generally high in analysis, and chemical incompatability
of the fertilizer materials is generally not a problem. Lastly, a variety of
nutrient ratios can easily be formulated.

A problem of some concern in bulk blending is the segregation of the
materials which could result in uneven distribution of the fertilizer
nutrients in the field. Care must be taken to use materials wherein the
granules are about the same size and density. Since this is not always
possible, special mixing hoppers have been developed.

Fertilizer materials commonly used in the bulk blending process are
urea, ammonium nitrate, ammonium sulfate, ammonium phosphates,
triple superphosphate, and potassium chloride.

LIQUID FERTILIZERS. Another innovation in the for-
mulating and handling of mixed fertilizers is the use of liquid fertilizers.

These materials are used mostly in California where the practice started and in the North Central States. As with bulk blending, liquid fertilizers have the advantage of low labor costs since the materials are handled in tanks and pumped out for transfer or for application. However, the cost per unit of nutrient element is usually higher, more sophisticated equipment is needed for storage and handling, and only relatively low analysis mixed fertilizers can be made. (For example, 5–10–10, 7–7–7, and 6–18–6 are common analyses.) Slightly higher analyses are possible by using superphosphoric acid or ammonium polyphosphates as a source of at least part of the phosphorus. Also, so called "suspension fertilizers," wherein a small amount of solids is suspended in the liquid, permit higher analyses such as 15–15–15.

19:12. EFFECT OF MIXED FERTILIZERS ON SOIL pH

ACID-FORMING FERTILIZERS. Most complete fertilizers, unless specially treated, tend to develop an acid residue in soils. This is mainly due to the influence of certain of the nitrogen carriers, especially those which supply ammonia or which produce ammonia when added to he soil. The major effect of NH_4 ions is exerted when they are nitrified. Upon oxidation the ammonium compounds tend to increase acidity as shown by the following reaction:

$$NH_4^+ + 2O_2 \longrightarrow 2H^+ + NO_3^- + H_2O$$

Two other effects of NH_4 ions are important, but to a lesser extent, in decreasing soil pH. For example, when ammonium sulfate is added to a soil, some of the NH_4 ions are readily adsorbed by the soil colloidal matter replacing equivalent quantities of other cations. If metallic cations are displaced, their loss by leaching is encouraged. This ultimately may result in a lowering of soil pH. On the other hand, if H ions are displaced, sulfuric acid appears in the soil solution. A similar development of sulfuric acid occurs if higher plants or microorganisms use the ammonium radical of the fertilizer to a greater extent than they do the sulfate.

In addition to ammonium compounds, materials such as urea and some of the organics, which upon hydrolysis yield ammonium ions, are potential sources of acidity. The phosphorus and potash fertilizers commonly used have little effect upon soil pH unless they also contain nitrogen.

NONACID-FORMING FERTILIZERS. In some instances, the acid-forming tendency of nitrogen fertilizers is completely counteracted by adding dolomitic limestone to the mixture. Such fertilizers are termed *neutral* or *nonacid-forming* and exert little residual effect on soil pH. Data are available in respect to nitrogen fertilizers that make it rather easy to calculate the approximate amount of dolomitic limestone necessary in any particular case.[6] It should be pointed out, however, that it is often economically preferable to use acid-forming fertilizers and to neutralize the soil acidity with separate bulk applications of lime.

19:13. THE FERTILIZER GUARANTEE

Every fertilizing material, whether it is a single carrier or a complete ready-to-apply mixture, must carry a guarantee as to its content of nutrient elements. The exact form is generally determined by the state in which the fertilizer is offered for sale. The *total nitrogen* is usually expressed in its *elemental form* (N). The phosphorus is quoted in terms of *available phosphorus* (P) or *phosphoric acid* (P_2O_5); the potassium is stated as *water-soluble potassium* (K) or *potash* (K_2O).

The guarantee of a simple fertilizer, such as sulfate of ammonia, is easy to interpret, since the name and composition of the material is printed on the bag or tag. When the amount of the nutrient element carried is noted, the purity of the fertilizer can usually be ascertained if a person is at all familiar wih the compounds present. For instance, if the material is nitrate of soda containing 16 per cent total nitrogen, it is apparent that the fertilizer is high-grade, since *chemically pure* sodium nitrate contains only slightly more than 16 per cent nitrogen.

The interpretation of an analysis of a complete fertilizer is almost as easy. The simplest form of guarantee is a mere statement of the relative amounts of N, P and K, or N, P_2O_5 and K_2O. Thus, an 8–16–16 fertilizer contains 8 per cent *total nitrogen,* 16 per cent *available* P_2O_5

---

[6] See W. H. Pierre, "Determination of Equivalent Acidity and Basicity of Fertilizers," *Analy. Ed., Ind. and Eng. Chem.,* 5:229–34, 1933.

It is, of course, very difficult to determine the exact potential acidity of a given fertilizer. The approximate acidifying capacity of a few materials are cited below. The values are in terms of pounds $CaCO_3$ per 20 pounds N supplied by the fertilizer.

Ammonium sulfate	107	Ammonium nitrate	36
Ammo-phos	100	Cottonseed meal	29
Anhydrous ammonia	36	Castor pomace	18
Urea	36	High grade tankage	15

The basicity in the same terms for certain fertilizers is as below:

Nitrate of soda	36	Tobacco stems	86
Calcium cyanamid	57	Cocoa meal	12

(7 per cent available P), and 16 per cent *water-soluble* K_2O (13 per cent water-soluble K). In some states, figures as to *water-soluble nitrogen, water-insoluble nitrogen,* and *available insoluble nitrogen* are required by law.

An *open formula* guarantee is used by some companies. Such a guarantee not only gives the usual chemical analysis but also a list of the various ingredients, their composition, and the pounds of each in a ton of the mixture. Such a type of guarantee is given in Table 19:7 for an 8–16–16 fertilizer with the nutrients expressed as N, P_2O_5 and K_2O.

Commercial fertilizers are sometimes grouped according to their nutrient *ratio.* For instance, a 5–10–10, an 8–16–16, a 10–20–20, and a 15–30–30 all have a 1–2–2 ratio. These fertilizers should give essentially the same results when suitably applied in equivalent amounts. Thus, 1,000 lbs. of 10–20–20 furnishes the same amounts of N, P and K as does a ton of 5–10–10.

This grouping according to ratios is valuable when several analyses are offered and the comparative costs become the deciding factor as to which should be purchased. Moreover, fertilizer recommendations are sometimes made on the basis of the ratio, the particular analysis being decided on later.

19:14. FERTILIZER INSPECTION AND CONTROL

So many opportunities are open for fraud, either as to availability or the actual quantities of ingredients present, that laws controlling the sale of fertilizers are necessary. These laws apply not only

Table 19:7. An Open Formula Guarantee of an 8–16–16 (Acid-forming) Fertilizer

Pounds of Ingredients per Ton	Total N	Available P_2O_5	P	Soluble K_2O	K
300 lbs. nitrogen solution	120				
100 lbs. sulfate of ammonia	20				
100 lbs. diammonium phosphate	20	52	22		
300 lbs. treble superphosphate		135	58		
666 lbs. superphosphate		133	57		
534 lbs. muriate of potash				320	266
2,000 lbs. 8–16–16	160	320	138	320	266

to the ready-mixed goods but also to the separate carriers. Such regulations protect not only the public but also the reliable fertilizer companies, since goods of unknown value are kept off the market.

Certain provisions are more or less common to the various state fertilizer laws in this country. In general, there is a license fee or tonnage tax on all fertilizers selling for a certain price or over. In addition, the manufacturer must print the following data on the bag or on an authorized tag:

1. Number of net pounds of fertilizer to a package.
2. Name, brand, or trade-mark.
3. Chemical composition guaranteed.
4. Potential acidity in terms of lbs. of $CaCO_3$ per ton.
5. Name and address of manufacturer.

An example of how this information often appears on the fertilizer bag is shown in Fig. 19:5.

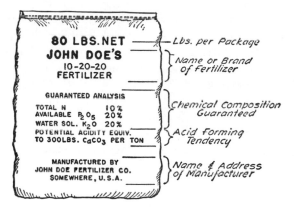

Figure 19:5. A fertilizer bag on which is printed the information commonly required by law in most states. Note the acid-forming tendency of this particular fertilizer.

For the enforcement of such laws, the various states usually provide adequate machinery. The inspection and analyses may be in the hands of an agency such as the state department of agriculture, the agricultural experiment station, or the state chemist's office. In any case, inspectors take samples of the fertilizers on the market throughout the state. These samples are analyzed in order to ascertain whether the goods are up to the guarantee. The expense of the inspection and control of fertilizers is usually defrayed by a license fee or a tonnage tax.

If a fertilizer falls below the guarantee—allowing, of course, for any variation permitted by law—the manufacturer is subject to prosecution in the state courts.

A more effective check on fradulent guarantees, however, is in publicity. The state law usually provides for the publication each year of a bulletin containing the "guaranteed" and "found" analyses of all brands inspected. This has proved to be very effective in preventing fraud. It protects not only the fertilizer user but also the manufacturer, as his guarantees thus receive an official sanction. The "found" analysis of most fertilizers is generally up to or more often above the guarantee.

19:15. FERTILIZER ECONOMY

HIGH VS. LOW ANALYSES. Whether buying mixed fertilizers or the various separate carriers, such as nitrate of soda, sulfate of ammonia, and the like, it is always important to obtain high-analysis goods. Price data indicate that the higher the grade, especially of a mixed fertilizer, the greater is the amount of the various nutrients obtained for every dollar expended. This is a price rule well worth remembering. It holds because the overhead is about the same for every ton of fertilizer, regardless of the amount of nutrients that it contains. Concentration, therefore, reduces the overhead per unit of nutrient carried. This is shown graphically in Fig. 19:6. Obviously, from the standpoint of economy, an 8–16–16 fertilizer furnishes more nutrients *per dollar* than a 4–8–8 or a 5–10–10.

In the past, certain disadvantages of high-analysis fertilizers have somewhat hampered their increased usage. For example, the equipment used to place the fertilizer in the soil was too crude to distribute satisfactorily the smaller amounts of the more concentrated materials. Also, when improperly placed, the more concentrated goods often resulted in injury to young seedlings. Modern fertilizer placement machinery, plus an increasing tendency to bulk spread at least part of the fertilizer, has largely overcome these difficulties. Hence, the savings which result from the use of higher analysis materials seem to far outweigh any associated disadvantages that may now exist.

RELATIVE COSTS OF N, P_2O_5, AND K_2O. Another price factor to remember in purchasing fertilizers is the relative costs of N, phosphorus, and potassium. Nitrogen has generally been more expensive than the other two constituents. This price differential has been somewhat reduced, however, due to the production of synthetic nitrogen carriers. Phosphorus per unit of P_2O_5 is next expensive, and potassium is the least expensive of all. It should be remembered, however, that there is considerable variation in the cost of different carriers for

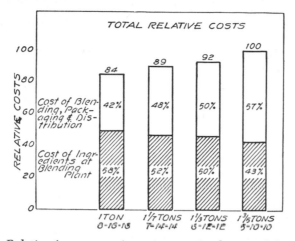

Figure 19:6. Relative farm costs of nutrients in fertilizer of different concentrations. Note that the same amount of nutrients is supplied by the indicated quantities of each fertilizer. These nutrients are furnished more cheaply by the higher analysis goods, mainly because of the lower handling costs.

a given element. Thus, the manufactured cost of nitrogen in some solid carriers (e.g., sodium nitrate) is about double that of anhydrous ammonia. Likewise, sulfate of potash is considerably more expensive than an equivalent amount of potassium chloride.

PURCHASING OF SEPARATE MATERIALS. In many instances a saving can be effected by purchasing the separate materials and applying them to the soil. Anhydrous ammonia, nitrogen solutions, ammonium nitrate, nitrate of soda, and sulfate of ammonia are employed to advantage in orchards, as top-dressings on meadows and pastures, and as a side-dressing in vegetable production and the growing of such field crops as cotton. When farm manure is available, the use of superphosphate with lime and manure in a legume rotation is generally desirable. The separate fertilizers may thus be effectively applied without the necessity of mixing and some saving thereby effected.

The bulk handling of separate carriers as well as mixtures thereof has already been mentioned. In some sections of the country these and other developments have essentially revolutionized the production and distribution of fertilizers.

19:16. THE MOVEMENT OF FERTILIZER SALTS IN THE SOIL

To fully understand the reasons for some of the specific methods of applying fertilizers (see next section), the movement of fertilizer salts within the soil should be reviewed. As previously pointed out, phosphorus compounds tend to move but little, except in the more sandy soils. (See p. 214.) Consequently, for maximum effectiveness this element should be placed in the zone of root development. Surface applications, unless worked into the soil, do not supply the deeper roots with phosphorus. Also, due to phosphorus immobility, the total quantity of this element necessary for a given season can be applied at one time without fear of loss by leaching.

On the other hand, potassium, and to an even greater extent, nitrogen, tend to move from their zones of placement. This movement is largely *vertical,* the salts moving up or down depending upon the direction of water movement. These translocations greatly influence the time and method of applying nitrogen and potassium. For example, it is often undesirable to supply nitrogen all in one annual application because of the leaching hazard. This tendency for the downward movement of nitrates is taken advantage of, however, in subsequent *top-dressings* where this fertilizer is applied on the surface of the ground. Water movement in the latter case is depended upon to carry the dissolved nitrate salts down to the plant roots. Top dressings of nitrogen solutions and urea may present problems in some cases due to the danger of volatilization (see p. 449).

The movement of nitrogen, and, to a lesser degree, potassium, must be considered in the *placement* of the fertilizer with respect to the seed. If the fertilizer salts are located in a band directly under the seeds, the upward movement of nitrates and some of the potassium salts by capillary water often results in injury to the stand. Rain immediately after planting followed by a long dry spell encourages such damage to seedlings. Placing the fertilizer immediately above the seed or on the soil surface also may result in injury especially to row crops. The possibility of such injuries should be kept in mind in reading the following section.

19:17. METHODS OF APPLYING SOLID FERTILIZERS

Much emphasis is placed on the selection of the correct fertilizer ratio and on the adequate and economical amounts of the various fertilizers to be used. However, the method of application is equally as important and must not be overlooked. A fertilizer should be placed in the soil in such a position that it will serve the plant to the best advantage. This involves not only different zones of placement but also the time of the year the fertilizer is to be applied. The methods of application will be discussed on the basis of the crops to be fertilized.

ROW CROPS. Cultivated crops such as corn, cotton, and potatoes are usually fertilized in the *hill* or the *row*, part or all of the fertilizer being applied at the time of planting. If placed in the hill the fertilizer may be deposited slightly below and on one side, or better, on both sides of the seed. When applied to the row, the fertilizer usually is laid in as a narrow *band*, on one or both sides of the row, 2 or 3 inches away and a little below the seed level. (See Fig. 19:7.)

When the amount of fertilizer is large, it is often wise to broadcast part and thoroughly work it into the soil before the planting is done. In some cases the crop is side-dressed with an additional amount of fertilizer later in the season. This practice involves placing the fertilizer along the side of the row at a time most satisfactory to the crop. This requires experience and good judgment.

VEGETABLES. Vegetables are fertilized much the same as are other row crops. However, larger *total* amounts are usually applied and side-dressing is common, especially with a nitrogen fertilizer such as nitrate of soda. This is done after the crop is well started and is in addition to the regular fertilization. When the fertilizer is applied around the hill, as with such crops as melons, the treatment is called a *spot-application*.

SMALL GRAINS. With small grains and similar crops the drill is equipped with a fertilizer distributor, the fertilizer entering the

Figure 19:7. The best fertilizer placement for row crops is to the side and slightly below the seed. This eliminates danger of fertilizer "burn" and concentrates the nutrients near the seed. (Photo courtesy National Plant Food Institute, Washington, D.C.)

soil more or less in contact with the seed. As long as the fertilizer is low in analysis and the amount applied does not exceed 300 or 400 pounds per acre, germination injury is not serious. Higher rates, especially of high analysis fertilizers, may result in serious injury if the seed and fertilizer are placed together. The more modern grain drills are equipped to place the fertilizer alongside the seed rather than in contact with it.

PASTURES AND MEADOWS. With meadows, pastures, and lawns, it is advisable to fertilize the soil well at the time of seeding. The fertilizer may be applied with the seed, or better, broadcasted, and worked thoroughly into the soil as the seedbed is prepared. The latter method is preferable, especially if the fertilization is heavy. During succeeding years it may be necessary to top-dress such crops with a suitable fertilizer mixture. This requires care. The amount of fertilizer applied and the time of treatment should be so regulated as to avoid injury to the foliage and to the root crowns of the plants.

TREES. Orchard trees usually are treated individually, the fertilizer being applied around each tree within the spread of the branches but beginning several feet from the trunk. The fertilizer is worked into the soil as much as possible. When the orchard cover-crop needs fertilization, it is treated separately, the fertilizer being drilled in at the time of seeding or broadcast later.

Ornamental trees are often fertilized by what is called the *perforation* method. Numerous small holes are dug around each tree, within the outer half of the branch-spread zone and extending well into the upper subsoil. Into these holes, which are afterward filled up, is placed a suitable amount of an appropriate fertilizer. This method of application places the nutrients within the root zone and avoids an undesirable stimulation of the grass that may be growing around ornamental trees.

PLOW-SOLE FERTILIZATION. Larger quantities of fertilizer are often required than can be safely applied in bands at planting time. One method used to supply the extra fertilizer is that of plowing under and thereby placing part of the application on the *plow sole* before the crop is planted. This type of application is probably most widely used as a supplementary measure rather than to replace the customary methods. Adverse weather conditions may seriously reduce the effectiveness of this procedure, however.

19:18. THE APPLICATION OF LIQUID FERTILIZERS

The use of liquid materials as a means of fertilization is assuming considerable importance in certain areas of this country. Three primary methods of applying liquid fertilizers have been used: (1) direct application to the soil; (2) application in irrigation water; and (3) the spraying of plants with suitable fertilizer solutions.

DIRECT APPLICATION TO SOIL. The practice of making direct applications of anhydrous ammonia, nitrogen solutions, and mixed fertilizers to soils is rapidly increasing throughout the United States. In each case equipment is needed designed specifically to handle the chemical in question. Carbon steel or plastic-lined containers are used for mixed fertilizers, whereas aluminum containers are needed for most of the nitrogen solutions, and mild steel is used for anhydrous ammonia. Pumps are needed to transfer and apply the aqua ammonia, liquid mixes, and no-pressure solutions. Anhydrous ammonia and pressure solutions must be injected into the soil to prevent losses by volatilization. Depths of 6 and 2 inches, respectively, are considered adequate for these two materials.

IN IRRIGATION WATER. In the West, particularly in California and Arizona, there is some application of liquid fertilizers in irrigation waters. Liquid ammonia, nitrogen solutions, phosphoric acid, and even complete fertilizers are allowed to dissolve in the irrigation stream. The nutrients are thus carried into the soil in solution. This requires no added application costs and allows the utilization of relatively inexpensive nitrogen carriers. Increased usage of these materials attest the growing popularity of the irrigation method of application. Some care must be used, however, to prevent ammonia loss by evaporation.

APPLIED AS SPRAY ON LEAVES. The direct application of micronutrients or urea to plants as a spray has been made. This type of fertilization is unique. Nor does it involve any extra procedures or machinery since the fertilizer is applied simultaneously with the insecticides. Apple trees seem to respond especially well to urea as much of the nitrogen is absorbed by the leaves. Moreover, that which drips or is washed off is by no means lost for it falls on the soil from which it may later be absorbed by plants.

19:19. FACTORS INFLUENCING THE KIND AND AMOUNT OF FERTILIZERS TO APPLY

The agricultural value of a fertilizer is necessarily uncertain, since a material so easily subject to change is placed in contact with two wide variables, the *soil* and the *crop*. Soil conditions are constantly fluctuating, not only from year to year but progressively throughout the season. The kind and the amount of the fertilizer applied should, as nearly as possible, meet these changes.

Also, the soil and the added fertilizer react with each other often very vigorously, both chemically and biologically. The reversion of phosphoric acid is an example of the first; the microbial hydrolysis of urea illustrates the latter. The result may be an increase or, more often, a decrease in the effectiveness of the fertilizer. Due allowance should be made for these reactions when deciding on the kind and amount of fertilizer to apply.

Again there is the *weather* which has a tremendous effect on the soil, upon the crop, and upon the fertilizer applied. If there is either an excess or deficiency of moisture, full efficiency of the fertilizer cannot be expected. In fact, any factor which may tend to limit plant growth will necessarily reduce fertilizer efficiency, and consequently the crop response to fertilization. It is only when other factors are not limiting that the amounts of fertilizers can be estimated with any degree of certainty.

In spite of the complexity of the situation, however, certain *guides* can be used in deciding the kind and amounts of fertilizers to be applied. The following are especially pertinent:

1. Kind of crop to be grown
   - economic value
   - nutrient removal
   - absorbing ability

2. Chemical condition of the soil in respect to
   - total nutrients
   - available nutrients

3. Physical state of the soil, especially as to
   - moisture content
   - aeration

The last of these factors in most cases has an indirect effect on fertilizer usage and has been discussed sufficiently elsewhere (pp. 199 and 254). Consequently, only the first two will be considered in the following sections.

19:20. KIND OF CROP TO BE FERTILIZED

Crops of high economic value such as vegetables justify larger fertilizer expenditures per pound of response obtained. Consequently, for these crops complete fertilizers are used in rather large amounts. As much as 2,000 pounds of analyses such as 8–16–16 are often recommended.

With crops having a low economic value per acre, much lower rates of fertilizer application are generally advisable. The extra yields obtained by applying large amounts of fertilizer are not usually sufficient, especially with such crops as natural pastures and meadows, to pay for the additional plant nutrients used.

It must always be remembered that the very highest yields obtainable under fertilizer stimulation are not always the ones that give the best return on the money invested (see Fig. 19:8). In other words, the law of diminishing returns is a factor in fertilizer practice regardless of the crop being grown. Therefore, the application of moderate amounts of fertilizer is to be urged for all soils until the maximum paying quantity that may be applied for any given crop is approximately ascertained.

If the nutrient removal by a given crop is high, fertilizer applications are usually increased to compensate for this loss. The extra fertilizer may

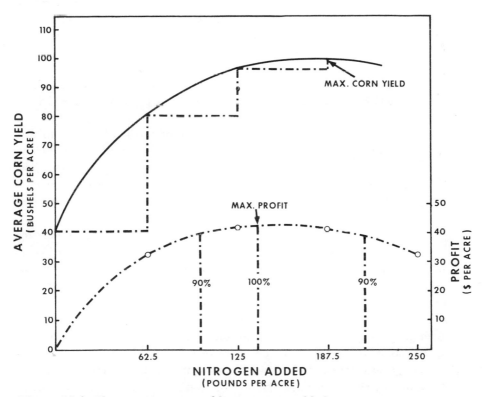

Figure 19:8. The average corn yield response to added nitrogen on 21 experiments in North Carolina and the calculated profit or net return to fertilizer. Note that maximum profit is obtained at a lower fertilizer rate than maximum yield. (From O. P. Engelstad. "Agronomic Response to Bulk Blended Fertilizers," A chapter in New Frontiers in Fertilizer Technology and Use, *Tennessee Valley Authority, 1964.*)

be applied directly to the particular crop under consideration or to some preceding and more responsive crop in the rotation. It should not be implied that in all cases an attempt should be made to return nutrients in amounts equivalent to those that have been removed. Sometimes advantage can be taken of the nutrient-supplying power of the soil. This source is usually insufficient, however, and extra fertilizer additions must be made. In fact, due to the vigorous reaction of phosphorus with soils, additions of this element in considerable excess of the amounts removed by crops and in other ways are usually economically sound.

Tremendous differences exist in the ability of plants to absorb nutrients from a given soil. For example, lespedeza and peanuts, both of which are legumes, can readily absorb adequate potassium under much lower soil potash levels than can alfalfa or soybeans. Consequently, responses to additions of potassium usually are much greater with the latter two crops. Obviously, crop characteristics deserve very careful study.

19:21. CHEMICAL CONDITION OF THE SOIL — TOTAL VS. PARTIAL ANALYSES

To determine the kind and quantity of fertilizer to add to soil, it is necessary to know what nutrient elements (or element) are deficient. At first thought this might appear to be a very simple proposition. Chemistry has to its credit so many wonderful accomplishments it would seem mere routine to analyze the soil for the various nutrient elements and immediately identify those that are deficient.

As will appear later, however, this is asking rather too much unless the chemical data are extensively supplemented by information from other sources. No phase of soil science has received so much popular recognition as has chemical analysis; nor has any other *technical soil procedure* been so generally overrated in the minds of the general public. Nevertheless, certain of these tests (especially the "quick tests") are of considerable value when properly run and when interpreted by competent specialists who have information of a practical nature at their command.

Two general types of chemical analyses of soils are commonly made— *total* and *partial*. In a *total analysis* the entire amount of any particular constituent present in the soil is determined, regardless of its form of combination and its availability. Such data are of great value in studying soil formation and other phases of soil science. Ordinarily, however, they give little if any information on the availability of the essential elements to plants. Analyses suitable for measuring only the available portion of a given nutrient constituent must be employed. Such analyses are called *partial,* because only a portion of the total quantity of a soil constituent is determined.

19:22. TESTS FOR AVAILABLE SOIL NUTRIENTS — QUICK TESTS

Many procedures for the *partial analyses* of soils have been developed during the past half century. In general, these procedures attempt to extract from the soil amounts of certain fertility elements which are correlated with those removed by plants. The large number of extracting solutions which have been employed in trying to measure nutrient availability is mute testimony of the difficulties involved. The extraction solutions employed have varied from strong acids such as H_2SO_4 to weak solutions of CO_2 in water. Buffered salt solutions such as sodium or ammonium acetate are the extracting agents now most commonly used.

QUICK TESTS—GENERAL CONSIDERATION. The group of tests most extensively used for nutrient availability are the so-called *rapid* or *quick tests.* As the name implies, the individual determinations are quickly made, a properly equipped laboratory being able to handle thousands of samples a year. Since these tests are the only ones having practical possibilities for widespread usage, their limitations as well as their merits will be critically reviewed.

A weak extracting solution such as buffered sodium acetate is generally employed in rapid tests and only a few minutes are allowed for the extraction. Most of the nutrients removed are those rather loosely held by the colloidal complex. The test for a given constituent may be reported either in general terms, such as *low, medium,* or *high,* or more specifically, in pounds per acre. The constituents most commonly tested for are phosphorus, potassium, calcium, and magnesium, and aluminum, iron, and manganese are frequently included.

LIMITATIONS OF QUICK TESTS. Perhaps the first limitation is the difficulty of properly *sampling soils* in the *field.* Generally only a very small sample is taken, perhaps a pint or so from an area of land often several acres in size. The chances of error, especially if only a few borings are made, are quite high. In general, at least 15 to 20 borings are suggested for each sample in order to increase the probability that a representative portion of the soil has been obtained.

A second limitation of these tests is the fact that their chemical procedures are somewhat *arbitrary.* It is essentially impossible to extract from a soil sample in a few minutes the amount of a nutrient, or even a constant proportion thereof, that a plant will absorb from that soil in the field during the entire growing season. To make matters worse, serious *technical difficulties* are sometimes encountered in accurately determining the amounts of the several nutrients even after they are extracted. This emphasizes the importance of good scientific equipment as well as technical knowledge and skill in making rapid tests.

Perhaps the biggest hurdle to overcome in the successful employment of quick tests is the *interpretation* of the chemical data obtained. Since the results are arbitrary, they must be correlated with crop responses before reliable fertilizer recommendations can be made. Even then the recommendations must be made in light of a practical knowledge of the crop to be grown, the characteristics of the soil under study, and other environmental conditions. Two soils testing exactly the same in respect to a given constituent have been found to respond quite differently in terms of crop yields to identical fertilizer treatments in the field.

TRAINED PERSONNEL SHOULD MAKE AND INTERPRET TESTS. Obviously, it is unwise to place any particular confidence in fertilizer recommendations when the tests are made and interpreted by an amateur. Not only might the novice make inaccurate determinations, but he is sure to lack the knowledge and judgment necessary for a rational interpretation in terms of fertilizer needs. The interpretation of quick test data is best accomplished by experienced and technically trained men, who fully understand the scientific principles underlying the common field procedures.

As already suggested, it is essential that a person have considerable related information in order to make the proper use of quick test data. Examples of supplementary data desirable are shown by the sample information sheet in Fig. 19:9. This supplementary information may be as helpful as the actual test results in making fertilizer recommendations.

MERITS OF RAPID TESTS. It must not be inferred from the preceding discussion that the limitations of rapid tests outweigh their advantages. In fact, when the precautions already cited are observed, rapid tests are an invaluable tool in making fertilizer recommendations. Moreover, these tests will become of even greater importance insofar as they are correlated with the results of field fertilizer experiments. Such field trials undoubtedly will be expanded to keep pace with the increasing use of the rapid tests.

19:23. THE BROADER ASPECTS OF FERTILIZER PRACTICE

It is obvious that fertilizer practice involves many intricate details regarding soils, crops, and fertilizers. In fact, the interrelations of

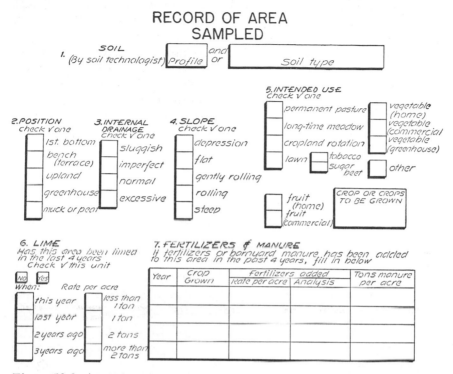

Figure 19:9. *A satisfactory interpretation of a quick test analysis of a soil cannot be made without certain pertinent field data. The record sheet above suggests the items that are most helpful to the expert in making a fertility recommendation. (Modified from a form used by the Ohio Agr. Exp. Sta.)*

these three are so complicated and far reaching that a practical grasp of the situation requires years of experience. The unavoidable lack of exactness in fertilizer decisions should ever be kept in mind.

Leaving the details and viewing the situation in a broad way, it seems to be well established that any fertilizer scheme should be built around the effective use of the most expensive of the fertilizer elements, nitrogen. Applications of phosphorus and potassium should be made to balance and supplement the nitrogen supply, whether it be from the soil, crop residues or added fertilizers.

A second aspect relates to economics. Farmers do not use fertilizers just to grow big crops or to increase the nutrient content of their soils. They do so to make a living. As a result, any fertilizer practice, no matter how sound it may be technically, which does not give a fair economic return will not long stand the test of time.

From this follows another important point. Fertilizers are added because of their effects on crops. For that reason it is inappropriate to think only in terms of the soil-fertilizer interactions. The nature of the crop, its requirements and economic value must be considered.

Not only must the soil, the crop, and the fertilizer receive careful study, but the crop rotation employed and its management should be considered in addition. Obviously, also the fertilizer applications must be correlated with the use of farm manure, crop residues, green manure, trace elements, and lime. Moreover, the residues of previous fertilizer additions must not be forgotten. In short, fertilizer practice is only a phase, but a very important one, of the fertility management of soils.

Chapter 20

Farm Manure and Green Manure

Farm manure is one of the most important agricultural by-products. By its utilization, part of the unused portion of the crop may enter the soil, there to exert an influence far greater than its nutrient content would lead one to expect. The world has already entered an era in which the prevention of agricultural waste is becoming necessary. Therefore, up-to-date farm management demands a more careful handling, as well as a wiser utilization of the manure produced on the farm.

20:1. THE CHEMICAL COMPOSITION OF FARM MANURE

The term *farm manure* is employed in reference to the refuse from all animals of the farm, although as a general rule the bulk of the manure which ultimately finds its way back to the land is produced by cattle. This is supplemented to a greater or less extent by manure from horses, hogs, sheep, and poultry.

Farm manure consists of two original components, the *solid* and the *liquid,* in about the ratio of 3 to 1. On the average, a little more than *one half the nitrogen,* almost *all of the phosphoric acid,* and about *two fifths of the potash* are found in the solid manure. (See Fig. 20:1.) Neverthe-

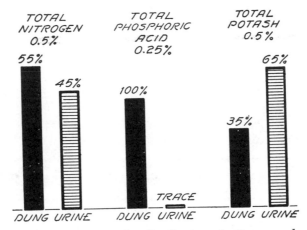

Figure 20:1. *Diagram showing the distribution of nitrogen, phosphoric acid, and potash between the solid and liquid portions of average farm manure.*

less, this apparent advantage of the solid manure is offset by the ready availability of the constituents carried by the urine, giving the latter about an equal agricultural value with the solid excrement. Such figures are suggestive of the care that should be taken of the liquid manure.

[1] The composition of fresh animal-excrement[a]

			Percentage of		
Excrement, percentage		H₂O	N	P₂O₅	K₂O
Horse	Solid, 80	75	0.55	0.30	0.40
	Urine, 20	90	1.35	Trace	1.25
	Whole manure	78	0.70	0.25	0.55
Cow	Solid, 70	85	0.40	0.20	0.10
	Urine, 30	92	1.00	Trace	1.35
	Whole manure	86	0.60	0.15	0.45
Sheep	Solid, 67	60	0.75	0.50	0.45
	Urine, 33	85	1.35	0.05	2.10
	Whole manure	68	0.95	0.35	1.00
Swine	Solid, 60	80	0.55	0.50	0.40
	Urine, 40	97	0.40	0.10	0.45
	Whole manure	87	0.50	0.35	0.40
Hens	Whole manure	55	1.00	0.80	0.40

[a] L. L. Van Slyke, *Fertilizers and Crop Production* (New York: Orange Juidd, 1932), pp. 216–26.

Although extended data are available as to the chemical composition of the liquid and solid portions of the excreta from the various farm animals,[1] it is extremely difficult to quote reliable average figures on mixed farm manure as it ordinarily is applied to the land. This is because a number of variable factors may radically change the amounts and proportions of nitrogen, phosphoric acid, and potash present. The more important of these factors are: (1) kind of animal; (2) age, condition, and individuality of animals; (3) food consumed; (4) litter used; and (5) the handling and storage which the manure receives before it is spread on the land.

In spite of the marked variability of farm manure, representative composition figures will be ventured. For purposes of calculation and discussion, average farm manure ready for field application will be considered as containing *0.5 per cent of nitrogen, 0.25 per cent of phosphoric acid,* and *0.5 per cent of potash.* The tentative nature of such figures, however, must always be kept in mind. Besides nitrogen, phosphorus, and potassium, farm manure contains calcium, magnesium, sulfur, and probably all of the trace elements. The latter are in some cases extremely important in the maintenance of a balanced nutrient condition in soils so treated.

20:2. OUTSTANDING CHARACTERISTICS OF FARM MANURE[2]

As a farm manure is essentially a fertilizer, it is logical to contrast it with the ready-mixed commercial fertilizers on the market. In such a comparison, six characteristics are outstanding: (1) the moist condition of manure; (2) its variability; (3) its low analysis; (4) its unbalanced nutrient condition; (5) the residual influence exerted by farm manure; and (6) its rapid fermentative processes.

MOISTURE AND VARIABILITY. Of the above characteristics the first two may be disposed of quickly. The variability of farm

---

[2] Data as to the amounts of manure likely to be produced by the different classes of farm animals are often useful in fertility calculations.

Tons of Manure Produced Annually by Farm Animals per 1,000 Pounds Live Weight[a]

Animal	Weight of Excrement	Weight of Bedding	Total Weight
Horse	9.00	3.0	12.00
Cow	13.50	1.5	15.00
Pig	15.25	3.0	18.25
Sheep	6.25	3.5	9.75
Steer	7.50	1.5	9.00
Hen	4.75	—	4.75

[a] L. L. Van Slyke, *op. cit.,* p. 287.

manure has already been sufficiently emphasized since it is a condition ordinarily to be expected. As to the moisture, whether in fresh or well-rotted manure, the amount may vary from 50 to 80 per cent depending on conditions.

LOW ANALYSIS. Since representative farm manure is considered to contain 0.5 per cent of nitrogen, 0.25 per cent of phosphoric acid, and 0.5 per cent of potash, a ton of this material supplies only 10, 5, and 10 pounds of total nitrogen, phosphoric acid, and potash, respectively. It is without doubt a low-analysis material when compared to the commercial fertilizers commonly on the market, such as an 8–16–16 for instance, which supplies 160, 320, and 320 pounds per ton, respectively, of these three constituents.

It must not be assumed, however, that the amounts of the three fertilizer elements added to an acre of land in an ordinary application of farm manure are correspondingly small. Because of the large acre applications of this fertilizer (10, 15, or even 20 tons an acre), the quantities of the nutrient elements added are comparatively large. For example, 10 tons of representative farm manure will supply in total about 100 pounds of nitrogen, 50 pounds of phosphoric acid, and 100 pounds of potash.

In such a comparison, however, it is well to remember that only a part of the nutrient constituents of farm manure is readily available. In general, only about *one half of the nitrogen, one sixth of the phosphoric acid,* and a little more than *one half of the potash* are readily available (during the first season) to plants. On the basis of readily available nutrients, 1 ton of average farm manure supplies approximately 5 pounds of N, 1 pound of P_2O_5, and 5 pounds of K_2O.

NUTRIENTS UNBALANCED. The phosphoric acid of most mineral soils is not only low but rather unavailable. Moreover, the phosphorus added in fertilizers is adsorbed rather strongly by the soil complex and is likely to become partly inactive. As a consequence, it seems necessary for a complete fertilizer to carry as much or even more phosphoric acid than nitrogen or even potash. The ratio of a ready-mixed complete commercial fertilizer in respect to these three constituents (N–P_2O_5–K_2O) ordinarily is seldom less than 1–1–1 or 1–2–1, while in some cases the ratio is as high as 1–3–1.

Farm manure with an availability ratio of 5–1–5 is obviously too low in phosphoric acid to be fully effective and for that reason is considered unbalanced. It is often advisable, especially when the farm manure is used for cereal crops, to correct this condition by reinforcing it with suitable amounts of superphosphate or some other phosphatic fertilizer. (See p. 571.)

RESIDUAL EFFECTS. The length of time through which the effects of an application of farm manure may be detected in crop growth is surprising. Hall[3] cites data from the Rothamsted experiments in which the effects of eight yearly acre applications of 14 tons each were apparent 40 years after the last treatment. This, of couurse, is an extreme case. Ordinarily, profitable increases may be obtained from manure only for three or four years after the treatment.

The sixth outstanding characteristic of farm manure, its fermentative and decay activities, will be considered in the following section.

20:3. THE FERMENTATION OF MANURE

In the process of digestion, the food of animals becomes more or less decomposed. This condition comes about partly because of the digestive processes themselves and partly from the concurrent bacterial action that takes place. Consequently, the fresh excrement consists of decayed or partially decayed plant materials. This is more or less intimately mixed with litter and the whole mass is moistened with the urine carrying considerable quantities of soluble compounds of nitrogen, potassium, and other nutrients. Moreover, the whole mass is teeming with bacteria and other organisms.

AEROBIC FERMENTATION. When manure is first produced, it is usually somewhat loose, especially if considerable litter is present. The first microbial changes are, therefore, likely to be largely aerobic in nature. These tranformations usually are rapid and are accompanied by considerable heat.

The simple nitrogenous compounds are influenced first, although the more complicated constituents are by no means unaffected. Carbon dioxide is given off in large quantities. The urea of the urine is readily influenced by aerobic activities and quickly undergoes hydrolysis. The ammonium carbonate which results is unstable and promptly produces ammonia. The odor of this gas in horse stables gives evidence of such a change.

$$CO(NH_2)_2 + 2H_2O \longrightarrow (NH_4)_2CO_3$$
$$(NH_4)_2CO_3 \longrightarrow 2NH_3\uparrow + CO_2\uparrow + H_2O$$

If conditions are favorable for nitrification, and such is likely to be the case, nitrates may appear in abundance. Since such compounds of nitrogen are very soluble and subject to but little adsorption, serious leach-

---

[3] A. D. Hall, *Fertilizers and Manures* (New York: Dutton, 1928), p. 234.

ing losses may occur. Hence, in the earlier and better aerated decomposition stages, farm manure may be depleted of its nitrogen in two forms —ammoniacal and nitrate.

ANAEROBIC DECAY. In a manure the gaseous oxygen is gradually used up while carbon dioxide is released. The decay now changes from aerobic to anaerobic, it becomes slower, and the temperature tends to fall. New organisms may now function, although many of those active under aerobic conditions probably continue to be effective. The products become changed to a considerable degree. Carbon dioxide, of course, is still evolved in large amounts, but instead of ammonia being formed, the nitrogenous matter is converted, at least in part, into the usual putrefactive products.

REDUCTION IN BULK. Because of the great loss of carbon dioxide and water during these decay processes, there is a considerable reduction in the bulk of the manure. Fresh excrement readily loses from 20 to 40 per cent in bulk by partial rotting and perhaps 50 per cent as it becomes more thoroughly decomposed. It is often argued that, if the manure is properly stored, this rapid loss of carbon dioxide and water should raise the percentage amounts of the fertilizer elements present. This may be true for potash and phosphoric acid. But in practice the losses in handling due to leaching and fermentation sometimes are so pronounced as to place well-rotted manure at a disadvantage as far as its total supply of plant nutrients is concerned. This is especially likely to be the case in respect to nitrogen which is subject to losses by both volatilization and leaching.

WELL-DECAYED VS. FRESH MANURE. In many cases, however, well-rotted manure[4] is more desirable than the fresh material. This is especially true if the fresh manure is strawy. The addition of straw to a soil may widen its carbon-nitrogen ratio and reduce as well as prevent the formation of nitrate nitrogen (p. 148). Strawy manure apparently tends to produce the same effect, and a crop immediately following its application may show nitrogen starvation. Under such conditions the well-decayed product is more desirable. When manure is used as a top-dressing, as is sometimes the case with fall wheat and other crops, well-rotted material should always be applied if possible. In trucking and vegetable gardening, well-decomposed manure is generally preferred. Such is also the case with home gardens, flower beds, lawns, and

---

[4] A change of a biological nature which takes place if the manure dries out too much is *fire-fanging*. Many people consider this to be due to actual combustion, as the manure is very light in weight and has every appearance of being burned. This condition, however, is produced by fungi and the dry and dusty appearance of the manure is due to the mycelia, which penetrate in all directions and use up the valuable constituents. Manure thus affected is of little value either as a fertilizer or as a soil amendment.

greenhouses. *Composting,* which is largely a biological process, is often resorted to, especially in the latter cases, farm manure being used in building up the compost pile. Because of its high organic content and the influence of its nitrogen and microorganisms, manure is especially valuable for such purposes.

A compost is commonly made of alternate layers of manure and the vegetable matter that is to be decayed. Layers of sod or of soil high in organic matter may also be introduced to advantage. The manure supplies especially active decay organisms which, in the presence of nitrogen, cause a rapid and effective humification. The foundation of such a compost is usually soil, and the pile is preferably capped with earth.

The mass should be kept moist in order to reduce the loss of ammonia and elemental nitrogen and to encourage vigorous bacterial action. Superphosphate is often added to balance up the mixture and make it more effective. A nitrogen fertilizer may also be employed with profit as well as ground limestone.

20:4. NUTRIENT LOSSES DURING MANURIAL PRODUCTION

A certain amount of every crop is lost before it is consumed by animals. Such loss is usually small on most farms, especially when compared to the nutrients retained by the livestock. Attention is therefore particularly directed toward those losses sustained by the food as it undergoes normal digestion, and is about to be voided.

As might be expected, the data bearing on this phase is variable, since so much depends on the age, conditions, individuality, and class of animal, and the character of the food. As a generalization and for purposes of calculation, it may be considered that *three fourths of the nitrogen, four fifths of the phosphorus, nine tenths of the potash,* and *one half of the organic matter* are recovered in the voided excrement. This means losses of about 25, 20, 10, and 50 per cent, respectively, for these constituents. (See Fig. 20:2.)

20:5. LOSSES DURING THE HANDLING AND STORAGE OF FARM MANURE

Since approximately one half of the nitrogen and three fifths of the potash of average farm manure are in a soluble condition, the possibility of loss by leaching is usually great, even though the manure is not

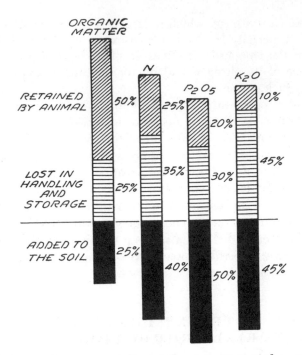

Figure 20:2. *A tentative representation of the proportion of the organic matter, nitrogen, phosphoric acid, and potash originally presented in the feed (1) retained by the animals, (2) lost in handling and storage of the manure, and (3) applied to the soil.*

exposed to especially heavy rainfall. In addition, decomposition, both of an aerobic and anaerobic nature, will cause a rapid waste of nitrogen in the ammonium, nitrate, and elemental forms. Packing and moistening the manure in the pile will change the decay from aerobic to anaerobic, thus reducing somewhat the waste of gaseous nitrogen while encouraging the simplification of the manurial constituents. Tight floors in the stables and impervious bottoms under the manure pile should considerably diminish leaching losses.

While the figures are extremely variable, it is probable that *one half* of the *nitrogen, potash,* and *organic matter* and at least *one third* of the *phosphoric acid* of farm manure are lost even under fairly careful methods of storage. On farms where manure remains outside for several months, the losses will, of course, be higher. Thus, at least one half of the nutrient constituents of the manure may often be wasted. This represents considerably over one half of the fertilizer value, since the elements removed are those most readily available to plants.

If we consider the losses which the food sustains during digestion and the waste of the manure in handling and storage, we cannot expect that more than 25 *per cent of the organic matter,* 40 *per cent of the nitrogen,* 50 *per cent of the phosphoric acid,* and 45 *per cent of the potash* of the original crop as removed from the land will, under ordinary conditions, reach the soil. (See Fig. 20:2.) This is a fairly conservative estimate.

20:6. PRACTICAL HANDLING AND STORAGE OF FARM MANURE

REDUCING LIQUID LOSSES. Considerable loss of manurial constituents occurs in the stable, due to leaching. Therefore, the first care is to the bedding, which should be chosen for its absorptive properties, its cost, and its capacity to keep animals clean.

Coordinated with this are the floors, which should be tight so that the free liquid will be held in contact with the absorbing materials. Preservation in stalls with tight floors has been for years a common method of handling farm manure in England. The trampling of the animals and the continued addition of litter as the manure accumulates aid in the preservation.

APPLY DIRECTLY TO THE FIELD. When it is possible to haul the manure directly to the field, this practice is to be advised. This system saves time and labor, and very largely obviates leaching losses since the soluble portions of the manure are carried directly into the soil. Such a practice, however, will not prevent some losses by volatilization.

It should not be assumed that daily spreading will always result in the greatest conservation of nutrients. For example, consider the areas where, during the winter months, manure is spread on frozen ground or on snow over frozen ground. In the spring the snow melts and the water often runs off the land before the soil thaws. This melt water carries much of the soluble potash and nitrogen of the manure with it, especially on land that is quite sloping. As much as about 25 per cent of the potash supplied in manure may be lost in this manner.

STORAGE IN PILES. It is often necessary to store manure outside, fully exposed to the weather. When this is the case, certain precautions should be observed. In the first place, the pile should be located on level ground far enough from the eaves of any building so that it receives no extra water in times of storm. The sides of the heap should be steep enough to shed water readily, while the depth of the pile should be such as to allow little leaching even after heavy storms. The earth under the manure may be slightly dished in order to prevent loss of excess water. If possible, the soil of the depression should be puddled, or better, covered with cement.

MANURE PITS. Some European farmers have constructed manure pits of concrete. These pits are usually rectangular in shape with a shed covering. One or even both ends may be open to facilitate the removal of the manure. In such a structure, leaching is prevented by the solid bottom while the roof allows a better control of moisture conditions. By keeping the manure carefully piled and well moistened, decomposition may proceed with a minimum waste. Large losses of nitrogen and especially of carbon (as CO_2), however, will still take place.

COVERED BARNYARDS. Another method of storage is in covered barnyards or in sheds where animals are fed and bedded. The floor of such a structure should be more or less impervious. The manure is kept thoroughly packed as well as damp by the animals. This is a common method of handling manure in the fattening of steers in the Middle West and elsewhere and allows a minimum loss.

It is evident from this consideration that well-protected and carefully preserved manure will be higher in available plant nutrients than that carelessly handled. Since hauling directly to the field affords less chance of loss by leaching and fermentation, this mode of handling should be adopted wherever feasible. If storage must be resorted to, the precautions already suggested should be observed insofar as possible.

20:7. ECONOMIC UTILIZATION OF FARM MANURE

METHOD AND RATE OF APPLICATION. In the application of manure to the land, the same general principles observed in the use of any fertilizer should be kept in mind. Of these, fineness of division and evenness of distribution are of prime importance. The efficiency of the manure may be raised considerably thereby.

A third important factor is the rate of application. Since the supply of manure is often limited in diversified farming, it is usually better, especially with field crops, to decrease the amounts at each spreading and cover a greater acreage. Thus, instead of adding 20 tons to the acre, 10 tons may be applied and twice the acreage covered. Applications can then be made oftener and a larger and quicker net return realized for each ton of manure.

MANURE SPREADER. Evenness of application and fineness of division are greatly facilitated by the use of a manure spreader.

This also makes possible the uniform application of small amounts of manure, even as low as 5 or 6 tons to the acre. It is impossible, or course, to spread such small amounts by hand and obtain an even distribution.

SURFACE APPLICATION VS. PLOWING UNDER. Whether manure should be plowed under or not depends largely on the crop on which it is used. On meadows and pastures it is spread as a top-dressing. With certain other crops, however, it is commonly plowed under. This is particularly necessary if the manure is long, coarse, and not well rotted. If manure is fine and well decomposed, it may be harrowed into the surface soil as is sometimes done with wheat. Obviously, the method of application employed will depend on the crop, the soil, and the condition of the manure.

C:N RATIO. In the utilization of farm manure it is well to remember that its addition to the soil in large amounts may widen the carbon-nitrogen ratio. This is likely to be the case if the manure is unusually strawy. The delay in plant growth that is sometimes observed from the use of strawy manure may be due to the reduction of nitrate accumulation induced by the high carbon content of the materials added. If such is likely to be the case, a sufficient interval should elapse between the application of the manure and the planting of the crop in order that nitrification may again be active.

20:8. REINFORCEMENT OF FARM MANURE

REASONS FOR REINFORCEMENT. As already explained, average farm manure contains about five times more readily available nitrogen and potassium than available phosphorus. (See p. 564.) It is thus badly unbalanced. In comparison with a complete commercial fertilizer, there should be at least five times more available phosphoric acid in the manure than is usually present to be sure that its nitrogen and potassium are properly balanced. Hence, in order to obtain the most economical results with manure, liberal applications of phosphorus should be used in the rotation in connection with it. Sometimes, however, part of the phosphatic fertilizer is mixed with the manure before it is applied to the land. This is the practice that is spoken of as *reinforcement*.

RATE OF PHOSPHATE ADDITIONS. The amount of phosphatic fertilizers that should be added to a ton of farm manure depends on the acre-rate of application of the latter. Ordinarily from 500 to 600 pounds of 16 to 20 per cent superphosphate or its equivalent are applied to the acre in this way during the course of a field crop rotation. Thus, if

10 tons of manure are spread on an acre, each ton should be reinforced with 50 or 60 pounds of ordinary superphosphate. If 15 tons of manure are applied to an acre, the reinforcement may be at the rate of 35 to 40 pounds of superphosphate a ton. If raw rock phosphate is used instead, it generally is applied at double the rate of superphosphate because of the less ready availability of the rock.

If the superphosphate is added each day in the stable in the case of dairy cows, 2 pounds per cow will amount to a reinforcement of about 50 pounds to the ton of manure. With this as a gauge any desired rate of superphosphate application to the land may be decided on, provided, of course, the tons of manure that are to go on each acre of land are known in advance. Thus, if the rate of manuring is to be 10 tons, 2 pounds of superphosphate daily per cow would mean the application of 500 pounds of superphosphate to each acre of land receiving the manure.

20:9. CROPS THAT RESPOND TO FARM MANURE

Since manure is available in limited amounts on the average farm and as mineral fertilizers give good results on grass and legumes, it is often considered judicious to reserve most of the manure for other crops of the rotation. This is especially the case when a feed crop such as corn or such cash crops as cabbage, tobacco, cotton, or potatoes are grown.

The top-dressing of the meadows with farm manure is allowable, especially with a new seeding or when the sod is soon to be plowed under for a cultivated crop. When the soil is acid and lime cannot be applied, it is practically necessary to top-dress the new seeding in order to insure a good stand of clover. Manure thus takes the place of lime, in a way, and strengthens and protects the crop. In many communities a large proportion of the farm manure is applied to the meadows, no doubt for the reasons just suggested.

The value of manure in orchards should not be overlooked, especially on sandy soils, as the maintenance of organic matter as well as nitrogen is a vital factor in orchard practice. In most cases, however, the fertility of an orchard soil can be maintained adequately by means of leguminous cover-crops and a nitrogenous commercial fertilizer, thus releasing what farm manure there is for use in the regular field rotation or for vegetables.

With trucking, garden, and greenhouse crops, the applications of large amounts of manure when obtainable have always proved advisable. As a matter of fact, manure when correctly handled, has shown itself one of the best fertilizers for intensive operations. This is due not only to the nutrients carried by the manure, but also to the large quantities of easily decomposed organic matter that are at the same time introduced. As large amounts of highly phosphatic fertilizers usually accompany or follow the manure in such cases, direct reinforcing is unnecessary.

20:10. FARM MANURE AND THE MAINTENANCE OF SOIL FERTILITY

The value of farm manure is determined not only by the organic matter it furnishes but especially by the quantity of nitrogen that it supplies. The nitrogen, when released by microbial activity, is used as a nutrient by higher plants. In addition, it makes possible the maintenance of a higher soil organic matter level than would otherwise be the case. Thus, even though farm manure no doubt has a very considerable influence on the physical and biological properties of the soil, it must be considered particularly as a nitrogen fertilizer and to a lesser degree one of potash also.

Viewed in this light the question immediately arises: Can the fertility problems of the representative general or dairy farm be solved by the use of farm manure even if it should be reinforced adequately with super phosphate? The answer, of course, is "No," especially if a more or less permanent fertility system is in operation. There are several reasons for such an answer.

In the first place, hardly one half of the nitrogen, potash, and phosphoric acid removed from the soil by the crops fed to animals is returned to the land in farm manure. (See Fig. 20:2.) And, of course, not all crops are used for animal food. Thus, the utilization of farm manure alone would obviously result in a gradual reduction of soil fertility unless other sources of nutrients were resorted to. Reinforcement with superphosphate would only delay the evil hour. It is only when farm manure is properly coordinated with lime, commercial fertilizers, and legumes as well as with good tillage, weed elimination, and soil-water and erosion control, that the fullest benefits from this valuable farm by-product are to be realized.

20:11. GREEN MANURES—DEFINED

From time immemorial the turning under of a green crop to better the condition of the soil has been a common agricultural practice.

Records show that the use of beans, vetches, and lupines for such a purpose was well understood by the Romans, who probably borrowed the idea from other nations. The art was lost in Europe to a great extent during the Middle Ages, but was revived again as the modern era was approached.

This practice of turning into the soil undecomposed green plant tissue is referred to as *green-manuring.* Material so added, if the soil is in a proper condition and well managed, brings about a number of favorable effects and may aid materially in maintaining or raising the crop-producing capacity of a soil.

20:12. THE BENEFITS OF GREEN-MANURING

SUPPLIES ORGANIC MATTER. The influence exerted by green-manuring which is generally mentioned first relates to the organic supply of the soil. When there is a shortage of farm manure, the practice becomes of special importance since roots and other crop residues may not be adequate to maintain the humus content of the land.

ADDITION OF NITROGEN. The plowing under of a green manure not only adds organic carbon to the soil but also returns soil nitrogen. The amount of nitrogen may be large or small, depending on conditions. If the crop turned under is a legume and the nodule organisms have been active, the store of soil nitrogen may be thereby increased. The organic matter content is also augmented since the amount of soil humus finally formed is determined to a considerable degree by the amount of organic nitrogen present (see p. 150).

BIOCHEMICAL BENEFITS. The organic material added in green manures also acts as a food for soil organisms, and tends to stimulate biological changes sometimes to a marked degree. Such biochemical action is of special consequence in the production of carbon dioxide, ammonium, nitrates, and perhaps other simple compounds. The response of the general-purpose flora of the soil and of the *Azotobacter* to carbonaceous and nitrogenous materials is well known. Even in peat soils, made up largely of organic matter, organisms may be definitely activated by the turning under of a green-manuring crop.

CONSERVATION AND AVAILABILITY OF NUTRIENTS. A growing green-manuring crop exerts a conserving influence on the nutrients of the soil since it takes up soluble constituents that might otherwise be lost in drainage or by erosion. In this respect it func tions as a *cover-crop*.[5] The presence of a green manure crop on the soil at a time when it might otherwise be bare is highly desirable.

The increased availability of the inorganic constituents of the soil is a phase that should not be forgotten in this connection. Jensen[6] found that the addition of 3 per cent of green manure to the soil raised the solubility of lime and phosphoric acid 30 to 100 per cent. This was over and above the mineral constituents which came directly from the decomposing green crop. Potassium, magnesium, and iron may also be markedly influenced in the same manner.

20:13. INFLUENCE OF LEGUMINOUS GREEN MANURES ON SOIL NITROGEN

When a nonlegume is turned under as a green manure, nitrogen originally in the soil is merely returned in an organic form. There is no gain. But if a legume is so utilized, there is a possibility of increasing temporarily the soil nitrogen to the extent of the symbiotic fixation. Since an increase in the organic nitrogen of the soil means an increase in fertility as well as a possible rise in humus, the probable magnitude of the fixation is worthy of some attention.

AMOUNTS OF NITROGEN FIXED. Data have already been cited (p. 154) which indicate that the nodule organisms of a vigorous crop of alfalfa might fix above 200 pounds of nitrogen an acre. Comparable figures for red clover are perhaps 100 to 150 pounds an acre. Soybeans compare rather well with red clover but hairy vetch and field beans ordinarily will acquire from the air only a half or a third as much nitrogen. If these crops are turned under, the soil, of course, gains in organic nitrogen to the extent of the microbial fixation. For instance, a ton of dry red clover contains from 40 to 50 pounds of nitrogen. If a green-manuring crop equivalent to 2 tons of such dry substance an acre should be turned under, there would be a gain in soil nitrogen of 80 to 100 pounds.

INCREASE IN HUMUS. Assuming the latter figure and a carbon-nitrogen ratio of 12 to 1, this amount of organic nitrogen should support an increase in humus of perhaps 1,800 pounds if it were all used

---

[5] A *cover-crop* is one planted for the purpose of covering or protecting the soil at certain times of year, especially from erosion hazards.

A *catch-crop* is one that follows the main crop. It must be rapid in growth as it can occupy the soil only a relatively short time. Both a cover-crop and a catch-crop may, on occasion, be used as a green manure.

[6] C. A. Jensen, "Effect of Decomposing Organic Matter on the Solubility of Certain Inorganic Constituents of the Soil," *Jour. Agr. Res.*, 9:253–68, May 1917.

in this way. Concurrently, of course, there is the stimulation of soil organisms of all kinds. This activation, common to all green manures when properly used, is especially characteristic of those of a leguminous nature.

20:14. THE DESIRABLE CHARACTERISTICS OF A GREEN MANURE

An ideal green-manuring crop should possess three major characteristics: (1) rapid growth; (2) abundant and succulent tops; and (3) the ability to grow well on poor soils. The more rapid the growth, the greater the chance of fitting such a crop into the rotation and of using it economically as a means of soil improvement. Abundant tops and roots are, of course, a necessary feature. And as already suggested, the higher the moisture content of the green manure the more rapid is the decay and the more quickly are benefits obtained. As the need of organic matter is especially urgent on poor land, a hardy crop has great advantages.

When other conditions are equal, it is better to make use of a leguminous green manure in preference to a nonleguminous one, because of the nitrogen gained by the soil and the organic activity it promotes. A little additional nitrogen is sometimes of tremendous importance.

However, it is often difficult to obtain a catch of some legumes and they may be so valuable as animal feed, that it is poor management to turn the stand under. Again, the seeds of many legumes are expensive, almost prohibiting the use of such crops as green manures. Moreover, some legumes do not fit into the common rotations in such a way as to be turned under conveniently as a green manure.

20:15. PLANTS SUITABLE AS GREEN MANURES

Some of the plants utilized in the various parts of the United States as green manures are listed in Table 20:1. Their value, of course, depends in part on climate, some of those mentioned being unsuited to northern regions as vice versa.

The growing of two crops together for green-manuring purposes is sometimes recommended. If properly chosen in respect to growth habits, climatic adaptation, and soil requirements, the advantages are noteworthy. Not only can larger amounts of green material be produced but also, if one of the crops is a legume, nitrogen fixation may be taken ad-

Table 20:1. List of Possible Green-manuring Crops

Legumes		Nonlegumes	
Southern Section Especially	*Wide Range*	*Wide Range in Most Cases*	
Crimson clover	Alfalfa	Rye	Ryegrass
Bur clover	Red Clover	Oats	Sudan grass
Lespedeza	Sweet clover	Barley	Mustard
Crotalaria	Soybean	Millet	Rape
Smooth vetch	Canadian field	Buckwheat	Weeds
Austrian winter	pea	Wheat	Winter oats and
pea	Cowpea		barley

vantage of. Also one crop may offer physical support to the other, a factor of no mean importance when dealing with plants that tend to lodge.

Oats and peas, and rye and vetch are excellent examples of such green-manure combinations. The two nonlegumes in these cases are highly desirable because of their rapid, abundant, and succulent growth and because they may be accommodated to almost any rotation. These non-legumes are hardy and will start under adverse weather conditions and in a poorly prepared seedbed. They are thus extremely valuable on poor soils. Moreover, their influence is notably enhanced by sowing a legume with them. In any case, the mixture should be plowed under when at midgrowth or soon after, as at that time their carbon-nitrogen ratio is comparatively narrow.

20:16. THE PRACTICAL UTILIZATION OF GREEN MANURES

The turning under of green crops must be judicious in order that the soil may not be clogged with too much undecayed matter. Once or twice in a rotation is usually enough for such treatments. Good drainage should always be assured as aeration is of vital importance in the proper decay of plant residues in the soil.

IN REGIONS OF LOW RAINFALL. In regions where rainfall is scanty, great caution must be observed in the use of green manures. The available moisture that should go to the succeeding crop may be used by the green manure itself or in the processes of decay, and the soil left light and open. In the drier portions of the United States, it is doubtful whether green manures are of any real value because of this.

CONDITIONS AT TIME OF TURNING. It is generally best to turn green crops under when their succulence is near the maximum and yet at a time when suitable tops have been produced. With most green manure this occurs at about or a little beyond the half-mature stage. The content of lignin and other compounds which may resist microbial attack is still low. Moreover, the carbon-nitrogen ratio of the green manure is comparatively narrow at this time.

Again, the succulence encourages a rapid and more or less satisfactory decay, with the maximum production of humus and other products. The plowing should be done, if possible, at a season when a plentiful supply of rain occurs. The effectiveness of this type of manuring is thereby much enhanced as the moisture conditions are such as to insure a rapid and effective decomposition.

Whether to fall- or spring-plow a green-manuring crop is of practical concern and is decided largely by such factors as climate, the nature of the soil, and the crop used. Fall plowing seems to be of some advantage in the northern states as measured by nitrate accumulations during the following summer. The reverse seems to be true farther south where the winters are milder and shorter and where the spring and summer seasons are longer. Whether the soil is sandy or clayey must also be considered.

ROTATION CONSIDERATIONS. Whether or not a crop can be used advantageously as a green manure often is determined by the character of the rotation. In the northern states, due to the shorter season, it is often somewhat of a problem whether a green manure may be introduced without seriously interfering with the regular crops of the rotation. Not only is the period for the growth of the green manure very short, but the time interval between the turning under of the green substance and the planting of the next crop is often inadequate. In our southern states, this disadvantage is not encountered to such an extent, since the season is much longer and the rotation less likely to offer interference.

20:17. GREEN-MANURING AND THE MAINTENANCE OF SOIL FERTILITY

It cannot be emphasized too strongly that green manuring is only one of the several practices that may be employed in an attempt to maintain, or partially maintain, the fertility of arable lands. Moreover, it usually is the last of the various methods so employed to be resorted to. Crop residues, especially roots, and farm manure under ordinary conditions supply most of the organic matter found in mineral arable soils, and if the nitrogen level is high, these should suffice as far as organic matter maintenance is concerned. Whether or not green manures are used should depend in part on the adequacy of these sources of plant tissue. The plowing under of green plants, therefore, may be considered as a supplementary measure, very important in some cases but ordinarily not so essential in the general fertility scheme as are certain other practices.

Chapter 21

Soils and the World's Food Supply[1]

Hunger is not new to the world. It has always been a threat to man's survival. At some place on earth through the centuries scarcity of food has brought misery, disease, and even death to man. But never in recorded history has the threat of mass starvation been greater than it is today. This threat is not due to the reduced capacity of the world to supply food. Indeed, this capacity is greater today than it has ever been and is continuing to grow at a reasonable rate. The problem lies in the even more rapid rate at which world population is increasing. World food production per person is at best holding its own. In selected areas it is declining.

[1] Perhaps the most comprehensive review of the world food supply problem is contained in three volumes of a report of the President's Science Advisory Committee Panel on World Food Supply, "The World Food Problem," The White House, May 1967. Much of the material contained in Chapter 21 has as its basis the report of this panel, on which this text's junior author was privileged to serve.

21:1. EXPANSION OF WORLD POPULATION

Science is largely responsible for the marked expansion in world population growth, and especially that which has occurred in the so-called developing nations. Until the near midpoint of the twentieth century, high birth rates in most of South America, Africa, and Asia were largely negated by equally high death rates. High infant mortality, poor health facilities, inadequate medical personnel, and disease spreading insects each took their toll. Population expansion was held in check.

During the past few decades advances in medical science and their application throughout the world have drastically changed this situation (see Fig. 21:1). Death rates have been drastically reduced, especially

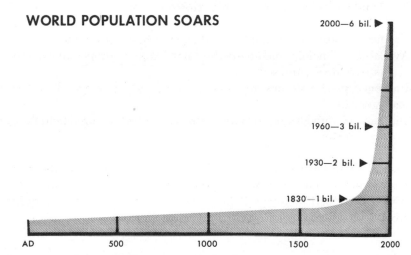

Figure 21:1. From the beginning of the human race until 1960, the world's population increased to 3 billion. Population estimates indicate that only forty years will be needed to provide the second 3 billion. Furthermore, most of the population growth will occur in countries already struggling to feed themselves. (Adapted from L. R. Brown, "Man, Land and Food," Foreign Agr. Econ. Report No. 11, U.S. Dept. of Agric., Econ. Res. Service, 1963.)

among the young. Pesticides have held in check mosquitoes and other disease-carrying pests. Medical services heretofore unheard of in remote areas of the developing nations have been initiated. The result is unprecedented population growth. The population is doubling every 18 to 27 years in the developing areas where two-thirds of the world's population now live. Experts predict the world's population will be between 6 and 7 billion by the year 2000—double that of today. Furthermore, *more than 90 per cent of this increase will occur in developing nations* where food supplies are already critical and where the technology for increased food production is wholly inadequate. It is no wonder that the world food supply is considered by some to be mankind's most serious problem.

21:2. FACTORS INFLUENCING WORLD FOOD SUPPLIES

The ability of a nation to produce food is determined by a multitude of variables. These include a complex of social, economic, and political factors, most of which affect the farmer's incentive to produce and his supply of production inputs. Also included are a number of physical and biological factors such as the following:

1. The natural resources available, and especially soil and water.
2. Available technology including the knowledge of proper management of plants, animals, and soils.
3. Improved plant varieties and animal breeds which respond to proper management.
4. Supplies of production inputs such as fertilizer, insecticides, and irrigation water.

Each of these factors are affected by the quantity and quality of soils —their natural productivity and response to management. There is good reason to place satisfactory soil properties high on the list of requisites to provide an adequate world food supply.

21:3. THE WORLD'S LAND RESOURCES

There is a total of thirty-two and a half billion acres of land in the major continents (see Table 21:1). However, most of it is not suited for cultivation. About half of it is completely nonarable. It is mountainous, too cold or too steep for tillage; it may be swampland; or it is desert country, too dry for any but the sparsest of vegetation.

About one-quarter of the land area supports enough vegetation to provide grazing for animals but for various reasons cannot be cultivated. This leaves only about 25 per cent of the land with the physical potential for cultivation (see Table 21:1). And only half of this potentially arable land is actually under cultivation. It is obvious that the kind of soils and

Table 21:1. World land area in different climatic zones[a]

Area in billions of acres

Climatic zone	Potentially arable	Grazing	Nonarable	Total
I Polar and subpolar	0	0	1.38	1.38
II Cold-temperate boreal	.12	.47	4.28	4.87
III Cool-temperate	2.24	2.46	2.48	7.18
IV Warm-temperate sub-tropical	1.37	2.08	3.38	6.83
V Tropical	4.13	4.02	4.08	12.23
Total	7.86	9.02	15.60	32.50

[a] From "World Food Problem", Vol. II, Report of the Panel on World Food Supply, a report of the President's Science Advisory Committee, Washington, D.C., p. 423.

their response to management may eventually hold the key to adequate food production, at least in some areas.

CONTINENTAL DIFFERENCES. Data in Table 21:2 suggest the role which soils may play in helping to meet the world food requirements. While the *total* potentially arable land is more than double that being cultivated today, there is great variation from continent to continent. In Asia and Europe, where population pressures have been strong for years, most of the potentially arable land is under cultivation. In contrast, only 2 per cent of the potentially arable land is cultivated in Australia and New Zealand. Comparable figures are 11 per cent for South America and 22 per cent for Africa. In these last four areas the physical potential for greater utilization of arable land is indeed great.

It is unfortunate that there is not better distribution of arable land in relation to population densities. The area of cultivated land *per person* is high in North America, the U.S.S.R., and Australia and New Zealand. It is low in Asia and Europe and not much higher in South America and Africa. This does not present a serious problem in Europe or the more economically developed parts of Asia. They can readily purchase food from the countries with excess supply. Only the transportation, trade and marketing problems must be overcome.

In developing countries of Asia, Africa, and Latin America the situation is much more critical. Their populations are increasing far more rapidly than their food production. Countries which formerly exported food crops now must import them. And their national economic growth rate is too slow to provide the resources to pay for the needed food. They must either be provided with food aids by their more fortunate neighbors, or must increase dramatically their capacity to produce food.

Table 21:2. *Present population and cultivated land on each continent, compared with potentially arable land*[a]

Continent	Population in 1965 (millions of persons)	Area in billions of acres			Acres of cultivated land per person	Ratio of cultivated to potentially arable land (percent)
		Total	Potentially arable	Cultivated		
Africa	310	7.46	1.81	0.39	1.3	22
Asia	1,855	6.76	1.55	1.28	.7	83
Australia and New Zealand	14	2.03	.38	.04	2.9	2
Europe	445	1.18	.43	.38	.9	88
North America	255	5.21	1.15	.59	2.3	51
South America	197	4.33	1.68	.19	1.0	11
U.S.S.R.	234	5.52	.88	.56	2.4	64
Total	3,310	32.49	7.88	3.43	1.0	44

[a] From report on World Food Supply, Vol. II, *op. cit.*, p. 434.

CHOICES OF ACTION. There are two routes which nations may follow to utilize land to increase their food production: (*a*) they may clear and cultivate arable land which has heretofore not been tilled, or (*b*) they may intensify production on lands already under cultivation. Some nations, notably those in Europe and Asia, have only the latter choice. They have little opportunity to expand land under cultivation since most of their arable land is already in use. Only by increasing annual yields per acre can they produce more food.

In areas outside Asia and Europe, the physical potential for increasing land under cultivation is great. For example, in Africa and South America where current land utilization per person is not high, there are about 3 billion acres of arable land which are not now being cultivated. Unfortunately, much of this land is inaccessible to modern transportation. The cost of clearing the land, of transporting the fertilizer and other inputs needed to it, and distributing the food produced from it, is high. Also large areas on these continents have humid, tropical climates and tropical soils—the optimum management of which man has yet to learn.

For these reasons, in most areas of the world, intensification of land already under cultivation is the preferred immediate method of increasing food production. In time, however, as economic development, transportation, and knowledge of soil management progress, expansion of land under cultivation is almost certain to occur. Our attention will now be turned to general kinds and acreage of soils found where food production is most critical.

21:4. POTENTIAL OF BROAD SOIL GROUPS

In Table 21:3 are shown the acreages dominated by different broad major soil groupings. Note that in terms of total area, shallow soils and sands are most prevelant (8.7 billion acres) followed closely by a variety of Latosols (Oxisols) found in tropical areas. There are vast areas of deserts soils and associated dry areas (Aridisols). Podzols (Spodosols) and podzolic soils make up the next most expansive grouping.

While the total area of different soil groupings is interesting, the potential utilization is of much greater practical importance. For example 82 per cent of the 6.73 billion acres of shallow Lithosols are considered nonarable, not even fit for grazing. In contrast, only about 9 per cent of the Chernozem and related soils (Mollisols) are classed as nonarable.

More than half the dark colored, base-rich soils with which the Chernozems are grouped are potentially arable. A similar proportion of Alluvial soils are so classed. It is interesting to note that man has long recognized the productivity of the dark colored, base-rich soils and especially the Alluvial soils. Alluvial soils are being utilized throughout the world but are especially important in lowland rice culture. Their location with respect to river and ground water make irrigation relatively easy and their productivity is generally high. The Chernozemic and related soils (Mollisols) are the bulwark of agriculture in North America, the U.S.S.R., and parts of South America.

Table 21:3. Total acreage of Broad Soil groups in the major continents and the percentage that are arable, nonarable but suitable for grazing, and nonarable[a]

Broad Soil Groupings	Total Acres (billions)	Approximate percentage of acreage		
		Potentially arable	*Grazing*	*Non-arable*
Light colored, base-rich Desert	5.26	20.3	43.0	36.7
Dark colored, base-rich				
Chernozem, Brunizem	2.03	56.7	34.5	8.8
Grumusol, Terra Rosa	0.81	53.1	33.3	13.6
Brown Forest, Rendzina	0.25	24.0	52.0	24.0
Moderately Weathered, leached				
Non-calcic Brown	0.72	38.0	47.9	14.1
Ando	0.06	28.6	42.8	28.6
Highly weathered, leached				
Podzol	4.85	16.3	25.6	58.1
Red-yellow podzolic	0.96	33.0	50.5	16.5
Latosols	6.18	42.4	28.5	29.1
Shallow Soils and Sands				
Lithosols	6.73	2.8	15.2	82.0
Regosols	1.90	7.9	18.9	73.2
Alluvial	1.47	53.7	29.3	17.0
Tundra	1.28	0	0	100.0
Total	32.50	24.2	27.8	48.0

[a] Calculated from the report on World Food Supply, Vol. II, *op. cit.*, Table 7:1, p. 423.

The arability of areas dominated by the light colored, base-rich soils of dry areas is determined to a considerable extent by the availability of irrigation water. The soils are often quite fertile and will respond to management if supplemental water can be applied. The remarkable progress that has been made in irrigation expansion in India and West Pakistan illustrates the productivity potential of these soils. Vast acreages are physically located where they can be irrigated if water can be stored and distributed economically. There are more than one billion acres of these soils which can be cultivated successfully if water and other production inputs are available.

The greatest potential for increasing land under cultivation is found in tropical areas dominated by Latosols (Oxisols). Scientists estimate that 40 per cent of the more than 6 billion acres of these soils are potentially arable (see Table 21:3). Another 1.75 billion acres are suitable for grazing. The potential here for increasing food production is enormous. We shall consider in more detail later how this potential might be achieved.

POTENTIAL BY CONTINENTS. Table 21:4 provides us with estimates of the potentially arable land by soil groupings and by continent. Again one is impressed with the total area of arable Latosols (Oxisols), the sizeable arable acreages of arid lands (desert, Aridisols), chernozemic and related soils (Mollisols), and Alluvial soils.

Europe and Asia are already utilizing most of their arable land. North America and Australia and the U.S.S.R. are either excess food producing areas or have the potential to become so. For these reasons, we shall concentrate our attention on Africa and South America where food shortages are occurring and where the soil resources are far under-utilized.

The light colored, base-rich soils of dry areas provide considerable food production potential for both continents, provided irrigation water is available. Potential exists for increased irrigation in southern South America and in tropical Africa. Doubling or even tripling the acreage under irrigation on these continents would appear to be economically feasible. Problems of storing and distributing the water are immediate limiting factors, but in time are likely to be overcome. In both Africa and South America vast areas of Latosols (Oxisols) have yet to be exploited. Most of the unused arable Latosols of the world are found in these two continents—more than two and a half billion acres. Furthermore, there are food population problems in tropical areas near these soil resources. For example, northeast Brazil is an economically depressed food shortage area. In that country literally millions of acres of uncleared Latosols are available. In time, total economic development of the inland areas where these soils are found will make possible realization of the production potential of that country. A similar statement might be made of central Africa whose Latosols are largely unutilized. However, as the next section will show, there are some unique problems in tropical areas which must be solved before full use can be made of these natural resources.

21:5. PROBLEMS AND OPPORTUNITIES IN THE TROPICS

One cannot help but wonder why soils of the humid tropics have not been more widely exploited. They seemingly have many advantages

SOILS AND THE WORLD'S FOOD SUPPLY [Ch. 21

Table 21:4. Estimates of acreage of potentially arable land by soil groups and continents[a]

Broad Soil Groupings	Millions of acres of arable land[b]							
	Africa	Asia	Australia	Europe	North America	South America	U.S.S.R.	Total
Light colored, base-rich Desert	340	250	110	30	50	90	210	1,080
Dark colored, base-rich Chernozem, Brunizem	0	120	30	30	400	180	390	1,150
Grumusol, Terra Rosa	130	60	140	20	70	20	—	440
Brown Forest, Rendzina	10	10	0	20	20	10	10	80
Moderately weathered, leached Non-calcic Brown	20	160	20	40	20	10	—	270
Ando	0	10	0	—	0	10	—	20
Highly weathered, leached Podzol	—	50	2	280	250	—	220	802
Red-yellow Podzolic	20	90	10	—	190	10	—	320
Latosols	1,030	250	30	—	40	1,270	—	2,620
Shallow Soils and Sands Lithosols	20	70	10	10	30	40	10	190
Regosols	120	10	10	10	10	—	10	170
Alluvials	130	480	0	10	80	60	30	790
Total	1,820	1,560	362	450	1,160	1,700	880	7,932

[a] From report on World Food Supply, Vol. II, *op. cit.*, p. 430.
[b] Blank spaces indicate soil group not present on the continent while 0 indicates essentially no potentially arable land in this group on the continent.

over their temperate zone counterparts. The crop growing season is commonly year round. In many areas ample moisture is available throughout the growing season. And some of the soils have physical characteristics far superior to the soils of the temperate zones. The hydrous oxide and kaolinitic type clays which dominate permit cultivation under very high rainfall conditions.

LIMITING FACTORS. There appear to be many reasons for man's failure to utilize more fully many of the humid tropical areas. In the first place, the environment of the wet tropics has not been too favorable for man and his domesticated plants and animals. Not only is the hot humid climate a source of discomfort, but it encourages diseases and pests, and it results in rapid decay and breakdown of tools and equipment man needs for production. Most of those factors which favor domesticated crop and animal production also support competitors in the environment.

Another very important limiting factor to agricultural development in the tropics is the absence or inadequacy of quality transportation. Regardless of the productivity of a given soil area, if there are no highways or railroads connecting it to cities and towns where the customers are, and from whence fertilizers, pesticides, and other inputs come, agriculture will not be likely to succeed.

Coupled with transportation are all other aspects of economic and social development. The package of inputs which have been so essential in the more developed areas of the world are no less essential for agriculture in the developing countries of the tropics. Capital is needed to clear the land, build the roads, construct the irrigation dams and canals, and to build the fertilizer and pesticide plants and distributing systems. Economic development in other segments of the economy is required if money is to be available to purchase the farmer's produce. Marketing systems must be developed to move perishable foods from farms to cities and to distribute them to hungry people. And last but not least, we must have research and education related specifically to the problems of the tropics.

THE SPECIAL PROBLEM OF TROPICAL SOILS. There are special problems associated with soils of the tropics. In the first place, all too little is known about them and their management. Research on tropical soils, in relation to their areal expanse and probable complexities, is insignificant compared to that on temperate region soils. Our knowledge of their characteristics makes possible identifying only the broadest categories of classification. More intensive study will undoubtedly show many different kinds of soils where we now are able to identify only a few.

The little we have learned about tropical soils merely reminds us of our ignorance. For example, some of the soils (Oxisols) of Hawaii and of the Philippines are excellent for pineapple and sugar cane production. They respond well to modern management and mechanization. In contrast, modern mechanized farming was a dramatic failure for the so-called "Groundnut Scheme" carried out by the British in Tanganyika following World War II. Apparently in the latter case, exposing the cleared soil to tropical rains resulted in catastrophic erosion. Knowledge of the nature of the soil might well have prevented much of the one hundred million dollar loss this project suffered.

There is a good likelihood that more intensive study will identify complexities among tropical soils similar to those known for temperate regions. We already know of the great variability among soils of tropical areas. Some are deep friable, easily manipulated and tilled. At the other extreme are the lateritic soils which when denuded of their upper horizon expose layers which harden, leaving a surface resembling a pavement (see Fig. 21:2). Such soils are essentially worthless from an agricultural point of view.

Figure 21:2. An exposed laterite area in central India. The pavement-like surface is barren and will not permit crop production. Sizeable acreages of such Latosols (Oxisols) with laterite layers are found in India, Africa, South America, and Australia.

The chemical characteristics of Latosols (Oxisols) differ drastically from those of soils of temperate regions. The high hydrous oxide content dictates enormous phosphate-fixing capacities. The low cation exchange capacities and heavy rainfall result in removal, of not only macronutrients but micronutrients as well. Indeed the level of technology needed to manage Latosols is fully as high as that required for temperate zone soils.

SOIL AND CROP MANAGEMENT SYSTEMS IN THE TROPICS. The *plantation* system of agriculture has been successful in raising crops such as bananas, sugar cane, pineapples, rubber, coffee, and cacao. This system generally imports the best known technology from developed countries and sometimes has associated with it sizeable research staffs to gain new knowledge for improved technology. While it has been generally successful in producing and marketing crops and animals, social and political problems have plagued this system.

At the opposite extreme from the plantation approach, are indigenous systems which require little from the outside and which have evolved mostly by trial and error of the native cultivators. One of the most widespread of these systems—that of *shifting cultivation*—will be described briefly to illustrate what the natives have learned from centuries of experience.

While there are variations in the practice of shifting cultivation, in general it involves three major steps:

1. The cutting and burning of trees or other native plants, leaving their ashes on the soil. Sometimes only the vegetation in the immediate area is burned. In other cases this is supplemented with plants brought in from nearby areas.
2. Growing crops on the cleared area for a period of one to five years, thereby utilizing nutrients left from the clearing and burning of native plants. Vegetation from outside the area may be brought in and burned between plantings.
3. Fallowing the area for a period of 5 to 12 years thereby permitting regrowth of the native trees and other plants, and the consequent "rejuvenation" of the soil. Nutrients are accumulated in the native plants and some, such as nitrogen, are released to the soil. The cutting and burning is repeated and the cycle starts again.

Shifting cultivation is primarily a system of nutrient conservation, accumulation and recycling. The native plants absorb available nutrients from the soil and from the atmosphere. Some are nitrogen fixers. Others are deep rooted and bring nutrients from lower horizons to the surface. All help protect the soil from the devastating effects of rain and sunshine. Also, the cropped area is generally small in size and is surrounded by native vegetation. This reduces the chances of gully formation or severe sheet erosion from runoff water.

There are other benefits of the system other than those relating to nutrients and erosion control. The burning is likely to destroy some weed seeds and even some unwanted insects and disease organisms. The short period of actual cropping (1 to 5 years out of 10 to 20 years discourages the buildup of weeds, insects, and diseases harmful to the cultivated crops.

While shifting cultivation seems primitive, it deserves careful study. In some tropical areas it is more successful than the seemingly more efficient temperate zone systems. Experimentation may permit improvement and alteration of the shifting cultivation system. Perhaps the nutrients accumulated in the native plants can be supplemented with compost or fertilizers. Seeding the fallowed area with plants selected for their beneficial effects rather than allowing natural invasion may also be a forward step.

Some soils in the tropics must have continuous vegetative cover to remain productive. If they dry out and especially if erosion removes the surface layers, the doughy laterite layers beneath harden irreversibly making plant growth impossible. This turn of events may be prevented by planting the crop desired amongst native or other crop plants without completely removing the latter. Since the plants involved are in most cases trees, this system has been termed the *mixed tree crop* system. The desired crop or crops are introduced by removing some of the existing plants and replacing them with crop plants. In time a given area may be planted entirely to a number of crop plants. The essential feature of system, however, is that at no time should the soil be free of vegetation. As primitive as this system may appear, up to now science has not been able to develop more successful alternatives for the management of laterite-containing soils. (See Fig. 21:2)

THE POTENTIAL OF TROPICAL AGRICULTURE. In spite of our inadequate knowledge of tropical agriculture in general, one cannot help but be optimistic about the future of agriculture in the tropics. The basic requirements for maximum year-round production appear to be higher in the humid tropics than anywhere else. Total annual solar radiation provides unmatched photosynthetic potential. The unused soil resources are plentiful (see Table 21:5). There is an increasing tendency to grow several crops a year in a given land area of the tropics. This is of special importance to food production since the practice can be followed by small land holders whose production almost invariably involves some food crops.

Already researchers have developed new crop varieties especially adapted to the tropics. Adaptive research is identifying means of controlling pests. And fertilizer usage is becoming more common in tropical areas. The potential for food production there is enormous. Its realization depends only on man's ability to exploit this potential.

Table 21:5. Total acreage by continents of different soil groups in the tropical zone and estimates of the areas potentially arable[a]

Soil Groups	Africa	Asia	Latin America	Australia & New Zealand	Total
Light-colored, base rich soils[b]	160	80	50	40	330
Dark-colored, base rich soils	267	60	125	20	345
Moderately weathered and leached soils	20	135	15	20	190
Highly weathered and leached soils	1200	270	1135	40	2645
Shallow soils and sands	90	30	40	30	190
Alluvial soils	105	285	40	—	430
Total	1715	260	1405	150	4130

[a] From report on World Food Supply, Vol. II. *op. cit.*, p. 483.
[b] Assumes application of irrigation water.

21:6. REQUISITES FOR THE FUTURE

The world's ability to feed itself depends upon many factors not the least of which is improved agricultural technology in the developing nations of the world. This technology is in turn dependent largely on science and more specifically on research and education. Furthermore, the research and education must have direct relevance to the developing countries and not be a mere transplant of what is available in the more developed nations. Too often the mistake is made of assuming that the technology of western Europe or of the United States can be transferred directly to the underdeveloped countries. Disastrous failures have shown the fallacy of this concept.

THE PACKAGE APPROACH. Most importantly, improved technologies must provide a package of all the inputs, cultural techniques, incentives, etc., upon which a successful food production system depends. The law of limiting factors described briefly in Chapter 2 is applicable here. Each of the dozens of economic, social, political, and biological factors which effect a successful agricultural system must be considered.

Assuming for the moment that the social, economic, and political factors can be made reasonably favorable, let us turn briefly to those components of the biological package which have some bearing on soil utilization.

CROP VARIETIES. New crop varieties adapted to conditions in the developing areas along with methods of pest control are among the first elements of the package. For example, the new dwarf Mexican wheats, which are highly responsive to fertilizer applications have set a new plateau for wheat yields over a wide geographic area. The average yield of wheat in Mexico has doubled as a result of introducing these new varieties, especially in irrigated areas. Luckily, these new varieties are adapted to food deficit countries such as India and Pakistan and have been widely adopted there with unprecedented speed. Disease and insect problems are being attacked through the use of pesticides and through the development of resistant varieties.

IRRIGATION AND DRAINAGE. Water supply is a critical factor in crop production in most areas of the world. In some cases, only supplemented moisture is needed to meet temporary deficits or to lengthen the growing season. At other locations, irrigation must be looked to for the bulk of the growing season moisture. Such locations may be in a year-round dry climatic area which is traversed by rivers flowing from areas of higher precipitation. Or there may be a dry period during part of an otherwise wet year. There is a growing recognition that, coupled with irrigation, soil drainage systems are also often essential.

Remarkable progress has been made in expanding irrigation. Worldwide acreage under irrigation in 1968 was about four times that of 1900. In Pakistan and India, two countries with the most serious food problems, 69 and 27 million acres respectively are under irrigation. Much of that increase has come in the past fifteen years. This acreage is being expanded annually, not only with major dam and reservoir projects but with "tube" wells which utilize ground water and which require only the simplest of distribution systems. The potentially irrigable land, in comparison to that currently irrigated, is near double for Pakistan and triple for India. Similar potentials and plans for their realization exist for parts of South America, Africa, and Australia.

FERTILIZER. It has been estimated[2] that "less than 15 per cent of the world's fertilizer is used in areas whose agriculture must feed half the world's people." To move from yields common in subsistence agriculture to those dictated by today's food requirements demands dramatic increases in supplies of fertilizer nutrients. It also demands widespread information on soil characteristics to determine the kinds of fertilizers that are needed. In highly leached areas, evaluations must be

2 World Food Supply Report, Vol. II, *op. cit.*, p. 379.

made of micronutrient deficiencies as well as those for N, P, K and lime. And attention must be given to fertilizer which resists rapid reaction with the soil or volatilization by microbial action.

While the use of manufactured fertilizers is to be encouraged, economic considerations may dictate alternate sources, especially of nitrogen. Native and improved legumes can and should be used. And animal manures will help supplement the manufactured fertilizers.

SOIL MANAGEMENT. In some areas there are serious soil management problems which need attention. For example, the so-called "Black Cotton" soils of India and of the Sudan (classified as Vertisols) are heavy textured and probably contain a high proportion of 2:1 type silicate clays. These soils are sticky when wet and hard when dry. The primitive implements and small draft animals used to plow and cultivate them do not permit timely soil manipulation. This means that much of the potential productive capacity of these soils is lost. Methods of incorporating organic matter into the surface of these soils must be sought. And tractors and other machines must be used, perhaps by cooperatives of small land owners, to permit timely tillage of these soils.

Agricultural development activities have emphasized the critical need for the characterization of soils. For example, the salinity and alkalinity status can well determine the likely success of an irrigation project. Nutrient deficiencies can be identified as can the potential for erosion and drainage problems. The time and effort being devoted to soil characterization is insignificant compared to the needs for this kind of information.

SOIL SURVEYS. Reliable soil survey information is inadequate or unavailable in most of the developing areas. In part this is due to lack of information of the soil characteristics upon which a classification scheme can be based. More frequently it is due to ignorance of the significance and value of the soil survey. Planners sometimes look upon soils as soils, without regard to the vast differences that exist among them—differences that could affect markedly the plans that are made.

Soil surveys will be of special significance in two ways. First, they will make possible the extrapolation of research results from a given area to other areas where the same kinds of soil are found. Second, they will provide one of the criteria to determine the economic feasibility of clearing and preparing for tillage lands which have as yet been unexploited.

MANPOWER. A final requisite for increased food production is trained manpower. The range needed goes from basic scientists (from whose test tubes and field plots new technologies and perhaps new food products are to come) to the cultivators and their assistants. We must have researchers whose interest relates directly to the solution of the world food problem. We must have technicians, farm managers, field service men, and individuals trained in processing and marketing trades. And we must have educators to teach not only the students but the farmers as well.

The fight to feed the world is not yet lost. But to win it will require technological and scientific inputs of a magnitude not yet realized. And among the most important of these inputs are those relating to soils and soil science.

Glossary of Soil Science Terms[1]

A horizon. The surface horizon of a mineral soil having maximum organic matter accumulation, maximum biological activity and/or eluviation of materials such as iron and aluminum oxides and silicate clays.

ABC soil. A soil with a distinctly developed profile, including A, B, and C horizons.

AC soil. A soil having a profile containing only A and C horizons with no clearly developed B horizon.

accelerated erosion. See *erosion.*

---

[1] This glossary was compiled from several sources including the following: (1) J. F. Lutz (Committee Chairman) "Glossary of Soil Science Terms" *Soil Sci. Soc. Amer. Proc.* 29:330–351, 1965; (2) *Soil, The 1957 Yearbook of Agriculture,* U.S. Department of Agriculture, Washington, D.C. 1957; and (3) Soil Survey Staff, *Soil Classification, A Comprehensive System—7th Approximation,* U.S. Department of Agriculture, 1960 and *Supplement to Soil Classification System (7th Approximation),* 1967.

acid soil. A soil with a preponderance of hydrogen and aluminum ions in proportion to hydroxyl ions. Specifically, soil with a pH value < 7.0. For most practical purposes a soil with a pH value < 6.6. (The term is usually applied to the surface layer or to the root zone unless specified otherwise.)

acidity, active. The activity of hydrogen ion in the aqueous phase of a soil. It is measured and expressed as a pH value.

acidity, potential. The amount of acidity that must be neutralized to bring an acid soil to neutrality or to some predetermined higher pH value. It is approximated by the sum of the absorbed hydrogen and aluminum. Usually expressed in milliequivalents per unit mass of soil.

actinomycetes. A group of organisms intermediate between the bacteria and the true fungi that usually produce a characteristic branched mycelium. Any organism belonging to the order of Actinomycetales.

adsorption. The attraction of ions or compounds to the surface of a solid. Soil colloids adsorb large amounts of ions and water.

adsorption complex. The group of substances in soil capable of adsorbing other materials. Colloidal particles account for most of this adsorption.

aerate. To impregnate with a gas, usually air.

aeration, soil. The process by which air in the soil is replaced by air from the atmosphere. In a well-aerated soil, the soil air is very similar in composition to the atmosphere above the soil. Poorly aerated soils usually contain a much higher percentage of carbon dioxide and a correspondingly lower percentage of oxygen than the atmosphere above the soil. The rate of aeration depends largely on the volume and continuity of pores within the soil.

aerobic. (i) Having molecular oxygen as a part of the environment. (ii) Growing only in the presence of molecular oxygen, as aerobic organisms. (iii) Occurring only in the presence of molecular oxygen (said of certain chemical or biochemical processes such as aerobic decomposition).

aggregate (soil). Many soil particles held in a single mass or cluster such as a clod, crumb, block or prism.

agric horizon. Horizon immediately below the plow layer of cultivated soils containing accumulated clay and humus to the extent of at least 15 per cent of the horizon volume. (new comprehensive classification system)

agronomy. A specialization of agriculture concerned with the theory and practice of field-crop production and soil management. The scientific management of land.

air-dry. (i) The state of dryness (of a soil) at equilibrium with the moisture content in the surrounding atmosphere. The actual moisture content will depend upon the relative humidity and the temperature of the surrounding atmosphere. (ii) To allow to reach equilibrium in moisture content with the surrounding atmosphere.

air porosity. The proportion of the bulk volume of soil that is filled with air at any given time or under a given condition, such as a specified moisture tension. Usually the large pores; that is, those drained by a tension of less than approximately 100 cm of water. See *moisture tension.*

albic horizon. A light-colored surface or lower horizon from which clay and free iron oxides have been removed or so segregated as to permit the color to be determined primarily by the primary sand and silt particles. (new comprehensive classification system)

Alfisols. Mineral soils that have no mollic epipedon, or oxic, or spodic horizon, but do have an argillic or natric horizon which is at least 35 per cent base saturated. Most soils classified as Gray-Brown Podzolic, Noncalcic Brown, and Gray Wooded in the old classification system belong in this soil order. (new comprehensive classification system)

alkali soil. (i) A soil with a high degree of alkalinity (pH of 8.5 or higher) or with a high exchangeable sodium content (15 per cent or more of the exchange capacity), or both. (ii) A soil that contains sufficient alkali (sodium) to interfere with the growth of most crop plants. See *saline-sodic soil* and *sodic soil.*

alkaline soil. Precisely any soil that has a pH value > 7. Practically, a soil with a pH of > 7.3. The term is usually applied to surface layer or root zone but may be used to characterize a horizon or a sample thereof.

alkalization. The process whereby the exchangeable sodium content of a soil is increased.

Alluvial soil. A soil developing from recently deposited alluvium and exhibiting essentially no horizon development or modification of the recently deposited materials.

Alpine Meadow soils. A great soil group of the intrazonal order, comprised of dark soils of grassy meadows at altitudes above the timberline. (1949 classification system)

alumino-silicates. Compounds containing aluminum, silicon, and oxygen as main constituents. An example is microcline, $KAlSi_3O_8$.

amendment, soil. Any substance such as lime, sulfur, gypsum, and sawdust used to alter the properties of a soil, generally to make it more productive. Strictly speaking, fertilizers are soil amendments, but the term is used most commonly for materials other than fertilizers.

amino acids. Nitrogen-containing organic acids which couple together to form proteins. Each acid molecule contains one or more amino groups ($-NH_2$) and at least one carboxyl group ($-COOH$). In addition, some amino acids contain sulfur.

ammonification. The biochemical process whereby ammoniacal nitrogen is released from nitrogen-containing organic compounds.

ammonium fixation. The adsorption or absorption of ammonium ions by the mineral or organic fractions of the soil in such a manner that they are relatively insoluble in water and relatively unexchangeable by the usual methods of cation exchange.

anaerobic. (i) The absence of molecular oxygen. (ii) Living or functioning in the absence of air or free oxygen.

anion-exchange capacity. The sum total of exchangeable anions that a soil can adsorb. Expressed as milliequivalents per 100 grams of soil (or of other adsorbing material such as clay).

anthropic epipedon. A thick, dark surface horizon, which is more than 50 per cent saturated with bases, has a narrow C/N ratio and more than 250 ppm of P_2O_5 soluble in citric acid. It is formed under long continued cultivation where large amounts of organic matter and fertilizers have been added.

antibiotic. A substance produced by one species of organism that, in low concentrations, will kill or inhibit growth of certain other organisms.

apatite. A naturally occurring, complex calcium phosphate which is the original source of most of the phosphate fertilizers. Formulas such as $3Ca_3(PO_4)_2 \cdot CaF_2$ illustrate the complex compounds which make up apatite.

argillic horizon. A diagnostic illuvial subsurface horizon characterized by an accumulation of silicate clays. (new comprehensive classification system)

Aridisols. Soils characteristic of dry places. Includes soils such as Desert, Red Desert, Sierozems and Solochak in the old classification system. (new comprehensive classification system)

artificial manure. See *compost.* (In European usage may denote commercial fertilizers.)

association, soil. See *soil association.*

autotrophic. Capable of utilizing carbon dioxide or carbonates as the sole source of carbon and obtaining energy for life processes from the oxidation of inorganic elements or compounds such as iron, sulfur, hydrogen, ammonium, and nitrites, or from radiant energy. Contrast with *heterotrophic.*

available nutrient. That portion of any element or compound in the soil that can be readily absorbed and assimilated by growing plants. ("Available" should not be confused with "exchangeable.")

available water. The portion of water in a soil that can be readily absorbed by plant roots. Considered by most workers to be that water held in the soil against a pressure of up to approximately 15 bars. See *field capacity* and *moisture tension.*

azonal soils. Soils without distinct genetic horizons. A soil order under the 1949 classification system.

B horizon. A soil horizon usually beneath the A which is characterized by one or both of the following: (1) an accumulation of silicate clays, iron and aluminum oxides, and humus, alone or in combination; (2) a blocky or prismatic structure.

bar. A unit of pressure equal to one million dynes per square centimeter.

base-saturation percentage. The extent to which the adsorption complex of a soil is saturated with exchangeable cations other than hydrogen and aluminum. It is expressed as a percentage of the total cation-exchange capacity.

BC soil. A soil profile with B and C horizons but with little or no A horizon. Most BC soils have lost their A horizons by erosion.

bedding (soil). Arranging the surface of fields by plowing and grading into a series of elevated beds separated by shallow depressions or ditches for drainage.

bedrock. The solid rock underlying soils and the regolith in depths ranging from zero (where exposed by erosion) to several hundred feet.

bench terrace. An embankment constructed across sloping fields with a steep drop on the down slope side.

Black Earth. A term used by some as synonymous with "Chernozem"; by others (in Australia) to describe self-mulching black clays.

Black Soils. A term used in Canada to describe soils with dark surface horizons of the black (Chernozem) zone; includes Black Earth or Chernozem, Wiesenboden, Solonetz, etc.

bleicherde. The light-colored, leached A2 horizon of Podzol soils.

blown-out land. Areas from which all or almost all of the soil and soil material has been removed by wind erosion. Usually unfit for crop production. A miscellaneous land type.

Bluff Podzol. See *Depression Podzol.*

bog iron ore. Impure ferruginous deposits developed in bogs or swamps by the chemical or biochemical oxidation of iron carried in solution.

Bog soil. A great soil group of the intrazonal order and hydromorphic suborder. Includes muck and peat. (1949 classification system)

border-strip irrigation. See *irrigation methods.*

bottomland. See *flood plain.*

breccia. A rock composed of coarse angular fragments cemented together.

broad-base terrace. A low embankment with such gentle slopes that it can be farmed, constructed across sloping fields to reduce erosion and runoff.

Brown Earths. Soils with a mull horizon but having no horizon of accumulation of clay or sesquioxides. (Generally used as a synonym for

"Brown Forest soils" but sometimes for similar soils acid in reaction.)

Brown Forest soils. A great soil group of the intrazonal order and calci-morphic suborder, formed on calcium-rich parent materials under deciduous forest, and possessing a high base status but lacking a pronounced illuvial horizon. (1949 classification system) (A much more narrow group than the European Brown Forest or Braunerde.)

Brown Podzolic soils. A zonal great soil group similar to Podzols but lacking the distinct A_2 horizon characteristic of the Podzol group. (1949 classification system) (Some American soil taxonomists prefer to class this soil as a kind of Podzol and not as a distinct great soil group.)

Brown soils. A great soil group of the temperate to cool arid regions, composed of soils with a brown surface and a light-colored transitional subsurface horizon over calcium carbonate accumulation. (1949 classi-fication system) They develop under short grasses.

Brunizem. Synonymous with *Prairie soils.* (1949 classification system)

buffer compounds, soil. The clay, organic matter, and compounds such as carbonates and phosphates which enable the soil to resist appreciable change in pH.

bulk density, soil. The mass of dry soil per unit bulk volume including the air space. The bulk volume is determined before drying to constant weight at 105° C.

buried soil. Soil covered by an alluvial, loessal, or other deposit, usually to a depth greater than the thickness of the solum.

C horizon. A horizon generally beneath the solum which is relatively little affected by biological activity and pedogenesis and is lacking properties diagnostic of an A or B horizon. It may or may not be like the material from which the A and B have formed.

calcareous soil. Soil containing sufficient calcium carbonate (often with magnesium carbonate) to effervesce visibly when treated with cold $0.1N$ hydrochloric acid.

calcic horizon. A horizon of secondary carbonate accumulation more than 6 inches in thickness, with a $CaCO_3$ equivalence of more than 15 per cent and at least 5 per cent more $CaCO_3$ than the C horizon. (new comprehensive classification system)

caliche. A layer near the surface, more or less cemented by secondary carbonates of calcium or magnesium precipitated from the soil solu-tion. It may occur as a soft thin soil horizon, as a hard thick bed just beneath the solum, or as a surface layer exposed by erosion.

cambic horizon. A horizon which has been altered or changed by soil form-ing processes. It usually occurs below a diagnostic surface horizon (epipedon). (new comprehensive classification system)

capillary conductivity. See *hydraulic conductivity.*

capillary porosity. The small pores, or the bulk volume of small pores, which hold water in soils against a tension usually > 60 cm of water. See *moisture tension.*

capillary water. (Obsolete) The water held in the "capillary" or *small* pores of a soil, usually with a tension > 60 cm of water. See *moisture tension.*

carbon cycle. The sequence of transformations whereby carbon dioxide is fixed in living organisms by photosynthesis or by chemosynthesis, liberated by respiration and by the death and decomposition of the fixing organism, used by heterotrophic species, and ultimately returned to its original state.

carbon-nitrogen ratio. The ratio of the weight of organic carbon (C) to the weight of total nitrogen (N) in a soil or in organic material.

"Cat" Clays. Wet clay soils high in reduced forms of sulfur which upon being drained become extremely acid due to the oxidation of the sulfur compounds.

catena. A sequence of soils of about the same age, derived from similar parent material, and occurring under similar climatic conditions, but having different characteristics due to variation in *relief* and in *drainage.*

cation exchange. The interchange between a cation in solution and another cation on the surface of any surface-active material such as clay or organic matter.

cation-exchange capacity. The sum total of exchangeable cations that a soil can adsorb. Sometimes called "total-exchange capacity," "base exchange capacity," or "cation-adsorption capacity." Expressed in milliequivalents per 100 grams of soil (or of other adsorbing material such as clay).

cemented. Indurated; having a hard, brittle consistency because the particles are held together by cementing substances such as humus, calcium carbonate, or the oxides of silicon, iron, and aluminum.

channery. Thin, flat fragments of limestone, sandstone, or schist up to 6 inches in major diameter.

chelate. (Gk., claw) A type of chemical compound in which a metallic ion is firmly combined with a molecule by means of multiple chemical bonds.

Chernozem. A zonal great soil group consisting of soils with a thick, nearly black or black, organic matter-rich A horizon high in exchangeable calcium, underlain by a lighter colored transitional horizon above a zone of calcium carbonate accumulation; occurs in a cool subhumid climate under a vegetation of tall and midgrass prairie. (1949 classification system) *chert.* A structureless form of silica, closely related to flint which breaks into angular fragments.

Chestnut soil. A zonal great soil group consisting of soils with a moderately thick, dark-brown A horizon over a lighter colored horizon that is above a zone of calcium carbonate accumulation. They develop under mixed tall and short grasses in a temperate to cool and subhumid to semiarid climate. (1949 classification system)

chisel, subsoil. A tillage implement with one or more cultivator-type feet to which are attached strong knifelike units used to shatter or loosen hard, compact layers, usually in the subsoil, to depths below normal plow depth. See *subsoiling.*

chlorosis. A condition in plants relating to the failure of chlorophyll (the green coloring matter) to develop. Chlorotic leaves range from light green through yellow to almost white.

chroma. The relative purity, strength, or saturation of a color; directly related to the dominance of the determining wavelength of the light and inversely related to grayness; one of the three variables of color. See *Munsell color system, hue,* and *value, color.*

class, soil. A group of soils having a definite range in a particular property such as acidity, degree of slope, texture, structure, land-use capability, degree of erosion, or drainage. See *Soil texture* and *soil structure.*

classification, soil. The systematic arrangement of soils into groups or categories on the basis of their characteristics. Broad groupings are made on the basis of general characteristics and subdivisions on the basis of more detailed differences in specific properties.

clay. (i) A soil separate consisting of particles < 0.002 mm in equivalent diameter. (ii) Soil material containing more than 40 per cent clay, less than 45 per cent sand, and less than 40 per cent silt.

clayey. Containing large amounts of clay or having properties similar to those of clay.

clay mineral. Naturally occurring inorganic material (usually crystalline) found in soils and other earthy deposits, the particles being of clay size; that is, < 0.002 mm in diameter.

claypan. A compact slowly permeable layer in the subsoil having a much higher clay content than the overlying material, from which it is separated by a sharply defined boundary. Claypans are usually hard when dry, and plastic and sticky when wet.

clod. A compact, coherent mass of soil produced artificially, usually by the activity of man by plowing, digging, etc., especially when these operations are performed on soils that are either too wet or too dry for normal tillage operations.

coarse texture. The texture exhibited by sands, loamy sands, and sandy loams except very fine sandy loam.

cobblestone. Rounded or partially rounded rock or mineral fragments between 3 and 10 inches in diameter.

colloid, soil. (Gk. glue like) Organic and inorganic matter with very small particle size and a correspondingly large surface area per unit of mass.

colluvium. A deposit of rock fragments and soil material accumulated at the base of steep slopes as a result of gravitational action.

compost. Organic residues, or a mixture of organic residues and soil, that have been piled, moistened, and allowed to undergo biological decomposition. Mineral fertilizers are sometimes added. Often called "artificial manure" or "synthetic manure" if produced primarily from plant residues.

concretion. A local concentration of a chemical compound, such as calcium carbonate or iron oxide, in the form of a grain or nodule of varying size, shape, hardness, and color.

conductivity, hydraulic. See *hydraulic conductivity*.

consistence. The combination of properies of soil material that determine its resistance to crushing and its ability to be molded or changed in shape. Such terms as loose, friable, firm, soft, plastic, and sticky describe soil consistence.

consumptive use. The water used by plants in transpiration and growth, plus water vapor loss from adjacent soil or snow, or from intercepted precipitation in any specified time. Usually expressed as equivalent depth of free water per unit of time.

contour. An imaginary line connecting points of equal elevation on the surface of the soil. A contour terrace is laid out on a sloping soil at right angles to the direction of the slope and nearly level throughout its course.

creep. Slow mass movement of soil and soil material down relatively steep slopes primarily under the influence of gravity, but facilitated by saturation with water and by alternate freezing and thawing.

crotovina. A former animal burrow in one soil horizon that has been filled with organic matter or material from another horizon (also spelled "krotovina").

crumb. A soft, porous, more or less rounded natural unit of structure from 1 to 5 mm in diameter.

required crushing strength. The force required to crush a mass of dry soil or, conversely, the resistance of the dry soil mass to crushing. Expressed in units of force per unit area(pressure).

crust. A surface layer on soils, ranging in thickness from a few millimeters to perhaps as much as an inch, that is much more compact, hard, and brittle, when dry, than the material immediately beneath it.

crystal. A homogeneous inorganic substance of definite chemical composition bounded by plane surfaces that form definite angles with each other, thus giving the substance a regular geometrical form.

crystal lattice. See *lattice structure.*

crystalline rock. A rock consisting of various minerals that have crystallized in place from magma. See *igneous rock* and *sedimentary rock.*

deflocculate. (i) To separate the individual components of compound particles by chemical and/or physical means. (ii) To cause the particles of the *disperse phase* of a colloidal system to become suspended in the *dispersion medium.*

Degraded Chernozem. A zonal great soil group consisting of soils with a very dark brown or black A1 horizon underlain by a dark gray, weakly expressed A2 horizon and a brown B (?) horizon; formed in the forest-prairie transition of cool climates. (1949 classification system)

denitrification. The biochemical reduction of nitrate or nitrite to gaseous nitrogen either as molecular nitrogen or as an oxide of nitrogen.

desalinization. Removal of salts from saline soil, usually by leaching.

desert crust. A hard layer, containing calcium carbonate, gypsum, or other binding material, exposed at the surface in desert regions.

Desert soil. A zonal great soil group consisting of soils with a very thin, light-colored surface horizon, which may be vesicular and is ordinarily underlain by calcareous material; formed in arid regions under sparse shrub vegetation. (1949 classification system)

desorption. The removal of sorbed material from surfaces.

diatoms. Algae having siliceous cell walls that persist as a skeleton after death. Any of the microscopic unicellular or colonial algae constituting the class Bacillariaceae. They occur abundantly in fresh and salt waters and their remains are widely distributed in soils.

diatomaceous earth. A geologic deposit of fine, grayish, siliceous material composed chiefly or wholly of the remains of diatoms. It may occur as a powder or as a porous, rigid material.

diffusion. The transport of matter as a result of the movement of the constituent particles. The intermingling of two gases or liquids in contact with each other takes place by diffusion.

disintegration. The breakdown of rock and mineral particles into smaller particles by physical forces such as frost action.

disperse. (i) To break up compound particles, such as aggregates, into the individual component particles. (ii) To distribute or suspend fine particles, such as clay, in or throughout a dispersion medium, such as water.

diversion dam. A structure or barrier built to divert part or all of the water of a stream to a different course.

double layer. In colloid chemistry, the electric charges on the surface of the disperse phase (usually negative), and the adjacent diffuse layer (usually positive) of ions in solution.

drift. Material of any sort deposited by geological processes in one place after having been removed from another. Glacial drift includes material moved by the glaciers and by the streams and lakes associated with them.

drumlin. Long, smooth cigar-shaped low hills of glacial till, with their long axes parallel to the direction of ice movement.

dryland farming. The practice of crop production in low-rainfall areas without irrigation.

duff. The matted, partly decomposed organic surface layer of forest soils.

duripan (hardpan). An indurated horizon cemented by materials such as aluminum silicate, silica, $CaCO_3$, and iron.

dust mulch. A loose, finely granular, or powdery condition on the surface of the soil, usually produced by shallow cultivation.

ectotrophic mycorrhiza. A mycorrhizal association in which the fungal hyphae form a compact mantle on the surface of the roots. Mycelial strands extend inward between cortical cells and outward from the mantle to the surface soil.

edaphology. The science that deals with the influence of soils on living things, particularly plants, including man's use of land for plant growth.

electrokinetic potential. In a colloidal system, the difference in potential between the immovable layer attached to the surface of the dispersed phase and the dispersion medium.

eluviation. The removal of soil material in suspension (or in solution) from a layer or layers of a soil. (Usually, the loss of material in *solution* is described by the term "leaching.") See *leaching.*

endotrophic. Nourished or receiving nourishment from within, as fungi or their hyphae receiving nourishment from plant roots in a mycorrhizal association.

endotrophic mycorrhiza. A mycorrhizal association in which the fungal hyphae are present on root surfaces only as individual threads that may penetrate directly into root hairs, other epidermal cells, and occasionally into cortical cells. Individual threads extend from the root surface outward into the surrounding soil.

Entisols. Soils which have no natural genetic horizons or only the beginning of such horizons. Typified by Grumusols in the old classification system. (new comprehensive classification system)

epipedon. A diagnostic surface horizon which includes the upper part of

the soil that is darkened by organic matter, or the upper eluvial horizons or both. (new comprehensive classification system.)

erosion. (i) The wearing away of the land surface by running water,
wind, ice, or other geological agents, including such processes as
gravitational creep. (ii) Detachment and movement of soil or rock
by water, wind, ice, or gravity. The following terms are used to
describe different types of water erosion:

accelerated erosion. Erosion much more rapid than normal, natural,
geological erosion, primarily as a result of the influence of the activities of man or, in some cases, of animals.

gully erosion. The erosion process whereby water accumulates in
narrow channels and, over short periods, removes the soil from this
narrow area to considerable depths, ranging from 1 or 2 feet to as
much as 75 to 100 feet.

natural erosion. Wearing away of the earth's surface by water, ice, or
other natural agents under natural environmental conditions of
climate, vegetation, etc., undisturbed by man. Synonymous with
geological erosion.

normal erosion. The gradual erosion of land used by man which does
not greatly exceed natural erosion. See *natural erosion.*

rill erosion. An erosion process in which numerous small channels of
only several inches in depth are formed; occurs mainly on recently
cultivated soils. See *rill.*

sheet erosion. The removal of a fairly uniform layer of soil from the
land surface by runoff water.

splash erosion. The spattering of small soil particles caused by the
impact of raindrops on very wet soils. The loosened and separated
particles may or may not be subsequently removed by surface
runoff.

eutrophic. Having concentrations of nutrients ·optimal (or nearly so)
for plant or animal growth. (Said of nutrient solutions or of soil solutions.)

evapotranspiration. The combined loss of water from a given area, and
during a specified period of time, by evaporation from the soil surface
and by transpiration from plants.

exchange acidity. The titratable hydrogen and aluminum that can be replaced from the adsorption complex by a neutral salt solution. Usually
expressed as milliequivalents per 100 grams of soil.

exchange capacity. The total ionic charge of the adsorption complex
active in the adsorption of ions. See *anion-exchange capacity* and
cation-exchange capacity.

exchangeable-sodium percentage. The extent to which the adsorption
complex of a soil is occupied by sodium. It is expressed as follows:

$$ESP = \frac{\text{Exchangeable sodium (meq/100 g soil)}}{\text{Cation-exchange capacity (meq/100 g soil)}} \times 100$$

fallow. Cropland left idle in order to restore productivity, mainly through accumulation of water, nutrients, or both. Summer fallow is a common stage before cereal grain in regions of limited rainfall. The soil is kept free of weeds and other vegetation thereby conserving nutrients and water for the next year's crop.

family, soil. In soil classification one of the categories intermediate between the great soil group and the soil series.

fertility, soil. The status of a soil with respect to the amount and availability to plants of elements necessary for plant growth.

fertilizer. Any organic or inorganic material of natural or synthetic origin which is added to a soil to supply certain elements essential to the growth of plants.

fertilizer grade. The guaranteed minimum analysis, in per cent, of the major plant nutrient elements contained in a fertilizer material or in a mixed fertilizer. (Usually refers to the percentage of $N-P_2O_5-K_2O$ but proposals are pending to change the designation to the percentage of N–P–K.)

fertilizer requirement. The quantity of certain plant nutrient elements needed, in addition to the amount supplied by the soil, to increase plant growth to a designated optimum.

field capacity (field moisture capacity). The percentage of water remaining in a soil 2 or 3 days after having been saturated and after free drainage has practically ceased.

fine texture. Consisting of or containing large quantities of the fine fractions, particularly of silt and clay. (Includes all clay loams and clays; that is, clay loam, sandy clay loam, silty clay loam, sandy clay, silty clay, and clay textural classes.)

first bottom. The normal flood plain of a stream.

fixation. The process or processes in a soil by which certain chemical elements essential for plant growth are converted from a soluble or exchangeable form to a much less soluble or to a nonexchangeable form; for example, phosphate "fixation." Contrast with *nitrogen fixation.*

fixed phosphorus. That phosphorus which has been changed to a less-soluble form as a result of reaction with the soil; moderately available phosphorus.

flood plain. The land bordering a stream, built up of sediments from overflow of the stream and subject to inundation when the stream is at flood stage.

fluorapatite. A member of the apatite group of minerals rich in fluorine. Most common mineral in rock phosphate.

fragipan. Dense and brittle pan or layer in soils that owe their hardness mainly to extreme density or compactness rather than high clay content or cementation. Removed fragments are friable, but the material in place is so dense that roots cannot penetrate and water moves through it very slowly.

friable. A soil consistency term pertaining to the ease of crumbling of soils.

fulvic acid. A term of varied usage but usually referring to the mixture of organic substances remaining in solution upon acidification of a dilute alkali extract from the soil.

furrow irrigation. See *irrigation methods*.

Genesis, soil. The mode of origin of the soil, with special reference to the processes responsible for the development of the solum, or true soil, from the unconsolidated parent material.

geological erosion. See *erosion*.

gilgai. The microrelief of soils produced by expansion and contraction with changes in moisture. Found in soils that contain large amounts of clay which swells and shrinks considerably with wetting and drying. Usually a succession of microbasins and microknolls in nearly level areas or of microvalleys and microridges parallel to the direction of the slope.

glacial drift. Rock debris that has been transported by glaciers and deposited, either directly from the ice or from the melt-water. The debris may or may not be heterogeneous.

glacial till. See *till*.

glaciofluvial deposits. Material moved by glaciers and subsequently sorted and deposited by streams flowing from the melting ice. The deposits are stratified and may occur in the form of outwash plains, deltas, kames, eskers, and kame terraces.

Gley soil. Soil developed under conditions of poor drainage resulting in reduction of iron and other elements and in gray colors and mottles.

granular structure. Soil structure in which the individual grains are grouped into spherical aggregates with indistinct sides. Highly porous granules are commonly called crumbs. A well-granulated soil has the best structure for most ordinary crop plants.

gravitational water. Water which moves into, through, or out of the soil under the influence of gravity.

Gray-Brown Podzolic soil. A zonal great soil group consisting of soils with a thin, moderately dark A1 horizon and with a grayish-brown A2 horizon underlain by a B horizon containing a high percentage of bases and an appreciable quantity of illuviated silicate clay; formed on relatively young land surfaces, mostly glacial deposits, from material relatively rich in calcium, under deciduous forests in humid temperate regions. (1949 classification system)

Gray Desert soil. A term used in Russia, and frequently in the United States, synonymous with Desert soil. See *Desert soil.*

Great soil group. Any one of several broad groups of soils with fundamental characteristics in common. Examples are Chernozems, Gray-Brown Podzolic, and Podzol. (1949 classification system)

Great Group. A category in the new comprehensive classification system between that of the suborder and the subgroup.

green manure. Plant material incorporated with the soil while green, or soon after maturity, for improving the soil.

groundwater. Water that fills all the unblocked pores of underlying material below the water table, which is the upper limit of saturation.

Ground-Water Laterite soil. A great soil group of the intrazonal order and hydromorphic suborder, consisting of soils characterized by hardpans or concretional horizons rich in iron and aluminum (and sometimes manganese) that have formed immediately above the water table. (1949 classification system)

Ground-Water Podzol soil. A great soil group of the intrazonal order and hydromorphic suborder, consisting of soils with an organic mat on the surface over a very thin layer of acid humus material underlain by a whitish-gray leached layer, which may be as much as 2 or 3 feet in thickness, and is underlain by a brown, or very dark-brown, cemented hardpan layer; formed under various types of forest vegetation in cool to tropical humid climates under conditions of poor drainage. (1949 classification system)

gully erosion. See *erosion.*

gypsic horizon. A horizon of accumulation of secondary $CaSO_4$, more than 6 inches thick which has at least 5 per cent more gypsum than the C or underlying stratum, and in which the product of thickness in inches and the per cent gypsum is at least 60 per cent-inches. (new comprehensive classification system)

Half-Bog soil. A great soil group, of the intrazonal order and hydromorphic suborder consisting of soil with dark-brown or black peaty material over grayish and rust mottled mineral soil; formed under conditions of poor drainage under forest, sedge, or grass vegetation in cool to tropical humid climates. (1949 classification system)

halomorphic soil. A suborder of the intrazonal soil order, consisting of saline and alkali soils formed under imperfect drainage in arid regions and including the great soil groups Solonchak or Saline soils, Solonetz soils, and Soloth soils. (1949 classification system)

hardpan. A hardened soil layer, in the lower A or in the B horizon, caused by cementation of soil particles with organic matter or with materials such as silica, sesquioxides, or calcium carbonate. The hardness does not change appreciably with changes in moisture content and pieces of the hard layer do not slake in water. See *caliche, claypan,* and *duripan.*

heavy soil. (Obsolete in scientific use) A soil with a high content of the fine separates, particularly clay, or one with a high drawbar pull and hence difficult to cultivate.

heterotrophic. Capable of deriving energy for life processes only from the decomposition of organic compounds and incapable of using inorganic compounds as sole sources of energy or for organic synthesis. Contrast with *autotrophic.*

histic epipedon. A horizon at or near the surface, saturated with water at some season and containing a minimum of 20 per cent organic matter if no clay is present and at least 30 per cent organic matter if it has 50 per cent or more of clay. (new comprehensive classification system)

Histisols. Soils characterized by their high organic matter content. Bog soils and half-bog soils are included in this soil order. (new comprehensive classification system)

horizon, soil. A layer of soil, approximately parallel to the soil surface, with distinct characteristics produced by soil-forming processes.

hue. One of the three variables of color. It is caused by light of certain wavelengths and changes with the wavelength. See *Munsell color system, chroma,* and *value, color.*

humic acid. A mixture of variable or indefinite composition of dark organic substances, precipitated upon acidification of a dilute-alkali extract from soil.

Humic Gley soil. Soil of the intrazonal order and hydromorphic suborder that includes Wisenboden and related soils, such as Half-Bog soils, which have a thin muck or peat O_2 horizon and an A1 horizon. Developed in wet meadow and in forested swamps. (1949 classification system.

humification. The processes involved in the decomposition of organic matter and leading to the formation of humus.

humus. That more or less stable fraction of the soil organic matter remaining after the major portion of added plant and animal residues have decomposed. Usually it is dark colored.

hydraulic conductivity. An expression of the readiness with which a liquid such as water flows through a soil in response to a given potential gradient.

hydromorphic soils. A suborder of intrazonal soils, all formed under conditions of poor drainage in marshes, swamps, seepage areas, or flats. (1949 classification system) *hydrous mica.* A silicate clay with 2:1 lattice structure, but of indefinite chemical composition since usually part of the silicon in the silica tetrahedral layer has been replaced by aluminum and containing a considerable amount of potassium which serves as an additional bonding between the crystal units, resulting in particles larger than normal in montmorillonite and, consequently, in a lower cation-exchange capacity. Sometimes referrred to as illite.

hydroxyapatite. A member of the apatite group of minerals rich in hydroxyl groups. A nearly insoluble calcium phosphate.

hygroscopic coefficient. The amount of moisture in a dry soil when it is in equilibrium with some standard relative humidity near a saturated atmosphere (about 98 per cent), expressed in terms of percentage on the basis of oven-dry soil.

igneous rock. Rock formed from the cooling and solidification of magma, and that has not been changed appreciably since its formation.

illite. A hydrous mica. See *hydrous mica.*

illuvial horizon. A soil layer or horizon in which material carried from an overlying layer has been precipitated from solution or deposited from suspension. The layer of accumulation.

immature soil. A soil with indistinct or only slightly developed horizons because of the relatively short time it has been subjected to the various soil-forming processes. A soil that has not reached equilibrium with its environment.

immobilization. The conversion of an element from the inorganic to the organic form in microbial tissues or in plant tissues, thus rendering the element not readily available to other organisms or to plants.

impervious. Resistant to penetration by fluids or by roots.

Inceptisols. Soils with one or more diagnostic horizons that are thought to form rather quickly and that do not represent significant illuviation or eluviation or extreme weathering. Soils classified as Brown Forest, Subarctic Brown Forest, Ando, Sols Bruns Acides, and associated Humic Gley and Low-Humic Gley soils are included in this order. (new comprehensive classification system)

infiltration. The downward entry of water into the soil.

infiltration rate. A soil characteristic determining or describing the *maximum* rate at which water *can* enter the soil under specified conditions, including the presence of an excess of water.

intergrade. A soil that possesses moderately well-developed distinguishing characteristics of two or more genetically related great soil groups.

intrazonal soils. A soil with more or less well-developed soil characteristics that reflect the dominating influence of some local factor of relief, parent material, or age, over the normal effect of climate and vegetation. (1949 classification system) *ions.* Atoms, groups of atoms, or compounds, which are electrically charged as a result of the loss of electrons (cations) or the gain of electrons (anions).

iron-pan. An indurated soil horizon in which iron oxide is the principal cementing agent.

irrigation efficiency. The ratio of the water actually consumed by crops on an irrigated area to the amount of water diverted from the source onto the area.

irrigation methods. The manner in which water is artificially applied to an area. The methods and the manner of applying the water are as follows:

> *border-strip.* The water is applied at the upper end of a strip with earth borders to confine the water to the strip.
>
> *check-basin.* The water is applied rapidly to relatively level plots surrounded by levees. The basin is a small check.
>
> *corrugation.* The water is applied to small, closely-spaced furrows, frequently in grain and forage crops, to confine the flow of irrigation water to one direction.
>
> *flooding.* The water is released from field ditches and allowed to flood over the land.
>
> *furrow.* The water is applied to row crops in ditches made by tillage implements.
>
> *sprinkler.* The water is sprayed over the soil surface through nozzles from a pressure system.
>
> *subirrigation.* The water is applied in open ditches or tile lines until the water table is raised sufficiently to wet the soil.
>
> *wild-flooding.* The water is released at high points in the field and distribution is uncontrolled.

isomorphous substitution. The replacement of one atom by another of similar size in a crystal lattice without disrupting or changing the crystal structure of the mineral.

kame. An irregular ridge or hill of stratified glacial drift.

kaolin. An aluminosilicate mineral of the 1:1 crystal lattice group; that is, consisting of one silicon tetrahedral layer and one aluminum oxide-hydroxide octahedral layer.

lacustrine deposit. Material deposited in lake water and later exposed either by lowering of the water level or by the elevation of the land.

land. Land is a broader term than soil. In addition to soil, its attributes include other physical conditions such as mineral deposits and water supply; location in relation to centers of commerce, populations, and other land; the size of the individual tracts or holdings; and existing plant cover, works of improvement, and the like.

land classification. The arrangement of land units into various categories based upon the properties of the land or its suitability for some particular purpose.

land-use planning. The development of plans for the uses of land that, over long periods, will best serve the general welfare, together with the formulation of ways and means for achieving such uses.

Latosol. A suborder of zonal soils including soils formed under forested, tropical, humid conditions and characterized by low silica-sesquioxide ratios of the clay fractions, low base-exchange capacity, low activity of the clay, low content of most primary minerals, low content of soluble constituents, a high degree of aggregate stability, and usually having a red color. (1949 classification system)

lattice structure. The orderly arrangement of atoms in a crystalline material.

leaching. The removal of materials in solution from the soil. See *eluviation.*

light soil. (Obsolete in scientific use) A coarse-textured soil; a soil with a low drawbar pull and hence easy to cultivate. See *coarse texture* and *soil texture.*

lime (agricultural). In strict chemical terms, calcium oxide. In practical terms, it is a material containing the carbonates, oxides and/or hydroxides of calcium and/or magnesium used to neutralize soil acidity.

lime requirement. The mass of agricultural limestone, or the equivalent of other specified liming material, required per acre to a soil depth of 6 inches (or on 2 million pounds of soil) to raise the pH of the soil to a desired value under field conditions.

limestone. A sedimentary rock composed primarily of calcite ($CaCO_3$). If dolomite ($CaCO_3 \cdot MgCO_3$) is present in appreciable quantities it is called a dolomitic limestone.

Lithosols. A great soil group of azonal soils characterized by an incomplete solum or no clearly expressed soil morphology and consisting of freshly and imperfectly weathered rock or rock fragments. (1949 classification system)

loam. The textural class name for soil having a moderate amount of sand, silt, and clay. Loam soils contain 7 to 27 per cent of clay, 28 to 50 per cent of silt, and less than 52 per cent of sand.

loamy. Intermediate in texture and properties between fine-textured and coarse-textured soils. Includes all textural classes with the words "loam" or "loamy" as a part of the class name, such as clay loam or loamy sand. See *loam* and *soil texture.*

loess. Material transported and deposited by wind and consisting of predominantly silt-sized particles.

luxury consumption. The intake by a plant of an essential nutrient in amounts exceeding what it needs. Thus if potassium is abundant in the soil, alfalfa may take in more than is required.

lysimeter. A device for measuring percolation and leaching losses from a column of soil under controlled conditions.

macronutrient. A chemical element necessary in large amounts (usually > 1 ppm in the plant) for the growth of plants and usually applied artificially in fertilizer or liming materials ("macro" refers to quantity and not to the essentiality of the element.) See *micronutrient.*

marl. Soft and unconsolidated calcium carbonate, usually mixed with varying amounts of clay or other impurities.

marsh. Periodically wet or continually flooded areas with the surface not deeply submerged. Covered dominantly with sedges, cattails, rushes, or other hydrophytic plants. Subclasses include fresh-water and salt-water marshes.

mature soil. A soil with well-developed soil horizons produced by the natural processes of soil formation and essentially in equilibrium with its present environment.

maximum water-holding capacity. The average moisture content of a disturbed sample of soil, 1 cm high, which is at equilibrium with a water table at its lower surface.

mechanical analysis. (Obsolete) See *particle-size analysis* and *particle-size distribution.*

medium-texture. Intermediate between fine-textured and coarse-textured (soils). (It includes the following textural classes: very fine sandy loam, loam, silt loam, and silt.)

mellow soil. A very soft, very friable, porous soil without any tendency toward hardness or harshness. See *consistence.*

metamorphic rock. A rock that has been greatly altered from its previous condition through the combined action of heat and pressure. For example, marble is a metamorphic rock produced from limestone, gneiss is one produced from granite, and slate is produced from shale.

micas. Primary alumino-silicate minerals in which two silica layers alternate with one alumina layer. They separate readily into thin sheets or flakes.

microfauna. That part of the animal population which consists of individuals too small to be clearly distinguished without the use of a microscope. Includes protozoa and nematodes.

microflora. That part of the plant population which consists of individuals too small to be clearly distinguished without the use of a microscope. Includes actinomycetes, algae, bacteria, and fungi.

micronutrient. A chemical element necessary in only extremely small amounts (< 1 ppm in the plant) for the growth of plants. Examples are: B, Cl, Cu, Fe, Mn, and Zn.) ("micro" refers to the amount used rather than to its essentiality.) see *macronutrient*.

microrelief. Small-scale, local differences in topography, including mounds, swales, or pits that are only a few feet in diameter and with elevation differences of up to 6 feet. See *gilgai*.

mineralization. The conversion of an element from an organic form to an inorganic state as a result of microbial decomposition.

mineral soil. A soil consisting predominantly of, and having its properties determined predominantly by, mineral matter. Usually contains < 20% organic matter, but may contain an organic surface layer up to 30 cm thick.

minor element. (Obsolete) See *micronutrient*.

moderately-coarse texture. Consisting predominantly of coarse particles. (In soil textural classification, it includes all the sandy loams except the very fine sandy loam.) See *coarse texture*.

moderately-fine texture. Consisting predominantly of intermediate-size (soil) particles or with relatively small amounts of fine or coarse particles. (In soil textural classification, it includes clay loam, sandy loam, sandy clay loam, and silty clay loam.) See *fine texture*.

moisture equivalent. The weight percentage of water retained by a previously saturated sample of soil 1 cm in thickness after it has been subjected to a centrifugal force of one thousand times gravity for 30 min.

moisture tension (or pressure). The equivalent negative pressure in the soil water. It is equal to the equivalent pressure that must be applied to the soil water to bring it to hydraulic equilibrium, through a porous permeable wall or membrane, with a pool of water of the same composition.

mollic epipedon. A thick, dark surface layer, more than 50 per cent base saturated (dominantly with bivalent cations), having a narrow C/N ratio (17/1 or less in virgin state and 13/1 and less with cultivated soils), a strong soil structure, a relatively soft consistence when dry, and less than 250 ppm of P_2O_5 soluble in citric acid. This horizon characterizes the Mollisol Soil Order, but is found in other orders as well.

Mollisols. Soils characterized by a thick, dark mineral surface horizon which is dominantly saturated with bivalent cations and has moderate to strong structure. Includes soils such as Chernozem, Prairie, Chestnut in the old classification system. (new comprehensive classification system)

montmorillonite. An aluminosilicate clay mineral with a 2:1 expanding crystal lattice; that is, with two silicon tetrahedral layers enclosing an aluminum octahedral layer. Considerable expansion may be caused along the C axis by water moving between silica layers of contiguous units.

mor. Raw humus; a type of forest humus layer of unincorporated organic material, usually matted or compacted or both; distinct from the mineral soil, unless the latter has been blackened by washing in organic matter.

morphology, soil. The constitution of the soil including the texture, structure, consistence, color, and other physical, chemical, and biological properties of the various soil horizons that make up the soil profile.

mottling. Spots or blotches of different color or shades of color interspersed with the dominant color.

muck. Highly decomposed organic material in which the original plant parts are not recognizable. Contains more mineral matter and is usually darker in color than peat. See *muck soil, peat.*

muck soil. An organic soil in which the organic matter is well decomposed (U.S. usage).

mulch. Any material such as straw, sawdust, leaves, plastic film, and loose soil that is spread upon the surface of the soil to protect the soil and plant roots from the effects of raindrops, soil crusting, freezing, evaporation, etc.

mulch farming. A system of farming in which the organic residues are not plowed into or otherwise mixed with the soil but are left on the surface as a mulch.

mull. A humus-rich layer of forested soils consisting of mixed organic and mineral matter. A mull blends into the upper mineral-layers without an abrupt change in soil characteristics.

Munsell color system. A color designation system that specifies the relative degrees of the three simple variables of color: hue, value, and chroma. For example: 10YR 6/4 is a color (of soil) with a hue = 10YR, value = 6, and chroma = 4. These notations can be translated into several different systems of color names as desired. See *chroma, hue,* and *value, color.*

mycorrhiza. The association, usually symbiotic, of fungi with the roots of seed plants. See *ectotrophic mycorrhiza* and *endotrophic mycorrhiza.*

natric horizon. A special argillic horizon which has prismatic or columnar structure and is more than 15 per cent saturated with exchangeable sodium. This is common in Solonetz and solodized-Solonetz soils. (new comprehensive classification system)

necrosis. Death associated with discoloration and dehydration of all or parts of plant organs, such as leaves.

nematodes. Very small worms abundant in many soils and important because many of them attack and destroy plant roots.

neutral soil. A soil in which the surface layer, at least to normal plow depth, is neither acid nor alkaline in reaction. See *acid soil, alkaline soil, pH,* and *reaction, soil.*

nitrification. The biochemical oxidation of ammonium to nitrate.

nitrogen assimilation. The incorporation of nitrogen into organic cell substances by living organisms.

nitrogen fixation. The conversion of elemental nitrogen (N_2) to organic combinations or to forms readily utilizable in biological processes.

nodule bacteria. See *rhizobia.*

nucleic acids. Complex compounds found in the nuclei of plant and animal cells and usually combined with proteins as nucleoproteins.

O horizon. Organic horizon of mineral soils.

ochric epipedon. A light-colored surface horizon generally low in organic matter which includes the eluvial layers near the surface. It is often hard and massive when dry. Although characteristic of Aridisols, it is found in several of the other soil orders. (new comprehensive classification system)

order. The highest category in soil classification. The three orders are zonal soils, intrazonal soils, and azonal soils (1949 classification system) Ten orders are recognized in the new comprehensive classification system: Entisol, Vertisol, Inceptisol, Aridisol, Mollisol, Spodisol, Alfisol, Ultisol, Oxisol, and Histisol.

organic soil. A soil which contains a high percentage (> 20%) of organic matter throughout the solum.

ortstein. An indurated layer in the B horizon of Podzols in which the cementing material consists of illuviated sesquioxides (mostly iron) and organic matter.

osmotic. A type of pressure exerted in living bodies as a result of unequal concentration of salts on both sides of a cell wall or membrane. Water will move from the area having the least salt concentration through the membrane into the area having the highest salt concentration and, therefore, exerts additional pressure on this side of the membrane.

oven-dry soil. Soil which has been dried at 150°C until it reaches constant weight.

oxic horizon. A highly-weathered diagnostic subsurface horizon from which most of the combined silica has been removed leaving a mixture dominated by hydrous oxide clays with some 1:1 type silicate minerals and quartz present. (new comprehensive classification system)

Oxisols. Soils of tropical and subtropical regions characterized by the

presence of a horizon (oxic) from which most of the combined silica
has been removed by weathering leaving oxides of iron and aluminum
and some quartz. Includes soils referred to as Latosols and some called
Ground-Water Laterites. (new comprehensive classification system)

pans. Horizons or layers, in soils, that are strongly compacted, indurated,
or very high in clay content. See *caliche, claypan, duripan, fragipan,*
and *hardpan.*

parent material. The unconsolidated and more or less chemically
weathered mineral or organic matter from which the solum of soils
is developed by pedogenic processes.

particle density. The mass per unit volume of the soil particles. In technical work, usually expressed as grams per cubic centimeter.

particle size. The effective diameter of a particle measured by sedimentation, sieving, or micrometric methods.

particle-size analysis. Determination of the various amounts of the different separates in a soil sample, usually by sedimentation, sieving,
micrometry, or combinations of these methods.

particle-size distribution. The amounts of the various soil separates in a
soil sample, usually expressed as weight percentages.

parts per million (ppm). Weight units of any given substance per one
million equivalent weight units of oven-dry soil; or, in the case of
soil solution or other solution, the weight units of solute per million
weight units of solution.

peat. Unconsolidated soil material consisting largely of undecomposed, or
only slightly decomposed, organic matter accumulated under conditions of excessive moisture.

ped. A unit of soil structure such as an aggregate, crumb, prism, block,
or granule, formed by natural processes (in contrast with a clod,
which is formed artificially).

pedalfer. (Obsolete) A subdivision of a soil order comprising a large
group of soils in which sesquioxides increased relative to silica during
soil formation.

pedocal. (Obsolete) A subdivision of a soil order comprising a large
group of soils in which calcium accumulated during soil formation.

peneplain. A once high, rugged area which has been reduced by erosion
to a low, gently rolling surface resembling a plain.

penetrability. The ease with which a probe can be pushed into the soil.
(May be expressed in units of distance, speed, force, or work depending on the type of penetrometer used.)

percolation, soil water. The downward movement of water through soil.
Especially, the downward flow of water in saturated or nearly saturated
soil at hydraulic gradients of the order of 1.0 or less.

permafrost. (i) Permanently frozen material underlying the solum. (ii) A perenially frozen soil horizon.

permanent charge. The net negative (or positive) charge of clay particles inherent in the crystal lattice of the particle; not affected by changes in pH or by ion-exchange reactions.

permeability, soil. The ease with which gases, liquids, or plant roots penetrate or pass through a bulk mass of soil or a layer of soil.

pF. (Obsolete) The logarithm of the soil moisture tension expressed in centimeters height of a column of water.

pH, soil. The negative logarithm of the hydrogen-ion activity of a soil. The degree of acidity (or alkalinity) of a soil as determined by means of a glass, quinhydrone, or other suitable electrode or indicator at a specified moisture content or soil-water ratio, and expressed in terms of the pH scale.

pH-dependent charge. That portion of the total charge of the soil particles which is affected by, and varies with, changes in pH.

phase, soil. A subdivision of a soil type or other unit of classification having characteristics that affect the use and management of the soil but which do not vary sufficiently to differentiate it as a separate type. A variation in a property or characteristic such as degree of slope, degree of erosion, and content of stones.

photomap. A mosaic map made from aerial photographs with physical and cultural features shown as on a planimetric map.

physical properties (of soils). Those characteristics, processes, or reactions of a soil which are caused by physical forces and which can be described by, or expressed in, physical terms or equations. Examples of physical properties are bulk density, water-holding capacity, hydraulic conductivity, porosity, pore-size distribution, etc.

plaggen epipedon. Man-made surface layer more than 20 inches thick and produced by long continued manuring. Common in Europe but unknown in the U.S.

Planosol. A great soil group of the intrazonal order and hydromorphic suborder consisting of soils with eluviated surface horizons underlain by B horizons more strongly eluviated, cemented, or compacted than associated normal soil. (1949 classification system)

plastic soil. A soil capable of being molded or deformed continuously and permanently, by relatively moderate pressure, into various shapes. See *consistence.*

platy. Consisting of soil aggregates that are developed predominately along the horizontal axes; laminated; flaky.

plinthite (brick). A highly weathered mixture of sesquioxides of iron and aluminum with quartz and other diluents which occurs as red mottles and which changes irreversibly to hardpan upon alternate wetting and drying.

Podzol. A great soil group of the zonal order consisting of soils formed in cool-temperate to temperate, humid climates, under coniferous or mixed coniferous and deciduous forest, and characterized particularly by a highly-leached, whitish-gray A2 horizon. (1949 classification system)

podzolization. A process of soil formation resulting in the genesis of Podzols and Podzolic soils.

pore-size distribution. The volume of the various sizes of pores in a soil. Expressed as percentages of the bulk volume (soil plus pore space).

porosity. The volume percentage of the total bulk not occupied by solid particles.

potassium fixation. The process of converting exchangeable or water-soluble potassium to a form not easily exchanged from the adsorption complex with a cation of a neutral salt solution.

Prairie soils. A zonal great soil group consisting of soils formed under temperate to cool-temperate, humid regions under tall grass vegetation. (1949 classification system)

primary mineral. A mineral that has not been altered chemically since deposition and crystallization from molten lava.

prismatic soil structure. A soil structure type with prismlike aggregates that have a vertical axis much longer than the horizontal axes.

productivity, soil. The capacity of a soil for producing a specified plant or sequence of plants under a specified system of management. Productivity emphasizes the capacity of soil to produce crops and should be expressed in terms of yields.

profile, soil. A vertical section of the soil through all its horizons and extending into the parent material.

protein. Any of a group of nitrogen-containing compounds that yield amino acids on hydrolysis and have high molecular weights. They are essential parts of living matter and are one of the essential food substances of animals.

puddled soil. Dense, massive soil artificially compacted when wet and having no regular structure. The condition commonly results from the tillage of a clayey soil when it is wet.

reaction, soil. The degree of acidity or alkalinity of a soil, usually expressed as a pH value.

Extremely acid	Below 4.5
Very strongly acid	4.5–5.0
Strongly acid	5.1–5.5
Medium acid	5.6–6.0
Slightly acid	6.1–6.5

Neutral	6.6–7.3
Mildly alkaline	7.4–7.8
Moderately alkaline	7.9–8.4
Strongly alkaline	8.5–9.0
Very strongly alkaline	9.1 and higher

Red Desert soil. A zonal great soil group consisting of soils formed under warm-temperate to hot, dry regions under desert-type vegetation, mostly shrubs. (1949 classification system)

Red-Yellow Podzolic soils. A zonal great soil group consisting of soils formed under warm-temperate to tropical, humid climates, under deciduous or coniferous forest vegetation and usually under conditions of good drainage. (1949 classification system)

regolith. The unconsolidated mantle of weathered rock and soil material on the earth's surface; loose earth materials above solid rock. (Approximately equivalent to the term "soil" as used by many engineers.)

Regosol. Any soil of the azonal order without definite genetic horizons and developing from or on deep, unconsolidated, soft mineral deposits such as sands, loess, or glacial drift. (1949 classification system)

Rendzina. A great soil group of the intrazonal order and calcimorphic suborder consisting of soils with brown or black friable surface horizons underlain by light-gray to pale-yellow calcareous material; developed from soft, highly calcareous parent material under grass vegetation or mixed grasses and forest in humid and semiarid climates. (1949 classification system)

residual material. Unconsolidated and partly weathered mineral materials accumulated by disintegration of consolidated rock in place.

reticulate mottling. A network of streaks of different color; most commonly found in the deeper profiles of Lateritic soils.

rhizobia. Bacteria capable of living symbiotically with higher plants, usually legumes, from which they receive their energy, and capable of using atmospheric nitrogen; hence, the term symbiotic nitrogen-fixing bacteria. (Derived from the generic name *Rhizobium.*)

rhizosphere. That portion of the soil in the immediate vicinity of plant roots in which the abundance and composition of the microbial population are influenced by the presence of roots.

rill. A small, intermittent water course with steep sides; usually only a few inches deep and, hence, no obstacle to tillage operations.

rill erosion. See *erosion.*

rock. The material that forms the essential part of the earth's solid crust, including loose incoherent masses such as sand and gravel, as well as solid masses of granite and limestone.

rough broken land. Land with very steep topography and numerous intermittent drainage channels but usually covered with vegetation.

runoff. That portion of the precipitation on an area which is discharged from the area through stream channels. That which is lost without entering the soil is called *surface runoff* and that which enters the soil before reaching the stream is called *ground water runoff* or *seepage flow* from ground water. (In soil science "runoff" usually refers to the water lost by surface flow; in geology and hydraulics "runoff" usually includes both surface and subsurface flow.)

salic horizon. A horizon at least 6 inches thick with secondary enrichment of salts more soluble in cold water than gypsum. (new comprehensive classification system)

saline-sodic soil. A soil containing sufficient exchangeable sodium to interfere with the growth of most crop plants and containing appreciable quantities of soluble salts. The exchangeable-sodium percentage is > 15, the conductivity of the saturation extract > 4 millimhos per centimeter (at 25° C), and the pH is usually 8.5 or less in the saturated soil.

saline soil. A nonsodic soil containing sufficient soluble salts to impair its productivity.

salinization. The process of accumulation of salts in soil.

sand. A soil particle between 0.05 and 2.0 mm in diameter.

second bottom. The first terrace above the normal flood plain of a stream.

secondary mineral. A mineral resulting from the decomposition of a primary mineral or from the reprecipitation of the products of decomposition of a primary mineral. See *primary mineral.*

sedimentary rock. A rock formed from materials deposited from suspension or precipitated from solution and usually being more or less consolidated. The principal sedimentary rocks are sandstones, shales, limestones, and conglomerates.

self-mulching soil. A soil in which the surface layer becomes so well aggregated that it does not crust and seal under the impact of rain but instead serves as a surface mulch upon drying.

separate, soil. One of the individual-size groups of mineral soil particles —sand, silt, or clay.

series, soil. See *soil series.*

shear. Force, as of a tillage implement, acting at right angles to the direction of movement.

sheet erosion. See *erosion.*

Sierozem. A zonal great soil group consisting of soils with pale-grayish A horizons grading into calcareous material at a depth of 1 foot or less, and formed in temperate to cool, arid climates under a vegetation of desert plants, short grass, and scattered brush. (1949 classification system)

silica-alumina ratio. The molecules of silicon dioxide (SiO_2) per molecule of aluminum oxide (Al_2O_3) in clay minerals or in soils.

silica-sesquioxide ratio. The molecules of silicon dioxide (SiO_2) per molecule of aluminum oxide (Al_2O_3) plus ferric oxide (Fe_2O_3) in clay minerals or in soils.

silt. (i) A soil separate consisting of particles between 0.05 and 0.002 mm in equivalent diameter. (ii) A soil textural class.

silting. The deposition of water-borne sediments in stream channels, lakes, reservoirs, or on flood plains, usually resulting from a decrease in the velocity of the water.

site index. A quantitative evaluation of the productivity of a soil for forest growth under the existing or specified environment.

slick spots. Small areas in a field that are slick when wet, due to a high content of alkali or of exchangeable sodium.

sodic soil. A soil that contains sufficient sodium to interfere with the growth of most crop plants, and in which the exchangeable-sodium percentage is 15 or more.

$$\textit{sodium-adsorption ratio} (SAR) = \frac{Na^+}{\dfrac{\sqrt{Ca^{2+} + Mg^{2+}}}{2}}$$ where the cation concentrations are in milliequivalents per liter.

soil. (i) A dynamic natural body on the surface of the earth in which plants grow, composed of mineral and organic materials and living forms. (ii) The collection of natural bodies occupying parts of the earth's surface that support plants and that have properties due to the integrated effect of climate and living matter acting upon parent material, as conditioned by relief, over periods of time.

soil air. The soil atmosphere; the gaseous phase of the soil, being that volume not occupied by solid or liquid.

soil alkalinity. The degree or intensity of alkalinity of a soil, expressed by a value > 7.0 on the pH scale.

soil association. A group of defined and named taxonomic soil units occurring together in an individual and characteristic pattern over a geographic region, comparable to plant associations in many ways.

soil complex. A mapping unit used in detailed soil surveys where two or more defined taxonomic units are so intimately intermixed geographically that it is undesirable or impractical, because of the scale being used, to separate them. A more intimate mixing of smaller areas of individual taxonomic units than that described under *soil association.*

soil conservation. A combination of all management and land use methods which safeguard the soil against depletion or deterioration by natural or by man-induced factors.

soil genesis. The mode of origin of the soil with special reference to the processes or soil-forming factors responsible for the development of the solum, or true soil, from the unconsolidated parent material.

soil geography. A subspecialization of physical geography concerned with the areal distributions of soil types.

soil horizon. See *horizon, soil.*

soil management. The sum total of all tillage operations, cropping practices, fertilizer, lime, and other treatments conducted on or applied to a soil for the production of plants.

soil map. A map showing the distribution of soil types or other soil mapping units in relation to the prominent physical and cultural features of the earth's surface.

soil mechanics and engineering. A subspecialization of soil science concerned with the effect of forces on the soil and the application of engineering principles to problems involving the soil.

soil microbiology. A subspecialization of soil science concerned with soil-inhabiting microorganisms and with their relation to agriculture, including both plant and animal growth.

soil monolith. A vertical section of a soil profile removed from the soil and mounted for display or study.

soil morphology. The physical constitution, particularly the structural properties, of a soil profile as exhibited by the kinds, thickness, and arrangement of the horizons in the profile, and by the texture, structure, consistency, and porosity of each horizon.

soil porosity. See *porosity.*

soil reaction. See *reaction, soil* and *pH, soil.*

soil salinity. The amount of soluble salts in a soil, expressed in terms of percentage parts per million, or other convenient ratios.

soil science. That science dealing with soils as a natural resource on the surface of the earth including soil formation, classification and mapping, and the physical, chemical, biological, and fertility properties of soils *per se;* and these properties in relation to their management for crop production.

soil separates. See *separate, soil.*

soil series. The basic unit of soil classification being a subdivision of a family and consisting of soils which are essentially alike in all major profile characteristics except the texture of the A horizon.

soil solution. The aqueous liquid phase of the soil and its solutes consisting of ions dissociated from the surfaces of the soil particles and of other soluble materials.

soil structure. The combination or arrangement of primary soil particles into secondary particles, units, or peds. These secondary units may be, but usually are not, arranged in the profile in such a manner as to give a distinctive characteristic pattern. The secondary units are characterized and classified on the basis of size, shape, and degree of distinctness into classes, types, and grades, respectively.

soil survey. The systematic examination, description, classification, and mapping of soils in an area. Soil surveys are classified according to the kind and intensity of field examination.

soil texture. The relative proportions of the various soil separates in a soil.

soil type. The lowest unit in the natural system of soil classification; a subdivision of a soil series and consisting of or describing soils that are alike in all characteristics including the texture of the A horizon.

solodized soil. A soil that has been subjected to the processes responsible for the development of a Soloth and having at least some of the characteristics of a Soloth. (1949 classification system)

Solonchak soils. An intrazonal group of soils with high concentrations of soluble salts in relation to those in other soils, usually light-colored, without characteristic structural form, developed under salt-loving plants, and occurring mostly in a subhumid or semiarid climate. (1949 classification system)

Solonetz soils. An intrazonal group of soils having surface horizons of varying degrees of friability underlain by dark hard soil, ordinarily with columnar structure (prismatic structure with rounded tops). This hard layer is usually highly alkaline. Such soils are developed under grass or shrub vegetation, mostly in subhumid or semiarid climates.

soluble-sodium percentage (SSP). The proportion of sodium ions in solution in relation to the total cation concentration, defined as follows:

$$SSP = \frac{\text{Soluble-sodium concentration (meq/liter)}}{\text{Total cation concentration (meq/liter)}} \times 100$$

solum (plural: sola). The upper and most weathered part of the soil profile; the A and B horizons.

splash erosion. See *erosion.*

spodic horizon. A subsurface diagnostic horizon containing an illuvial accumulation of free sesquioxides of iron and aluminum and of organic matter. (new comprehensive classification system)

Spodosols. Soils characterized by the presence of a spodic horizon, an eluvial horizon in which active organic matter and amorphous oxides of aluminum and iron have precipitated. These soils include most Podzols, Brown Podzolics, and Ground Water Podzols of the old classification system. (new comprehensive classification system)

sprinkler irrigation. See *irrigation methods.*

stratified. Arranged in or composed of strata or layers.

strip cropping. The practice of growing crops which require different types of tillage, such as row and sod, in alternate strips along contours or across the prevailing direction of wind.

structure, soil. See *soil structure.*

stubble mulch. The stubble of crops or crop residues left essentially in place on the land as a surface cover before and during the preparation of the seedbed and at least partly during the growing of a succeeding crop.

subirrigation. See *irrigation methods.*

subsoil. That part of the soil below the plow layer.

subsoiling. Breaking of compact subsoils, without inverting them, with a special knife-like instrument (chisel) which is pulled through the soil at depths usually of 12 to 24 inches and at spacings usually of 2 to 5 feet.

surface runoff. See *runoff.*

surface soil. The uppermost part of the soil, ordinarily moved in tillage, or its equivalent in uncultivated soils and ranging in depth from 3 to 4 inches to 8 or 10. Frequently designated as the "plow layer," the "Ap layer," or the "Ap horizon."

symbiosis. The living together in intimate association of two dissimilar organisms, the cohabitation being mutually beneficial.

talus. Fragments of rock and other soil material accumulated by gravity at the foot of cliffs or steep slopes.

tensiometer. A device for measuring the negative pressure (or tension) of water in soil *in situ;* a porous, permeable ceramic cup connected through a tube to a manometer or vacuum gauge.

tension, soil-moisture. The equivalent negative pressure of suction of water in soil.

terrace. (i) A level, usually narrow, plain bordering a river, lake, or the sea. Rivers sometimes are bordered by terraces at different levels. (ii) A raised, more or less level or horizontal strip of earth usually constructed on or nearly on a contour and designed to make the land suitable for tillage and to prevent accelerated erosion.

texture. See *soil texture.*

thermal analysis (differential thermal analysis). A method of analyzing a soil sample for constituents, based on a differential rate of heating of the unknown and standard samples when a uniform source of heat is applied.

thermophilic organisms. Organisms which grow readily at temperatures above 45° C.

till. (i) Unstratified glacial drift deposited directly by the ice and consisting of clay, sand, gravel, and boulders intermingled in any proportion. (ii) To plow and prepare for seeding; to seed or cultivate the soil.

tilth. The physical condition of soil as related to its ease of tillage, fitness as a seedbed, and its impedance to seedling emergence and root penetration.

toposaic. A photomap on which topographic or terrain-form lines are shown, as on standard topographic quadrangles. See *photomap.*

toposequence. A sequence of related soils that differ, one from the other, primarily because of *topography* as a soil-formation factor.

topsoil. (i) The layer of soil moved in cultivation. See *surface soil.* (ii) Presumably fertile soil material used to topdress roadbanks, gardens, and lawns.

trace elements. (Obsolete) See *micronutrient.*

truncated. Having lost all or part of the upper soil horizon or horizons.

tuff. Volcanic ash usually more or less stratified and in various states of consolidation.

tundra. A level or undulating treeless plain characteristic of arctic regions.

Tundra soils. (i) Soils characteristic of tundra regions. (ii) A zonal great soil group consisting of soils with dark-brown peaty layers over grayish horizons mottled with rust and having continually frozen substrata; formed under frigid, humid climates, with poor drainage, and native vegetation of lichens, moss, flowering plants, and shrubs. (1949 classification system)

type, soil. See *soil type.*

Ultisol. Soils of humid areas characterized by the presence of either an argillic horizon or a fragipan each of which is less than 35 per cent saturated with bases. They have no spodic horizon and no oxic or natric horizons. They include soils formerly classified as Red-Yellow Podzolics, Reddish-Brown Laterites, and Rubrozems. (new comprehensive classification system)

umbric epipedon. A thick, dark surface layer which is less than 50 per cent saturated with bases. Ando soils have umbric epipedons. (new comprehensive classification system)

unsaturated flow. The movement of water in a soil which is not filled to capacity with water.

value, color. The relative lightness or intensity of color and approximately a function of the square root of the total amount of light. One of the three variables of color. See *Munsell color system, hue,* and *chroma.*

varnish, desert. A glossy sheen or coating on stones and gravel in arid regions.

varve. A distinct band representing the annual deposit in sedimentary materials regardless of origin and usually consisting of two layers, one a thick, light-colored layer of silt and fine sand and the other a thin, dark layer of clay.

Vertisols. Soils high in swelling clays which crack widely upon drying resulting in shrinking, shearing and soil mass movement. (new comprehensive classification system)

virgin soil. A soil that has not been significantly disturbed from its natural environment.

volume weight (Obsolete) See *bulk density.*

waterlogged. Saturated with water.

water-stable aggregate. A soil aggregate stable to the action of water such as falling drops, or agitation as in wet-sieving analysis.

water table. The upper surface of ground water or that level below which the soil is saturated with water; locus of points in soil water at which the hydraulic pressure is equal to atmospheric pressure.

weathering. All physical and chemical changes produced in rocks, at or near the earth's surface, by atmospheric agents.

wilting point (*or permanent wilting point*). The moisture content of soil, on an oven-dry basis, at which plants (specifically sunflower plants) wilt and fail to recover their turgidity when placed in a dark humid atmosphere.

windbreak. A planting of trees, shrubs, or other vegetation, usually perpendicular or nearly so to the principal wind direction, to protect soil, crops, homesteads, roads, etc., against the effects of winds, such as wind erosion, and the drifting of soil and snow.

xerophytes. Plants that grow in or on extremely dry soils or soil materials.

zeta potential. See *electrokinetic potential.*

zonal soil. A soil characteristic of a large area or zone. (1949 classification system)

Index

Absorption by plants
 form in which nutrients are taken up,
  37
 influenced by cation exchange, 102
 influenced by soil aeration, 252
 luxury consumption of potassium, 494
 of ammonium, 37
 of calcium ions, 37
 of carbonate ions, 37
 of nitrate nitrogen, 37
 of organic materials, 146
 of organic nitrogen compounds, 146,
  451
 of organic phosphorous compounds,
  142, 476, 488
 of phosphate ions, 37
 of potassium ions, 37
 of sulfate ions, 38
 of water, 175, 252
Acidity (see Soil acidity)
Acre-furrow-slice

energy of, 138
organic and mineral soils compared,
 7, 365, 371
pounds of nutrients in, 23, 24
pounds of organic matter in, 24, 25
relation to profile, 5
weight of, mineral soils, 54
weight of, peat soils, 365
Actinomycetes of soil (see also Soil
 organisms)
cause of disease, 127, 403, 404
condition for growth, 123
importance in soils, 124
nature of, 123
numbers and weight of, 124
relation to pH, 123, 397, 398, 403
Adhesion
water retention by, 165
Adsorption of anions by soils
mechanism of, 483
of phosphorus, 483

631